STARS AND STELLAR SYSTEMS
Compendium of Astronomy and Astrophysics

(IN NINE VOLUMES)

GERARD P. KUIPER, *General Editor*
BARBARA M. MIDDLEHURST, *Associate General Editor*

CONTRIBUTORS

HALTON C. ARP

A. BLAAUW

VICTOR M. BLANCO

J. DELHAYE

OLIN J. EGGEN

T. ELVIUS

JESSE L. GREENSTEIN

F. J. KERR

ROBERT P. KRAFT

W. J. LUYTEN

S. W. McCUSKEY

R. MINKOWSKI

GUIDO MÜNCH

J. H. OORT

J. L. PAWSEY

L. PLAUT

NANCY G. ROMAN

MAARTEN SCHMIDT

STEWART SHARPLESS

P. J. VAN RHIJN

G. WESTERHOUT

L. WOLTJER

RICHARD WOOLLEY

GALACTIC STRUCTURE

Edited by

ADRIAAN BLAAUW

and

MAARTEN SCHMIDT

THE UNIVERSITY OF CHICAGO PRESS

CHICAGO & LONDON

This publication has been supported in part by the

NATIONAL SCIENCE FOUNDATION

Library of Congress Catalog Card Number: 64-23428

THE UNIVERSITY OF CHICAGO PRESS, CHICAGO & LONDON
The University of Toronto Press, Toronto 5, Canada

Preface to the Series

THE SERIES "Stars and Stellar Systems, Compendium of Astronomy," comprising nine volumes, was organized in consultation with senior astronomers in the United States and abroad early in 1955. It was intended as an extension of the four-volume "Solar System" series to cover astrophysics and stellar astronomy. In contrast to the "Solar System" series, separate editors have been appointed for each volume. The volume editors, together with the general editors, form the editorial board that is responsible for the over-all planning of the series.

The aim of the series is to present stellar astronomy and astrophysics as basically empirical sciences, co-ordinated and illuminated by the application of theory. To this end the series opens with a description of representative telescopes, both optical and radio (Vol. 1), and of accessories, techniques, and methods of reduction (Vol. 2). The chief classes of observational data are described in Volume 3, with additional material being referred to in succeeding volumes, as the topics may require. The systematic treatment of astronomical problems starts with Volume 4, as is apparent from the volume titles. Theoretical chapters are added where needed, on dynamical problems in Volumes 4, 5, and 9, and on astrophysical problems in Volumes 6, 7, and 8. In order that the chapters may retain a greater degree of permanence, the more speculative parts of astronomy have been de-emphasized. The level of the chapters will make them suitable for graduate students as well as for professional astronomers and also for the increasing number of scientists in other fields requiring astronomical information.

The undersigned wish to thank both the authors and the volume editors for their readiness to collaborate on this series, which it is hoped will stimulate the further growth of astronomy.

The editors wish to acknowledge the support by the National Science Foundation both in defraying part of the costs of the editorial offices and in providing a publication subsidy.

GERARD P. KUIPER
BARBARA M. MIDDLEHURST

Preface to Volume 5

THE present volume reviews progress and problems in the principal fields of galactic research, with emphasis on the observational aspects. Chapters 1–4 present accounts of the classical investigations of the space distribution and motions of the stars in general in the part of the Galaxy usually referred to as the solar neighborhood. Chapters 5–20 deal with the space distribution and motions of the various components of the galactic population. The general order in which these are given is one of gradual transition from the flat systems to the spheroidal ones. Thus, problems concerning the young populations of stars with their uneven space distribution, and the radio and optical investigations of the interstellar gas, are dealt with first, and next, the older populations. The last chapter of this group describes the concept of the "stellar populations" with reference to the preceding data on motions and space distribution. Chapters 21–23 deal, respectively, with some of the principal fields of dynamical investigation, with the model of the mass distribution in the Galaxy, and with the role of magnetic fields in the Galaxy. The Appendix gives some particulars about Kapteyn's Plan of Selected Areas which may continue to serve useful purposes in future galactic researches.

Although much of the emphasis in modern galactic research is on problems bearing on evolution *in* the Galaxy, the editors have, after some hesitation, refrained from concluding the book with a chapter devoted especially to the evolution of the Galaxy as a whole. The principal reasons were that such a chapter would seem to fit better in the context of a presentation of problems of the evolution of stellar systems in general, possibly in a later volume of this series, and that it appeared unlikely that we would find an author willing to, and able to, devote the necessary time to such a comprehensive and difficult task.

The editors have felt that this volume on galactic research, probably more than other ones of this compendium, should help fill the gap owing to the lack of a good textbook. Existing textbooks are either largely outdated or cover only part of the many aspects of this domain of astronomy. Therefore, an attempt has been made to obtain a certain degree of completeness and homogeneity—although we are aware that we have only partly succeeded in this—and cross-references have been added to the original manuscripts.

"New" galactic coordinates are used throughout, even in diagrams based on the old system, taken from existing literature; in such cases approximate values of l^{II} are added. In diagrams of the projected space distribution on the galactic plane, we have consistently adopted an orientation with the direction of the galactic center pointing downward; some diagrams were redrawn for this purpose. Uniformity of symbols has also been aimed at, but this is a difficult problem; different schools of investigators consistently use their own set of symbols and this is reflected in the present book.

For a book like the present one with twenty-three authors, the dates of completion of the manuscripts range over a considerable lapse of time, from three years ago to rather recently, and deadlines are of restricted value. A well-known galactic astronomer has defined the deadline as "the date when the editor falls dead if he has received a manuscript." Our authors have generously collaborated in avoiding this risk. Many of them had extensive responsibilities, either in research or administration, and could devote little time to writing their chapters. We are grateful for their contributions.

We wish to express our indebtedness to Miss Barbara M. Middlehurst, the associate general editor, for her unfailing and stimulating collaboration. Our thanks are also due to Mr. J. B. van Wijk of the Kapteyn Laboratory for his careful assistance in the proofreading and to our secretarial staff for their careful preparation of the manuscripts.

We deeply regret the deaths of Dr. J. L. Pawsey and Dr. P. J. van Rhijn. Although the natural development of the fields of research covered by their chapters did suggest certain revisions, we have decided to maintain these chapters almost unchanged.

ADRIAAN BLAAUW
MAARTEN SCHMIDT

Table of Contents

23. DYNAMICS OF GAS AND MAGNETIC FIELDS; SPIRAL STRUCTURE . . . 531
L. Woltjer

CHAPTER 1

Distribution of Common Stars in the Galactic Plane

S. W. McCUSKEY

Warner and Swasey Observatory, Case Institute of Technology

§ 1. INTRODUCTION

THE *common stars* are here defined as those populating the main sequence and the ordinary giant branch of the Hertzsprung-Russell diagram as it is usually formed for stars brighter than a given apparent magnitude. We exclude from discussion the supergiants of spectral classes later than B, the novae, the white dwarfs, the large numbers of M stars revealed by infrared photography, the carbon stars, S stars, high-velocity stars, and the variables. These special classes are discussed elsewhere in this volume. The O and B stars at the high-luminosity end of the main sequence will be considered but not in any great detail.

Our discussion will be restricted to the stellar population near the galactic equator. High and intermediate latitude distributions are discussed by Elvius in chapter 3 of this volume. New galactic coordinates l^{II}, b^{II} (Blaauw *et al.* 1959) will be used as far as possible.

§ 2. THE GENERAL STELLAR POPULATION

Van Rhijn has indicated briefly in chapter 2 of this volume the space density near the galactic plane for stars of all spectral classes together. Before considering the spatial distribution of the common stars in groups according to spectral type, therefore, we shall summarize in somewhat more detail the information on galactic structure available from general star counts near the galactic plane. When the common stars of all spectral classes are included in general star counts, they constitute well over 95 per cent of the stars observed in areas near the galactic plane. By *general star counts* we shall mean counts of stars irrespective of spectral type.

Given $A(m)$, the number of stars per unit area between magnitudes $m - \frac{1}{2}$ and $m + \frac{1}{2}$; $\varphi(M)dM$, the luminosity function or the number of stars per cubic

1

parsec in the solar neighborhood in the absolute magnitude range M to $M +$ dM; and the interstellar absorption as a function of distance, one can calculate the relative density in space at distance r parsecs. Van Rhijn has indicated, in chapter 2, methods for solving the fundamental integral equation of stellar statistics which yields the space density function $D(r)$. In the following discussion we shall assume that the interstellar absorption has been evaluated in each area and has been included in the analysis.

The analyses of general star counts suffer from a lack of resolving power. The luminosity function is somewhat uncertain, its variability with position in space is not known with high precision, and there is always the difficulty of properly allowing for the amount and distribution of interstellar absorbing material. In spite of these difficulties, some knowledge of the over-all stellar population in the region surrounding the sun to a distance of 2500 or 3000 parsecs can be deduced from star counts. In this section, therefore, we shall sketch the run of space density of stars as deduced from general star counts. In succeeding sections we shall consider the space distribution of stars in separate spectral groups.

Table 1 indicates the run of average relative space density $D(r)$ as a function of galactic longitude l^{II} (to convert to l^{I}, subtract 32°). The third line of the table gives the number of areas from which the average $D(r)$ values have been obtained. The values of $D(r)$ quoted are averages over ranges in l^{II} varying from 4° to 15° depending on the data available. Data for this summary have been derived from the investigations by the following: van Rhijn (1936), Miller (1937), Miller and Hynek (1939), Baker (1939), Bok (1939), Baker (1941), Kiefer and Baker (1941), Baker and Kiefer (1942), Risley (1943), Baker and Nantkes (1944), Bok and Rendall-Arons (1945), Nantkes and Baker (1948), McCuskey (1939, 1945, 1949, 1951, 1952a, 1954), McCuskey and Seyfert (1947), Calvert (1951), and Heeschen (1951).

In all of these investigations the standard luminosity function derived by van Rhijn (1936) and modified, where required, for variations with distance from the galactic plane has been used. The run of interstellar absorption with distance in each region was determined and applied in the star count analysis. Usually the absorption was determined from an analysis of the color excesses of early-type stars in the region concerned.

The conclusions we may draw from an inspection of Table 1 are:

a) In the northern Milky Way, $l^{II} = 21°$ to 218°, there appears to be a modest density increase in the range 100 to 300 parsecs. The average $D(r)$ for all longitudes at 300 parsecs is 1.17. Thereafter there is a steady decrease to a distance of 1000 parsecs. Beyond 1000 parsecs the average density for all longitudes remains sensibly constant and equal to about 0.5 that near the sun.

b) A high density region of large radial extent exists in the Monoceros region of the Milky Way. In the longitude range $210° < l^{II} < 215°$, the value $D(r) \cong$ 1.0 is maintained to a distance of 2500 parsecs from the sun.

TABLE 1

Relative Density Gradients from General Star Counts

Distance (parsecs)	l^{II} b^{II} No. Areas	21° −2°.3 2	48° −1°.0 3	67° +1°.8 4	101° +0°.6 5	122° −1°.0 6	142° +1°.6 4	170° −0°.7 4	181° −1°.7 4	195° −1°.2 4	203° −1°.1 3	213° −0°.4 4	218° −0°.3 3
100		1.0	1.0	1.0	1.16	1.0	1.15	1.20	1.63	1.38	1.0	1.0	1.17
300		2.0	0.81	1.27	1.05	0.77	1.32	1.24	1.49	1.43	0.87	1.08	0.99
500		1.95	0.53	1.07	0.97	0.74	1.31	1.11	1.04	0.94	0.60	0.88	0.92
1000		0.70	0.43	0.54	0.58	0.60	0.72	0.61	0.33	0.43	0.47	0.85	0.87
1500		0.93	0.53	0.39	0.47	0.48	0.44	0.48	0.19	0.29	0.33	0.98	0.73
2000		0.82	0.65	0.43	0.40	0.46	0.30	0.52	0.18	0.31	0.28	1.11	0.67
2500		0.45	0.62	0.70	0.34	0.10	0.28	0.63	0.16	0.33	0.23	1.10	0.59

c) In Auriga-Taurus ($170° < l^{II} < 200°$) at distances greater than 1000 parsecs there is a marked deficiency of stars compared to the region around the sun.

The data for individual regions from which the average $D(r)$ values have been deduced indicate large local fluctuations of density within 1000 parsecs of the sun. The Cygnus cloud ($l^{II} = 67°$), the Perseus-Cassiopeia complex ($l^{II} = 142°$), and the Auriga-Taurus region ($l^{II} = 182°$) stand out particularly in this regard.

From these trends one may conclude that there is evidence from the general star counts for a somewhat elongated relatively high density region near the sun with its maximum about 300–500 parsecs from the sun and toward the galactic anti-center.

The variations of space density with distance in the southern Milky Way are not represented in Table 1. Sufficiently detailed recent and homogeneous studies of the stellar distribution for this range in galactic longitude are not available. Two investigations, however, should be mentioned. Bok (1932) has made star counts to the 16th photographic magnitude in the surroundings of η Carinae ($l^{II} = 286°$, $b^{II} = 0°$). On the assumption of a uniform absorption of 0.4 magnitude per kiloparsec, he finds a stellar space density at 1000 parsecs of two to three times that in the solar neighborhood. And even at greater distances from the sun, the relative density $D(r)$ remains, in general, ≥ 1.0.

A second study by Bok (1931) of the Selected Areas in the southern Milky Way indicates that between longitudes $l^{II} = 340°$ and $0°$ there occurs a rapid decrease of relative density to 0.2 at 600 parsecs followed by a rise again to $D(r) = 1.00$ beyond 3000 parsecs. This analysis also was carried out on the assumption of a uniform absorption of 0.4 mag per kiloparsec. The uncertainty in the density function arising from this assumption precludes a satisfactory comparison with the more detailed analyses shown in Table 1. To the extent that these results can be combined, it appears, however, that the decline in density for short distances toward the galactic center in the range $l^{II} = 340°$ to $0°$ reinforces the statement above concerning the location of the sun relative to the local density maximum.

§ 3. DISTRIBUTION OF STARS ACCORDING TO SPECTRAL TYPE

3.1. LARGE-SCALE INVESTIGATIONS

Many years ago Shapley and Cannon (1924) studied the surface distribution of the stars of different spectral types from data presented in the newly completed *Henry Draper Catalogue*. This comprehensive and relatively homogeneous body of data was divided into the groupings of Table 2, which have proved useful for statistical studies ever since. These exemplify what we have designated as "the common stars." The *Catalogue* contains many more stars than the number exhibited in the table. But for the sake of obtaining a relatively homogeneous body of data, Shapley and Cannon limited their discussion to the stars with apparent visual magnitude brighter than 8.25.

This pioneering investigation revealed certain characteristics of the stellar distribution which may be summarized as follows:

a) The B stars are divided into two groups. The stars brighter than $m_v = 5.25$ show a distinct concentration toward a plane inclined about 16° to the galactic plane. This the authors designated as the "local system." The fainter B stars, however, are concentrated toward the galactic plane itself. Figures 1 and 2 adapted from the papers by Shapley and Cannon show clearly this local clustering effect in the bright B star population. The concentration of bright B stars toward a great circle in the sky was studied by B. A. Gould in 1879 and has been named Gould's belt.

b) Stars of type A brighter than $m_v = 6.5$ are distributed with remarkable uniformity in galactic longitude. There is little or no evidence for the clumpiness

TABLE 2

GROUPINGS OF HENRY DRAPER SPECTRAL CLASSES
INTRODUCED BY SHAPLEY AND CANNON (1924)

Spectral Class	Subdivisions	Numbers of Stars $m < 8.25$	Percentage
B........	B0 to B5	2061	4
A........	B8 to A3	15884	27
F........	A5 to F2	6536	11
G........	F5 to G0	8776	15
K........	G5 to K2	20760	35
M.......	K5 to M8	4491	8
B–M.....	....	58508	100

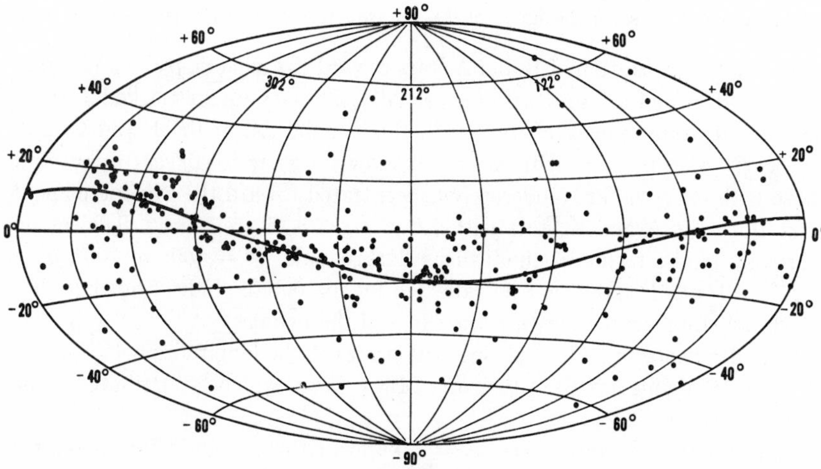

FIG. 1.—Galactic distribution of B stars brighter than visual magnitude 5.25 according to Shapley and Miss Cannon. The curve represents approximately the circle of concentration of these stars and illustrates the so-called "local system."

or clustering tendency such as that found for the B stars. This is not true for the fainter stars. Undoubtedly the brighter A stars are near enough so that the patchiness due to the interstellar absorption is not noticeable in their surface distribution.

c) The brighter stars of class A ($m_v < 6.5$) also show a tendency to deviate systematically from the galactic plane in the same sense as the bright B stars. But the inclination of the great circle about which they are concentrated is only about 5° as compared to 16° for the B stars. The fainter stars of class A0 show a high degree of concentration to the galactic plane.

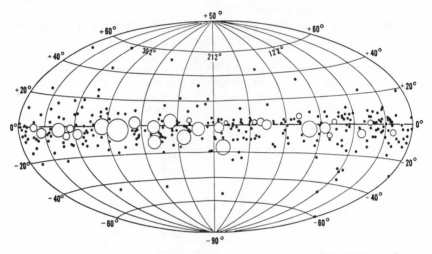

FIG. 2.—Galactic distribution of B stars fainter than visual magnitude 6.25 according to Shapley and Miss Cannon. These fainter stars are clearly concentrated along the galactic plane. Circles represent groups or clusterings of B stars. Dots represent individual stars.

d) The concentration of B and A stars toward the galactic plane and a similar concentration for faint stars of nearly all spectral types are marked. Little or no concentration, however, appears in the distribution of the F and G stars. The early M-type stars with $m_v < 8.0$ show no galactic concentration while those with $m_v > 8.0$ are moderately concentrated toward the galactic plane.

e) Both the A and K stars with $7.0 < m_v < 8.25$ are clearly deficient numerically in the region of the Taurus dark nebula ($l^{II} = 160°$ to 200°, $b^{II} = -11°$). Classes F and G are not affected by the nebula, indicating that these are dwarf stars located between the sun and the nebula.

f) A deficiency of stars of all spectral classes in the longitudes between $l^{II} = 10°$ and 55° delineates the rift in the Milky Way, which is attributed to obscuring matter.

g) Giant stars brighter than $m_v = 7.0$ appear to show the effect of the rift, which suggests that it is not more than 200 parsecs distant.

h) The fainter stars of class M show a strong preference for the region of

Sagittarius, which is apparently an indication of their high luminosity and a spatial concentration toward the galactic center.

These, in brief, give a picture of the surface distribution of the various spectral classes over the sky as determined from the data of the *Henry Draper Catalogue*. Charlier (1927) and Seydl (1929) have also provided detailed statistical data derived from the *Henry Draper Catalogue* from which similar conclusions could be drawn.

Among the other large-scale investigations prior to 1930 of the spatial distribution of common stars according to spectral type, that by Pannekoek (1929) should be mentioned. This important work discusses the space distribution primarily of the A, K, and B stars as determined from the data of the *Henry Draper Catalogue* and the *Extension*. Pannekoek made counts of stars in specified divisions of the sky according to apparent magnitude for classes B8 to A3 (A stars), and classes K0–K3 (K stars). The B stars were treated individually. On the assumption of a mean absolute magnitude for each spectral group (0.9 for A and 0.7 for K), the stars were distributed into spatial cells and an average density computed for each cell. The region within 300 parsecs of the sun is covered by the investigation of the A and the K stars. In the case of the latter, Pannekoek excluded on the basis of proper motion data those K stars which were probably dwarfs. Hence the analysis refers to the stars of the gK group.

The stars of types A and K exhibit marked clusterings or concentrations in the neighborhood of the galactic plane. Figures 3 and 4, adapted from those shown by Pannekoek, indicate this clearly. These figures give the average space density, stars per 10,000 cubic parsecs, at the centers of the space cells embracing a region extending 30 parsecs on either side of the galactic plane. Full curves indicate the high concentrations of stars of each spectral group. Dotted contours indicate regions of low density. By a study of these diagrams the reader may judge for himself the complexity of the galactic structure in the solar neighborhood. Much of this undoubtedly arises from the irregularity of the obscuring clouds. There appears from Figures 3 and 4 to be little similarity between the local space distribution of the A stars and that of the K stars. Where the density is low, the agreement between the two diagrams is closer. This, of course, is probably due to the intervening interstellar matter.

The well-known clusterings of B stars, already mentioned above, are clearly exhibited by Pannekoek's study. Some of these now are recognized as the stellar associations defined by Ambarzumian (1949, 1950). A list of these has been given by Morgan, Whitford, and Code (1953) and by Alter, Ruprecht, and Vanýsek (1958). These clusterings of high-luminosity stars are discussed by Sharpless in chapter 7 of this volume. Interstellar absorption was entirely neglected in the broad analyses described above. At the time of these studies, however, the idea of a general interstellar medium had not been widely accepted. Not until Trumpler (1930) evaluated the absorption coefficient in a fairly definitive way could its effect on stellar density calculations be included.

3.2. Stellar Distributions of Spectral Groups

3.2.1. *The B stars.*—The work by Shapley and Cannon and by Pannekoek, together with the investigations by Charlier (1916), Struve (1927), and by Merrill and Burwell (1933), clearly confirmed the conclusions drawn by John Herschel (1847) and by Gould (1879) regarding the phenomenon now called Gould's belt. The bright B stars ($m_v < 6.25$) are concentrated toward a plane which is inclined to that of the Galaxy. The fainter B stars do not show this phenomenon (Figs. 1, 2).

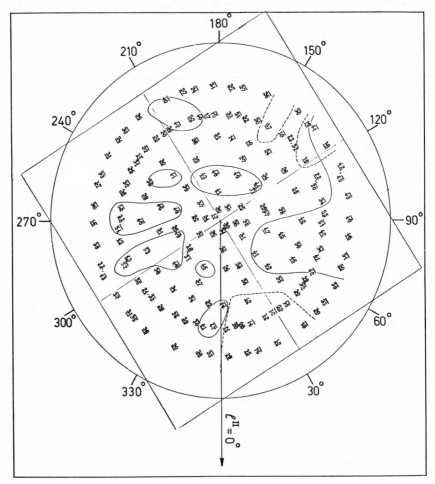

Fig. 3.—Space density of A stars in the region of the galactic plane according to Pannekoek. The numbers refer to the number of stars per 10^4 cubic parsecs. A bar above or below the number indicates that the element of volume referred to is above or below the galactic plane. The outer circle of numbers refers to a distance of 300 parsecs from the sun. Full contours represent concentrations; dotted contours represent deficiencies in stellar density.

A recent study of the O–B5 stars within 600 parsecs of the sun between galactic longitudes $l^I = 340°$ and $200°$, $l^{II} = 12°$ to $232°$ in the northern sky has been made by Blaauw (1956). The stars were divided into distance groups on the basis of their absolute magnitudes as derived from proper motion and radial velocity data, and their space distribution was determined. Blaauw's conclusions may be summarized as follows:

a) Nearly all of the B stars between these galactic longitudes in the range 0 to 200 parsecs from the sun are below the galactic plane. They clearly mark Gould's belt. These stars are more numerous in the longitude range $80° < l^I < 200°$, $112° < l^{II} < 232°$ than between $l^I = 340°$ and $80°$, $l^{II} = 12°$ to $112°$.

b) Between longitudes $l^I = 80°$ and $170°$, $l^{II} = 112°$ and $202°$, there is a

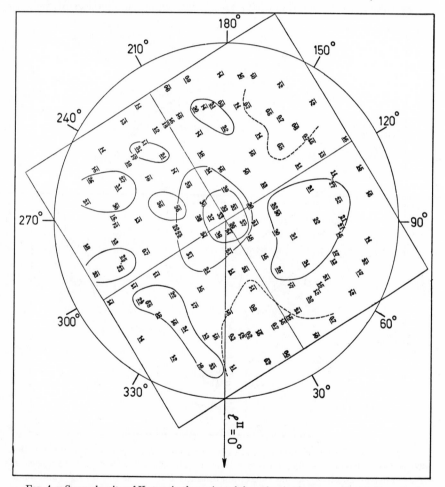

Fig. 4.—Space density of K stars in the region of the galactic plane according to Pannekoek. The numbers and contours have the same significance as in Figure 3.

grouping of stars within the distance limit of 200 parsecs which has a very small velocity dispersion compared to the velocity dispersion found for the O–B5 stars in general. This is called the Cassiopeia-Taurus group. It thins out appreciably in the distance range 200–400 parsecs.

  c) In the distance range 200–400 parsecs there are nearly 10 times as many O–B3 stars between longitudes $l^{\mathrm{I}} = 340°$ and 80°, $l^{\mathrm{II}} = 12°$ to 112° as there are among the stars within 200 parsecs.

  A deficiency of early B stars between longitudes $l^{\mathrm{I}} = 100°$ and 150°, $l^{\mathrm{II}} = 132°$ and 182° extends throughout the distance range 200 to 600 parsecs. This has been pointed out by Weaver (1953) in his study of the high luminosity stars in relation to galactic spiral structure. Figure 5, taken from Blaauw's paper, shows the distribution of the O–B3 stars within 400 parsecs of the sun

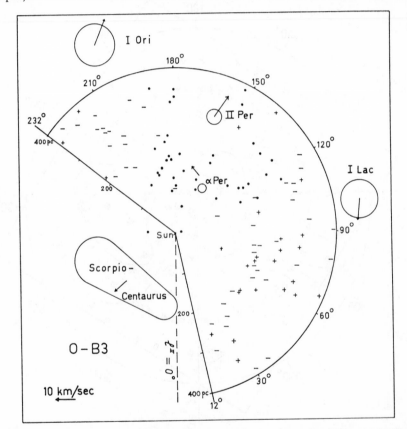

Fig. 5.—Distribution of stars B3 and earlier projected on the galactic plane and within 400 parsecs of the sun according to Blaauw. Dots indicate stars in the Cassiopeia-Taurus group (dots in parentheses have the most uncertain distances from the sun). Plus signs and minus signs indicate, respectively, field stars at positive and negative galactic latitudes. The α Persei cluster is marked. The locations of the nearest associations are shown by the large circles.

projected on the galactic plane. The Cassiopeia-Taurus group is evident as is the clumpiness of the over-all space distribution of these objects. The total number of stars involved in this analysis is 292.

In the summary of a series of papers on the stellar luminosity function, Mc-Cuskey (1956) has presented the variation of space density with distance from the sun for the stars of spectral class B5 in several relatively smooth regions near the galactic plane. Figure 6 shows the projection on the galactic plane of these regions and the density functions derived from this analysis. The spectral types for stars brighter than $m_{pg} = 12.5$ were observed in a homogeneous sys-

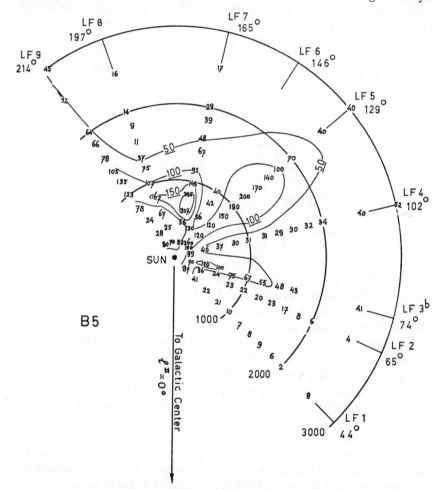

Fig. 6.—The space density distribution of the B5 stars in the galactic plane as determined from the LF Region survey made at the Warner and Swasey Observatory. Contours indicate approximately regions of equal density. The density is expressed in units of number of stars per 10^7 cubic parsecs.

tem based on the MK classification system. Contours shown in Figure 6 indicate that a region of relatively high space density of these objects occurs at longitudes $l^{II} = 112°$ to $147°$. This region extends to a distance of some 2500 parsecs from the sun. Local condensations within 1000 parsecs of the sun occur in Cygnus ($l^{II} = 74°$) and in Auriga ($l^{II} = 165°$). The latter is in the same general direction but considerably beyond the a Persei cluster and the II Persei association shown in Figure 5.

An analysis by Bok (1939) of the B0–B5 stars in Selected Areas 8, 9, 18, and 19 ($l^{I} = 92°, 107°, 68°, 81°; l^{II} = 124°, 139°, 100°, 113°$) confirms the extensive region of high space density shown at $l^{II} = 129°$ in Figure 6. At a distance of 1600 parsecs in S.A. 8, the relative density is 1.16 that near the sun. In the other Selected Areas the decrease in space density with distance is marked.

In the southern Milky Way the *space* distribution of early B stars is not so well known. Around the η Carinae nebula ($l^{II} = 286°$) a marked concentration

TABLE 3

NUMBERS OF B STARS IN SOME SOUTHERN AREAS

m_{pg}	MONOCEROS $l^{II} = 212°$ (67 square deg.)		S.A. 193 $l^{II} = 293°$ (6 square deg.)		FIELD II $l^{II} = 281°$ (6 square deg.)	
	B0–B2	B3–B5	B0–B2	B3–B5	B0–B2	B3–B5
8.0–9.0.........	1	5	3	6	2	1
9.0–10.0........	5	23	5	18	0	1
10.0–11.0........	2	33	3	18	1	0

of these objects was noted by, among others, Shapley and Cannon (1924) and by Charlier (1916). Later studies by Bok (1932, 1956) and by Bok and van Wijk (1952) indicate that the center of the concentration in Carina is at a distance of 1300 to 1500 parsecs from the sun.

This region of high B-star concentration surrounding S.A. 193 ($l^{II} = 293°$) has been compared by Bok and Wright (1945) with their results for a field in Monoceros ($l^{II} = 212°$) and another, Field II, at $l^{II} = 281°$, $b^{II} = +0°.8$ in the Carina region. Table 3 exhibits the numbers of stars in these areas. Making due allowance for the differing areas involved, it is found that the population of early B stars near S.A. 193 is 5 or 6 times that in the Monoceros region and much larger than in Field II. Bok and van Wijk (1952) found that the B-star concentration in Carina-Vela has a sharp boundary at $l^{II} = 282°$. This appears to be a real spatial effect and not due to overlying nebulosity. It is clearly apparent in the small number of B stars in Field II as exhibited in Table 3.

In the region of Sagittarius and Scorpio the principal clustering of O–B5 stars occurs in the Large Sagittarius Cloud at $l^{II} = 0°$. This is not as extensive as the concentration near η Carinae. Bok (1956) concludes that this apparent outcropping of bright stars probably indicates only a higher transparency for the region of the Large Sagittarius Cloud than in the surroundings. In an area of about 60 square degrees, the number of O–B5 stars brighter than the eleventh magnitude is 172 or about 3 per square degree. This may be compared with the surface density near S.A. 193 which is 9 stars per square degree.

A more detailed analysis of the distribution of the early B stars is given in chapter 7 of this volume.

3.2.2. *The A stars.*—The broad aspect of the spatial distribution of the A stars has been discussed above in consideration of the work by Shapley and Cannon (1924) and by Pannekoek (1929). While the 2450 B8 to A3 stars brighter than $m_v = 6.5$ of the *Henry Draper Catalogue* show very little concentration toward the galactic plane (Shapley and Cannon 1921), the fainter stars are strongly concentrated toward this plane.

During the past 30 years, many studies of selected regions in low galactic latitudes have been made. In particular the work by the Swedish astronomers based upon the spectral and luminosity classification system developed by Lindblad (1925, 1926), that by the Harvard investigators, and that carried on at the Warner and Swasey Observatory should be mentioned. In some of the investigations only an estimate of the interstellar absorption was made. In others, stellar colors were used to obtain an evaluation of the absorption for the regions concerned. Among the former were the analyses by Schalén (1928, 1932, 1935) and those by F. Becker (1939). Because of the uncertainty due to lack of detailed knowledge of the absorption, we shall not include their results in the present summary.

Table 4 summarizes the space density distributions for A-type stars obtained by those investigators who have included an adequate evaluation of the interstellar absorption in their analyses. The entries of the table give the *number of stars per 1000 cubic parsecs* at the distances listed. Several regions of high space density at considerable distances from the sun are apparent: (*a*) The Scutum cloud shows up at $l^{II} = 26°$, $b^{II} = -1°4$; the stellar density at 2000 parsecs is nearly 3.5 times that at 100 parsecs. (*b*) There is a relatively large population of A stars in Cygnus ($l^{II} = 85°$ to $95°$), but they appear to be within 500 parsecs of the sun. (*c*) Similar but more extended regions of high density exist in Cepheus ($l^{II} = 102°$), Perseus ($l^{II} = 139°$), and Auriga ($l^{II} = 160°$) in the northern sky. (*d*) In Monoceros ($l^{II} = 216°$) a relatively constant density of about 2.5 times that in the solar neighborhood extends to a distance of at least 1000 parsecs from the sun. (*e*) In the region of Selected Area 193 ($l^{II} = 293°$) in the southern sky, an extensive A-star concentration at distances exceeding 1000 parsecs appears.

The studies of space density of the A stars, carried on at the Warner and Swasey Observatory, have been summarized by McCuskey (1956). Figures 7, 8, and 9 show the distribution of B8–A0 and A2–A5 stars, respectively. Numbers refer to the space density in units of stars per 10^5 cubic parsecs. Contours have

TABLE 4

SPACE DENSITY OF A STARS NEAR THE GALACTIC PLANE
(No. of Stars per 1000 Cubic Parsecs)

Distance (parsecs)	lII −2°, bII −5°.6 B8-A0	15° +1°.5 A1-A5	26° −1°.4 B8-A6	26° −3°.8 B8-A6	32° +2°.2 A0	49° +1°.7 A0	54° −2°.8 B8-A0	54° −2°.8 A2-A5	85° +0°.8 A0	93° −7°.0 A0	100° +7°.0 A0	102° −2°.8 B8-A0	102° −2°.8 A2-A5
100	.06	.058	.42	.42	.061	.061	.70	1.30	.122	.244	.049	.12	.44
200	.095	.054	.35	.34	.056	.061	.29	.55	.348	.385	.046	.16	.47
300	.10	.074	.28	.26	.051	.061	.15	.35	.311	.278	.046	.15	.50
500	.07	.060	.13	.08	.044	.061	.12	...	.101	.162	.046	.13	.45
700	.055	...	.36	.12	.039	.045	...	...	.087	.118	.046	.10	.24
1000	(.17)	...	.71	.17	...	.021	...	...	...	...	.037	.06	...
1500	.04	...	1.05	.29	...	...	...	...	...	...	...	...	...
2000	.02	...	1.43	.32	...	...	...	...	...	...	...	...	...
Reference*	(1)	(2)	(3)	(3)	(4)	(4)	(5)		(4)	(4)	(4)	(6)	

TABLE 4—*Continued*

Distance (parsecs)	102° −7°.8 A0	102° −7°.8 A2-A3	112° −0°.7 A0	116° −2°.2 B8-A0	116° −2°.2 A2-A5	124° −2°.1 A0	139° +2°.4 A0	152° −7°.4 A0	160° −0°.2 A0	166° +8°.1 A0	216° +1°.1 B8-A0	216° +1°.1 A1-A7	281° +0°.8 B8-A0	281° +0°.8 A1-A7	293° +0°.9 B8-A0	293° +0°.9 A1-A7
100	...	...	.061	.054	.21	.061	.061	.061	.122	.043	.15	.34	.14	.35	.07	.30
200	.31	.277	.061	.050	.074	.028	.226	.061	.305	.026	.18	.27	.19	.29	.12	.25
300	.20	.185	.089	.040	.058	.024	.305	.061	.230	.015	.18	.28	.21	.32	.15	.19
500	.133	.160	.204	.047	.060	.035	.191	.082	.106	.012	.15	.23	.18	.31	.15	.19
700	.165	.222	.345	.049	.054	.043	.043	.087	.076	.012	.13	...	.15	...	.27	.18
1000	.080	...	.107	.023	.012	.049	.012	...	.049	.012	(.06)	...	(.10)	...	.32	(.18)
1500	.020	...	...	.004	...	...	...	...	...	...	...	...	...	...	.17	...
2000	...	...	...	...	...	...	...	...	...	...	...	...	...	...	(.08)	...
Reference*	(7)		(4)	(8)		(4)	(4)	(4)	(4)	(4)	(9)		(10)		(1)	

* (1) Bok (1956), (2) Pronyk (1960), (3) Russell (1953), (4) van Rhijn (1955), (5) Iwaniszewska (1960), (6) Risley (1949), (7) Ramberg (1957), (8) Ampel (1959), (9) Bok and Rendall-Arons (1945), (10) Bok and Wright (1945).

been drawn to show the main features of the concentrations and the regions of low density. The fields denoted by LF1 to LF9 were selected so as to be as free as possible of obvious obscuring nebulosity. Conspicuous features of the stellar distribution indicated by these figures are:

a) The highly concentrated group of B8–A0 stars (Fig. 7) at distances within 500 parsecs of the sun and between longitudes $l^{II} = 85°$ and $145°$. This undoubtedly is a continuation of the Cygnus group of early A stars at a distance, uncorrected for absorption, of about 400 parsecs already noted by Pannekoek (1929) and by Malmquist and Hufnagel (1933), among others. It is interesting to note that in the region between $l^{II} = 60°$ and $l^{II} = 130°$ the B8–A0 star population at distances between 1000 and 2000 parsecs from the sun remains sensibly constant (Fig. 8). These results are, of course, a confirmation of those outlined above from Table 4.

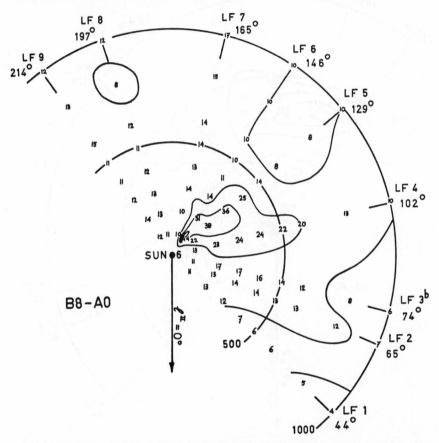

Fig. 7.—The space distribution in the galactic plane of the B8–A0 stars within 1000 parsecs of the sun according to the LF Region survey. Contours of equal density are shown. The density values are in units of stars per 10^5 cubic parsecs. The arrow points to the galactic center.

b) The A2–A5 stars (Fig. 9) are concentrated also in the region from $l^{II} =$ 60° to 130° but at greater distances than the early A star group. In some respects the distribution of A2–A5 stars resembles that of the B5 stars shown in Figure 6.

c) The distribution of B8–A0 stars exhibited in Figure 8 shows a large concentration between 1000 and 2000 parsecs in the range $l^{II} = 160°$ to 210°. Here the space density averages four to five times that in the solar neighborhood. This aggregate of A stars coincides closely with the junction between the local spiral arm of the Galaxy and the Perseus arm as shown by Morgan (1955). This is the region in which Morgan, Whitford, and Code (1953) have found concentrations of blue supergiant stars.

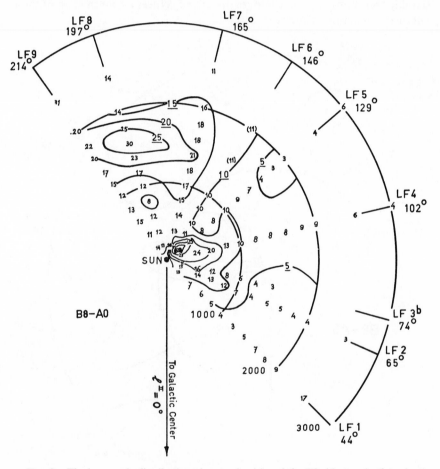

FIG. 8.—The large-scale distribution of space densities of the B8–A0 stars in the galactic plane according to the LF Region survey. Units of density are stars per 10^5 cubic parsecs. Contours of equal space density are shown.

Along the recognized spiral arm toward Cygnus the density of A stars is constant at large distances and is low on the average. It does not differ greatly from the density between the local arm and the Perseus arm, say at $l^{II} = 130°$. One cannot clearly associate the early A star population determined from this survey with the spiral characteristics of the Galaxy as defined by the aggregates of O and B stars. This is in conformity with the conclusion drawn by van Rhijn (1956) from his study of the distribution of A and K stars.

The high density of A stars at longitudes $l^{II} = 160°$ to $210°$ coincides with a concentration of hydrogen as shown by van de Hulst, Muller, and Oort (1954). Similarly the region of low space density of stars in LF4 and LF5 at distances of 1000 to 2000 parsecs coincides with a region of low hydrogen density. But there appears in the analysis above no increase in the population of A stars be-

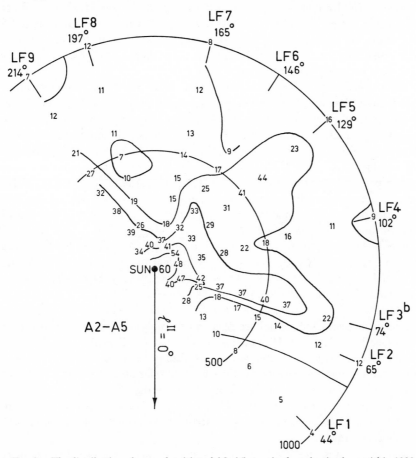

FIG. 9.—The distribution of space densities of A2–A5 stars in the galactic plane within 1000 parsecs of the sun according to the LF Region survey. Units of density are stars per 10⁵ cubic parsecs.

tween 2000 and 3000 parsecs comparable to the high density of hydrogen in this longitude interval at these large distances. Van Rhijn (1955) has found a weak but nevertheless rather definite correlation between the space densities of the A stars near the galactic plane and the density of interstellar hydrogen.

The sampling nature of the analysis sketched here must always be kept in mind. Interpolation between density values derived for the LF regions is approximate at best, and the interpretation of contours should be made accordingly. One should also bear in mind that a change in the mean absolute magnitudes and dispersions used in the analysis for the LF regions would modify the absolute density functions. The parameters used here for the B8–A0 stars are $M_0 = +0.5$, $\sigma_0 = 0.8$; for the A2–A5 stars $M_0 = +2.0$, $\sigma_0 = 0.8$. Photographic magnitudes were used throughout. The general picture we get from the analysis of the LF regions is a rather uniform density of A stars, about 0.08 per 1000 cubic parsecs, on which are superposed concentrations ranging from 1.5 to 5 times the average background density. Any correlation between the distribution of A stars and classes of objects which delineate the spiral arms of our Galaxy is not yet clearly apparent.

3.2.3. *The F stars.*—The stars of spectral classes F0, F2, F5 form an interesting group. Excluding the rare supergiants, they occupy a place on the Hertzsprung-Russell diagram near $M_{pg} = +3.5$. In nearly every direction from the sun, density analyses show a decrease in the space population of these objects. This is exhibited in Figure 10, where in part (*a*) the average of the densities determined by McCuskey (1956) for the LF regions is plotted against the distance, and in part (*b*) the gradients found by Bok and Rendall-Arons (1945), Risley (1949), Bok and Wright (1945), and Ampel (1959) are shown. On the average, the space density at 500 parsecs from the sun amounts to about 25 per cent of that in the solar neighborhood.

Figure 11 shows the distribution on the galactic plane of the F0–F5 stellar densities determined for the LF regions. Notable is the concentration extending beyond 500 parsecs at $l^{II} = 130°$. In every other direction the density decrease continues to distances of the order of 1000 parsecs.

3.2.4. *The G and K giants.*—In 1929, Pannekoek called attention to the dissimilarity between the spatial arrangement of the gK stars and that of the A stars (see Figs. 3 and 4). His conclusion was that the K-giant stars, while occurring in condensations, were not concentrated in the same regions of space as the A stars. There was a central grouping in the solar neighborhood, a region of higher than average density in Cygnus and another high density region in Puppis-Carina, all within 300 parsecs of the sun. These results, however, are somewhat vitiated by the fact that no account of the effects of interstellar absorption was taken.

Recently van Rhijn (1956) has determined the space densities of the giant K stars from counts in the Selected Areas. Table 5 summarizes the results for northern areas near the galactic plane. Comparable values for the areas in the southern Milky Way are not available. The entries of Table 5 are values of the *relative space density*, the density near the sun being taken as unity. These may be converted to absolute densities by multiplication by the factor 0.25, which is the number of stars per 1000 cubic parsecs near the sun. It is clear from Table 5 that a region of relatively high density extends to a distance of 300 parsecs in the longitude range $l^{II} = 80°$ to 160°. This is particularly noticeable at $l^{II} = 93°$ in the border between Cygnus and Cepheus. As van Rhijn has pointed out,

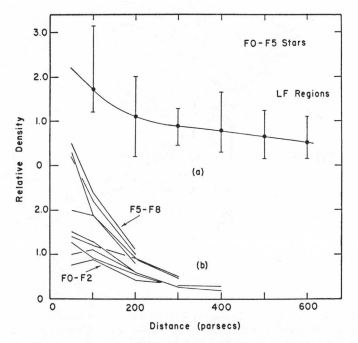

FIG. 10.—Density gradients for F0–F5 stars in the galactic plane: (*a*) The average relative density function for the LF regions; the vertical lines indicate the ranges of the data entering the averages. (*b*) The relative density functions found by other investigators.

there appears to be no distinct correlation between the space density of gK stars as determined from Selected Area data and the density of interstellar hydrogen. And there appears to be little correlation between the space density of gK stars and that of the A-star group as determined from the Selected Area data. In all of this investigation, due account was taken of the interstellar absorption in the regions concerned.

In the survey of spectral types in the LF regions, however, there does appear to be a coincidence of high density regions for both the gF8–K3 stars and the B8–A0 stars in the longitude range $l^{II} = 100°$ to 150° and within 500 parsecs of the sun. The distribution of gF8–K3 stars (McCuskey 1956) is shown in Figure 12. The reader may compare this with Figure 7 for the B8–A0 stars. In each

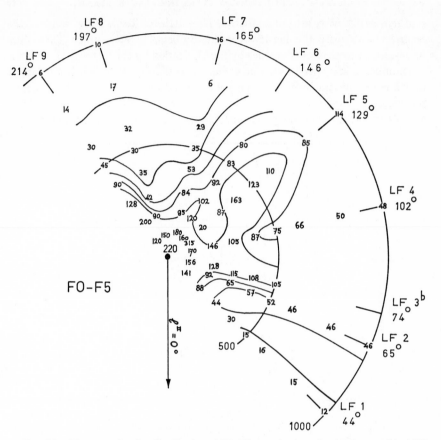

Fig. 11.—The space density distribution of F0–F5 stars in the galactic plane within 1000 parsecs of the sun according to the Cleveland LF Region survey. Contours of equal density are shown. Units of density are stars per 10^5 cubic parsecs.

TABLE 5

RELATIVE SPACE DENSITY FUNCTIONS FOR THE GIANT K-STARS
(According to van Rhijn)

Distance (parsecs)	l^{II} b^{II}	79° +9°5	85° +0°8	93° −7°0	100° +7°0	112° −0°7	124° −2°1	139° −2°4	152° −7°4	160° −0°2	166° +8°1
100.....	.......2.00		2.00	2.00	2.00	2.00	1.50	1.00	2.00	1.00	0.75
200.....	.......2.30		2.30	4.00	2.15	3.00	1.65	1.85	2.15	1.00	.40
300.....	.......1.27		1.39	2.77	1.32	1.50	0.89	1.66	2.00	1.00	.40
500.....	.......1.00		1.34	2.50	1.10	1.84	0.72	0.80	1.58	0.66	.40
700.....	.......1.50		2.00	2.43	1.08	0.93	0.64	0.59	1.00	0.37	.35
1000.....	.......1.40		.....	.....	1.00	.....	0.55	0.40	.....	.....	0.30

case the peak density occurs at a distance of 200 parsecs from the sun. Except for this condensation, the background density of gF8–K3 stars is sensibly uniform to a distance of 500–700 parsecs from the sun.

In contrast to the rather constant background density of the gF8–K3 stars shown in Figure 12, we exhibit in Figure 13 the variation of space density with distance found by other observers. The caption for the figure identifies the sources. Here we note, in general, a modest decrease in the number of stars per 1000 cubic parsecs in the first 500 parsecs from the sun. In the investigation by Ramberg (1957), however, at $l^{II} = 102°$, the space density of giant stars rises appreciably between 500 and 1000 parsecs. This area nearly coincides in longitude with LF4 but is at $b^{II} = -7°8$ as contrasted with $b^{II} = -2°8$ for LF4. Figure 12 shows an extended region of nearly constant density in this galactic longitude.

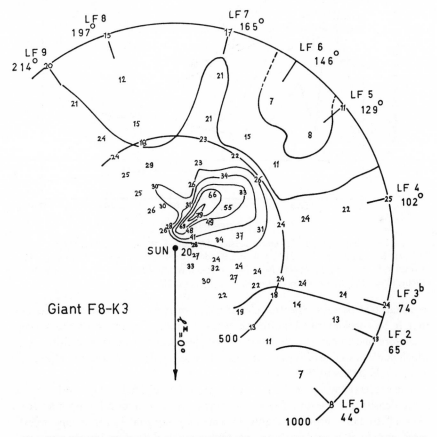

FIG. 12.—The distribution in space of the gF8–K3 stars in the galactic plane within 1000 parsecs of the sun as determined in the LF Region survey. Units of density are stars per 10^5 cubic parsecs. Contours of equal density are shown.

We conclude from these exhibits that, within a section of the Milky Way extending from $l^{II} = 30°$ to $l^{II} = 230°$ and out to a distance of 1000 parsecs from the sun, the space distribution of gG and gK stars is sensibly uniform except for a high concentration within 200 parsecs at $l^{II} = 130°$.

3.2.5. *The main-sequence G and K stars.*—Our knowledge of the space density at large distances of the dwarf stars of late spectral class is necessarily limited because of their low intrinsic luminosity. In a spectral survey which reaches stars of $m_{pg} = 13.5$, a dwarf G star would be visible only at a distance

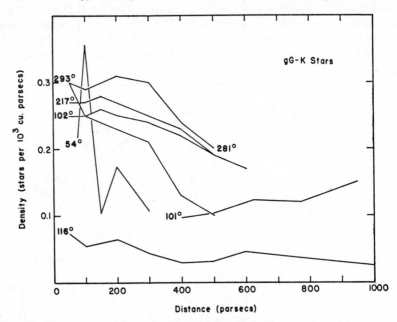

FIG. 13.—The general trend in space density of the gG–K stars with distance from the sun. The sources of data are: $l^{II} = 217°$, Bok and Rendall-Arons (1945); $l^{II} = 102°$, Risley (1949); $l^{II} = 293°$, Bok and Wright (1945); $l^{II} = 281°$, Bok and Wright (1945); $l^{II} = 54°$, Iwaniszewska (1960); $l^{II} = 116°$, Ampel (1959); $l^{II} = 101°$, Ramberg (1957).

less than 600 parsecs. Spectral classification of it as a dG star would require that it be considerably brighter than the limiting magnitude of the survey. Therefore one might say that 500 parsecs is about the maximum distance to which our knowledge of these stars extends. For the dK stars, the corresponding limit would be about 200 parsecs.

The spectral survey of the nine LF regions has yielded the general trend of space density for the dwarf G and K stars, averaged over all longitudes from $l^{II} = 44°$ to 232°, shown in Figure 14. One may say that in the region investigated, within 500 parsecs of the sun, there is little departure from a fairly uniform distribution of these main-sequence stars. Dashed lines in Figure 14 indicate the maximum and minimum values of the density entering into the average. The wide fluctuation in depth from region to region is obvious.

The calculation of space density functions for giant stars and for main-sequence stars separately requires a knowledge of the relative numbers of these objects in any spectral group. For the fainter stars this separation cannot be made by examination of the spectra because the luminosity criteria are not sufficiently pronounced. Therefore some independent determination of the percentage of dwarf stars among the entire spectral class is necessary. This can be done from studies of stellar motions.

It is well known that the percentage of dwarf stars among those of classes G and K changes markedly with apparent magnitude and with galactic latitude. The percentage at low latitudes is considerably less than in high galactic latitudes because of the well-known concentration of the giant stars of late spectral classes toward the galactic plane.

The variation of the percentage of dwarf stars as a function of apparent magnitude for spectral classes G and K is shown in Figure 15. The curves are for

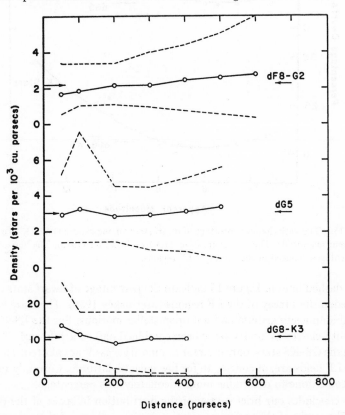

Fig. 14.—The trend of the space density with distance for the dG and dK stars in the galactic plane averaged over $l^{II} = 44°$ to 232° as determined in the LF Region survey. Dashed lines indicate the maximum and minimum values of density. Arrows indicate the mean density for the entire distance range.

high latitude and have been drawn from data compiled by W. Becker (1942). These reflect the studies made by many investigators and are based on proper motions. It should be noted that the class labeled K includes late-type as well as early-type K stars. It has been pointed out elsewhere (McCuskey 1952*b*) that if the early G stars are treated separately from those of class G5 the percentage of dwarf stars among them rises to something like 85 per cent. The percentage of dwarfs drops rapidly with progressively later spectral types in this range.

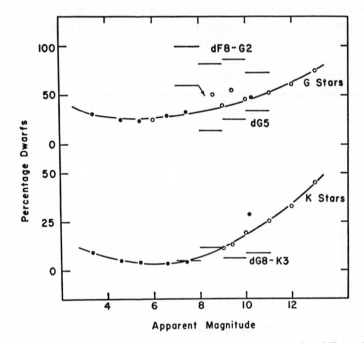

Fig. 15.—The variation in percentage of dwarf stars among classes G and K as a function of apparent magnitude. The curves are from data by W. Becker (1942). The horizontal lines are percentages deduced in the survey of LF regions.

The dashed lines in Figure 15 indicate the percentage of dwarf stars actually observed in the survey of the LF regions (McCuskey 1956). These are based on spectral luminosity criteria and not upon stellar motions. For the F8–G2 stars, luminosity classes IV and V have been combined and called "dwarfs." For the G5 and the G8–K3 stars, only data for luminosity class V are plotted. These data for the LF fields are, of course, all for low galactic latitude. Certainly much remains to be done to determine more adequately this percentage.

This concludes our brief survey of the distribution in space of the common stars. The study of the stellar population in the environs of the sun is still far from complete. The southern sky presents almost virgin territory for exploration. With the advent of large and powerful telescopes in Australia, Indonesia, and South Africa, spectral surveys to provide homogeneous data on many faint stars should be forthcoming in the not too distant future. Our knowledge of the "common stars" awaits enhancement through these sources.

REFERENCES

ALTER, G.,
  RUPRECHT, J., and
  VANÝSEK, V.   1958   *Catalogue of Star Clusters and Associations* (Prague: Czechoslovakia Academy of Science).

AMBARZUMIAN, V. A.   1949   *A.J. U.S.S.R.*, **26**, 3.
                       1950   *Ibid.*, **27**, 228.

AMPEL, R.   1959   *Bull. Astr. Obs. N. Copernicus Univ. Torun*, No. 20.

BAKER, R. H.   1939   *Harvard Circ.*, No. 424.
                       1941   *Ap. J.*, **94**, 493.

BAKER, R. H., and
  KIEFER, L.   1942   *Ap. J.*, **96**, 224.

BAKER, R. H., and
  NANTKES, E.   1944   *Ap. J.*, **99**, 125.

BECKER, F.   1939   *Zs. f. Ap.*, **19**, 50.

BECKER, W.   1942   *Sterne und Sternsysteme* (Dresden and Leipzig: Verlag Steinkopff), p. 227.

BLAAUW, A.   1956   *Ap. J.*, **123**, 408.

BLAAUW, A., *et al.*   1959   *Ap. J.*, **130**, 702.

BOK, B. J.   1931   *Harvard Circ.*, No. 371.
                       1932   *Harvard Reprint*, No. 77.
                       1939   *Ap. J.*, **90**, 249.
                       1956   *Vistas in Astronomy* (London and New York: Pergamon Press), **2**, 1522.

BOK, B. J., and
  RENDALL-ARONS, J. M. 1945   *Ap. J.*, **101**, 280.

BOK, B. J., and
  VAN WIJK, U.   1952   *A.J.*, **57**, 213.

BOK, B. J., and
  WRIGHT, F. W.   1945   *Ap. J.*, **101**, 300.

CALVERT, R. L.   1951   *Ap. J.*, **114**, 123.

CHARLIER, C. V. I   1916   *Lund Medd.*, Ser. II, No. 14.
                       1927   *Ibid.*, No. 36.

GOULD, B. A.   1879   *Uranometria Argentina*, p. 355.

HEESCHEN, D. S.   1951   *Ap. J.*, **114**, 132.

HERSCHEL, J.   1847   *Cape Observations*, p. 385.

HULST, H. C. VAN DE,
  MULLER, C. A., and
  OORT, J. H.   1954   *B.A.N.*, **12**, 117.

IWANISZEWSKA, C.   1960   *Bull. Astr. Obs. N. Copernicus Univ. Torun*, No. 24.

KIEFER, L., and
  BAKER, R. H.   1941   *Ap. J.*, **94**, 482.
LINDBLAD, B.   1925   *Nova Acta Reg. Soc. Sci. Uppsala*, Ser. IV, **6**,
                                No. 5.

                        1926   *Uppsala Medd.*, No. 11.

MALMQUIST, K. G., and
  HUFNAGEL, L.   1933   *Stockholms Obs. Ann.*, Vol. **11**, No. 9.
McCUSKEY, S. W.   1939   *Ap. J.*, **89**, 568.

                        1945   *Ibid.*, **102**, 32.

                        1949   *Ibid.*, **109**, 139 and 414.

                        1951   *Ibid.*, **113**, 672.

                        1952a   *Ibid.*, **115**, 479.

                        1952b   *A.J.*, **57**, 147.

                        1954   *Ap. J.*, **120**, 139.

                        1956   *Ibid.*, **123**, 458.

McCUSKEY, S. W., and
  SEYFERT, C. K.   1947   *Ap. J.*, **106**, 1.
MERRILL, P. W., and
  BURWELL, C.   1933   *Ap. J.*, **78**, 87.
MILLER, F. D.   1937   *Harvard Ann.*, **105**, 297.
MILLER, F. D., and
  HYNEK, J. A.   1939   *Contributions Perkins Obs.*, No. 13.
MORGAN, W. W.   1955   *Sci. Amer.*, **192**, No. 5, p. 42.
MORGAN, W. W.,
  WHITFORD, A. E., and
  CODE, A. D.   1953   *Ap. J.*, **118**, 318.
NANTKES, E., and
  BAKER, R. H.   1948   *Ap. J.*, **107**, 113.
PANNEKOEK, A.   1929   *Pub. Amsterdam*, No. 2.
PRONYK, I. I.   1960   *Pub. Crimean Astrophys. Obs.*, **23**, 46.
RAMBERG, J. M.   1957   *Stockholms Obs. Ann.*, Vol. **20**, No. 1.
RHIJN, P. J. VAN   1936   *Pub. Kapteyn Astr. Lab. Groningen*, No. 47.

                        1955   *Ibid.*, No. 57.

                        1956   *Ibid.*, No. 59.

RISLEY, A. M.   1943   *Ap. J.*, **97**, 277.

                        1949   *Ibid.*, **109**, 314.

RUSSELL, J. A.   1953   *A.J.*, **58**, 89.
SCHALÉN, C.   1928   *Uppsala Medd.*, No. 37.

                        1932   *Ibid.*, No. 55.

                        1935   *Ibid.*, No. 61.

SEYDL, O.   1929   *Pub. Obs. Nat. Prague*, No. 6.
SHAPLEY, H., and
  CANNON, A. J.   1921   *Harvard Circ.*, No. 226.

                        1924   *Harvard Reprint*, No. 6.

STRUVE, O.   1927   *A.N.*, **231**, 17.
TRUMPLER, R. J.   1930   *Lick Obs. Bull.*, No. 420.
WEAVER, H. F.   1953   *A.J.*, **58**, 177.

CHAPTER 2

Classical Methods for the Determination of Luminosity Function and Density Distribution

P. J. VAN RHIJN†

Kapteyn Laboratory, Groningen

§ 1. DETERMINATION OF THE DENSITY DISTRIBUTION

THE density distribution, in a specific direction of the galactic plane, of a given kind of stars is usually derived using the equation

$$A(m) = \omega \int_0^\infty \varphi(M) D(r) r^2 dr, \qquad (1.1)$$

where

  m = apparent magnitude;

  M = absolute magnitude = $m + 5 - 5 \log r - a(r)$; $\qquad$ (1.2)

  r = distance from the sun;

  $a(r)$ = the absorption of light in magnitudes between the sun and the distance r;

  $A(m)$ = number of stars between the apparent magnitudes $m - \frac{1}{2}$ and $m + \frac{1}{2}$ on the area of the sky ω;

  $\varphi(M)$ = the luminosity function, i.e., the number of stars per unit volume near the sun between the absolute magnitudes $M - \frac{1}{2}$ and $M + \frac{1}{2}$;

  $D(r)$ = the density of the stars at the distance r expressed in the density near the sun as a unit.

Equation (1.1) is proved as follows. $\varphi(M)$ is the number of stars per unit volume near the sun between the absolute magnitudes $M \pm \frac{1}{2}$. Therefore,

† Deceased May 9, 1960. Dr. van Rhijn's manuscript was submitted in the fall of 1959. In the process of coordinating this chapter with others in the volume, the editors have somewhat shortened the manuscript in so far as it dealt with items covered more comprehensively elsewhere.

$\varphi(M) D(r)$ is the number of stars per unit volume between the absolute magnitudes $M \pm \frac{1}{2}$ at the distance r; it is assumed that the density depends only on the distance and is independent of the absolute magnitude. The number of stars between the absolute magnitudes $M \pm \frac{1}{2}$ at distance r and in the element $\omega r^2 \, dr$ is therefore

$$A_r(m) \, dr = \varphi(M) D(r) \omega r^2 dr \,. \qquad (1.3)$$

These stars have apparent magnitudes between $m - \frac{1}{2}$ and $m + \frac{1}{2}$, if M and m are related by means of (1.2). The total number of stars between the apparent magnitudes $m \pm \frac{1}{2}$ in ω is found by integrating the expression (1.3) over all distances; the result is (1.1).

The density at the distance r in a specific direction is found by solving the integral equation (1.1); $A(m)$, $\varphi(M)$, and $a(r)$ are assumed to be known. The derivation of these functions will be discussed below. Equation (1.1) can be solved by trial and error, as is more fully explained by Bok (1937, pp. 26 ff.). An approximate function $D(r)$ is assumed, and the numbers of stars $A(m)$ are computed according to (1.1) by numerical integration for the values of m for which $A(m)$ is known. If the agreement of the computed and observed values of $A(m)$ is insufficient, $D(r)$ must be changed to assure it. We cannot expect a perfect agreement and must be satisfied if most of the differences between the computed and the observed numbers do not exceed the mean errors of the latter and if, when arranged according to values of the magnitude, they have a random character. The statistical mean error of the observed number is of the order of the square root of the number, if the latter is not small (see, for instance, Trumpler and Weaver 1953, p. 167). Crowder (1959) has devised a method of solving (1.1) by means of an electronic computer.

If the dispersion of the luminosity function is large, as occurs when stars of all spectral classes are taken together, the shape of the density distribution function cannot be determined with high accuracy. Neglecting absorption, for the moment, if all stars had the same absolute magnitude, stars of a specific apparent magnitude m would be at the same distance r, and any irregularity in the density distribution at distance r would appear clearly in the numbers of stars at the corresponding apparent magnitude. But if the dispersion in absolute magnitudes is large, the stars of apparent magnitude m are located at widely different distances, and different density functions $D_1(r)$ and $D_2(r)$ may yield practically the same distribution of apparent magnitudes, the positive excess in the numbers at distance r in solution $D_1(r)$ over solution $D_2(r)$ being compensated for by a negative excess at a neighboring distance (Trumpler and Weaver 1953, p. 471). An accurate determination of the density function can only be made for stars with a small dispersion in absolute magnitude as, for instance, stars of a specific spectral or spectrum-luminosity class.

Analytical methods have been proposed, to solve equation (1.1) (Bok 1937, pp. 14 and 15), but certain formulae would have to be adopted for the luminosity function and density distribution, whose validity is doubtful, in most cases.

The Swedish school has often used the method for the determination of the density devised by Malmquist (1925, 1936), which can be described, in the main, as follows. It is supposed that the distribution of the absolute magnitudes M per unit volume is Gaussian:

$$\varphi(M) = \frac{1}{\sigma(2\pi)^{1/2}} \exp\left[-\frac{(M-M_0)^2}{2\sigma^2}\right], \qquad (1.4)$$

where σ and M_0 are known constants independent of the distance. If the second and higher derivatives of $\log A(m)$ are small, then the distribution of the absolute magnitudes of stars of apparent magnitude m is also Gaussian (Malmquist 1936):

$$\varphi_m(M) = \frac{1}{\sigma_m(2\pi)^{1/2}} \exp\left[-\frac{(M-M_m)^2}{2\sigma_m^2}\right], \qquad (1.5)$$

where

$$\sigma_m^2 = \sigma^2 + \frac{\sigma^4}{\text{Mod}} \frac{d^2 \log A(m)}{dm^2}, \qquad (1.6)$$

and

$$M_m = M_0 - \frac{\sigma^2}{\text{Mod}} \frac{d \log A(m)}{dm}. \qquad (1.7)$$

Formula (1.5) is valid within the solid angle considered, if the absorption depends only on the distance, not on the direction.

The distribution of the absolute magnitudes of stars between the limits of apparent magnitude $m \pm \frac{1}{2}$ can be found by using equations (1.5) to (1.7) for various values of m. The resulting (m, M) table can be transformed into an (m, r) table by means of (1.2); the adopted differences between the values of $\log r$ for the centers of successive shells amount to 0.10, for instance. By adding the values of the table corresponding to different values of m in a given shell, we obtain the total number of stars in the shell, which, when divided by the volume of the shell, gives the density.

Thus, it appears that the data needed for the determination of the densities are the numbers of stars $A(m)$, the luminosity function $\varphi(M)$, and the absorption of light in magnitudes as a function of distance.

§ 2. THE LUMINOSITY FUNCTION FOR ALL SPECTRAL CLASSES COMBINED

2.1. METHODS

The luminosity function is defined as the number of stars per unit volume in the region near the sun where the density is considered constant, but considerable difficulty in determining it arises from our lack of accurate distances of the stars. It can be derived by means of trigonometric parallaxes, spectroscopic parallaxes, mean parallaxes of stars of given proper motion and apparent magnitude, and by means of a comparison of the distribution of proper motions and tangential velocities.

2.1.1. *Trigonometric parallaxes.*—This method, which has been explained
and used by the author in *Groningen Publications*, No. 38, can be applied only to
stars near the sun; we will therefore restrict the investigation to objects with a
total proper motion $\mu > \mu_0$. The value of μ_0 will be discussed presently. The
distribution of the trigonometric parallaxes of stars between the apparent magnitudes $m \pm \frac{1}{2}$ and $\mu > \mu_0$, called the (m, π) table, is derived, for various values
of m, from the parallax catalogue; it must be corrected for two errors:

a) That arising from incompleteness of the stars with measured parallax
between $\pi \pm \Delta\pi$ and apparent magnitude $m \pm \frac{1}{2}$. In order to arrive at the
correct (m, π) table, each star is considered as f stars where

$$f = \frac{\text{total number of stars } (m, \mu)}{\text{number of stars } (m, \mu) \text{ with known trigonometric parallax}} \text{ ,}$$

μ is the proper motion of the star considered, and "number of stars (m, μ)"
means the number of stars in the interval of proper motion $\mu \pm \Delta\mu$ between the
magnitudes $m \pm \frac{1}{2}$.

In this procedure, it is assumed that the stars, with an observed parallax,
within a μ group, have not been selected on the basis of the parallax. The de-
nominator of f can be derived from counts in the parallax catalogue; the numera-
tor must be found from other sources. The errors in the numbers of the (m, π)
table are multiplied by the factor f; in order to avoid large errors in the final
result, f must not be allowed to exceed a certain limit. This condition can be
satisfied by a proper choice of μ_0.

b) The distribution of the parallaxes of the (m, π) table as found under (a)
must be corrected for accidental errors of observation separately for each magnitude group (Trumpler and Weaver 1953, p. 121). Since the probable errors of the
best parallax determinations are of the order of $\pm 0\overset{''}{.}005$, the distribution of the
parallaxes for $\pi < 0\overset{''}{.}010$ is of little value.

The (m, π) table, thus found, gives the numbers of stars between apparent
magnitudes $m \pm \frac{1}{2}$ and the parallax limits $\pi \pm \Delta\pi$ for objects with a proper
motion exceeding μ_0. These numbers must be corrected for the missing stars
with proper motion $< \mu_0$ by multiplication with the factor F defined by

$$F = \frac{\text{number of stars in the } (m, \pi) \text{ group whatever the proper motion}}{\text{number of stars in the } (m, \pi) \text{ group with proper motion} > \mu_0}$$

$$= \frac{\text{total number of stars in the } (m, \pi) \text{ group}}{\text{number of stars in the } (m, \pi) \text{ group with transverse linear velocity} > (4.74\mu_0)/\pi_0} \text{,}$$

where π_0 is the mean parallax of the group. The velocity is expressed in km/sec,
the proper motion in $''$/year and the parallax in seconds of arc. The last ratio in
the expression for F can be inferred from the solar velocity and the constants of
the Schwarzschild velocity ellipsoid of the group (see Delhaye, chap. 4 of this
volume).

The value of F depends on π_0, μ_0 being determined by the above considerations. With decreasing π_0, the value of $(4.74\,\mu_0)/\pi_0$ and hence of the factor F, increases. It is clear that large values of F must be avoided, because the errors in the numbers are multiplied by this factor in the final result. As described above, the (m, π) table to be used in the determination of the luminosity function is restricted to parallaxes exceeding $0\overset{''}{.}010$. The factors F are moderate for these cases.

We thus find the number of stars between the apparent magnitudes $m \pm \frac{1}{2}$ and the parallaxes $\pi \pm \Delta\pi$ for the parallax groups $\pi > 0\overset{''}{.}010$. These numbers are identical with those between the absolute magnitudes $M \pm \frac{1}{2}$ in the parallax group $\pi \pm \Delta\pi$ if

$$M = m + 5 + 5 \log \pi_0 ,$$

where π_0 is the mean parallax of the stars in a parallax group. Dividing these numbers by the volume of the parallax group between the parallaxes $\pi \pm \Delta\pi$, we find the numbers $\varphi(M)$ of the luminosity function.

Several values of $\varphi(M)$ are found for approximately the same value of M, each originating from one of the (m, π) groups. They must be averaged with certain weights, which will not be considered here.

2.1.2. *Spectroscopic parallaxes.*—The spectroscopic absolute magnitudes M are derived from the intensity ratios of a number of Fraunhofer lines; the spectroscopic parallaxes π_s are then found by using

$$M = m + 5 + 5 \log \pi_s - a(\pi_s) . \tag{2.1}$$

Since the spectral class is always known for the stars considered, we can obtain the luminosity function for stars of each spectral class separately. If all spectral classes are investigated, the luminosity function irrespective of spectral class can be found by adding the numbers in the various spectral classes for each absolute magnitude.

The luminosity function is derived by the same method as is used for determining the trigonometric parallaxes, with the following differences:

a) Let us denote by N_r the number of stars per cubic parsec between the absolute magnitudes $M \pm \frac{1}{2}$ as a function of the distance r. The luminosity function $\varphi(M)$ represents N_r near the sun, or rather within the limit of r, say r_0, where N_r may be considered to be independent of r. The largest distance, used in the determination of the luminosity function by means of trigonometric parallaxes, does not exceed this limit, and the numbers N_r, found in the preceding section, therefore represent values of $\varphi(M)$. But in the case of the spectroscopic parallaxes, the distances extend to 500 parsecs or even farther, and it cannot be assumed that N_r is independent of r within this distance. The values of N_r at distances exceeding r_0 must therefore be multiplied by the ratio

$$\frac{\text{number } N_r \text{ at distance} < r_0}{\text{number } N_r \text{ at distance } r} ,$$

which one usually assumes to be independent of the absolute magnitude for stars of a specific spectral class; the adopted value is the mean value for all values of M. For later spectral classes, the ratio can be determined separately for giants and dwarfs.

 b) We find, by simple counts, the numbers of stars between the apparent magnitudes $m \pm \frac{1}{2}$ and the limits of the logarithm of the parallax, $\log \pi_s \pm \Delta \log \pi_s$. Their distribution must be corrected for the observational errors in $\log \pi_s$. We shall neglect, for argument's sake, the error in the parallax caused by that in the absorption and assume that the errors in the spectroscopic absolute magnitudes for stars of a given true absolute magnitude follow a Gaussian distribution with a known dispersion ϵ. It follows that the errors in $\log \pi_s$ for stars of a given true parallax are distributed according to a Gaussian curve with dispersion $\epsilon/5$. The corrected distribution of $\log \pi_s$ can then be found according to the methods discussed by Trumpler and Weaver (1953, p. 121).

The spectroscopic absolute magnitudes M_s are derived from certain line intensity ratios I, a given value of M_s corresponding to a given value of I. The reduction of I to M_s can be made by one of two different methods, either the impartial or the partial one (Russell and Moore 1938; van Rhijn 1939; see also Blaauw's chap. 20 of Vol. III of this series). The supposition that the errors in $\log \pi_s$ for stars of a given true parallax are distributed according to a Gaussian curve holds only if we follow the impartial method of reduction. In practice, partially reduced absolute magnitudes must often be used. The correction to the observed values of $\log \pi_s$ can then be made following Russell and van Rhijn.

The difference between the distributions of the impartially and partially reduced spectroscopic absolute magnitudes must be emphasized: If the true absolute magnitudes are distributed according to a Gaussian curve, both kinds of spectroscopic absolute magnitudes are also so distributed. For the impartially reduced absolute magnitudes, however, the dispersion of the observed values is larger and for those partially reduced it is smaller than that of the true absolute magnitudes. For a more detailed discussion of these effects, see the above mentioned chapter on the calibration of luminosity criteria in Volume III of this series.

 2.1.3. *Method of* $\pi_{m,\ \mu}$.—In this method, as outlined in *Groningen Publications*, No. 38, the stars are divided into groups of apparent magnitude and proper motion, and for each group the following functions are assumed as given: (*a*) the mean parallaxes $\pi_{m,\ \mu}$; (*b*) the distributions of the true parallaxes around $\pi_{m,\ \mu}$; (*c*) the numbers of stars between apparent magnitudes $m \pm \frac{1}{2}$ and proper motions $\mu \pm \Delta\mu$.

The distribution of the true parallaxes in each magnitude-proper motion group is found by using (*a*), (*b*), and (*c*), and that of the true parallaxes in each magnitude group, by summation of these distributions over all values of the proper motion. We thus find the numbers of stars between the apparent magnitudes $m \pm \frac{1}{2}$ and the parallax limits $\pi \pm \Delta\pi$; they are identical with the numbers between the absolute magnitudes $M \pm \frac{1}{2}$ and the same parallax limits. Dividing these numbers by the volume of the parallax group, we get the numbers per unit volume between the absolute magnitudes $M \pm \frac{1}{2}$ and the parallax limits $\pi \pm \Delta\pi$. The luminosity function $\varphi(M)$ is found by applying a correction similar to that discussed in section 2.1.2 under (a), and by taking the mean of the values derived for a given absolute magnitude in the various parallax groups.

2.1.4. *Comparison of distributions of proper motion components and tangential velocities.*—This method has been devised and extensively applied by Strömberg. We shall follow here Abrams' (1947) discussion of Strömberg's method.

First, the distribution of the absolute magnitudes of stars brighter than apparent visual magnitude m_0 is determined. Let

v = component of the proper motion in the direction of the solar antapex, corrected for the effect of galactic rotation, in "/year;

t = peculiar tangential linear velocity in the v direction in km/sec;

V_0 = solar motion in km/sec;

λ = angular distance to antapex;

π = parallax in seconds of arc.

Then $(4.74/\pi) v = V_0 \sin \lambda + t$, and $M = m + 5 + 5 \log \pi$, if we neglect the interstellar absorption. Eliminating π we find

$$\frac{47.4}{\sin \lambda} v 10^{m/5} = \left(V_0 + \frac{t}{\sin \lambda} \right) 10^{M/5} . \qquad (2.2)$$

Introducing the new variables

$$x = \frac{47.4}{\sin \lambda} v 10^{m/5} ,$$

$$y = V_0 + \frac{t}{\sin \lambda} , \qquad (2.3)$$

$$z = 10^{M/5} ,$$

we have

$$x = yz . \qquad (2.4)$$

If the distribution functions of y and z are not correlated, the relation between the distribution functions $\Phi(x)$ of x, $\chi(y)$ of y, and $\Psi(z)$ of z is

$$\Phi(x) = \int_0^\infty \chi(y) \Psi(z) \frac{dz}{z} ; \qquad y = \frac{x}{z} . \qquad (2.5)$$

The function $\Phi(x)$ is determined from the observations of stars brighter than a given apparent magnitude m_0, the value of x being known for each star; it must be corrected for errors of observation. The function $\chi(y)$ can be found from the solar velocity and the elements of the velocity ellipsoid of the group, which are both derived from the radial velocities. The function $\Psi(z)$ and hence the dis-

tribution of absolute magnitudes for the stars $m < m_0$ is then computed from
(2.5) by trial and error. The neglected dependence of y on z as well as the neglected interstellar absorption can easily be taken into account (see Abrams
1947). In applying this method, one may similarly use the distribution of the
total proper motions or that of the components of the proper motions perpendicular to the direction of the anti-apex. Thus, we find the numbers of stars
N between the absolute magnitudes $M \pm \frac{1}{2}$ and apparent magnitudes brighter
than m_0. The luminosity function $\varphi(M)$ is then derived by

$$\frac{N}{\varphi(M)} = 4\pi \int_r^{r_0} r^2 D(r)\, dr, \tag{2.6}$$

where r_0 is given by

$$5 \log r_0 + a(r_0) = m_0 + 5 - M, \tag{2.7}$$

$a(r_0)$ being the absorption at distance r_0, and $D(r)$, the density of the stars at
distance r (unit = density near the sun). It is assumed that the observational
data cover the whole sky. r_0 is determined by (2.7). The solution $\varphi(M)$ by using
equation (2.6) requires a knowledge of the density distribution, $D(r)$. If the
luminosity function has a Gaussian shape, it may be derived from the numbers
N by the method proposed by Malmquist (1924).

2.2. Results

For a detailed discussion of the problems involved in using the methods outlined above, and of their relative merits, the reader is referred to *Statistical
Astronomy* (Trumpler and Weaver 1953, pp. 367–409). Many studies have been
made of the luminosity function of stars irrespective of spectral class. Table 1
gives the luminosity function for photographic magnitudes as given by Luyten
(1938), van Rhijn (1936), and McCuskey (1956).

The Minnesota values (Luyten) were derived according to the method described in section 2.1.3; the Groningen values (van Rhijn) are averages derived
by the methods described in sections 2.1.1, 2.1.2, and 2.1.3. The Cleveland
values (McCuskey) hold for a distance of 100 pc from the sun in the galactic
plane. They were obtained by taking the sums of the numbers for each spectral
class separately. The latter values equal the total number per cubic parsec
multiplied by the luminosity function which is assumed to be Gaussian. The
constants of the function were derived by Russell and Moore (1938, 1940) according to a method not described here. The agreement between the separate
determinations is fairly good; the Groningen values are somewhat smaller than
the others between $M = 7$ and $M = 11$.

At the faint end of the luminosity curve, Luyten finds a maximum in the
curve for $M = 14.5$, but he notes that he is not certain that it is real (see also Luyten 1941). We have therefore quoted his values only down to $M_{pg} = 15.0$. Luyten's material for the stars of large proper motion in the southern hemisphere is
very valuable, and might be used to greater advantage, if more accurate apparent

magnitudes were known. Moreover, the poor knowledge of the parallaxes of faint stars with large proper motion is a serious disadvantage.

It will be difficult to obtain a good determination of the number of stars per cubic parsec near the sun for absolute magnitudes somewhat fainter than the maximum of Luyten's curve, e.g., between $M_{pg} = 17.5$ and $M_{pg} = 18.5$, because these stars are found among those of faint apparent magnitude ($m_{pg} = 18.5$ to 19.5) and large proper motion ($\mu > 0''5$). The luminosity curve for

TABLE 1

LUMINOSITY FUNCTION

The number of stars per cubic parsec near the sun between
the photographic absolute magnitudes $M - \frac{1}{2}$
and $M + \frac{1}{2}$ (: = uncertain values)

M_{pg}	log $\varphi + 10$		
	Minnesota	Groningen	Cleveland
$-$ 6.0......	....	2.10:	....
$-$ 5.0......	....	3.07:	....
$-$ 4.0......	....	3.65:	....
$-$ 3.0......	....	4.25	....
$-$ 2.0......	....	4.75	4.70
$-$ 1.0......	....	5.07	5.35
0.0......	....	6.34	6.40
$+$ 1.0......	....	6.34	6.40
$+$ 2.0......	6.89	6.77	6.77
$+$ 3.0......	7.04	6.86	7.01
$+$ 4.0......	7.18	7.19	7.16
$+$ 5.0......	7.34	7.35	7.20
$+$ 6.0......	7.46	7.49	7.45
$+$ 7.0......	7.57	7.53	7.67
$+$ 8.0......	7.68	7.46	....
$+$ 9.0......	7.76	7.49	....
$+$10.0......	7.84	7.64	....
$+$11.0......	7.91	7.81	....
$+$12.0......	7.96	7.97	....
$+$13.0......	8.01	8.01	....
$+$14.0......	8.04	8.06	....
$+$15.0......	8.04	....	....

$M_{pg} = 17.5$ to 18.5 could probably be found by searching for the stars, $m_{pg} = 18.5$ to 19.5, $\mu > 0''5$, using the blinking method and determining the parallaxes of a number of them.

There is also another method of finding the stars $M_{pg} = 17.5$ to 18.5. Most of these stars are probably M dwarfs. It has been suggested to me by W. Fricke that the M dwarfs among the apparently faint stars, for example down to $m = 19.0$, can be found by selecting, first, the giants as well as the dwarfs among the M stars by obtaining spectra with a large Schmidt telescope, and then selecting the dwarfs among them on the basis of their proper motion which is much larger for the dwarfs than for the giants. The luminosity curve $M_{pg} =$ 17.5 to 18.5 can probably be found by determining the parallaxes of a number of the M dwarfs thus selected.

The bright end of the luminosity function plays an important role in modern work on the theory of the initial luminosity function (Salpeter 1955, and others). It must be remembered that the values for stars brighter than $M = -3.0$ are very uncertain. They have been derived in Table 1 from obsolete values of the function for stars of spectral type B. More accurate values can be found by determining the luminosity function for stars of each of the spectral classes as discussed in the next section and adding the numbers for each luminosity over all the spectral classes. The luminosity function for the main-sequence stars, needed in the evolutionary work mentioned above, can best be obtained if first the functions for different spectrum-luminosity classes are determined.

The luminosity function given in Table 1 applies to the vicinity of the sun. It probably varies with position *in* the galactic plane, and it certainly does so with distance *from* the plane. The variations of the luminosity function in the galactic system have been discussed by McCuskey (1956), Oort (1932), and van Rhijn and Schwassmann (1935) among others. See also Elvius' chapter 3 in this volume.

§ 3. LUMINOSITY FUNCTION FOR A GIVEN SPECTRAL CLASS

Valuable results have been derived for the density distribution of stars of a given spectral class, including giant and dwarf classifications for the later-type stars; they are discussed in McCuskey's chapter 1 and Elvius' chapter 3 of this volume.

A summary of the luminosity functions for the spectral classes A, F, G, and K (giants and dwarfs separately for G and K) by Malmquist, Schalén and van Rhijn–Schwassmann has been given by Bok (1937, pp. 23 and 24). McCuskey (1956) has adopted luminosity functions based on more recent information. Although the data of the different authors agree fairly well in most cases, a re-determination of the luminosity function for each spectral class is highly desirable. This may be done by first determining the function for each spectrum-luminosity class, then adding the curves for all luminosity classes for B, A, and F stars and, for the G and K stars, the curves for the giant and dwarf branches, respectively.

Relative frequencies of the absolute magnitudes per unit volume of the G8 to G9 and K0 to K1 stars as a function of the absolute visual magnitude were derived by Halliday (1955). The absolute magnitudes were derived from "luminosity numbers," interpolated between adjacent Yerkes luminosity classes I, II, . . . , V with the aid of an oscilloscopic microphotometer. In both the G8, G9 and K0, K1 groups we find a minimum frequency between the giants and dwarfs.

§ 4. THE EFFECT OF INTERSTELLAR ABSORPTION

The space density of stars in a given area of the sky can be found by using equations similar to equation (1.1) if we know the interstellar absorption as a function of the distance in this direction. This knowledge must hold for the effective wavelength of the magnitudes m that have been used in the $A(m)$ curve. The determination of the absorption is discussed below.

It is usually assumed that the absorption depends only on the distance and not on the direction in the area, and that the mean absorption $a(m)$ for stars of magnitude m and for the effective wavelength concerned is equal to a constant χ multiplied by the mean color excess E'

$$a(m) = \chi E' , \qquad (4.1)$$

where the color excess, E, is defined by $E = CI - CI_0$; CI = color index and CI_0 = intrinsic color index. According to (1.2) and (4.1) we have

$$5(\log r)' - 5 = M_m - \chi E' , \qquad (4.2)$$

where primes denote averages for the stars of the types considered of apparent magnitude m. M_m is found by using equation (1.7). The mean distance r' is related to $(\log r)'$ by

$$\log r' = (\log r)' + \frac{\sigma_m^2}{50 \, \mathrm{Mod}} ; \qquad (4.3)$$

Mod = 0.434 and σ_m is the dispersion of the absolute magnitudes of stars of apparent magnitude m [cf. (1.6)]. If $\sigma_m \leq 0.5$, then $\log r' = (\log r)'$ approximately.

We find the mean distance r' by means of equations (4.2) and (4.3) and the corresponding mean absorption by using (4.1). Because of the smoothing effect of the averaging which is implied by this procedure, the results for the dependence of absorption on distance and for the density distribution can be regarded only as a first approximation. Greater accuracy can, however, be obtained. If we recompute the absorption for stars of a given apparent magnitude, starting from the first approximation for the absorption in dependence on distance, denoted by $a_1(r)$, and from the first results for the density distribution, then

$$a(m) = \frac{\int_0^\infty A_r(m) a_1(r) dr}{\int_0^\infty A_r(m) dr} = \frac{\int_0^\infty D(r) \varphi(M) a_1(r) r^2 dr}{\int_0^\infty D(r) \varphi(M) r^2 dr} . \qquad (4.4)$$

If the computed values of $a(m)$ do not agree with the observed ones, those of $a_1(r)$ must be altered so that there will be such agreement, and the computation of the density distribution must be repeated with this $a_1(r)$. This will in turn affect the computation of $a(m)$, but sufficient approximation of the functions to be solved is soon reached by this procedure.

§ 5. CONCLUDING REMARKS

As we have shown in section 1, the density distribution, when determined by the use of equation (1.1) for a group of stars with large dispersion in absolute magnitudes, is of limited value. For modern work it is preferable to use groups of stars selected according to certain spectral and luminosity criteria, for which the dispersion is small. It may be necessary to abandon the attempt to find the density distribution separately for *all* kinds of stars. This approach was discussed at the First I.A.U. Symposium on Coordination of Galactic Research (Blaauw 1955). New approaches can be based on

a) The Yerkes MK system (Morgan, Keenan, and Kellman 1943; Johnson and Morgan 1953);

b) The luminosity classifications developed in Sweden (Elvius 1955, 1956; Westerlund 1951, 1953);

c) The system developed by Chalonge and collaborators (Chalonge 1958);

d) The $H\gamma$ equivalent width plus spectral type (Petrie 1953; Petrie and Moyls 1956, and others);

e) The H and K emission reversals (Wilson and Bappu 1957; Wilson 1959);

f) The narrow-band photometry developed by Strömgren (1958) and Gyldenkerne (1958).

It is hardly possible for a single astronomer or even a single observatory to undertake a comprehensive investigation along these lines. It can only be accomplished successfully by several observatories cooperating in a joint project.

At the Stockholm Conference on the Coordination of Galactic Research (see *Symposium of the International Astronomical Union*, No. 7, 1959), a committee was appointed "whose task it will be to investigate how work on the density distribution for different components of the galactic population in both low and high latitudes can best be promoted." It is strongly urged that this committee will publish a plan in the near future for joint studies of the problems of density distribution as well as those of motions. There has been, so far, a great deal of wasted effort because different astronomers have chosen different fields of observation; we therefore know the spectral classes and magnitudes in some fields and only motions in others. This regrettable confusion of approach should be avoided in the future.

The areas at high latitudes to be investigated can be chosen to coincide with Kapteyn's Selected Areas. (See the Appendix to this volume.) The suitability of Kapteyn's areas *in* the galactic plane must be considered carefully; it is open to doubt, since Kapteyn, in making his choice, knew nothing of spiral structure or of the interstellar absorption. Both of these factors should undoubtedly influence the choice of the areas for observation.

REFERENCES

ABRAMS, J. W.	1947	*Ap. J.*, **105**, 268.
BLAAUW, A.	1955	*I.A.U. Symp.*, No. 1 (Cambridge: Cambridge University Press).

Bok, B. J.   1937   *The Distribution of the Stars in Space* (Chicago: University of Chicago Press).

Chalonge, D.   1958   *Ric. Astr. Specola Vaticana*, **5**, 345 ("Stellar Populations").

Crowder, H. K.   1959   *A.J.*, **64**, 22.

Elvius, T.   1955   *Stockholms Obs. Ann.*, **18**, No. 7.
                                    1956   *Ibid.*, **19**, No. 3.

Gyldenkerne, K.   1958   *Ann. d'ap.*, **21**, 26 and 77.

Halliday, I.   1955   *Ap. J.*, **122**, 222.

Johnson, H. L., and
   Morgan, W. W.   1953   *Ap. J.*, **117**, 313.

Luyten, W. J.   1938   *Pub. Astr. Obs. Univ. of Minnesota*, **2**, No. 7.
                                    1941   *Ann. New York Acad. Sci.*, **42**, 201.

Malmquist, K. G.   1924   *Medd. Lunds Astr. Obs.*, Ser. II, No. 32, p. 64.
                                    1925   *Ibid.*, Ser. I, No. 106.
                                    1936   *Stockholms Obs. Medd.*, No. 26.

McCuskey, S. W.   1956   *Ap. J.*, **123**, 458.

Morgan, W. W.,
   Keenan, P. C., and
   Kellman, E.   1943   *An Atlas of Stellar Spectra* (Chicago: University of Chicago Press).

Oort, J. H.   1932   *B.A.N.*, **6**, 249.

Petrie, R. M.   1953   *Pub. Dom. Ap. Obs. Victoria*, **9**, 251.

Petrie, R. M., and
   Moyls, B. N.   1956   *Pub. Dom. Ap. Obs. Victoria*, **10**, 287.

Rhijn, P. J. van   1936   *Pub. Kapteyn Astr. Lab. Groningen*, No. 47.
                                    1939   *Ibid.*, No. 49.

Rhijn, P. J. van, and
   Schwassmann, A.   1935   *Zs. f. Ap.*, **10**, 161.

Russell, H. N., and
   Moore, C. E.   1938   *Ap. J.*, **87**, 389.
                                    1940   *Ibid.*, **92**, 354.

Salpeter, E. E.   1955   *Ap. J.*, **121**, 161.

Strömgren, B.   1958   *Ric. Astr. Specola Vaticana*, **5**, 385 ("Stellar Populations").

Trumpler, P. J., and
   Weaver, H. F.   1953   *Statistical Astronomy* (Berkeley and Los Angeles: University of California Press).

Westerlund, B.   1951   *Uppsala Astr. Obs. Ann.*, **3**, No. 6.
                                    1953   *Ibid.*, No. 8 and No. 10.

Wilson, O. C.   1959   *Ap. J.*, **130**, 499.

Wilson, O. C., and
   Bappu, M. K. V.   1957   *Ap. J.*, **125**, 661.

CHAPTER 3

Distribution of Common Stars in Intermediate and High Galactic Latitudes

T. ELVIUS
Uppsala Observatory

§ 1. INTRODUCTION

Our knowledge of the three-dimensional distribution of the common stars in the galactic system is confined to a limited region around the sun. By *common stars* we shall mean main-sequence stars and ordinary giants of spectral types A–K. The overwhelming majority of objects recognizable in high and intermediate galactic latitudes belong to these groups. With the methods so far available for classifying stars of faint apparent magnitudes, we may be able to derive, in regions where the interstellar absorption is small, the distribution of the ordinary A stars or of the giants of types G and K up to two kiloparsecs, whereas for the K-dwarfs we can only reach a couple of hundred parsecs.

Most of the stars of these types are concentrated in a relatively narrow layer surrounding what is generally called the "galactic plane." The data concerning the distribution of the common stars *in* the galactic plane are described by McCuskey in chapter 1 of this volume. Their distribution off the plane is of considerable interest not only for the sake of completeness, but also in order to understand some of the dynamical properties of the stellar system in our vicinity (cf. chap. 21 of this volume).

In order to derive the three-dimensional distribution, we must analyze data concerning the apparent surface distribution in those galactic latitudes that are usually called "high" ($|b|$ approx. $> 40°$) and "intermediate" (approx. $40° > |b| > 10°$). Although the interstellar absorption in these latitudes has considerably less influence on the density analysis than in the "low" galactic latitudes (approx. $|b| < 10°$), it cannot be neglected. In early investigations the

41

influence of absorption on the interpretation of star counts $A(m)$ was estimated in a rather schematic manner, and this is still sometimes the case. Experience shows, however, that even at high latitudes, in order to obtain satisfactory results, we must determine the amount of interstellar matter and its distribution along the line of sight by accurate color studies. They must be made separately for every region to be investigated.

§ 2. THE COORDINATES AND THE SUN'S POSITION

When discussing the space distribution of stars, it is convenient to describe the position of a star, or of a volume element, by polar coordinates: galactic longitude l, galactic latitude b (coordinates in the "old system" are called l^I, b^I, and those in the "new" IAU system l^{II}, b^{II}), and the distance from the sun r along the line of sight, r being corrected for absorption.

In studies of the distribution of stars on levels above and below the galactic plane, it is profitable to use a linear coordinate, z, measured perpendicular to the galactic plane (defined by $b = 0$). $z = r \sin b$, and accordingly is counted positive on the northern side of the galactic plane, negative on the southern side.

It is not quite clear whether this galactic plane $z = 0$, in which the sun is situated by definition, really coincides with a plane defined as the symmetry surface for the masses in our surroundings. On the contrary, many results indicate that this surface undulates more or less around a "mean plane," and it is quite possible (see, for example, van Tulder 1942 and Blaauw 1960) that the sun is situated about 10 or 20 parsecs north of the mass-symmetry plane. To estimate the sun's position is an intricate problem, illustrated by the fact that Schilt (1950) found the sun to be somewhat south of this plane, whereas van Rnijn (1955, 1956), investigating the differences in density for positive and negative z-values, found the sun to be 18 parsecs north of the symmetry plane, from A stars, and 5 parsecs north, from K-giants. (Cf. F. Becker's, 1939, data in Tables 4 and 5.) It seems safe to conclude from present data that the sun is situated about 10 parsecs north of the symmetry plane defined by the mass distribution in the z-direction.

In some investigations dealt with in the present chapter, the z-coordinate is assumed to suffice as the only coordinate in describing the space distribution. This is the case, for instance, if the investigation is restricted to a relatively limited polar cap, or if it is assumed that the surfaces of constant density are planes parallel to the galactic plane. If deviations from these assumptions are to be studied, it is necessary to supplement z by cylindrical or rectangular coordinates in order to indicate the projection on the galactic plane of the star, or the volume element, in question. For the rectangular coordinates, x and y, one may use the conventional system based on the direction of the galactic center and the direction perpendicular to it in the galactic plane.

§ 3. METHODS FOR THE DENSITY ANALYSIS

There are two types of methods used to determine the density distribution according to z. One category comprises methods which are essentially the same as those used for regions close to the galactic plane: we attempt to find the relative density distribution $D(r)$ from the surface distribution $A(m)$ of the apparent magnitudes; the luminosity function $\varphi(M)$ is either assumed to be known or is derived in the process of the analysis. For the actual methods employed in solving the general equation,

$$A(m) = \omega \int_0^\infty \varphi(M)\, D(r)\, r^2 dr,$$

see van Rhijn's chapter 2 in this volume.

When $A(m)$ represents general star counts, we must use a general luminosity function, valid for all kinds of stars. [In this chapter, the term "general star counts" will refer to numbers $A(m)$ irrespective of spectral type.] This function has mainly been derived from relatively nearby stars, and hence represents a sample from layers close to the galactic plane. It was realized long ago that the density gradient $d \log D(z)/dz$ is quite different for different spectral and luminosity groups. In the analysis it will consequently be necessary to take into account the variation of $\varphi(M)$ with z.

This is not necessary if stars are separated into suitable intervals of spectral type and luminosity class (e.g., main-sequence A stars, FV stars, giants of G-type, and so on). In that case, $\varphi(M)$ will be characterized by a relatively small dispersion, $\sigma(M)$, around a mean absolute magnitude M_0, and to some extent $\varphi(M)$ may be assumed to be independent of z. This will be somewhat inaccurate because of the differing percentages of high-velocity stars, even if the spectral groups are meant to be homogeneous.

Interstellar absorption $a(r)$ is now usually taken into account by considering the observed distribution of color excesses in the relevant regions. An erroneous estimate of its amount will have serious consequences. As an example, let us assume that we have neglected an absorption of 0.5 magnitude; if we correct for it, we must decrease the observed apparent distance moduli $(m - M)$ for stars behind the absorbing cloud by 0.5 magnitude. As we have $\log r = 0.2 (m - M) - 0.2\, a(r) + 1$, $\log r$ must then be diminished by 0.1, which corresponds to a 20 per cent smaller distance for stars behind the absorption. Simultaneously, $\log D(r)$ will be increased by 0.3, that is, the densities will be increased by a factor of 2 for the volume elements behind the cloud. The effect on a graph of $\log D(z)$ as a function of z will be, at higher levels where the gradient is negative, that the curves become less steep when the correction for absorption is applied. It is interesting to note that the same effect on $D(r)$ and r will occur if the absolute magnitude is increased by 0.5 magnitude for stars beyond a certain distance, as this, too, corresponds to a contraction of the distance scale.

In another category of methods used in deriving $D(z)$, a dynamical condition is introduced (see chap. 21). We find, under certain equilibrium conditions, and for a specific class of stars, a relationship between the density gradient, $d \log D(z)/dz$, the mean square speed $\langle Z^2 \rangle$ in the z-direction, and the acceleration K_z produced by the gravitational field perpendicular to the galactic plane. If $\langle Z^2 \rangle$ does not change with z, the density distribution for this class of stars will then follow the law,

$$D(z) = D(0) \exp \left(\int_0^z K_z \, dz / \langle Z^2 \rangle \right).$$

This density function must be coordinated with the star numbers $A(m)$ and the luminosity function $\varphi(M)$, the above general equation between these quantities remaining valid. Since investigations of this kind will be discussed in chapter 21 of this volume, we shall only summarize results in this chapter.

§ 4. SOME EARLY DETERMINATIONS OF $D(z)$

Investigators of stellar distributions in directions other than those close to the galactic plane have usually focused their attention on the general decrease of density in the z-direction. Accounts of pioneering studies, which are usually attempts to present an over-all picture of the stellar system from general star counts, have been given by von der Pahlen (1937); more recent results have been summarized by W. Becker (1950).

In many of the earlier investigations, as well as in recent work, use has been made of the large amount of observational material gathered in Kapteyn's Selected Areas. Van Rhijn's tables (1929), which give the values of log $A(m)$ based on the Selected Area material for various galactic longitudes and latitudes, were particularly useful for the study of the three-dimensional density distribution. The extensive observational data published or still being collected in the Plan of Selected Areas will continue to be of great importance for this work. Reference to the Plan of Selected Areas is given in the Appendix to this volume.

The importance of investigations based on homogeneous spectral groups was first shown by Lindblad (1926) and by Petersson (1927), who found a much sharper decrease for the A stars than for the late-type giants, in spite of the rather small difference in absolute magnitudes.

Table 1 contains results for stars of all spectral classes combined. The second column gives the distribution for all absolute magnitudes as derived by Seares (1928) from counts of faint stars, and the next columns, the results for successive groups of absolute magnitudes given by van Rhijn and Schwassmann (1935), whose analysis was based on spectral data for a number of Selected Areas with an average galactic latitude of $+50°$. As they felt that the luminosity function for the apparently faint stars was not sufficiently well known, the authors attempted to estimate the percentage of dwarfs and giants from mean parallaxes.

The very different decrease in density with height over the galactic plane for stars of different absolute magnitudes is quite apparent from their results. The $D(z)$-distribution by Bok and MacRae (1941), also incorporated in Table 1, is based on material from the galactic polar caps and was originally published only in the form of graphs. Bok and MacRae made use of the available data pertaining to spectral groups to get "the best possible representation" of the star counts when interpreting them as sums of stars from different z-levels. Oort (1932), in an investigation of the gravitational force exerted by the system in the direction perpendicular to the galactic plane, derived $D(z)$ for some spectral groups, using the second method mentioned in Section 3. Some of these results are given in Table 2. More recent results are described below.

TABLE 1

DENSITY DISTRIBUTION PERPENDICULAR TO THE GALACTIC PLANE, $D(z)$, IN THE VICINITY OF THE SUN

z PARSECS	SEARES (1928)	VAN RHIJN AND SCHWASSMANN (1935)					BOK AND MACRAE (1941) (Published as curves)					
		$M =$					$M =$					
		-4	-2	0	$+4$	$+8$	-2	0	$+2$	$+4$	$+6$	$+8$
0....	1.00	1.00	1.00	1.00	1.00	1.00	1.00	1.00	1.00	1.00	1.00	1.00
125....	0.73	0.11	0.16	0.50	0.73	0.80	0.10	0.22	0.40	0.70	0.80	0.90
250....	0.40	0.03	0.05	0.16	0.33	0.50	0.03	0.10	0.14	0.35	0.54	0.72
500....	0.17	0.00	0.02	0.07	0.13	0.27	0.01	0.03	0.04	0.12	0.26	0.45
1000....	0.07	....	0.00	0.02	0.04	0.12	0.001	0.003	0.007	0.03	0.06	0.16
1500....	0.04	....	....	0.01	0.03	0.09	.....	.....	0.002	0.005	0.013	0.06

TABLE 2

DENSITY DISTRIBUTION $D(z)$ DERIVED BY OORT FROM DYNAMICAL CONSIDERATIONS

z PARSECS	OORT (1932)			OORT (1936) (Published as curves)
	A0–A9	F0–F9	Late Giants	Dwarfs $M_{pg} > +4.5$
0........	1.00	1.00	1.00	1.00
125........	0.58	0.83	0.89	0.85
250........	0.14	0.48	0.63	0.54
500........	0.03	0.14	0.29	0.21
1000........	....	0.02	0.07	0.06
1500........	....	0.01	0.02	0.024
2000........	....	....	0.01	0.014

§ 5. MODERN DETERMINATIONS OF $D(z)$

5.1. LATE-TYPE GIANTS

Because of their relatively high luminosity combined with their comparatively rich abundance on high levels, the late-type giants have been considered
especially valuable in studying the galactic structure far away from the galactic
plane. For this reason, they are treated in this section, before other types.

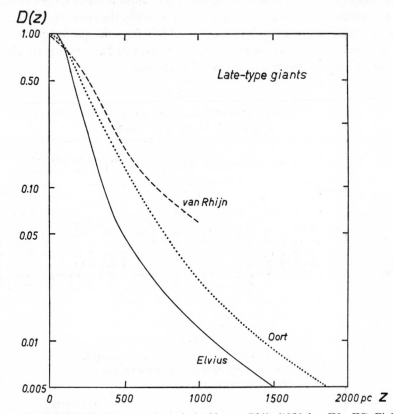

FIG. 1.—$D(z)$ curves for late-type giants derived by van Rhijn (1956, for gK0–gK5), Elvius
(1962, for gG5–gK6), and Oort (1960, for gK0, with dynamical considerations).

Table 3 contains recent results concerning $D(z)$ for the late-type giants. Some
of these are shown in Figure 1. Hill (1960) studied the density distribution and
the velocity distribution of K-type giants in determining the force K_z. Numbers
of the K-type giants, $A(m)$, were deduced from star counts of K-type stars,
combined with estimates of the percentage of giants from proper motion distributions. Hill's results indicate a steeper decrease of density with z than that
found by Oort (1932) (cf. Table 2).

The values for K_z found by Hill for $z > 500$ pc were incompatible with the requirements set by Poisson's equation. Oort (1960) investigated this matter in detail and found that a different interpretation of the star counts, which does not lead to a conflict with Poisson's equation, is possible. The corresponding density distribution (Table 3) shows a somewhat steeper decrease for $z > 500$ pc than the one derived by Hill. The two distributions are by no means independent, since the authors used the same luminosity function and the same velocity distribution, except for a component of high-velocity giants introduced by Oort.

TABLE 3

DENSITY DISTRIBUTION $D(z)$ FOR LATE-TYPE GIANTS NORMALIZED
TO UNITY AT z EITHER 0 OR 50 PARSECS

z PARSECS	ELVIUS gG5–gK6		VAN RHIJN (1956) gK0–gK5		HILL (1960)* gK	OORT (1960)* gK	UPGREN (1962)			
	(1951)	(1962)	Pos. z	Neg. z			G5–7 III	K0 III	K3–5 III	G5–M III
0............	1.00	......	1.00	1.00	1.00	1.00	......	......	......	......
50............	......	1.00	0.90	0.80	0.91	0.95	1.00	1.00	1.00	1.00
125............	0.52	0.68	0.71	0.61	0.70	0.73	1.00	0.54	0.96	0.56
250............	0.17	0.24	0.52	0.42	0.37	0.42	0.96	0.22	0.80	0.27
500............	0.041	0.047	0.17	0.21	0.13	0.13	0.71	0.07	0.50	0.12
1000............	0.011	0.012	0.06	0.05	0.035	0.025	0.57	0.03	0.07	0.05
1500............	......	0.005	......	......	0.016	0.008	......	......	......	......
Mean M_{pg} or M_B used.........	+1.7		about +2.0		+2.2	+2.2	+1.0	+1.8	+1.4	......
Absolute density corresponding to 1.00 in the table (stars/10^6 cub. pc.)......	400		300		......	......	3	140	6	270

* Published as curve.

The second column in Table 3 gives results by Elvius [1951, 1962; the revised values (1962) including material from the catalogues by Elvius (1955) and by Elvius and Lodén (1960)]. In contrast to most other investigators, Elvius determined luminosity classes for all stars of types G and K in his fields (Selected Areas), so that no further estimates of the relative number of giants and dwarfs are needed. The effective limiting magnitude for these spectral classifications is about 13.5 (pg). For each area, color data are available, and hence, the run of the absorption with distance can be determined. The data given by the author in Table 3 refer to high or intermediate latitudes in the sector $90° < l^{II} < 150°$. A curve $D(z)$ adopted on the basis of these results is drawn in Figure 1, for comparison with the results of other investigators, and in Figure 2 for comparison with other spectral groups. Special weight has been given to those areas in which the color excesses indicate small or insignificant amounts of absorption. As the areas of highest latitudes are found near $b = +60°$, the resulting $D(z)$ is not quite representative for a column in the immediate neighborhood of the sun, but only for a comparatively limited region in x, y at some distance from the sun in the sector mentioned above. This is illustrated in Figure 6, which shows the $D(z)$ curves of late-type giants found from Selected Areas; their directions differ from the direction of the galactic pole.

The data for K-giants given in Table 3, taken from van Rhijn (1956), which refer to latitude zones at $|b| > 20°$, were derived from counts of late-type stars in spectral catalogues. A general luminosity law for the K stars had been adopted, the division between giants and dwarfs having been taken at $M_{pg} = +3.5$ (the average value for the giants being between 1.5 and 2.0). The absorption was usually estimated from tables of the variation of color excess with galactic latitude (van Rhijn 1949). The asymmetry in $D(z)$ with respect to the galactic plane, mentioned in Section 2, is evident from the table.

Upgren (1962) has made a survey of the late-type stars to a limiting magnitude of about 13.0(pg) in the northern galactic polar cap, covering an area of nearly 400 square degrees. With the spectroscopic dispersion used, there were many cases in which Upgren was not able to discriminate between giants and dwarfs, especially for the fainter apparent magnitudes. He therefore tried to estimate the relative number of giants and dwarfs by comparison with Malmquist's catalogue (1960) which covers an area of nearly 70 square degrees around the north galactic pole. The spectral and luminosity determinations given by Malmquist were made by the same spectrophotometric analyses of short spectra as were used by Elvius. Down to the limiting magnitude of 13.5(pg), it was found that practically all late-type stars could be classified as to luminosity.

Analyzing the distribution of late-type giants from the star numbers so estimated, Upgren assumed that all of them are situated beyond the absorbing layer; he accepted Hubble's classical value for the absorption, 0.25 magnitude (pg) in the polar direction. In contrast to the Swedish investigators who have used a common mean absolute magnitude of $+1.7$(pg) for the giants, Upgren applied different values for the spectral subclasses. Upgren's $D(z)$, for all giants, has about the same slope for the higher levels as van Rhijn's and Hill's curves. For the lower levels, his results indicate a sharper gradient, but the density does not decrease as quickly as that found by Elvius. Upgren finds quite a different density decrease for different subtypes, as is shown in the selection of his values in Table 3. The absolute density values (number of stars per 10^6 cubic pc) corresponding to the unity used for $D(z)$ are also given in this table. It should be pointed out that both Upgren and Elvius normalized their density for z about 50 pc, as it is very difficult to find, with any reliability, the density dependence with z for the first 100 parsecs. According to Upgren, about 90 per cent of the giants close to the galactic plane belong to types K0 and K1–2 III, but at a level of 1000 parsecs, only 40 per cent fall within these spectral types. As this spectral group has the steepest density gradient, the low-level portion of the curve for all types taken together is also rather steep, but on the higher levels, the other types gain more influence. For G5–7 giants, the curve derived by Upgren is remarkably flat; this result might arise from the high number of stars which Upgren calls giants, classified as dwarfs by Malmquist. The high luminosity ($M = +1.0$ in the B-system) which Upgren adopts for the G giants also has a strong influence; for the early K stars he uses a value which is nearly one magnitude fainter.

The intricate problems concerning the $D(z)$ distribution of late-type giants may approach a solution when we have access to the results of the current investigation by Malmquist on the basis of his above-mentioned catalogue (1960). Preliminary results by Malmquist (1962) seem to indicate that the absorption in the direction of the north galactic pole is much heavier than has previously been thought. Color data as well as irregularities in the apparent star numbers, indicate that the absorption may be concentrated in two layers, one at a level of about 200 parsecs, the other at about twice this distance. Their total absorption may be about 0.6 magnitude (pg). These circumstances will influence the density analysis for both near and distant stars (cf. Ljunggren, 1965).

A comparison of the results in Table 3 reveals differences which are not easy to understand. It may be that investigations like those of Elvius, van Rhijn, and Oort in which the data for $D(z)$ represent a fairly wide region in x, y give a smoothed representation for $D(z)$ over a large volume, whereas, in a narrow column centered on the sun, there are irregularities in the density distribution. This matter is discussed in more detail in Section 6. Whether or not these irregularities are confined to the late-type giants or extend to other spectral groups also, may perhaps be settled in the future. Some discrepancies may possibly be traced back to classification differences.

In the investigations referred to, it has not been possible to establish the difference in $D(z)$ between the "weak-line" and the "strong-line" stars (Roman 1950, 1952), which would be expected from the different velocity dispersions of these types at $z = 0$, demonstrated, for instance, by Vyssotsky (1957) and Blaauw (1958). Upgren, at the Warner and Swasey Observatory, attacked this problem, but was unable to find suitable criteria, using short spectra. Investigators in Sweden are also studying this matter. Methods for the separation of apparently faint objects into such categories would greatly aid us in the study of the density distribution in the z-direction. A recent investigation by Yoss (1961) of late-type stars of comparatively bright apparent magnitudes indicates that giants with weak cyanogen absorption have higher dispersion in space velocity and less concentration toward the galactic plane than giant stars with normal cyanogen absorption.

5.2. THE A STARS

For the A stars, the density decreases much more steeply with increasing z than for the late-type giants (see Fig. 2). Some results are given in Table 4. Becker (1939) investigated the Selected Areas in the southern sky, and obtained, without correction for absorption, $D(z)$ from fields at high and intermediate latitudes, which he found to be somewhat different for positive and negative z.

Elvius (1951), investigating the Stockholm Selected Area observations, derived a $D(z)$ curve, taking into account the absorption in the individual areas. As these areas are rather small, the high-latitude regions comprise too few A stars, so that the main values given in Table 4 come from three areas with a

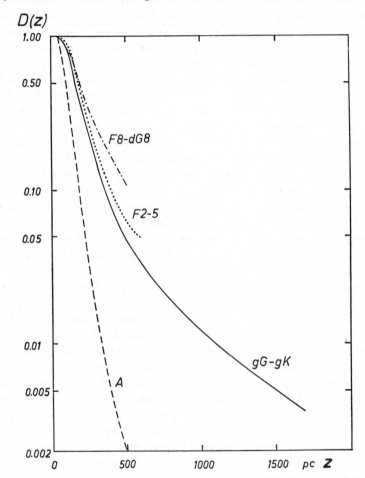

FIG. 2.—$D(z)$ curves for different spectral and luminosity groups as derived by Elvius (1962).

mean $|b|$ of about 17°. They may therefore possibly not represent the region close to the sun.

Van Rhijn (1955), in an investigation of the A0–A5 stars, similar to that of the gK stars mentioned in section 5.1, paid particular attention to a possible relation between star density and hydrogen density. A positive correlation was found to be present for z-levels close to the galactic plane. For levels beyond about 250 parsecs the correlation disappears. This result would imply that one

TABLE 4

DENSITY DISTRIBUTION $D(z)$ FOR THE A STARS, NORMALIZED
TO UNITY AT z EITHER 0 OR 50 PARSECS

z PARSECS	F. BECKER (1939) B8–A4		ELVIUS (1951) B8–A3	VAN RHIJN (1955) A0–A5			UPGREN (1962) A0–A5
	Pos. z	Neg. z		Hydrogen Density			
				Large	Small	Zero	
0..........	1.00	1.00	....	2.50	1.50	0.90	....
50..........	0.46	0.60	1.00	1.60	1.16	0.68	1.00
100..........	0.23	0.33	0.47	1.11	0.82	0.45	0.51
150..........	0.16	0.20	0.20	....	....	....	0.20
200..........	0.10	0.13	0.07	0.37	0.31	0.21	0.082
300..........	0.03	0.06	....	0.08	0.08	0.08	0.022
500..........	....	....	....	0.03	0.03	0.03	0.005
1000..........	....	....	....	....	....	....	0.001
Mean M_{pg}*.....	+0.7 (A0)		+1.1 (A0)	+0.6 (A0)			+1.0 for all
Absolute density corresponding to 1.00 in the table (stars/10⁶ cub. pc.)......	400		1500†	700			450

* Becker, Elvius, and van Rhijn assume varying mean absolute magnitude with spectral type.
† 750 if the mean absolute magnitude is shifted to +0.6 for A0.

will obtain different gradients over different x, y-regions, depending upon the amount of hydrogen present. In Table 4, van Rhijn's results for $D(z)$ have been given for large, small, and zero hydrogen density, respectively. The unit for $D(z)$ is valid for the region close to the sun.

Upgren (1962), in connection with the aforementioned investigation of late-type stars, has analyzed the material of early-type stars published by Slettebak and Stock (1959) for the nearly 400-square-degree region around the north galactic pole. He assumes that all stars belong to the main sequence and are situated behind the absorbing layer. For the A0–A5 stars, Upgren finds nearly the same steep gradient for the first couple of hundred parsecs as derived by Elvius and by van Rhijn. For higher levels, he confirms van Rhijn's curve, which flattens out gradually, even if the gradients remain higher for the A stars than for other types.

It seems worthwhile to point out that it is not quite clear whether this density distribution for levels far from the galactic plane represents the same kind of A stars as we find close to the galactic plane. When interpreting this density curve, it should be remembered that van Rhijn (1960) found that the dispersion in the linear velocities of the A stars increases with distance from the galactic plane. He was of the opinion that this is not caused by an admixture of sub-dwarfs to the normal A stars, yet he leaves the question open concerning possible astrophysical differences between the two groups of A stars with different dispersions and distributions which, he assumes, cause the observed phenomenon.

On the other hand, investigations by Woolley (1957) and collaborators, on the dependence between density and velocity dispersion of A stars, do not confirm these results of van Rhijn. Wayman (1961), studying radial velocities of A stars in the southern galactic cap, did not find a change with z in the velocity dispersion perpendicular to the galactic plane within the first 400 parsecs. Jones (1962), investigating the A0 stars in a cylinder centered on the sun with its axis in the z-direction, found the density of the A0 stars to be constant between a level about 60 parsecs below the sun to about 100 parsecs above it. The analysis of stars in the polar cap by Malmquist, referred to in the preceding subsection, will probably also help in outlining more of the structure of the density distribution of the A stars. For the southern polar cap see Bok and Basinski (1964).

5.3. The F Stars

The density dependence on z for F stars has been derived by some of the above investigators. It is tacitly assumed and supported by color investigations, that practically all F stars found in the surveys at high or intermediate latitudes belong to the main sequence. Upgren (1962) includes among F stars the late A subclasses according to Slettebak and Stock. These stars are probably classified as F0 by Elvius and Becker. Some results for the F stars are given in Table 5.

For the F0–F5 stars, Becker (1939) found somewhat different distributions for the northern and southern polar caps, as in the case of the A stars. Elvius' data (1962) for F2–F5 are the result of an attempt to summarize the analyses previously published (1951, 1955, 1956), with special emphasis on a certain, narrow region x, y. Since it was difficult to find a reliable luminosity calibration of the spectrophotometric measurements for the F0 stars, this subclass was excluded from the analysis. Upgren (1962) used the subclasses A7–F2; it is therefore not surprising that his $D(z)$ dependence is steeper than Elvius'. Moreover, Elvius has taken the interstellar absorption into full account, whereas Upgren has corrected for only a small amount. Up to about 400 parsecs, Elvius obtained nearly the same curve for the relative density as he found for all the late-type giants (see Fig. 2). Beyond this level, the curve for the F stars flattens out more than for the giants. All three investigators find about 800 stars per 10^6 cubic parsec for their respective groups in the solar neighborhood. Surprisingly, Ramberg (1957), in his Lacerta investigation, found only about a quarter of this density for the same group, using the same sort of observational material as Elvius.

Recently, Upgren (1963a) determined space densities near the northern galactic pole for the F5–G2 dwarfs and found a substantially steeper decline than for the G dwarfs. Bok and Basinski (1964), investigating the southern polar cap, found a similar density curve for a color group identified with the F stars.

5.4. Late-Type Dwarfs

We know less about the z-distribution for the G and K main-sequence types than for those previously discussed, because for higher levels we must rely on the

TABLE 5

Density Distribution $D(z)$ for the F and dG Stars, Normalized
to Unity at z Either 0 or 50 Parsecs

z PARSECS	F. Becker (1939) F0–F5		Elvius (1962) F2–F5	Upgren (1962) A7–F2	Elvius (1962) F8–dG8	Upgren (1963a) F5–G2V
	Pos. z	Neg. z				
0.............	1.00	1.00	....	....	....	....
50............	0.67	0.83	1.00	1.00	1.00	1.00
100...........	0.44	0.64	0.90	0.23	0.85	0.65
150...........	0.36	0.46	0.65	0.12	0.65	0.50
200...........	0.30	0.32	0.40	0.063	0.45	0.36
300...........	....	0.21	0.18	0.024	0.26	0.23
500.,.........	....	....	0.06	0.007	0.12	....
1000..........	....	....	....	0.001	....	....
Mean M_{pg}........	+3.3		+3.0	+3.0	+5.0	+4.5
Absolute density corresponding to 1.00 in table (stars/10^6 cub. pc.)........	750		800	900	5000	5500

results from integrated counts of faint stars, as the limiting magnitudes for the spectral surveys are too low to permit penetration to distances comparable to those we are able to reach for the other spectral groups. A good deal of information may therefore be obtained from Table 1. For dwarfs of absolute magnitude about +6, i.e., about dG8, the density falls to about $\frac{1}{20}$ of its value in the solar neighborhood within the first kiloparsec in z. For $M = +8$ the corresponding value is $\frac{1}{6}$. (See also the last column of Table 2.)

The spectral surveys available for the dwarfs show controversial results. Elvius (1956, 1962), from his Selected Areas material for the group F8–dG8 (see the last column of Table 5), found a density decrease in agreement with results by van de Kamp and Vyssotsky (1936) in their study of proper motions, as well as with the data in Table 1. Upgren (1962), on the other hand, found a rather constant density up to the limiting distance of his material which is about 200 parsecs in z for the earlier subclasses, dG5 and dG8, and successively less for the later spectral sequence.

Examination of the author's curves for a group of Selected Areas (Elvius 1956, p. 76) reveals rather different absolute densities for the individual areas, but at a level of about 100 parsecs the same general relative decrease with z exists. By combining the material from the areas studied, the author (1962) derived the general $D(z)$ curve for the F8–G8 dwarfs which is included in Figure 2 and tabulated in Table 5. In these results there are indications that the absolute density has a maximum (with a density of about 5000–8000 stars per 10^6 cubic pcs) somewhere between $z = 50$ and $z = 100$ parsecs. Near the sun these areas indicate lower density. Upgren finds a mean value of 1300 stars per 10^6 cubic parsecs for the dG5–dG7 stars up to a limiting z of 230 parsecs. Ramberg (1957) also found comparatively low values close to the sun, about 2000 for the types F8–dG8 in the field in Lacerta, pointing toward $l^{II} = 101°$ and $b^{II} = -8°$.

5.5 VARIATION OF $\varphi(M)$ WITH z

Upgren (1963b), on the basis of his investigations of the density variation with z of various spectral groups, has computed $\varphi(M, z)$ for M from -2 to $+5$ up to $z = 500$ pc. For distances less than 100 pc from the galactic plane, the luminosity function is in good agreement with that generally accepted for the solar neighborhood. For higher levels the variation is similar to that found by Bok and MacRae (1941). See Table 1.

§ 6. THREE-DIMENSIONAL DISTRIBUTION

The investigations of the three-dimensional distribution of the common stars can be divided into three groups. The first are the early attempts to obtain an over-all picture of what was then believed to be the whole galactic system, by Seeliger, Schwarzschild, Charlier, Kapteyn, and Seares. The comprehensive treatise on stellar statistics by von der Pahlen (1937) includes accounts of their work.

The second group contains studies in which the variation with x and y of the density distribution on different z-levels is derived from comparisons with the $D(z)$ obtained for the polar directions, i.e., for x and y close to zero. This method has been proposed by Vashakidze (1937) and Oort (1938). Oort's work, which is based on star counts in the Selected Areas and on corrections for absorption derived from nebular counts, is of special importance for the problems under consideration. By studying the available color data, especially for B stars, Oort concluded that one can assume the absorption to occur close to the galactic plane and in front of the stars in areas away from the galactic circle. He then derived the large-scale variations of stellar density by comparing the observed star counts with the numbers of stars expected, if the surfaces of equal density were parallel to the galactic plane. The expected number of stars, of apparent magnitude m_b at latitude b, denoted by $A_b(m_b)$, would be related to the number of stars in the same z-level at $b = 90°$, $A_{90}(m_{90})$ by the equation

$$A_b(m_b) = \operatorname{cosec}^3 b \, A_{90}(m_{90}) ,$$

where the two apparent magnitudes involved are related by

$$m_{90} = m_b + 5 \log \sin b - \delta(a) ,$$

$\delta(a)$ representing the difference in absorption between the two directions. It follows from Oort's conclusion regarding the position of the interstellar matter,

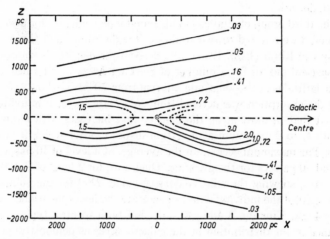

Fig. 3.—General density distribution of all types of stars together according to Oort (1938), in the intersection of the galactic system with a plane perpendicular to that of the Galaxy, passing through the sun and the center of the system. The dotted parts of the equidensity lines are extrapolated. Unit of density is the density near the sun.

that $\delta(a)$ is independent of m. It is of interest that this relation is independent of the variation of the luminosity function with z.

From the deviations between the star counts observed in various directions and the expected numbers of stars calculated according to the above relation, Oort derived the excess, or deficiency of stars as a function of the level z and the position x, y. For the high levels, Oort (1938) found that the surfaces of equal density are inclined on both sides of the galactic plane at an angle of about 10°, corresponding to an increase in density toward the galactic center. Closer to the galactic plane Oort found evidence that the sun is situated in a region of relatively low density. Figure 3 (from Oort's paper) shows the results projected on an x, z-plane (x-axis pointing to the galactic center).

The picture deviates from the early concept of the sun situated in a "local system." Bok and MacRae, van Rhijn, and Elvius, quoted below, also show that in levels above or below the galactic plane the stellar density in certain directions is higher than the values in the same levels above or below the immediate vicinity of the sun.

Bok and MacRae (1941) used methods similar to Oort's, adopting the $D(z)$ distribution of the polar cap and incorporating revised data on the amount and run of the absorption taken from various investigations. Their analysis takes into account the spread of distances for stars of a given apparent magnitude. In the sector $60° < l^{II} < 120°$, Bok and MacRae found densities increasing with increasing projected distance from the sun. In this sector, some of the summarizing figures for the galactic layer in McCuskey's chapter 1 also show high absolute densities.

In the third group of studies $D(r)$ is found independently for every direction. In section 5 we referred to two studies of the distribution of the A and the gK stars by van Rhijn (1955, 1956), who derived the density distribution $D(r)$ for these spectral groups for a number of Selected Areas in intermediate and low galactic latitudes in the longitude interval from 70° to 170° in l^{II}. The distribution of the absorption was derived from color data for each individual area. It appeared that in most areas the density first increases with r, and therefore also with z, to a maximum at a certain distance, after which it gradually decreases. The maximum occurs, on the average, at a level of 40 parsecs for the A stars and 50 parsecs for the gK stars. Diagrams, for a level of $+100$ and -100 parsecs in z, showing the relative density values $D(r)$ for the points where the lines of sight of the individual areas penetrate the levels mentioned are given in Figures 4 and 5 for the A and gK stars. For both spectral types, there is a resemblance to the distribution in the galactic layer as demonstrated in Figures 7 and 12 of McCuskey's chapter 1 in this volume.

As was indicated in the preceding section, van Rhijn found a correlation between the distribution of A stars in the region with high hydrogen intensity, using the radio data by van de Hulst, Muller, and Oort (1954), in the layers relatively close to the galactic plane.

An investigation of local deviations from the general density functions, $D(z)$, to which we referred in the preceding sections, is possible on the basis of the observations in Kapteyn's Selected Areas collected by the author. They cover the galactic latitudes from $-17°$ to $+58°$ within the longitude interval $85° < l^{II} < 160°$. For about 3100 stars in 19 areas, spectral types and luminosity classes have been determined to the limiting photographic magnitude 13.5; for all of them and for about 1000 additional stars down to magnitude 14.0, magnitudes and color indices have been measured (Elvius 1951, 1955; Elvius and Lodén 1960). Intrinsic colors have been determined by Elvius (1951) and Elvius

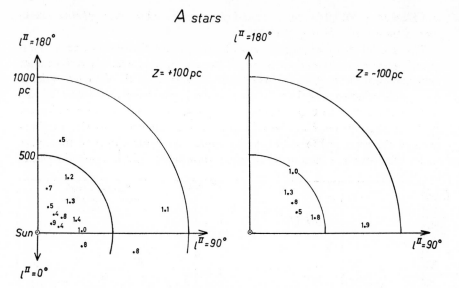

Fig. 4.—Density distribution of the A stars for the levels $z = +100$ pc and $z = -100$ pc found by van Rhijn (1955) from Selected Area data. Unit is the A-star density in the solar neighborhood.

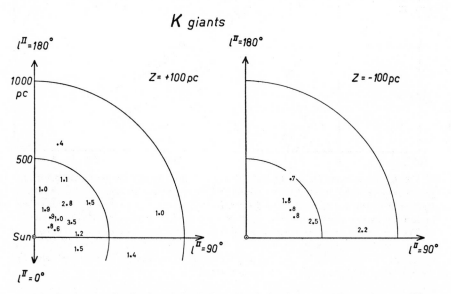

Fig. 5.—Density distribution of the K giants for the levels $z = +100$ pc and $z = -100$ pc found by van Rhijn (1956) from Selected Area data. Unit is the gK-star density in the solar neighborhood.

and Ekedahl (1961). Photographic and photoelectric observations for an extension of these data are also available.

The density distribution for the individual Selected Areas has been determined, allowing for the effect of interstellar absorption, which is derived from
color excesses. The results provide a basis for the study of the three-dimensional
density distribution. Considerable fluctuations in the density are found for surfaces of constant z. In Figure 6, the curves $D(z)$ for gG–gK stars for individual
areas, or mean curves for a few adjacent areas are shown. The different directions of the areas are indicated in the upper right-hand corner of the figure,
which shows the x, y coordinates at which the lines of sight intersect the planes

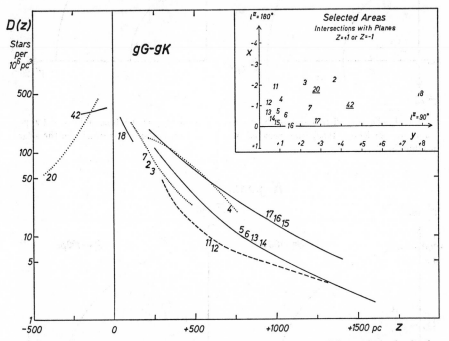

Fig. 6.—$D(z)$ curves for late-type giants in some directions at different latitudes in the
longitude interval $85° < l^{II} < 160°$, derived from Selected Area material by Elvius (1962).
Unit for $D(z)$ is the number of stars per $10^6\,pc^3$. The curves represent $D(z)$ along the line of sight
for individual areas or groups of areas as indicated by the S.A. numbers marking the curves.

The three-dimensional arrangement of points in the individual areas can be estimated from
the inserted diagram, showing the positions (x, y) of the intersections of the lines of sight with
the planes $z = +1$ or $z = -1$ parallel to the galactic plane. The positions are indicated by
the S.A. number; those with $z = -1$ are underlined.

$z = +1$ or $z = -1$. The numbers of the Selected Areas mark these intersections; those with the plane $z = -1$ are underlined.

The differences between the curves are considerable. They indicate real
fluctuations in the density at given levels of z. These fluctuations differ from

those in van Rhijn's investigation of the late giants, because he used statistical estimates of the percentages of giants among stars of these types, and only statistically determined corrections for the interstellar absorption within each area, or uncertain colors.

For the F and dG stars the author finds features of the three-dimensional distribution similar to those of the K giants, i.e., increased density at levels z above the galactic plane in some directions. (Cf. Elvius [1956], pp. 75 and 76.)

The data obtained by the author on the interstellar absorption support the view that it is caused by distinct clouds situated at various levels above and below the galactic plane. Where the limiting magnitude permits penetration to large distances, such layers of absorption have been located as high as 500 or 600 pc in z. They would strongly affect the derivation of the densities at high levels. When considering our knowledge of the three-dimensional distribution of the common stars, we recognize the need for more data, spectra as well as colors, for faint stars especially on the southern sky.

REFERENCES

BECKER, F.	1939	*Zs. f. Ap.*, **19**, 50.
BECKER, W.	1950	*Sterne und Sternsysteme* (Dresden and Leipzig: Steinkopff).
BLAAUW, A.	1958	*Ric. Astr. Specola Vaticana*, **5**, 333 ("Stellar Populations").
	1960	*M.N.*, **121**, 164.
BOK, B. J., and BASINSKI, J.	1964	*Mem. Mt. Stromlo Obs.*, No. 16.
BOK, B. J., and MACRAE, D. A.	1941	*Ann. New York Acad. Sci.*, **42**, Art. 2, 219.
ELVIUS, T.	1951	*Stockholms Obs. Ann.*, **16**, Nos. 4 and 5.
	1955	*Ibid.*, **18**, No. 7.
	1956	*Ibid.*, **19**, No. 3.
	1962	Unpublished.
ELVIUS, T., and EKEDAHL, Y.	1961	*Medd. Uppsala Obs.*, No. 135.
ELVIUS, T., and LODÉN, K.	1960	*Stockholms Obs. Ann.*, **21**, No. 2.
HILL, E. R.	1960	*B.A.N.*, **15**, 1.
HULST, H. C. VAN DE, MULLER, C. A., and OORT, J. H.	1954	*B.A.N.*, **12**, 117.
JONES, D. H. P.	1962	*Roy. Obs. Bull.*, No. 52 (Greenwich and Cape Observatories).
KAMP, P. VAN DE, and VYSSOTSKY, A. N.	1936	*A.J.*, **45**, 177.

KAPTEYN, J. C.   1906   *Plan of Selected Areas* (Groningen: Second impression, issued by P. J. van Rhijn, Kapteyn Astr. Lab. 1923).

LINDBLAD, B.   1926   *Medd. Uppsala Obs.*, No. 14.

LJUNGGREN, B.   1965   *Medd. Uppsala Obs.*, No. 151.

MALMQUIST, K. G.   1939   *Trans. I.A.U.*, **6**, 460.

     1960   *Uppsala Obs. Ann.*, **4**, No. 9.

     1962   *Medd. Uppsala Obs.*, No. 140.

OORT, J. H.   1932   *B.A.N.*, **6**, 249.

     1936   *Ibid.*, **8**, 75.

     1938   *Ibid.*, p. 233.

     1960   *Ibid.*, **15**, 45.

PAHLEN, E. VON DER   1937   *Lehrbuch der Stellarstatistik* (Leipzig: J. A. Barth).

PETERSSON, J. H.   1927   *Medd. Uppsala Obs.*, No. 29.

RAMBERG, J. M.   1957   *Stockholms Obs. Ann.*, **20**, No. 1.

RHIJN, P. J. VAN   1929   *Pub. Kapteyn Astr. Lab. Groningen*, No. 43.

     1949   *Ibid.*, No. 53.

     1955   *Ibid.*, No. 57.

     1956   *Ibid.*, No. 59.

     1960   *Ibid.*, No. 61.

RHIJN, P. J. VAN, and
SCHWASSMANN, A.   1935   *Zs. f. Ap.*, **10**, 161.

ROMAN, N. G.   1950   *Ap. J.*, **112**, 554.

     1952   *Ibid.*, **116**, 122.

SCHILT, J.   1950   *A.J.*, **55**, 97.

SEARES, F. H.   1928   *Ap. J.*, **67**, 123.

SLETTEBAK, A., and
STOCK, J.   1959   *Astr. Abhandlungen Hamburger Sternwarte*, **5**, No. 5.

TULDER, J. J. M. VAN   1942   *B.A.N.*, **9**, 315.

UPGREN, A. R.   1962   *A.J.*, **67**, 37.

     1963*a*   *Ibid.*, **68**, 194.

     1963*b*   *Ibid.*, p. 475.

VASHAKIDZE, M. A.   1937   *Bull. Abastumani Obs.*, **1**, 87.

VYSSOTSKY, A. N.   1957   *Pub. A.S.P.*, **69**, 109.

WAYMAN, P. A.   1961   *Roy. Obs. Bull.*, No. 36 (Greenwich and Cape Observatories).

WOOLLEY, R. V. D. R.   1957   *M.N.*, **117**, 198.

YOSS, K. M.   1961   *Ap. J.*, **134**, 809.

CHAPTER 4

Solar Motion and Velocity Distribution of Common Stars

J. DELHAYE*

Observatoire de Besançon

§ 1. INTRODUCTION, DEFINITIONS, LIST OF RECENT ANALYSES

Studies of stellar kinematics are in general based on either the proper motions or the radial velocities. The space velocity can be used if the parallax of a star is known, but at present this is possible only for a relatively small number of stars. Since, moreover, the trigonometric parallax programs usually are drawn up for a selection of nearby stars chosen on the basis of the size of the proper motions, effects of this observational selection may be present in the available space velocities for stars with trigonometric parallaxes. Samples of stars with spectroscopic parallaxes generally do not suffer from this kind of selection.

Fortunately, it is possible to study the kinematical properties of a group of stars either from the proper motions alone, or from the radial velocities alone. In this way, certain parameters characterizing the general properties of the velocity distribution may be determined, but an accurate determination of the structure of this distribution is hardly possible. Ambarzumian (1936) has suggested a method which to some extent allows the study of details using the radial velocities only, and this was taken up by Nahon (1956, 1957a, b).

A serious problem encountered in kinematical studies is that of classifying the stars into homogeneous physical groups. The practical impossibility of carrying out such a classification at the time when the kinematical investigations reported here were made is largely responsible for the somewhat unsatisfactory nature of many of the results to be presented in this chapter. The kinematical heterogeneity of some stellar groups, defined by the classifications used at the time of the investigation, often reveals their physical heterogeneity. This heterogeneity is sometimes subsequently confirmed by new spectroscopic evidence.

* Now at Observatoire de Paris.

This chapter reviews determinations of the solar motion and some results concerning the distribution of the peculiar motions of the stars. It is desirable first to define briefly some of the quantities involved. Let S be a point in the galactic plane, at the distance R from the center of the Galaxy, C. We shall assume that the point S does not participate in the internal motions of the Galaxy, its only motion being the translation of the whole Galaxy relative to the other stellar systems. We define, at the point S, a system of coordinate axes, fixed in direction, on which we project the velocities of stars situated at S at the epoch t (see Fig. 1). The component Π is in the direction of CS, Θ that in the direction of galactic rotation, and Z is perpendicular to the galactic

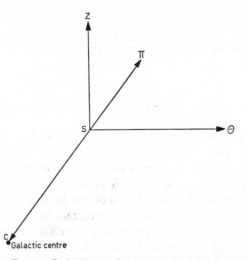

Fig. 1.—Definition of the system of coordinates

plane. If the motion of the star follows a circular orbit, the components of its velocity will have the values

$$\Pi = 0 , \qquad \Theta = \Theta_c , \qquad Z = 0 .$$

A second system of axes, that of the *local standard of rest*, is defined as follows: (*a*) at the moment considered, its origin coincides with S; (*b*) its axes have the same directions as the former system; (*c*) its origin describes a circular orbit around the galactic center, C, with the circular velocity Θ_c. If the velocity components of a star in the first coordinate system are Π, Θ, and Z, its components with respect to the local standard of rest are Π, $\Theta - \Theta_c$, and Z. For a star located at the point S at the moment of observation, we define *total velocity* as the velocity with respect to the fixed coordinate system, and *peculiar velocity* as the velocity with respect to the local standard of rest.

In dealing with the solar motion, we are in principle interested in its velocity components with respect to a reference system defined at the position of the sun, e.g., the local standard of rest. However, we always use observations of the sun with respect to stars or interstellar matter spread over a volume of space within which systematic differential motions occur. It is, therefore, in principle, always necessary to reduce the observed motions by eliminating these systematic differential effects. These effects must also be eliminated in studying the distributions of the peculiar motions in order to obtain results which are useful in the context of the dynamical theory of the Galaxy.

The position of the sun will be denoted by S_0, and the circular velocity at S_0 by $(\Theta_c)_0$. The components of the total velocity of the sun are Π_1, Θ_1, and Z_1; hence the sun's peculiar velocity will have the components Π_1, $\Theta_1 - (\Theta_c)_0$, and Z_1. The velocity of a star at S with respect to the sun, is then the sum of three vectors: (a) the peculiar velocity of the star with respect to the local standard of rest at S; (b) the differential velocity of the local standard of rest at S with respect to that at S_0; and (c) a vector equal but opposite to the peculiar velocity of the sun with respect to the local standard of rest at S_0. The only way we have at present of eliminating the part (b) is assuming circular motion and the galactic rotation curve as it has been found from 21-cm observations, and, for the solar neighborhood, the constants A and B of differential rotation. We do not have sufficient knowledge of the probably not negligible non-circular systematic deviations to take them into account. The above assumption requires, moreover, knowledge of the distances of the stars if we are dealing with radial velocities or space motions. The uncertainty just mentioned becomes more and more important when we study stars chosen from larger volumes. Studies of the stars nearer than 20 pc are not affected by it, but those of the rare types of stars are affected very much. In studying the velocity distributions it is not always clear whether the correct amount of systematic motion has first been eliminated; also, it must be assumed that essentially the same pattern of velocities occurs in different parts of the region surveyed. For a detailed discussion of some aspects of this problem we refer to Weaver (1961), who has shown that great care must be exercised in the application to large volumes of space of certain classical methods which in principle are defined for the study of the properties of the stars in a small element of volume. We further wish to point out that the use of radial velocities or of proper motions necessitates the incorporation, into one general solution, of observed distributions of quantities pertaining to different directions in space for different volumes of space.

The distribution of the peculiar velocities is usually described by means of certain probability parameters. Generally, these are the moments of the first and second order of the peculiar velocities. Those of the first order determine the centroid of the velocity distribution with respect to the local standard of rest. The ellipsoid defined by the moments of the second order may be called the ellipsoid of the residual velocities, or simply, the velocity ellipsoid. The direction of its major axis is called the vertex direction. The velocity ellipsoid

TABLE 1

DETERMINATIONS OF SOLAR MOTION AND VELOCITY DISPERSIONS

Type of Object	Reference	Type	No. of Stars Used	Assigned Weight (w)	S (km/sec)	l_A^{II}	b_A^{II}	disp Π (km/sec)	disp Θ (km/sec)	disp Z (km/sec)	l^{II}
Supergiants:											
B–K	Wilson (1941)	r	205	2.0	19.7	59°	16°				36°
O–B5	Parenago (1951)	s	35	0.7	16.6	56	13	12	11	9	18
F–M	Parenago (1951)	s	138	1.7	15.5	56	25	13	9	7	
Giants A–F:											
A	Parenago (1951)	s	15	0.4	20.5	41	30	22	13	9	27
F	Parenago (1951)	s	44	0.7	28.7	43	19	28	15	9	14
Giants G:											
G bright	Nordström (1936)	r	244	0.9	13.5	58	18	18	13	17	16
G faint	Nordström (1936)	r	100	0.7	13.9	48	22	25	15	15	4
G0–G8	Parenago (1951)	s	345	1.2	15.0	57	28	26	18	15	12
Giants K:											
K bright	Nordström (1936)	r	948	1.5	20.0	57	22	23	17	20	11
K faint	Nordström (1936)	r	342	1.0	16.7	75	26	28	16	18	15
K0–K2	Vyssotsky and Williams (1948)	p	2525	2.5		61	17				
K0–K2	Delhaye (1951)	pa	4439	3		66	19				8
K0–K2	Delhaye (1952)	pb	4439	3							359
G9–K1	Parenago (1951)	s	261	1.0	22.4	60	17	31	21	16	21
K2–K5	Parenago (1951)	s	394	1.2	20.8	63	18	31	21	17	14
Giants M:											
M bright	Nordström (1936)	r	179	0.7	22.0	65	19	27	19	19	359
M faint	Nordström (1936)	r	60	0.5	26.5	39	19	26	18	17	312
M	Parenago (1951)	s	266	1.0	19.8	76	18	31	23	16	7
Carbon stars	McLeod (1947)	r	68	0.5	17.4	95	18	48	23	16	
	Ikaunieks (1952)	s	25	0.1	25	83	–2	34	29	45	
	Vandervort (1958)	r	66	0.3	33.7	71	6				
Subgiants	Parenago (1951)	s	112	0.4	30.0	78	21	43	27	24	359
	Eggen (1960a)	s	114	0.4	36.4	75	15				

64

TABLE 1—*Continued*

Type of Object	Reference	Type	No. of Stars Used	Assigned Weight (w)	S (km/sec)	l_A^{II}	b_A^{II}	disp Π (km/sec)	disp Θ (km/sec)	disp Z (km/sec)	l_V^{II}
O and B stars:											
Oe5–B5	Nordström (1936)	r	464	3.6	20.3	59°	11°	11	9	6	307°
B0–B5	Parenago (1951)	s	40	1.3	18.2	51	24	10	8	5	22
	Filin (1957)	r, s	1270	5.9	18.6	57	21	10	9	6	310
Dwarfs A0:											
B8–B9	Nordström (1936)	r	234	1.9	21.2	54	19	14	10	8	314
B8–A3	MacRae and Nevin (1948)	r	457	2.7	17.1	62	25	15	9	9	15
B8–A3	Vyssotsky and Williams (1948)	p	1912	5.5		46	16				
B7–A2	Parenago (1951)	s	53	0.9	15.9	44	27	16	11	6	32
B8–A5	Delhaye (1951)	pa	5089	8.9		45	23				24
B8–A5	Delhaye (1952)	pb	5089	8.9							23
Dwarfs A5:											
A0–A9, bright	Nordström (1936)	r	686	2.9	16.3	45	25	17	12	9	31
A0–A9, faint	Nordström (1936)	r	207	1.1	18.3	50	20	17	8	13	43
A3–A8	Parenago (1951)	s	61	1.0	17.6	39	21	19	9	8	22
A0–F3	Wehlau (1957)	s	89	1.0	13.7	43	33	20	9	9	19
Dwarfs F0:											
A5–F5	Smart and Tannahill (1940)	p	3263	5.7		50	26				17
A9–F1	Parenago (1951)	s	110	1.1	17.2	44	25	24	13	10	21
A5–F5	Tannahill (1952)	p	4310	6.6		53	26				21
A5–F2	Vyssotsky and Williams (1948)	p	1117	3.3		42	23				
Dwarfs F5:											
F0–F9, bright	Nordström (1936)	r	414	1.7	17.2	47	19	25	16	12	13
F0–F9, faint	Nordström (1936)	r	394	1.3	18.6	53	28	22	18	15	10
F2–F4	Parenago (1951)	s	180	1.1	15.8	54	29	27	17	12	2
F5–F7	Parenago (1951)	s	177	0.8	20.8	72	22	32	21	17	356
F0–F9	Delhaye (1951)	pa	2748	3.4		53	24				13
F0–F9	Delhaye (1952)	pb	2748	0.7							358
F0–F9	Gliese (1956)	s	68	0.7	15.5	48	24				
F4–F8	Wehlau (1957)	s	88	0.6	17.1	51	23	27	17	17	13

TABLE 1—*Continued*

Type of Object	Reference	Type	No. of Stars Used	Assigned Weight (w)	S (km/sec)	l_A^{II}	l^{II}	disp Π (km/sec)	disp Θ (km/sec)	disp Z (km/sec)	l^{II}
Dwarfs G0:											
F8–G2	Parenago (1951)	s	188	0.6	33.3	64°	7°	46	28	23	17°
F9–G1	Wehlau (1957)	s	58	0.4	26.4	56	15	26	18	20	2
Dwarfs G5:											
G bright	Nordström (1936)	r	112	0.6	30.3	59	7	46	27	18	359
G faint	Nordström (1936)	r	302	1.0	32.2	52	7	46	33	17	22
G3–G7	Parenago (1951)	s	113	0.4	37.4	65	4	50	30	27	2
G	Gliese (1956)	s	97	0.7	34.8	50	9	...	...	...	...
G2–G7	Wehlau (1957)	s	58	0.5	23.9	70	11	32	17	15	14
Dwarfs K:											
K	Nordström (1936)	r	201	0.7	19.3	71	9	42	27	20	8
K	Parenago (1951)	s	100	0.4	36.4	63	15	52	31	23	5
K3–K6	Parenago (1951)	s	121	0.5	37.6	79	15	51	29	23	13
K0–K5	Gliese (1956)	s	119	0.5	26.8	69	14	...	...	...	...
G8–K2	Wehlau (1957)	s	53	0.7	19.8	55	23	28	16	11	3
K3–K6	Wehlau (1957)	s	59	0.5	25.0	68	14	35	20	16	11
Dwarfs M:											
M	Nordström (1936)	r	40	0.3	22.4	66	−1	60	8	23	16
M	Parenago (1951)	s	170	0.6	25.5	70	21	46	26	23	6
M	Vyssotsky (1946)	p	214	0.7	23	72	24	34	23	16	...
M	Mumford (1956)	p	825	1.4	19.7	69	24	31	25	18	...
M	Dyer (1956)	p	306	0.9	20.0	72	18	35	26	21	...
K6–M8	Gliese (1956)	s	93	0.5	33.5	63	16	...	...	...	...
K8–M2	Wehlau (1957)	s	72	0.4	17.3	68	25	32	21	19	8
M3–M6	Wehlau (1957)	s	40	0.3	23.3	64	23	31	23	16	353
Subdwarfs	Parenago (1949)	r	141	0.2	136	91	−4	100	75	50	...
	Fricke (1950)	r	78	0.2	148	107	−2	110	...	...	...
	Deeming (1961)	r	103	0.2	149	83	2	...	...	...	(0)

66

TABLE 1—Continued

Type of Object	Reference	Type	No. of Stars Used	Assigned Weight (w)	S (km/sec)	l_A^{II}	b_A^{II}	disp Π (km/sec)	disp Θ (km/sec)	disp Z (km/sec)	l_V^{II}
White dwarfs........	Parenago (1949)	p	50	0.3	45	64°	1°	45	28	20	.....
	Pavlovskaya (1956)	p	27	0.2	38	81	12	50	33	25	.....
Planetary nebulae...	Wirtz (1922)	r	96	0.5	31	74	14	(45)	(35)	(20)	.....
Classical cepheids....	Parenago (1947)	r	125	2.2	18.6	71	13	13	9	5	.....
	Raimond (1954)	r	70	1.7	21.9	67	21	...	10	...	.....
	Weaver (1954)	r	46	1.4	20.1	48	21	...	10	...	.....
	Stibbs (1956)	r	96	2.0	16.6	54	27	...	...	...	.....
Long-period variables:											
Per. <300 days.....	Wilson and Merrill (1942)	s	69	0.1	53.6	68	13	85	67	62	9°
	Kulikovsky (1948)	s	93	0.2	25	75	18	52	42	47	
	Safronov (1955)	s	36	0.1	25	88	7	62	43	44	
	Osvalds and Risley (1961)	s	109	0.2	47	49	11	79	59	55	
Per. >300 days.....	Wilson and Merrill (1942)	s	77	0.3	28.2	76	19	48	40	33	38
	Kulikovsky (1948)	s	40	0.2	12	81	0	34	32	30	
	Safronov (1955)	s	64	0.3	17	72	21	35	28	25	
	Osvalds and Risley (1961)	s	131	0.4	32	54	14	47	40	28	
Carbon variables....	Osvalds and Risley (1961)	s	24	0.2	29	56	24	54	42	31	
Se variables........	Ikaunieks (1950)	s	17	0.2	21	67	51	25	17	20	
	Osvalds and Risley (1961)	s	20	0.3	26	68	45	29	23	15	
RR Lyrae variables:											
Per. <0.45 day.....	Notni (1956)	r	39	0.1	56	32	4	46	42	23	
Per. >0.45 day.....	Notni (1956)	r	39	0.1	218	90	6	158	101	122	
Galactic clusters....	Barkhatova (1949)	r	26	0.8	21.8	70	22	15	12	6	
Globular clusters....	Kinman (1959)	r	70	0.1	182	87	2	...	115	...	
Interstellar Ca II....	Blaauw (1952)	r	...	1.5	20.1	52	24	...	6	...	

67

is usually described in terms of Laplace-Gaussian, or "normal," distributions
of the velocity components. The principal observed deviation from the normal
law is an asymmetry in the distribution of the components Θ. This asymmetry
is clearly revealed by the large velocities. See Figure 2, which gives, separately
for the A, gK, and dM stars, the distribution of the velocity components with
respect to the sun in the directions Π, Θ, and Z. The dashed lines at the velocities + 9, −12, and −7 km/sec mark the zero points of the local standard of
rest (sec. 2.1). The asymmetry is not usually described in terms of the moments of the third and higher order, but rather in terms connected with its
dynamical interpretation.

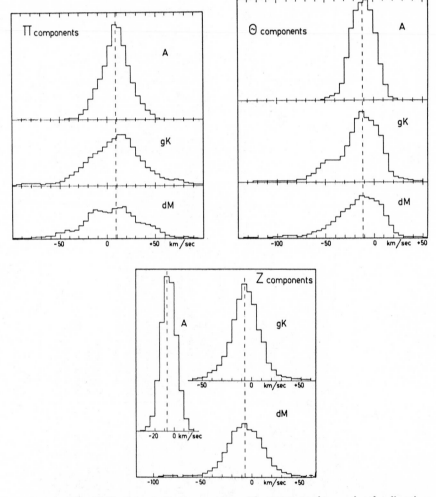

FIG. 2.—Distribution of velocity components with respect to the sun for the directions
Π, Θ, Z. Data for A and gK stars are from Vyssotsky and Janssen (1951), and for dM stars from
Dyer (1956). The dashed lines indicate the velocity components of the local standard of rest.

Apart from the considerations already mentioned with regard to the way of selecting the stars, it can be stated that, generally, the analysis of observed distributions of radial velocities is rather straightforward; the distributions can usually be simply expressed in the parameters defining the distribution of the space velocities. It is, however, different in the case of the proper motions, which represent angular velocities. Special methods have therefore been proposed for these, the three principal ones are those of Charlier (1926), Karl Schwarzschild (1907, 1908), and Blaauw (1939). In recent years Schwarzschild's and Blaauw's methods have been applied most. Schwarzschild used the statistics of the directions of the proper motions for different regions of the sky, whereas Blaauw used the dispersion of the residual proper-motion components derived from different areas. From a mathematical point of view, Schwarzschild's method is simple and rigorous; it is based on the fundamental property that the directions of the proper motions and those of the tangential velocities are identical, and that these directions are not affected by the distances of the stars. Blaauw's method is less rigorous, for it requires the elimination of the dispersion of the distances of the stars, which adds to the dispersion of the proper-motion components, but it is less sensitive to systematic errors in the system of proper motions. The distribution of the weights with which the stars enter is different in the two methods. In Schwarzschild's method, each star carries equal weight irrespective of the size of its proper motion, whereas in the dispersion method the stars of large proper motion, and hence those of the high velocities, carry more weight than the others. Due to these differences, the results of the two methods of analyses supplement each other in a valuable way.

For a detailed description of the methods for determining the solar motion we refer to Edmondson (1959), and for the methods for analyzing the ellipsoidal velocity distribution, to the quoted papers and to the general treatises by Eddington (1914), von der Pahlen (1937) and Smart (1938).

The results of part of the numerous more recent investigations of the solar motion and the ellipsoidal velocity distribution are collected in Table 1, in which they have been arranged in chronological order for each spectral type. The nature of the basic data (radial velocities, proper motions, or space motions) is indicated. The differences between the results of different authors are due to the different methods and to different basic observational data. The following quantities are listed:

Column   1: the type of object.
Column   2: the reference to the investigation.
Column   3: the type of observational data used:

> p = proper motions; pa = elements of the velocity ellipsoid from the direction of the proper motions; pb = the same elements from the dispersion of the proper motions; r = radial velocities; s = space velocities.

Column 4: the number of stars used.

Column 5: the weight assigned in subsequent use of these results in this chapter, defined by $W = \sqrt{n}/c$, in such a way that unit weight approximately corresponds to a probable error of 1 km/sec in S and in disp Π, disp Θ, and disp Z; to 4° in l_A^{II}, 3° in b_A^{II}, and 6° in l_V^{II}.

Column 6: the solar motion, S, with respect to the mean of the stars considered.

Column 7: the galactic longitude of the apex, l_A^{II}.

Column 8: the galactic latitude of the apex, b_A^{II}.

Columns 9 to 11: the dispersions of the residual velocities in the directions Π, Θ, and Z, respectively.

Column 12: the galactic longitude, l_V^{II} of the direction of the vertex.

§ 2. SOLAR MOTION

2.1. Solar Motion with Respect to Circular Velocity: Peculiar Motion

For the determination of the solar motion we select, on the basis of Table 1, the results given in Table 2. These do not include halo objects and variable stars, with the exception of the classical cepheids, so that only population I and some disk-population objects remain. References to the selected investigations are in the last column. The second column gives relative weights, the following three columns, the mean components Π_0, θ_0, and Z_0 of the solar motion, and the next three, the dispersions.

The simple model of the state of motion in the Galaxy described before, if one assumes the mean motion of each of the various groups of stars to be in the galactic plane in the direction of galactic rotation, implies that, in principle, identical values of the components Π_0 and Z_0 should be found, and that these should be the same as the components Π_1 and Z_1 in the fixed coordinate system. The component θ_0 in Table 2 represents the mean velocity of the sun in the Θ direction with respect to the stars considered. Assuming that the complications referred to in the preceding section may be disregarded so that the velocity field represented by the stars used is identical to that for the position of the sun, we may put $\theta_0 = \Theta_1 - \langle \Theta \rangle$, where $\langle \Theta \rangle$ is the mean velocity of the stars at S_0 in the Θ direction. This is not the same as the peculiar velocity of the sun, $\Theta_1 - (\Theta_c)_0$, which we shall denote by θ_1, since $\langle \Theta \rangle$ differs from $(\Theta_c)_0$. The difference is

$$(\Theta_c)_0 - \langle \Theta \rangle = \theta_0 - \theta_1 . \tag{1}$$

We are interested in finding θ_1, the velocity component with respect to the circular velocity. It may be estimated from the data in Table 2 in the following way. In the classical theory of the dynamics of the Galaxy as described in chapter 21, which in its simplest form assumes a stationary system with symmetry with respect to the galactic plane and the galactic center, a relation exists between $(\Theta_c)_0 - \langle\Theta\rangle$, the dispersion of the residual velocities, and the density gradient in the galactic plane toward the galactic center. Denoting the dispersions of the velocities in the directions Π, Θ, and Z by disp Π, disp Θ, and disp Z, respectively, and calling ν the density at the distance R from the center in the galactic plane for the category of stars considered, we have approximately, for $[(\Theta_c)_0 - \langle\Theta\rangle] \ll (\Theta_c)_0$,

$$(\Theta_c)_0 - \langle\Theta\rangle = \theta_0 - \theta_1 = -\frac{\text{disp}^2\,\Pi}{2(A-B)}\left[\frac{\partial \ln \nu}{\partial R} + \frac{1}{R_0}\left(1 - \frac{\text{disp}^2\,\Theta}{\text{disp}^2\,\Pi}\right)\right]. \quad (2)$$

For the derivation of this relation we refer to chapter 21. The component θ_1 may then be found from the values of θ_0 in Table 2 in combination with the available data on the velocity dispersions.

TABLE 2

ADOPTED COMPONENTS OF THE SOLAR MOTION AND VELOCITY DISPERSIONS

TYPE	WEIGHT	SOLAR MOTION (km/sec)				VELOCITY DISPERSIONS (km/sec)			
		Π_0	θ_0	Z_0	Ref.	disp Π	disp Θ	disp Z	Ref.
cO–cB5.........	0.7	− 9.0	+13.4	+ 3.7	1	12	11	9	1
cF–cM.........	1.7	− 7.9	+11.7	+ 6.5	1	13	9	7	1
gA.............	0.4	−13.4	+11.6	+10.3	1	22	13	9	1
gF.............	0.7	−19.7	+18.5	+ 9.5	1	28	15	9	1
gG.............	1.2	− 7.2	+11.1	+ 6.9	1	26	18	15	1
gK0............	1.0	−10.6	+18.6	+ 6.5	1	31	21	16	1
gK3............	1.2	− 9.0	+17.6	+ 6.4	1	31	21	17	1
gM.............	1.0	− 4.5	+18.3	+ 6.2	1	31	23	16	1
Carbon stars.....	0.3	−10.7	+31.8	+ 3.5	2	48	23	16	3
Subgiants........	0.4	− 8.0	+28.0	+ 8.0	4	43	27	24	1
B0.............	6	− 9.6	+14.5	+ 6.7	5	10	9	6	5
dA0............	2.7	− 7.3	+13.7	+ 7.2	6	15	9	9	6
dA5............	1.0	− 8.5	+ 7.8	+ 7.4	7	20	9	9	7
dF5............	0.6	−10.1	+12.3	+ 6.2	7	27	17	17	7
dG0............	0.4	−14.5	+21.1	+ 6.4	7	26	18	20	7
dG5............	0.5	− 8.1	+22.1	+ 4.3	7	32	17	15	7
dK0............	0.7	−10.8	+14.9	+ 7.4	7	28	16	11	7
dK5............	0.5	− 9.5	+22.4	+ 5.8	7	35	20	16	7
dM0............	0.4	− 6.1	+14.6	+ 6.9	7	32	21	19	7
dM5............	0.3	− 9.8	+19.3	+ 8.6	7	31	23	16	7
White dwarfs.....	0.2	− 6	+37	+ 8	8	50	33	25	8
Planetary nebulae.	0.5	− 8	+29	+ 8	9	45	35	20	9
Classical cepheids.	2.0	− 8.6	+12.0	+ 7.6	10	13	9	5	11
Interstellar Ca II.	1.5	−11.4	+14.4	+ 8.2	12	......	6	......	12

References: (1) Parenago (1951)
(2) Vandervort (1958)
(3) McLeod (1947)
(4) Eggen (1960a)
(5) Filin (1957)
(6) MacRae and Nevin (1948)

(7) Wehlau (1957)
(8) Pavlovskaya (1956)
(9) Wirtz (1922)
(10) Stibbs (1956)
(11) Parenago (1947)
(12) Blaauw (1952)

The weighted mean values of the Π and Z components in Table 2 are

$$\langle \Pi_0 \rangle = -9.2 \text{ km/sec} \pm 0.3 \text{ (p.e.)},$$

$$\langle Z_0 \rangle = +6.9 \text{ km/sec} \pm 0.2 \text{ (p.e.)}.$$

There is no evidence for significant deviations from these means.

Figure 3 shows the dependence of θ_0 on disp^2 Π. It is based on a number of normal points obtained by combining the data in Table 2, particulars of which are given in Table 3.

TABLE 3

NORMAL POINTS USED IN FIGURE 3

Type	Weight	θ_0 (km/sec)	disp Π (km/sec)
1. Supergiants............	2.4	+12.2	13
2. gA–gF...............	1.1	+16.0	26
3. gG–gM.............	4.4	+16.2	30
4. Carbon stars..........	0.3	+31.8	48
5. Subgiants.............	0.4	+28.0	43
6. B0..................	6	+14.5	10
7. dA.................	3.7	+12.1	16
8. dF–dM.............	3.4	+17.7	30
9. White dwarfs..........	0.2	+37	50
10. Planetary nebulae.......	0.5	+29	45
11. Classical cepheids.......	2.0	+12.0	13
12. Interstellar Ca II........	1.5	+14.4	6

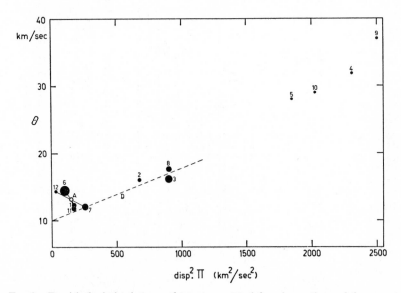

Fig. 3.—Empirical relation between the component θ of the solar motion and the square of the dispersion in the Π velocity components. For explanation of the numbers, see Table 3.

According to relations (1) and (2), θ_0 is a linear function of disp^2 II, apart from variation of the term $\partial \ln \nu / \partial R$ and of the ratio disp^2 Θ/disp^2 II. This latter ratio may be assumed to be constant on the basis of the general dynamical considerations set forth in chapter 21 of this volume. Hence, if the density gradient were the same for all groups, we would expect the intersection of the linear relation with the ordinate axis, corresponding to disp^2 II $= 0$, i.e., to strictly circular motion, to give the solar motion component θ_1 with respect to the local standard of rest as defined before. However, there is no observational evidence that these density gradients do not vary significantly, and we do know that, locally, irregularities in the space distribution occur which may involve irregularities in the distribution in velocity space (see chaps. 4, 5, and 21). Unfortunately, our knowledge of the space distribution of the concerned objects is too restricted to allow us to predict the size of the density-gradient effect.

A linear relation seems to hold approximately in Figure 3 for the objects with disp II ≥ 16 km/sec (abscissae ≥ 250), but we note considerable scatter for the objects with smaller velocity dispersion. These latter are the youngest stars that have well-determined solar motions, but whose density distribution is known to be non-uniform, except for that of the interstellar matter. If we disregard these objects and include only the dwarfs and giants of types A–M (groups 2, 3, 7, and 8), defining the dashed line marked D and allow a slight curvature of this empirical relation as it is indicated by the groups with large dispersion, then we find from the intersection with the ordinate axis that the value of θ_1 must be at least $+ 10$ km/sec. If, on the other hand, we attach some, but low, weight to the individual groups belonging to the cluster of dots marked 1, 6, 7, 11, and 12, all of which refer to the youngest objects and if we combine their average position marked A with the dots marked 2, 3, and 8, then we find a value at the intersection somewhat lower than $+13$ km/sec. It seems safe to conclude, therefore, that the true value of θ_1 lies between $+10$ and $+13$ km/sec. We adopt the value $+12$ km/sec and thus arrive at the following elements of the sun's peculiar motion:

$$\Pi_1 = - \ 9 \, \text{km/sec} ,$$

$$\theta_1 = + 12 \, \text{km/sec} ,$$

$$Z_1 = + \ 7 \, \text{km/sec} ,$$

corresponding with a total speed of 16.5 km/sec in the direction $l^{II} = 53°$, $b^{II} = +25°$.

2.2 STANDARD SOLAR MOTION

The standard solar motion is usually defined as the sun's motion with respect to the stars forming the majority in the general catalogues of radial velocities and proper motions (A to G main-sequence stars, giants, and supergiants). It is found to have the components

$$\Pi_s = - 10.4 \, \text{km/sec} , \quad \theta_s = + 14.8 \, \text{km/sec} , \quad Z_s = + 7.3 \, \text{km/sec} ,$$

corresponding to

$$S_s = 19.5 \text{ km/sec}, \qquad l_s^{II} = 56°, \qquad b_s^{II} = +23 .$$

Compared with the peculiar motion of the sun, the largest difference is in the Θ component and in the sense expected, because the sample used contains a certain fraction of stars with large velocity dispersion, which reveals itself also in the asymmetric drift (Fig. 2).

2.3. BASIC SOLAR MOTION

The basic solar motion is defined by the most frequently occurring velocities among the stars in the solar neighborhood. The notion of basic solar motion was introduced by Vyssotsky and Janssen (1951) and further applied by Dyer (1956) because of the good agreement found for the values derived from

TABLE 4

BASIC SOLAR MOTION

Type	Π_B (km/sec)	θ_B (km/sec)	Z_B (km/sec)	Authors
A.......	-9.4 ± 0.5	$+ 9.9$	$+5.6\pm0.2$	⎫
gK.....	-9.3 ± 0.9	$+10.7$	$+6.7\pm0.5$	⎬ Vyssotsky and Janssen (1951)
dM.....	....	$+12.6$	....	⎭
dM.....	-8 ± 2	$+10$	$+6 \pm2$	Dyer (1956)

A stars, K giants, and M dwarfs (see Table 4). The adopted values of the components are

$$\Pi_B = -9 \text{ km/sec}, \qquad \theta_B = +11 \text{ km/sec}, \qquad Z_B = +6 \text{ km/sec},$$

corresponding to

$$S_B = 15.4 \text{ km/sec}, \qquad l_B^{II} = 51°, \qquad b_B^{II} = +23°.$$

The difference between the basic solar motion and the peculiar solar motion is small and within the errors of the determination of the basic solar motion. It may be stated as an empirical result that the most frequently occurring velocities of the common stars in the solar neighborhood in the fixed-coordinate system are very close to the circular velocity in the Galaxy near the sun.

§ 3. DEPENDENCE OF KINEMATIC PROPERTIES ON STELLAR TYPE AND AGE

The variations of the kinematic properties of the stars with the position in the Hertzsprung-Russell diagram, which are apparent from the foregoing compilations, are shown in Figure 4. It shows the run of the three components Π_0, θ_0, and Z_0 of the solar motion and of the three velocity dispersions for the giant and the main-sequence spectral sequences. The data were taken from Table 2. The most conspicuous phenomena are the increasing velocity dispersions and increasing values of the solar motion component θ_0 as we proceed along the main sequence from the early to the late types.

3.1. Parenago's Discontinuity; the Work of von Hoerner

Parenago (1950) has suggested that, along the main sequence, a discontinuity occurs in the kinematic properties around type F5. As the larger

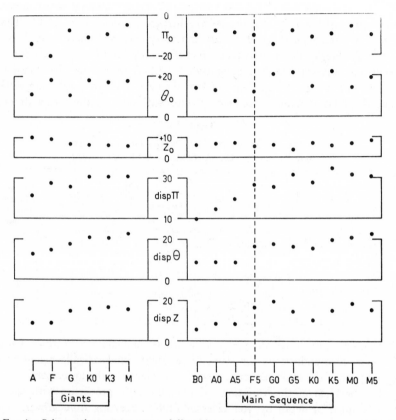

Fig. 4.—Solar-motion components and dispersions of the three velocity components for the main-sequence and giant-spectral types.

values found by him for the velocity dispersion of the later types may be partly a consequence of the observational selection of large proper-motion stars referred to before, we chose, in Table 2 and Figure 4, the results of Wehlau, who, in her analysis, has been careful to eliminate such effects. Probably as a consequence of this, the discontinuity noted by Parenago is less pronounced in Figure 4 than in Parenago's original diagram, but it is still noticeable in the three dispersions and in the component θ_0. Parenago and Massevitch (1950) have found support for the reality of the discontinuity in the existence of separate mass-luminosity and mass-radius relations for these two domains of the main sequence.

The occurrence of the discontinuity may also be interpreted in a different way. According to current theories of stellar evolution, the stars on the lower part of the main sequence have lifetimes as long as, or exceeding, the age of the Galaxy, whereas those on the upper main sequence are of more recent origin. The transition between the two age groups occurs at about visual absolute magnitude + 3.5 (see Sandage 1958) which corresponds to type F6. This is just about the type at which the discontinuity occurs. Closely related to this is also Salpeter's (1955) interpretation of the "knee" in the luminosity function occurring at visual absolute magnitude + 3.5. Thus, it may be stated that the stars above the discontinuity of Parenago are those with ages shorter than that of the Galaxy, and those below the discontinuity are the ones with longer

TABLE 5

KINEMATIC PROPERTIES OF GROUPS DISCRIMINATED
SPECTROSCOPICALLY, ACCORDING TO ROMAN (1952)

Type	Group	Num-ber	Prototype	Mean Speed Corrected for Solar Motion	Standard Deviation from Mean Speed
F5–G5 (excluding G2–G3, III–IV).......	Strong line	70	β Vir	28.4± 1.7 (p.e.)	14.5
	Weak line	61	ι Psc	42.7± 2.8	22.2
G5–K1; II, III, IV...	Strong line	91	HR 4126	24.7± 1.3	12.6
	Weak line	113	2 Dra	40.9± 2.3	24.1
	"4150"	25	HR 645	42.1± 8.3	41.6
	Weak CN	12	φ² Ori	95.6±13.7	47 4

lifetimes and, in the majority, nearly as old as the Galaxy as a whole. On this basis, we also understand that the normal giants kinematically belong to the upper part of the main sequence, and the subgiants to the lower part.

The problem of the variations of the kinematic properties with age has been studied in detail by von Hoerner (1960). Starting from groups in the HR diagram with known ages (derived from models of evolving stars), he found that the kinematic properties satisfy the relation

$$V(\tau) = \left(1 + \frac{\tau}{t_E}\right)^{1/3} V_0,$$

where $V(\tau)$ is the mean speed for stars of age τ, t_E is a constant determining the time scale, and V_0 the mean speed at the time of star formation. This relation is due to a theory of the velocity dispersion as an accumulating effect of encounters of stars with stars and gas complexes, developed by Spitzer and Schwarzschild (1953). The properties of the stars formed after the collapse of the primordial galactic cloud (see also Eggen, Lynden-Bell, and Sandage,

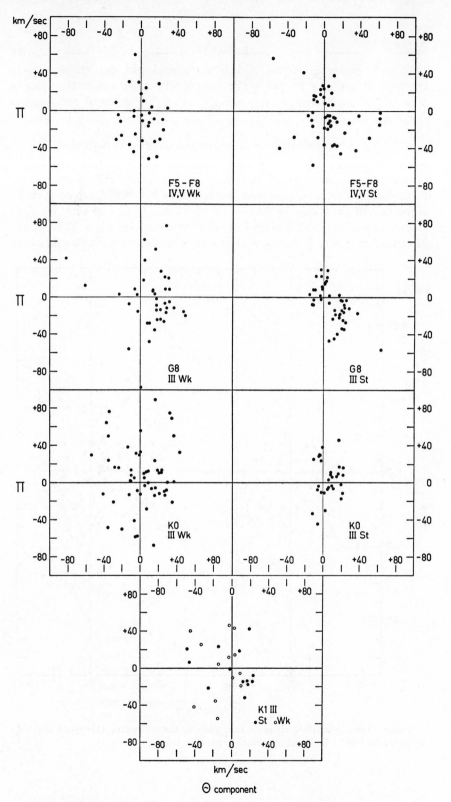

Fig. 5.—Velocity distributions in the Π, Θ plane for the weak-line (Wk) and the strong-line (St) stars after elimination of the standard solar motion, according to Blaauw (1958).

1962, and chapter 21 of this volume) correspond with the values $V_0 = 10$ km/sec and $t_E = 2 \times 10^8$ years. For stars of still earlier origin, the value of V_0 would be much larger, corresponding to the higher degree of turbulence in the gaseous medium.

3.2. Kinematic Heterogeneity of Certain Spectral Groups

Roman (1950, 1952) was the first to draw attention to the heterogeneity of certain groups selected on the basis of the position in the HR diagram. Kinematically different subgroups were discovered by her in the domain of main-sequence and giant stars of the spectral types late F, G, and early K. Their names, prototypes, and kinematic properties are described in Table 5 and illustrated in Figure 5. For faint G dwarfs, a similar differentiation has been

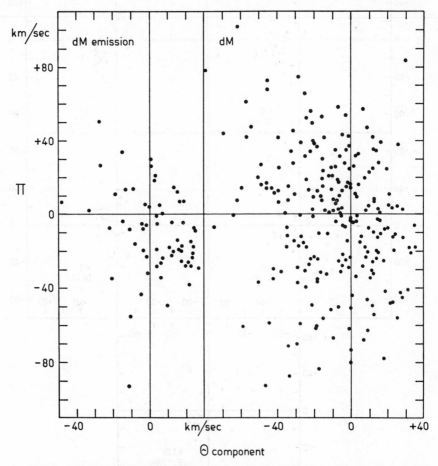

Fig. 6.—Velocity distributions in the Π, Θ plane for the dM and the dMe dwarfs according to Vyssotsky (1957). The basic solar motion was eliminated.

found by Vyssotsky and Skumanich (1953), and for faint K giants, by Yoss (1958).

Differences between the kinematic properties of the normal M dwarfs and Me dwarfs were discovered by Delhaye (1953) and confirmed by further work of Einasto (1954), Smak (1956), Gliese (1956, 1958), Vyssotsky and Dyer (1957), and Arakelian (1958). The Me dwarfs have considerably lower solar motion and velocity dispersion than the normal M dwarfs (see Fig. 6). For the former we find a mean speed with respect to the sun of 11 km/sec $\pm$ 2 (p.e.) with a standard deviation of 18 km/sec, and for the latter, a mean speed of 22 km/sec $\pm$ 1 (p.e.) with standard deviation of 30 km/sec.

Subdivision of main-sequence types into two kinematically different groups, independent of knowledge of spectroscopic details, had been proposed by

TABLE 6

KINEMATICAL SUBDIVISION OF MAIN-
SEQUENCE STARS ACCORDING
TO EINASTO (1954)

Type	Group I disp~14.5 km/sec (Per cent)	Group II disp~29.1 km/sec (Per cent)
A5–A9	100	0
F0–F4	98	2
F5–F7	89	11
F8–G2	58	42
G3–G9	39	61
K0–K7	74	26
M	86	14

Einasto (1954) on the basis of a description of the velocity distribution by means of two superposed velocity ellipsoids with different dispersion and mean velocity. The properties of the two subgroups, marked I and II, as found by Einasto are shown in Table 6. For group I the velocity dispersion in the direction of the major axis of the velocity ellipsoid is 14.5 km/sec, and for group II, 29.1 km/sec. The table shows the varying percentages of stars belonging to the two subgroups for the main-sequence types according to Einasto.

The existence of kinematically different subgroups among the classical spectral types was also indicated by the investigation of the vertex direction of the velocity ellipsoids. From simple dynamical considerations one would expect the vertex to be in the direction $l^{II} = 0°$. We see, however, from Table 1 that in many cases, and particularly in those of the main-sequence A stars, large deviations toward higher longitudes occur. It appears that the direction found sometimes depends on whether the method is based on the directions of the proper motions (Schwarzschild's method) or on their dispersions. Table 7 gives the two kinds of results for the A, F, and K stars of the seventh magni-

TABLE 7

LONGITUDE OF THE VERTEX (= THE VERTEX DEVIA-
TION) FOR SEVENTH MAGNITUDE A, F, AND K STARS
AS DETERMINED FROM THE DIRECTIONS OF THE
PROPER MOTIONS AND FROM THEIR DISPERSIONS

| | l_V^{II} | |
TYPE	From Directions of Proper Motions	From Dispersion of Proper Motions
B8–A5........	$23°.8 \pm 3°.3$	$22°.7 \pm 3°.1$
F0–F9........	11.0 ± 2.4	-2.2 ± 2.8
K0–K2........	8.0 ± 2.5	-3.4 ± 2.7

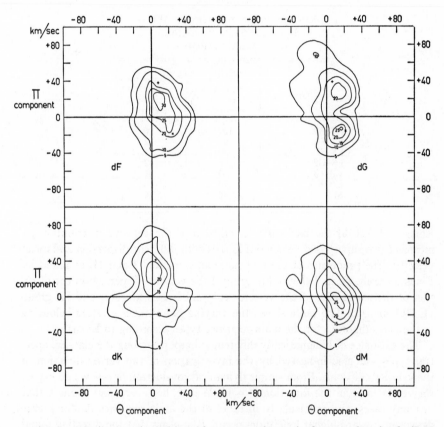

FIG. 7.—Distribution of velocities with respect to the sun in the Π, Θ plane for the F–M dwarfs within 20 pc according to Gliese (1956). Plus signs indicate the projected velocity of the Taurus stream; crosses that of the Ursa Major stream.

tude in the *General Catalogue* of B. Boss (Delhaye 1952). For types F and K, the differences between the results of the two methods far exceed their probable errors. A reasonable interpretation of these differences is, that the vertex deviation is largely due to the stars with low velocities (which enter with full weight in Schwarzschild's method) and does not occur among the high velocities which carry most of the weight in the dispersion method. Since the A-type stars have almost exclusively low velocities, the deviation is found here by both methods. Confirmation of this interpretation was found by Alexander

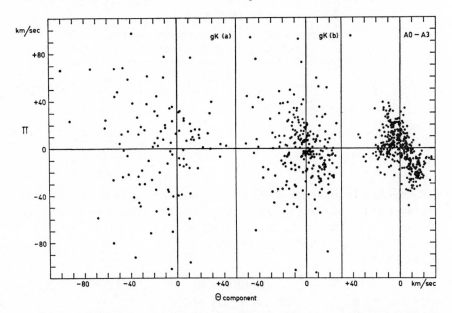

Fɪɢ. 8.—Distribution of velocities in the Π, Θ plane for the gK stars with high (gK(a)) and low (gK(b)) orbital inclination on the galactic plane, and for the A stars, with respect to the local standard of rest, according to Vyssotsky (1951).

(1958). Another confirmation is provided by Figure 7, which shows the curves of equal density in the velocity plane Π, Θ for stars of various spectral types within 20 pc (Gliese 1956). Analogous curves were given by Delhaye (1952).

Subdivision of the stars according to the inclination of their galactic orbits with respect to the galactic plane was carried out by Vyssotsky (1951). He found that the stars with low inclination show pronounced vertex deviation, comparable to the A stars, whereas those with high inclination do not show it (see Fig. 8). Since the strongly inclined orbits are generally those of the stars with high velocities with respect to the local standard of rest, the interpretation is essentially the same as in the preceding case.

Figures 5–8 show, apart from the amount of the vertex deviations, the occurrence of certain concentrations of velocity points. Although some of these may be due to observational selection, part of them must be real. These local structures in the velocity distributions are the more pronounced as we are dealing with the smaller velocity dispersions and larger vertex deviations.

Closely related to these concentrations in the velocity plane is the phenomenon of the moving groups. Their existence has been recently reinvestigated by Eggen (1958a–c, 1960b–e) and Eggen and Sandage (1959) whose results for five groups are summarized in Table 8. Eggen's evidence for the reality of these groups rests not only on the kinematic data, but also on their

TABLE 8

VELOCITIES OF MOVING GROUPS WITH RESPECT TO
THE SUN, ACCORDING TO EGGEN

Group	$U = \Pi - \Pi_1$ (km/sec)	$V = \theta - \theta_1$ (km/sec)	$W = Z - Z_1$ (km/sec)
Sirius (extended UMa group)......	-14	0	-12
Hyades........................	$+40$	-18	-2
ζ Herculis....................	$+54$	-45	-26
ϵ Indi......................	$+79$	-39	$+6$
61 Cygni.....................	$+92$	-53	-6

HR diagrams. In the region of the low and moderate velocities, we encounter the Sirius and Hyades groups. The occurrence of the first of these is confirmed by Figures 5–8. That of the Hyades group is somewhat less evident. For a more detailed discussion of these phenomena we refer to the following chapters of this volume.

REFERENCES

ALEXANDER, J. B.   1958   M.N., 118, 161.
AMBARZUMIAN, V. A.   1936   M.N., 96, 172.
ARAKELIAN, M. A.   1958   Izvestia Akad. Nauk Armenian S.S.R., Phys.-
                                   Mathem., 11, No. 5.
BLAAUW, A.   1939   B.A.N., 8, 305.
                          1952   Ibid., 11, 459.
                          1958   Ric. Astr. Specola Vaticana, 5, 333 ("Stellar Popu-
                                   lations").
BARKHATOVA, K. A.   1949   A.J. U.S.S.R., 26, 256.
CHARLIER, C. V. L.   1926   The Motions and Distributions of the Stars (Berke-
                                   ley: Univ. of California Press).
DEEMING, T. J.   1961   M.N., 123, 273.
DELHAYE, J.   1951   Bulletin Astronomique, 16, 1.
                          1952   Ibid., p. 221.
                          1953   Comptes Rendus, 237, 294.
DYER, E. R.   1956   A.J., 61, 228.
EDDINGTON, A. S.   1914   Stellar Movements and the Structure of the Universe
                                   (London: Macmillan).

EDMONDSON, F. K.   1959   *Hdb. d. Phys.*, **53**, 1.

EGGEN, O. J.   1958a   *M.N.*, **118**, 65.

                                1958b   *Ibid.*, p. 154.

                                1958c   *Ibid.*, p. 560.

                                1960a   *Ibid.*, **120**, 430.

                                1960b   *Ibid.*, p. 448.

                                1960c   *Ibid.*, p. 540.

                                1960d   *Ibid.*, p. 563.

                                1960e   *Vistas in Astronomy* (London and New York: Pergamon Press), **3**, 258.

EGGEN, O. J., and
  SANDAGE, A. R.   1959   *M.N.*, **119**, 255.

EGGEN, O. J., LYNDEN-
  BELL, D., and
  SANDAGE, A. R.   1962   *Ap. J.*, **136**, 748.

EINASTO, J.   1954   *Tartu Obs. Pub.*, **32**, No. 6.

FILIN, A. J.   1957   *A.J. U.S.S.R.*, **34**, 838.

FRICKE, W.   1950   *A.N.*, **278**, 121.

GLIESE, W.   1956   *Zs. f. Ap.*, **39**, 1.

                                1958   *Ibid.*, **45**, 293.

HOERNER, S. VON   1960   *Mitt. Astr. Rechen Inst. Heidelberg*, Ser. A. No. 13.

IKAUNIEKS, IA.   1950   *Pub. Inst. Phys., Math. Riga*, No. 2, p. 101.

                                1952   *A.J. U.S.S.R.*, **29**, 654.

KINMAN, T. D.   1959   *M.N.*, **119**, 559.

KULIKOVSKY, P. J.   1948   *Variable Stars, Moscow*, **6**, 225.

McLEOD, N. W.   1947   *Ap. J.*, **105**, 390.

MacRAE, D. A., and
  NEVIN, S.   1948   *A.J.*, **53**, 120.

MUMFORD, G. S.   1956   *A.J.*, **61**, 224.

NAHON, F.   1956   *Comptes Rendus*, **242**, 462.

                                1957a   *Ibid.*, **244**, 2688.

                                1957b   *Ibid.*, p. 2775.

NORDSTRÖM, H.   1936   *Meddel. Lund.* Ser. II, No. 79.

NOTNI, L.   1956   *Mitteilungen Jena Obs.*, No. 26.

OSVALDS, V., and
  RISLEY, A. M.   1961   *Pub. Leander McCormick Obs.*, **11**, 147.

PAHLEN, E. VON DER   1937   *Lehrbuch der Stellarstatistik* (Leipzig: J. A. Barth).

PARENAGO, P. P.   1947   *Variable Stars, Moscow*, **6**, 102.

                                1949   *Astr. Circ. U.S.S.R.*, Nos. 90–91, p. 8.

                                1950   *A.J. U.S.S.R.*, **27**, 150.

                                1951   *Pub. Sternberg Inst.*, **20**, 26.

PARENAGO, P. P., AND
  MASSEVITCH, A. G.   1950   *A.J. U.S.S.R.*, **27**, 137.

PAVLOVSKAYA, E.   1956   *A.J. U.S.S.R.*, **33**, 660.

RAIMOND, E.   1954   *B.A.N.*, **12**, 99.

Roman, N. G.	1950	*Ap. J.*, **112**, 554.
	1952	*Ibid.*, **116**, 122.
Safronov, V. S.	1955	*Variable Stars, Moscow*, **10**, 236.
Salpeter, E. E.	1955	*Ap. J.*, **121**, 161.
Sandage, A. R.	1958	*Ric. Astr. Specola Vaticana*, **5**, 41 ("Stellar Populations").
Schwarzschild, K.	1907	*Nachr. Kgl. Ges. d. Wissenschaften*, Göttingen, **1907**, 614.
	1908	*Ibid.*, **1908**, 191.
Smak, J.	1956	*Warsaw Obs. Repr.*, No. 56.
Smart, W. M.	1938	*Stellar Dynamics* (Cambridge: University Press).
Smart, W. M., and Tannahill, T. R.	1940	*M.N.*, **100**, 688.
Spitzer, L., and Schwarzschild, M.	1953	*Ap. J.*, **118**, 106.
Stibbs, D. W. N.	1956	*M.N.*, **116**, 453.
Tannahill, T. R.	1952	*M.N.*, **112**, 3.
Vandervort, G. L.	1958	*A.J.*, **63**, 311.
Vyssotsky, A. N.	1946	*Ap. J.*, **104**, 239.
	1951	*A.J.*, **56**, 62.
	1957	*Pub. A.S.P.*, **63**, 109.
Vyssotsky, A. N., and Dyer, E. R.	1957	*Ap. J.*, **125**, 297.
Vyssotsky, A. N., and Janssen, E. N.	1951	*A.J.*, **56**, 58.
Vyssotsky, A. N., and Skumanich, A.	1953	*A.J.*, **58**, 96.
Vyssotsky, A. N., and Williams, E. T. R.	1948	*A.J.*, **53**, 92.
Weaver, H. F.	1954	*A.J.*, **59**, 375.
	1961	*The Velocity Ellipsoid and the Determination of Its Parameters*, unpublished.
Wehlau, A. W.	1957	Thesis, Berkeley.
Wilson, R. E.	1941	*Ap. J.*, **93**, 212.
Wilson, R. E., and Merrill, P. W.	1942	*Ap. J.*, **95**, 248.
Wirtz, C.	1922	*A. N.*, **215**, 281.
Yoss, K. M.	1958	*A.J.*, **63**, 61.

CHAPTER 5

Motions of the Nearby Stars

RICHARD WOOLLEY
Royal Greenwich Observatory

§ 1. GENERAL REMARKS

FROM a practical point of view the motion of a star relative to the sun must be regarded as being compounded out of two components, the radial velocity in the line of sight and the transverse velocity perpendicular to the line of sight. Since the radial velocity is determined by spectroscopic observation, making use of Doppler's principle, it can be determined practically instantaneously, and the accuracy with which it can be determined is a characteristic of the spectral type of the star and of the spectrograph used. In the case of bright stars high dispersion can be employed, and if the star has sharp lines, which is generally the case if the spectral type is F7 or later, an accuracy superior to 1 km/sec is attainable; this is, of course, independent of the distance of the star. Such an accuracy is obtained with the use of coudé spectrographs. These have not in fact been employed in the determination of radial velocities of many stars, and the bulk of the available determinations of the velocity of stars, even bright ones, are of less accuracy than this, the probable error being 2 or 3 km/sec. Many published determinations are of even lower accuracy. The data given in R. E. Wilson's (1953) *Catalogue of Radial Velocities* include an estimate of the accuracy of the determination, which is an excellent guide. For stars of early type the spectral lines are as a rule broad, and the velocities derived from their measurement are poor compared with the late types; and, of course, for faint stars spectrographs of low dispersion must be used, so that the velocity found, even in the case of late type stars, has a probable error of several km/sec.

Turning to the determination of transverse velocity, several difficulties occur. Firstly, the velocity is seen as an angular displacement, which cannot be converted into a motion in km/sec unless the distance of the star is known. Secondly, if the star is a distant one the transverse motion in arc is small and hard to measure, even if the actual motion is large; and, in any case, an error in seconds

85

of arc per annum corresponds to a large error in kilometers per second. Lastly, the motion is measured relative to some system which itself may be subject to error and uncertainty. If the transverse motion is measured by meridian observation the planes of reference are defined by the solar system, but their practical realization presents difficulties which may be serious in relation to the small quantities involved. If the determination is photographic (that is to say is made by measurement of new and old photographic plates) the proper motion found for a particular star is a motion relative to whatever reference objects may be choosen. These may be reference stars whose motions have been determined by meridian instruments (and are supposed to be relative to invariable planes defined by the solar system) or they may be stars much fainter than the star under observation whose motions are supposed to be negligible. Recently a project has been undertaken by the Lick Observatory of measuring stellar motions relative to galaxies whose apparent motions in arc may indeed be supposed negligible. This project offers great promise.

Stellar distance is, unfortunately, ill-determined except in very favorable cases where the star is very close or else happens to be a member of a well-defined group of nearly parallel moving stars. Consequently, apart from these favorable cases, the transverse velocities in absolute units are not well known, even if the proper motions (angular displacement in seconds of arc per century) are exceptionally well-determined.

As a result of these well-known uncertainties in the determination of stellar motion briefly sketched above, analysis of stellar motions in the past has been largely statistical. Indeed, in many ways a statistical analysis of stellar motion is inevitable. Just as the present position of a particular star is a contingency of no significance as an isolated fact in itself, so is the motion. Even if we knew enough about the galactic field of force to calculate the galactic orbit of one star, this orbit, though of great interest because none such has yet been reliably computed, is still not a datum of general significance (since the galactic attraction has to be assumed before the orbit is calculated). One would expect, however, to be able to infer generalizations from a large number of stellar galactic orbits; and similarly one may be able to draw inferences from a large number of stellar motions. In default of stellar distances one may even draw important inferences from proper motions.

The statistical analysis of stellar motions was treated thoroughly, with reference to ideas current at the time, by A. S. Eddington in *Stellar Movements and the Structure of the Universe* published in 1914, a work of such importance that it should still be studied by serious students of stellar motion in spite of the fact that it was written fifty years ago. Today there are better data available, and the idea of the attraction of the Galaxy as a whole on the movements of stars in the neighborhood of the sun has entered as a dominant feature in the analysis. It is only in these respects that Eddington's ideas must be brought up to date.

§ 2. GALACTIC ORBITS OF NEARBY STARS

We have no guarantee, of course, that the gravitational field of the Galaxy has any cylindrical symmetry; indeed, the appearance of other galaxies might suggest that this is quite far from being the case. However, in default of detailed knowledge of the distribution of matter in those parts of the Galaxy which are far remote from the sun, it is necessary to assume some sort of symmetry in order to make any inquiry into the galactic orbits of stars. An enormous simplification results if one supposes that it is permissible to consider motion parallel to the plane of the Galaxy independently of motion perpendicular to the Galaxy.

Considering only the projection of the motion of a star on the galactic plane, let R be the distance from the galactic center and set $u = R^{-1}$. Let the component in the galactic plane of the attraction be $u^2 \mu(u)$. The equation of motion of the star is

$$\frac{d^2u}{d\vartheta^2} + u = \frac{\mu(u)}{h^2}, \tag{1}$$

where h is a constant (since the force may be assumed central) and ϑ is the galactic longitude with the center of the Galaxy as origin, counted positive in the direction in which the Galaxy is rotating.

This equation can be solved analytically if $\mu(u)$ is a constant or if it can be expressed as a power series in u with terms up to and including u^3, namely,

$$\mu(u) = a + \beta u + \gamma u^2 + \delta u^3 .$$

Such a formula for $\mu(u)$ may be a good representation of the galactic attraction for moderate values of u, though it must break down and fail to represent the attraction near the center of the Galaxy, where u takes very large values. If $\gamma = 0$ and $\delta = 0$ the solution of equation (1) is

$$u = R_0^{-1}[1 + e \cos n(\vartheta - \vartheta_0)],$$

where e and ϑ_0 are arbitrary constants and R_0 and n are given by

$$R_0 = \frac{h^2 - \beta}{a}, \qquad 1 - n^2 = \frac{\beta}{h^2}.$$

We shall return to this case later. If $\delta = 0$ (but $\gamma \neq 0$), the solution is

$$u = R_0^{-1}\{1 + e \, cn^2[n(\vartheta - \vartheta_0) \, k]\},$$

where the constants R, e, n, and ϑ_0, and the modulus k of the elliptic function $cn[n(\vartheta - \vartheta_0) \, k]$ can be found in terms of the two initial conditions of the orbit and of the three constants a, β, and γ (Woolley 1964). If δ is not equal to zero, the orbit is

$$\frac{u - a}{u - b} = c \, cn[m(\vartheta - \vartheta_0) \, k],$$

giving six constants to be determined.

In the remainder of this paper, however, we shall only consider small deviations from the circular motion, and we shall assume that a sufficient approximation to the galactic field is given by neglecting $d^2\mu/du^2$. The solution of (1) is then

$$u = R_1^{-1}[\, 1 + e \cos n(\vartheta - \vartheta_0)\,],\qquad(2)$$

where e and ϑ_0 are arbitrary constants, and

$$1 - n^2 = \frac{1}{\mu_1 R_1}\frac{d\mu}{du}.$$

Here μ_1 is the value of μ when $R = R_1$. In terms of the circular velocity Θ_c at $R = R_1$, we have

$$\mu_1 = R_1\Theta_c^2,$$

$$h = R_1\Theta_c.$$

Again from the definition, the Oort constants A, B are given by

$$2A = -\frac{d\Theta}{dR} + \frac{\Theta}{R},$$

$$2B = -\frac{d\Theta}{dR} - \frac{\Theta}{R}.$$

We find

$$n^2 = \frac{4B}{B - A}.$$

The motion may be described in terms of an epicycle as follows. Consider a point C (called the epicenter) moving with the circular velocity Θ_c at a distance R_1 from the galactic center O. Let P be a point whose rectangular coordinates are (ξ, η) in axes whose origin is C, such that the axis of ξ is OC produced and η is positive in the direction in which galactocentric longitude increases. Then if

$$\xi = -eR_1 \cos n(\vartheta - \vartheta_0),$$

$$\eta = \frac{2e}{n}R_1 \sin n(\vartheta - \vartheta_0),$$

the motion of P satisfies equation (2) (and therefore eq. [1]) if e^2 can be neglected.

The motion described by equation (2) and by its epicyclic representation is identical with that described in Lindblad's extensive researches. It is, however, convenient to adopt the epicyclic description in many contexts. In particular, if we take the present position of the star P as origin, and set up *non*-rotating rectangular coordinates with P as origin with x radial (positive outward) and y tangential (positive in the direction in which rotation takes place), then the coordinates of the epicenter are

$$x = eR_1 \cos n(\vartheta - \vartheta_0),\qquad y = -\frac{2e}{n}R_1 \sin n(\vartheta - \vartheta_0).$$

Again, if u is the velocity along the axis of x (again positive outward) and v is the velocity along the axis of y relative to the circular velocity Θ_P at *the star's place P* (both v and Θ being counted positive in the direction in which rotation takes place)

$$u = \Theta_P e n \sin n(\vartheta - \vartheta_0), \qquad v = \tfrac{1}{2}\Theta_P e n^2 \cos n(\vartheta - \vartheta_0).$$

Then, since $\Theta/R = (A - B)$ and $n^2 = 4B/(B - A)$, we have

$$\frac{x}{v} = -\frac{y}{u} = -\frac{1}{2B}.$$

Further, writing $\lambda = 2/n$,

$$u^2 + \lambda^2 v^2 = \Theta_P^2 e^2 n^2 .$$

These results are found quite simply. Details are given, for example, by Woolley (1960).

§ 3. THE VELOCITY ELLIPSOIDS

In the light of this analysis we may ask ourselves what we may expect to see in the statistics of the velocities of nearby stars. If there is a class of stars which move in very eccentric galactic orbits, the above analysis will tell us very little. However, there is reason to believe that most of the nearby stars do move in orbits whose velocities differ from the circular velocity by so small a fraction of itself that it is reasonable to neglect the square of this fraction (i.e., u^2/Θ^2 and v^2/Θ^2 small).

In the first place it is reasonable to suppose that the mean of the velocities radial to the center of the Galaxy (u velocities) is zero in any large set of stars of mixed origin. What goes out from the center of attraction must fall back again (unless indeed it has the velocity of escape). One can suppose that any group of stars with a common origin in space and time is now moving out from the center, or moving in: but in a mixture the inward and outward motions must cancel each other. (There is of course a non-zero average to be expected of the u component of the velocities relative to the sun; but this is a mere reflection of the component radial to the galactic center of the sun's own motion.) Actual statistics show for the nearby stars that the distribution of the u components, after the solar motion has been removed, approximates reasonably well to a Gaussian distribution, so that if there are ν stars of a certain kind per unit volume, of which $\nu(u)\,du$ have velocities between u and $u + du$,

$$\nu(u)\,du = \frac{j}{\sqrt{\pi}} \nu e^{-j^2 u^2}\,du ,$$

where the coefficient j may vary from one (spectral) class of stars to another.

We now remark that if the distribution of epicenters is independent of y but varies exponentially with x, or

$$\rho(x) = \rho \exp(-x/L)$$

for reasonably small values of x, then the exponential u distribution implies an exponential v distribution, namely,

$$\nu(v) = \frac{j\lambda}{\sqrt{\pi}} \exp[-j^2\lambda^2(v-v_1)^2],$$

where $v_1 = (4BLj^2\lambda^2)^{-1}$ (see Woolley 1960, eq. 3.25).

Historically, an ellipsoidal distribution of velocities was proposed by K. Schwarzschild in 1907, long before the appearance of the work of either Lindblad or Oort on the rotation of the Galaxy. Schwarzschild supposed that if U, V, W were three rectangular components of stellar velocity, it would be possible to find a distribution function of the form

$$\exp\{-[K^2U^2 + H^2(V^2+W^2)]\},$$

the axis of U being the "direction of star streaming" revealed by the observations of velocity themselves. The exponent is related to the equation of an ellipsoid (with two equal axes), namely,

$$K^2U^2 + H^2(V^2+W^2) = 1,$$

which is called "the velocity ellipsoid." Introduction of the ideas of stellar dynamics, either by direct consideration of stellar galactic orbits as above, or by an appeal to general theorems on stellar dynamics as in Smart's (1938), *Stellar Dynamics* (chap. 10), or elsewhere, tells us that if the distribution is Gaussian in one coordinate it is also Gaussian in another, the dispersion being different and in a manner related to the galactic gravitational field; see also chapter 21 of this volume. Also, the velocity ellipsoid should point to the center of the Galaxy. If we find it to be substantially tilted, we must inquire how this can occur.

The velocity ellipsoid can be determined from radial velocities alone, or from proper motions alone (Smart 1938, chap. 5; Trumpler and Weaver 1953, chap. 3). In the latter case it is necessary to introduce somewhere into the analysis a speed in kilometers per second. This can be done if the speed of the sun relative to the mean of the stars considered is supposed known, either from radial-velocity measurements or from the proper motions of stars of known parallax. However, Stromberg (1946) took the point of view that it is valuable to confine one's attention to stars so close to the sun that their trigonometrical parallaxes can be determined and all three components of the motion observed in kilometers per second. He accordingly examined 444 stars within 20 parsecs of the sun. These have parallaxes greater than 0″.050 which may be supposed to be determinable with some accuracy. More recently Gliese (1957) has published a catalogue of 1094 stars within 20 parsecs of the sun, of which 597 stars (or 742 stars counting all components of multiple stars separately) have all three components of the motion known. This material was analyzed by Gliese (1956) himself and also by Woolley (1958).

There are very few stars of spectral type A within 20 parsecs of the sun (Stromberg gave only 26), but for stars of this type the dispersion in absolute magnitude is small. If it is supposed that this dispersion is negligible, the relative distance of each star may be found from its apparent magnitude. Proceeding in this way Alexander (1958) investigated 475 stars of type A. By comparing the mean radial velocities with the proper motions he was able to determine the mean absolute magnitude, and then to work out the three components of velocity for each star from its apparent magnitude, proper motion, and radial velocity.

In Gliese's catalogue the u velocities are components of velocity directed toward longitude $l^{II} = 180°$ and zero latitude, the v toward longitude $l^{II} = 90°$ and zero latitude, and the w components directed toward the north galactic pole. If we have a catalogue of stellar velocities resolved into three rectangular coordinates, we can of course examine the distribution of any one component without any appeal to theory or hypothesis whatever—there is no need to suppose that the distribution is ellipsoidal. If it is found that the distribution is Gaussian in each of three components, then it is ellipsoidal; that is to say it is Gaussian in any direction, the parameters in various directions being related to the surface of an ellipsoid.

As a matter of fact, the u and w velocities in Gliese's catalogue do approximate well to Gaussian distributions, while the v velocities do not fit Gaussian distributions so well. In all three components, but especially in v, there are too many large velocities in comparison with a Gaussian distribution fitting the lower velocities.

In a Gaussian distribution

$$\nu(q) = \exp(-j^2 q^2),$$

the dispersion σ is defined by $2j^2\sigma^2 = 1$, and the median m is given by $jm = 0.4769$. Hence $\sigma = 1.483\ m$.

The present writer prefers the median to any other criterion of the best fit of a Gaussian distribution: it is not subjective, as a graphical method would be, and does not give high weight to very large entries, as the method of least squares does.

Table 1 shows the analysis of stellar velocities according to spectral type, the data for stars of type A being taken from Alexander's paper and those for remaining spectral types being taken from Woolley's discussion of the Gliese material. Unfortunately these results are affected by a selection effect, namely, that faint stars are put on parallax programs because they have been found to show large proper motion. Quite clearly if this is done, the stars known to be within 20 parsecs of the sun will have a larger velocity dispersion than the totality of stars within this distance of the sun so long as the list of stars remains incomplete. That the list is seriously incomplete is shown by the fact that the mean transverse-velocity dispersion of the M stars listed by Gliese is $\sqrt{5.2}$ times the mean radial-velocity dispersion, whereas it should be only $\sqrt{2.16}$ times (Woolley 1958). It is therefore an urgent matter to detect late-type dwarf stars of low proper motion. An important start has been made by Vyssotsky (1946), who classifies late-type stars into giants and dwarfs from their spectra.

The velocity ellipsoid can, of course, be tilted with respect to the radius vector from the galactic center. Considering only the components of motion in the galactic plane, u and v, the general expression

$$\nu(u,v)\,du\,dv = \text{const}\exp\{-[a(u-u_0)^2+2f(u-u_0)(v-v_0)$$
$$+b(v-v_0)^2]\}\,du\,dv$$

gives Gaussian distributions of the velocity component in any direction in the galactic plane. Suppose that both u and v components are found to exhibit Gaussian distributions. Then the principal axes of the velocity ellipse are found by rotating the (u, v) axes through an angle Ω given by

$$\tfrac{1}{2}\tan 2\Omega = \frac{\Sigma(u-u_0)(v-v_0)}{\Sigma(u-u_0)^2-\Sigma(v-v_0)^2},$$

the quantities u_0 and v_0 being the mean (or median) velocity relative to the sun. In any comparatively small sample, such as the nearby stars, the value of the

TABLE 1

ANALYSIS OF MOTIONS OF NEAREST STARS ACCORDING TO SPECTRAL TYPE

SPECTRAL TYPE	No. OF STARS	MEAN MOTION (km/sec)			DISPERSION (km/sec)			
		u_0	v_0	w_0	σ_u	σ_v	σ_w	σ_u^2/σ_v^2
A.........	475	+10	−14	−6	18	13	8	1.9
F.........	84	+10	−12	−6	29	16	13	3.3
G.........	136	+16	−20	−7	38	24	19	2.5
K.........	190	+15	−19	−9	37	20	16	3.4
M.........	292	+ 7	−16	−7	40	24	18	2.8

tilt Ω found in this way is vulnerable to the chance occurrence of particular stars with high values of the product $(u-u_0)(v-v_0)$, and the tilts found for most classes of stars are not definitely significant. However, Stromberg found a much larger tilt for stars of type A than for stars of other spectral types, and this tilt is confirmed by Alexander, who finds a tilt of about 30° to the direction of the center of the Galaxy, in the direction of increasing longitude.

This tilt may be accounted for by assuming that the (epicenters of the orbits of the) A stars are distributed in an arm of the Galaxy, or that they avoid a lane in the Galaxy, the arm or lane being inclined at some angle other than 0° or 90° to the direction of the galactic center. For suppose that the density of the epicenters (x, y) is given by the expression

$$\ln\rho(x, y) = \ln\rho - \frac{1}{L}(lx+my)l\pm\frac{1}{M^2}(lx+my)^2, \tag{3}$$

with $l^2 + m^2 = 1$, and with the understanding that the formula only applies to local values of x and y, i.e., considerably less than the distance to the galactic center. This distribution leads to

$$\nu(u,v) = \text{const} \exp[\, - j^2(u^2 + \lambda^2 v^2)$$

$$- \frac{1}{2BL}(lv - mu) \pm \frac{1}{4B^2M^2}(lv - mu)^2\,],$$

which may be rearranged as

$$\nu(u,v) = \text{const} \exp\Big[- j^2 \Big(1 \mp \frac{m^2}{k^2}\Big)(u - u_1)^2 - j^2\lambda^2 \Big(1 \mp \frac{l^2}{\lambda^2 k^2}\Big)(v - v_1)^2$$

$$\mp \frac{2\,j^2 lm}{k^2}(u - u_1)(v - v_1)\Big],$$

and, therefore, leads to a tilted velocity ellipse, the angle of tilt Ω being given by

$$\tfrac{1}{2}\tan 2\Omega = \pm \frac{lm}{k^2(1 - \lambda^2) \mp (m^2 - l^2)}, \tag{4}$$

in the sense of decreasing longitude, since the u axis is at $180°$ and the v axis at $90°$ of (new) longitude.

The ratio of the axes of the ellipse is λ_{eff} where

$$\lambda_{\text{eff}}^2(k^2 \mp m^2) = \lambda^2 k^2 \mp l^2.$$

The value of λ_{eff}^2 may be taken to be 2 for A stars (from the values of σ_u^2 and σ_v^2 in Table 1). Similarly, the value of λ^2 (for stars in general in the solar neighborhood) can be taken to be 3. Accordingly,

$$k^2 = \pm (l^2 - 2m^2). \tag{5}$$

Again, if we set $\Omega = 30°$, we have from equation (4)

$$- \frac{\sqrt{3}}{2} = \pm \frac{lm}{- 2k^2 \mp (m^2 - l^2)}. \tag{6}$$

Eliminating k^2 from equations (5) and (6),

$$l^2 - \frac{2}{\sqrt{3}} lm - 3m^2 = 0,$$

and

$$\frac{1}{m} = \frac{\sqrt{10} + 1}{\sqrt{3}} \qquad [\text{solution}(a)]$$

or

$$\frac{1}{m} = - \frac{\sqrt{10} - 1}{\sqrt{3}} \qquad [\text{solution}(b)].$$

Since k is real, solution (a) requires the upper sign in equation (5), and therefore in (3), and refers to a lane; equally, solution (b) refers to an arm. Since $l^2 + m^2 = 1$ the directions in both cases are known: according to solution (a) the lane is normal to (new) longitude $l^{\text{II}} = 157°$, and according to (b) the arm is normal to new longitude 219°. By (5) the value of k for solution (a) is 0.74. This value of k leads to a value for M, since $k^2 = 4j^2B^2M^2 = 2B^2M^2/\sigma_u^2$. With $\sigma_u = 18$ km/sec for A stars and $B = -10$ km/sec/kpc we find $M = 0.94$ kiloparsecs.

The distribution of 21 cm radiation does suggest a lane of hydrogen in the solar neighborhood generally in the direction of $l^{\text{II}} = 67°$ (van de Hulst, Muller, and Oort 1954), but the distribution of early-type stars given by McCuskey (1956) suggests rather an arm in the direction of $l^{\text{II}} = 129°$. It seems quite likely that the tilt in the velocity ellipse of A stars in the solar neighborhood is, in fact, a consequence of the irregularity of the space distribution of these stars.

§ 4. COLOR-MAGNITUDE ARRAYS AND ORBITAL CHARACTERISTICS

A correlation between the color-luminosity arrays (HR diagrams) and orbital characteristics of nearby stars has been pointed out by Woolley and Eggen (1958). If the distance of the sun to the center of the Galaxy is R, the closest approach to the center of the Galaxy made by a star in the neighborhood of the sun with velocities u, v relative to the circular velocity is

$$R + \frac{1}{2B}\left[\left(\frac{u^2}{\lambda^2} + v^2\right)^{1/2} - v\right], \tag{7}$$

$2B$ being negative. This is a result of the equations developed in Section 2 in which the square of the eccentricity e is neglected, so that the result is inaccurate for large values of u and v, but classification of stellar orbits according to perigalactic distance computed from this equation is some guide to the approaches made by stars to the galactic center, even if the division points given by (7) are inexact.

Woolley and Eggen classified the stars in the solar neighborhood by computing the velocity

$$v' = -v + \sqrt{\left(\frac{u^2}{\lambda^2} + v^2\right)},$$

and divided the stars as follows:

Class	v' (km/sec)
A	0– 9
B	10– 29
C	30– 59
D	60– 99
E	100–129
E+	≥ 130

If one adopts $-2B = 20$ km/sec/kpc and $R = 10$ kpc, the division point between D and E is halfway into the galactic center from the sun; but, as has been said, this is inexact, though the order A, B, C, . . . does represent increasing approach to the galactic center.

Having classified the stars in this way Woolley and Eggen constructed HR diagrams for the six classes. These show a gradual change from class A to class E+; these diagrams are reproduced in Figure 1.

The HR diagram of the class A stars resembles that of the Pleiades, and that of class E+ resembles the open cluster M67. These two open clusters are, in terms of the contemporary theory of stellar evolution, very young and very old, respectively. Accepting this interpretation, stars with more or less circular orbits in the neighborhood of the sun are of comparatively recent formation, while stars in the solar neighborhood which describe orbits that go halfway into the galactic center are much older.

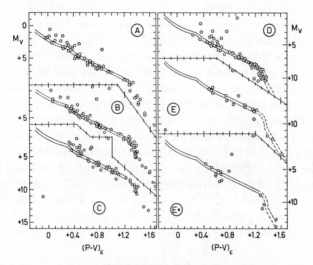

FIG. 1.—Color-luminosity arrays for stars of classes A, B, . . . , E+ (see text) for which the trigonometric parallax, from at least two determinations, is greater than 0″.05. The order A, B, . . . , E+ represents decreasing pericentric distance of the star's galactic orbit from the galactic center.

The motions of the nearby stars therefore support the view that young stars may be expected to be confined to regions of space where interstellar gas and dust are located, so that star formation is now confined to the spiral arms of our Galaxy (cf. Burbidge 1960). The occurrence of highly elliptic orbits among old stars and their absence among stars formed recently are natural consequences of a collapse of intergalactic matter, originally chaotic but settling down to its present shape on account of inelastic collisions between *gas* particles.

§ 5. THE MOVING CLUSTER IN TAURUS (THE HYADES)

We now leave aside the statistical analysis of stellar velocities, in relation to galactic forces, and consider in this section, and in the one which follows, cases where the motion is certainly not random, but where the stars move in some very orderly way which must have a connection with their original formation.

We do return to equilibrium considerations in Section 7, which deals with motion perpendicular to the galactic plane.

It has been known for a long time that the proper motions of a number of stars in the constellation Taurus are directed toward a certain point in the sky, called the radiant. The stars concerned occupy apparent places distributed over an area with a diameter of roughly twenty degrees. Since the average distance of the stars from the sun is roughly forty parsecs, judged by the trigonometrical parallaxes and also by a more refined argument that follows, the stars occupy a volume in space with a diameter of rather more than ten parsecs.

If the stars were not subject to galactic attraction, and had remained within such distances of each other for 10^9 years, their velocities would have to be equal and parallel within 10 meters per second (since 1 km/sec $\approx 10^{-6}$ parsecs/year). This argument is little affected by the presence of galactic forces: and even placing the age of the cluster as low as 10^8 years, the motions must agree within a tenth of 1 km/sec, unless the cluster is a fortuitous agglomeration of stars, which we cannot easily admit. Now if we do concede that the motions are equal and parallel (well within the limits of observational error) we can deduce the distance of each star from the sun (i.e., its parallax) from the observed proper motion and observed radial velocity, once the radiant has been fixed.

Let the angular distance of the star from the radiant be λ and let the common velocity of all the stars relative to the sun be V. Then the transverse velocity is $T = V \sin \lambda$ and the radial velocity is $V_r = V \cos \lambda$. But if the parallax in seconds of arc is p and the proper motion in seconds of arc per year is μ, and T is expressed in kilometers per second, $T = 4.74 \, \mu/p$. We have therefore

$$p = \frac{4.74 \mu \cot \lambda}{V_r}.$$

If the proper motion and radial velocity are both known to an accuracy of two per cent, which is possible in the best observed cases, we can determine the parallax to an accuracy of three per cent, which is far better than could be achieved by observation of trigonometrical parallax. (For a trigonometrical parallax of $0\overset{''}{.}025$ we might expect a probable error of $\pm 0\overset{''}{.}008$.)

Van Bueren (1952) gave a list of 132 stars which he regarded as having the motion of the Hyades cluster both as regards the direction of the proper motion and as regards the radial velocity. This list only extends to stars of spectral type K0, having an apparent visual magnitude of $+9.0$, and it is not possible to enumerate the Hyades stars fainter than this, for lack of adequate data on proper motion and radial velocity over the wide area of the sky occupied by the cluster. Nevertheless, van Bueren estimates the number of stars of types K and M by analogy with other clusters and finds that the total mass is 320 $\odot$; he states that the velocity of escape from the center of the cluster is 0.2 km/sec.

It is a question of cardinal interest, in discussing the motion of the cluster stars, whether or not they have the velocity of escape from one another. Van Bueren finds for the right ascension and declination of the radiant

$$a = 6^h18^m5 , \qquad \delta = 7°29'(1950),$$

and also finds $V = 43.95$ km/sec. He quotes such observations of radial velocity as were available to him at the time he was writing. In these, the median difference between the observed radial velocity and $V \cos \lambda$ is 2.3 km/sec. Either this is attributable to errors in the observations of radial velocity, or the stars are

TABLE 2

RADIAL VELOCITIES OF LATE-TYPE MEMBERS OF HYADES

Star H.D.	Spectrum (Wilson)	Observed Radial Velocity (km/sec)	Computed $V \cos \lambda$ (van Bueren) (km/sec)	O−C (km/sec)
		Giants		
27371..........	gG9	+39.5	+37.7	+1.8
27697..........	gG8	+39.9	+37.8	+2.1
28305..........	gG8	+39.7	+38.2	+1.5
28307..........	gG8	+39.4	+38.5	+0.9
		Dwarfs		
26345..........	dF6	+36.0	+36.7	−0.7
26784..........	dF7	+36.5	+37.5	−1.0
27149..........	dG3	+37.0	+37.2	−0.2
27383..........	dF7	+36.8	+37.7	−0.9
27406..........	dF9	+36.9	+37.4	−0.5
27808..........	dF6	+35.4	+37.4	−2.0
27989..........	dG4	+36.6	+38.1	−1.5
28205..........	dF8	+37.5	+38.4	−0.9
28237..........	dG0	+37.3	+38.8	−1.5
28406..........	dF7	+37.9	+38.4	−0.5
28608..........	dF6	+37.8	+39.0	−1.2
30810..........	dF7	+40.0	+40.7	−0.7

certainly not gravitationally bound together. More accurate radial velocities than those generally given in Wilson's catalogue may be determined, in the case of late-type stars which have sharp metallic lines, if high-dispersion spectrographs are used. A number of such determinations were made by Woolley, Jones, and Mather (1960), using spectra obtained with the coudé spectrographs attached to the 100-inch telescope at Mount Wilson (dispersion 10 A/mm) and the 200-inch telescope at Mount Palomar (dispersion 9 A/mm). The results are shown in Table 2.

It will be noticed that the four giant stars all show positive residuals from the calculated velocity $V \cos \lambda$, and the twelve dwarf stars all show negative residuals. The mean residual of the twelve dwarf stars is -1.0 ± 0.1 km/sec and the median departure from this mean is 0.4 km/sec. The system of these observations was tested by observing the radial velocity of the moon on ten spectrograms; it was found that the mean difference from the calculated radial velocity of sunlight reflected from the moon was $+0.2 \pm 0.3$ km/sec and the median departure of a single determination was 0.65 km/sec. Now the velocities determined for the dwarf Hyades stars are each the mean of three determinations, so that we should expect to find a median departure of 0.4 km/sec from the calculated velocity if the actual stellar velocities were zero. In fact, the median departure from $V \cos \lambda - 1.0$ km/sec is again 0.4 km/sec, showing that the real dispersion in radial velocities is too small to be detected. It can hardly exceed 0.3 km/sec. Accordingly the radial velocities of the dwarf stars indicate that these stars have *not* got the velocity of escape from the cluster. It can hardly be supposed that the four giant stars are really moving away from the cluster with a velocity of 2.5 km/sec, and it seems necessary to suppose that gas motions in the atmospheres of these giant stars produce an apparent shift in radial velocity. Since the system of radial velocities was calibrated by observing the spectrum of the moon, illuminated by a star of type dG2, it is to be supposed that the velocity indicated by the dwarf stars is in fact the kinematic velocity. If this is accepted, the observations of radial velocity indicate a correction to van Bueren's value of approximately -1.0 km/sec, giving

$$V = 43 \text{ km/sec}.$$

Turning to the proper motions of stars in the Hyades cluster, these have been re-examined by Wayman (unpublished) with the same question in mind, namely, whether or not *best determined* proper motions indicate an observable dispersion in velocity. Forty-three stars given as members of the Hyades occur in the *Catalogue of 5268 Standard Stars, 1950.0* known as *N30*, which was published by the Nautical Almanac Office of the U.S. Naval Observatory (Morgan 1952); they also occur in the *Albany General Catalogue* (Boss 1937) known as *GC*. The catalogue *GC* gives star positions for epoch 1900 which are still considered very accurate, though subject to small systematic errors which are believed known. *GC* also gives proper motions, based on nineteenth-century meridian observations and on twentieth-century meridian observations up to 1925. These proper motions were considered to be capable of improvement by the authors of *N30*, who derived new positions, with a mean epoch of 1930, from meridian observations made between 1917 and 1949. Combination of the *N30* positions (at about 1930) with *GC* positions (corrected for systematic error) (at about 1900) gives *N30* proper motions.

Table 3, which was very kindly supplied to me by Dr. Wayman, shows proper motions of the twenty Hyades stars which have the smallest probable errors in the position angle of their proper motion. These proper motions have been recomputed for the purpose from the data in *N30* and *GC* but are *N30* proper motions so far as system is concerned. The radiant computed from these proper motions is

$$\alpha = 6^h 17^m.5 \pm 2^m.1, \qquad \delta = + 7°41' \pm 14' \text{ (probable errors)},$$

which differs very little from van Bueren's radiant. The parallaxes shown are computed by taking $V = 43.0$ km/sec in each case.

TABLE 3

PROPER MOTIONS OF WELL OBSERVED HYADES STARS

STAR H.D.	ANNUAL PROPER MOTION (sec of arc)			RESIDUAL FROM RADIANT $\Delta \vartheta$	PROBABLE ERROR OF POSITION ANGLE, ϵ_ϑ	SIN λ	PARALLAX
	μ_α	μ_δ	μ				
24357...	+0".145	−0".026	0".147	+0°.1	0°.51	0.607	0".0251
26462...	+ .144	+ .016	.145	−0.6	.71	.534	.0282
26911...	+ .114	− .026	.117	+2.3	.91	.526	.0231
27176...	+ .095	− .031	.100	−2.0	.92	.542	.0191
27371...	+ .116	− .022	.118	−0.6	.33	.515	.0238
27397...	+ .116	− .019	.118	+0.5	.85	.508	.0242
27459...	+ .105	− .019	.107	−0.3	.91	.508	.0218
27697...	+ .106	− .028	.109	−0.2	.38	.508	.0223
27819...	+ .111	− .036	.117	+2.8	.68	.508	.0239
27934...	+ .098	− .046	.108	+1.9	.83	.522	.0214
27946..	+ .107	− .050	.118	+1.9	.82	.522	.0235
27962...	+ .108	− .032	.113	+0.2	.65	.500	.0235
28024...	+ .107	− .045	.116	−1.4	.70	.522	.0231
28305...	+ .108	− .037	.114	−0.2	.32	.500	.0237
28307...	..+ .103	− .026	.106	+0.4	.73	.485	.0227
28319...	+ .104	− .024	.107	−0.3	.73	.477	.0233
28485...	+ .103	− .022	.105	−0.9	.73	.477	.0229
28910...	+ .100	− .025	.103	+2.0	.68	.462	.0232
30780...	+ .080	− .034	.087	−1.0	.76	.415	.0217
32301...	+0".064	−0".042	0".077	−0°.4	0°.50	0.399	0".0200

In ten cases the residual between the position angle of the proper motion and the position angle of the radiant from the star's position is *less* than its probable error, and in eleven cases the residual is *greater* than its probable error. This again indicates that the true dispersion in the stellar velocities is too small to measure—as was found in the case of radial velocities. Since a displacement of half a degree in the direction of a velocity of 43 km/sec requires a vector addition of 0.375 km/sec, it seems safe to conclude from the proper motions of the stars (as well as from the radial velocities) that they have *not* got the velocity of escape from the cluster. Van Bueren's estimate of the velocity of escape is not at all likely to be an overestimate.

The extreme parallaxes shown in Table 3 are 0".0282 for HD 26462 and 0".0191 for HD 27176, corresponding to distances of 35.6 and 52.5 parsecs, respectively. Since Table 3 includes only a selection of the cluster members, these are not the extreme limits of the cluster. Before leaving the subject it must be pointed out that the entire business of determining proper motion is subject to systematic errors. Thus, Wayman's proper motions are about five per cent systematically smaller than van Bueren's. Also, in this part of the sky there is a considerable systematic difference between $N30$ proper motions and GC proper motions; in fact for R.A. 4^h5 and Dec. $+20°$ we have

$$N30–GC , \qquad \Delta\mu \text{ in R.A.} = -0\overset{.}{''}0043 \text{ per year} ,$$

$$\Delta\mu \text{ in Dec.} = +0\overset{.}{''}0025 \text{ per year} ,$$

so that the $N30$ proper motions place the Hyades about four per cent closer than the GC proper motions. We may expect the $N30$ system to be superior of the two, but we may suppose that further meridian work may produce fresh modifications of one or two per cent in the proper motions and therefore in the distances.

§ 6. STELLAR GROUPS

The existence of stars quite widely separated from the Hyades but moving with the same velocity as the cluster has been suspected for a long time. The subject has been discussed recently in two very important papers by Eggen. In the first of these (Eggen 1958a), the author examines certain stars to find out whether there is a number of stars, greater than that given by chance, whose proper motion is directed toward the radiant of the Hyades cluster and whose radial velocity is equal to the projection of the radial velocity of the Hyades in the direction of the star—both within the limits of experimental error. Clearly, since there are three components of space velocity, there are three conditions to be satisfied if the vector motion of a star is equal to that of a definite group: but since parallax is usually badly determined or even unknown we are compelled to eliminate one condition. The *direction* of the proper motion and radial velocity are chosen on the two conditions that must be satisfied if parallel motion is to be established.

In a later paper (Eggen 1960) the question is raised whether motion perpendicular to the galactic plane is relevant to group membership—or, as the author puts it, whether the w motion is not "uncoupled" from the u and v motions. The inner members of the Hyades are held together by their mutual attraction, but if there are any stars which are so far removed from the cluster that they have the velocity of escape, yet continue to share the galactic motion of the cluster sufficiently to remain within a kiloparsec of the center of the cluster for many revolutions around the center of the Galaxy, these stars must describe orbits which have nearly the same galactic period as has the cluster itself. The periods are determined by the velocities u and v (and the distance of the star from the galactic center), so that stars in approximately the same place, and with approximately the same values of u and v, will have nearly the same galactic periods even if they have quite different velocities w perpendicular to the galactic plane.

As a result of a number of discussions with Dr. Eggen, the present writer came to the conclusion (Woolley 1961) that it is the v component of a star's velocity that is most indicative of common origin and group membership. Consider the formation of a number of stars in a restricted area in the Galaxy and within a comparatively short space of time. By formation of the stars is meant in this connection the separation of a certain mass from the gas cloud and its condensation to a sufficient density for the resulting protostar to pursue a galactic orbit, little influenced by the remaining interstellar gas or by magnetic fields if present. The protostars will move off on individual orbits each of which will have a maximum and a minimum distance from the galactic center and a maximum distance above and below the galactic plane; or, the orbits will all be contained within a certain envelope. Initially the protostar envelope will be confined in longitude as well as in radius and height, but ultimately (unless the galactic periods are identically equal) the stars will spread right around the Galaxy. During the spreading process those with shortest periods will lead, and those with longest periods will trail the stars with average period. Hence, if any observer encounters the configuration, which we will now call a group, by overtaking or by being overtaken by it, he will see, within a few hundred parsecs of himself, only a sample of the group. If the encounter takes place soon after the formation of the group the sample seen will depend on the initial conditions of the group; but if the encounter takes place so long after the formation of the group that it has been drawn out in longitude by separation of stars with different periods, the observer will only see stars whose periods were just right to bring the stars concerned to the observer's longitude at the time that he occupies it. The sharpness of selection will depend on the original size of the group and on the original dispersion of the velocities, but as time goes on these become progressively less important, and in very old groups only galactic period matters. As the selection proceeds and sharpens, the observer sees a smaller number of group members at any time.

Let ω be the angular velocity of the epicenter of a star's orbit at a distance R_1 from the center of the Galaxy, and let φ be the galactocentric longitude of the star. Since, according to Section 2,

$$\eta = \frac{2e}{n} R_1 \sin n (\vartheta - \vartheta_0),$$

we have

$$\varphi = \vartheta + \frac{2e}{n} \sin n (\vartheta - \vartheta_0),$$

where ϑ may now be considered to be the galactocentric longitude of the epicenter. Let ϑ', φ' be the values of ϑ and φ at $t = 0$, the time of formation of the group. At any subsequent time t we have

$$\vartheta = \vartheta' + \omega t, \qquad \varphi = \vartheta' + \omega t + \frac{2e}{n} \sin n (\vartheta' + \omega t - \vartheta_0).$$

The star is seen in the longitude of the observer φ_1 if

$$\varphi_1 = \vartheta' + \omega t + \frac{2e}{n} \sin n (\vartheta' + \omega t - \vartheta_0),$$

so that for the star to be seen

$$\varphi_1 - \frac{2e}{n} < \vartheta' + \omega t < \varphi_1 + \frac{2e}{n}.$$

Also ϑ' must lie between certain limits, set by the original dimensions of the group; let us say that the initial conditions are

$$\vartheta_1 - \beta < \vartheta' < \vartheta_1 + \beta,$$

ϑ_1 being the galactocentric longitude of the center of the region of star formation. These conditions impose extreme limits for ωt, namely,

$$\varphi_1 - \frac{2e}{n} - (\vartheta_1 + \beta) < \omega t < \varphi_1 + \frac{2e}{n} - (\vartheta_1 - \beta).$$

The mean angular velocity of the group seen is given by

$$\langle \omega t \rangle = \varphi_1 - \vartheta_1,$$

and the extreme ranges of angular velocity seen are

$$\langle \omega \rangle \pm \Delta\omega,$$

where

$$t\Delta\omega = \frac{2e}{n} + \beta.$$

Accordingly, as t increases the range $\Delta\omega$ decreases.

Now if R_* is the distance of the observer from the center of the Galaxy, and if he sees in his immediate neighborhood a star with velocity v relative to the circular velocity at R_*, the distance of the star's epicenter from the center of the Galaxy is

$$R_* - \frac{v}{2B}.$$

Since, in general, if ω is the angular velocity of the epicenter distant R from the center of the Galaxy,

$$\frac{d\omega}{dR} = -\frac{2A}{R},$$

the range $\Delta\omega$ in members of the group seen implies a range of values of v seen, namely,

$$t\Delta v = \left| \frac{B}{A} \right| R \left(\frac{2e}{n} + \beta \right).$$

To see what restriction this might be expected to effect in practice, we must adopt some values for the fractions $2e/n$ and β, characteristic of the initial configuration of the group. If we take both fractions equal to 1/20 (or 500 pc at a distance of 10 kpc from the galactic center) and take $|B/A| = \frac{1}{2}$, then

$$l\Delta v = \tfrac{1}{20}R.$$

Then with $R = 10$ kpc, we have, since 1 km/sec $\approx$ 1 pc in 10^6 years the results of Table 4.

In a table of ages of clusters published by Burbidge (1960) the age of the Hyades is given from 3×10^8 years to 1.1×10^9 years by different authorities. We should therefore expect the Hyades group (if coeval with the cluster) to have v velocities within a range of about ± 1 km/sec. Other groups described by Eggen (1958b) are, to judge by their HR diagrams, as old as M67, whose age is given from 4 to 5×10^9 years in Burbidge's table. In these groups one would expect to find a v selection of only a few tenths of ± 1 km/sec.

The Hyades group has the velocities $u = +40$, $v = -18$, and $w = -2$ km/sec relative to the sun, and therefore about $u = +29$, $v = -1$, and $w = +5$

TABLE 4

SPREAD IN VELOCITY FOR STELLAR
GROUPS OF DIFFERENT AGE

Age of Group (years)	Spread in Velocity (km/sec)
10^8	± 5
10^9	± 0.5
10^{10}	± 0.05

km/sec relative to the circular velocity in the neighborhood of the sun. The large positive value of u is rather surprising, as it implies that the epicenter of the group is at least a kiloparsec behind the present position of the cluster, and if the group were part of the debris of a large object one would expect the epicenters to be drawn out in longitude, and to find other values of u in the solar neighborhood. However, Eggen has in effect suggested this; see, for example, Figure 2 of Eggen (1960), where a number of dwarf A-type stars have the same v as the Hyades, but have values of u ranging from $+25$ to $+10$ km/sec relative to the sun, or $+14$ to -1 km/sec relative to the circular velocity.

The Sirius group has velocities $u = -14$, $v = 0$, and $w = -12$ km/sec relative to the sun, and therefore has the same galactic period as the sun. One may suggest that the sun is actually a member of the group; the age of this group given in Burbidge's table, already referred to, is 4×10^8 years which, no doubt, is too short a value for the age of the earth.

A further feature remains to be pointed out. Equality of galactic period only implies equality of v if the stars are at the same place. If their present positions differ in x (distance from the galactic center), there is a gradient of v

$$\frac{dv}{dx} = -(A - B)$$

or about 3 km/sec per 100 parsecs. So far it has not been possible to find any clear observational evidence for this.

The general view entertained here is that the stellar groups are debris of old spiral arms. If any large mass of gas succeeds in forming a large number of stars, these stars, even if originally in a spherically symmetrical pattern, will be drawn out in galactic longitude. At a moderate time after the star formation, the configuration will look like a spiral arm. Ultimately it must be so dissipated in longitude as to mingle with other arms and lose its special identity. Only the common v velocities will mark the stars as members of an old arm; Eggen's groups are, as it were, the ghosts of old spiral arms.

§ 7. THE MOTION OF STARS PERPENDICULAR TO THE GALACTIC PLANE

The following discussion makes a return to the study of the statistics of stellar motion, and might have preceded the sections dealing with special motions in groups. However it is, as will be seen, developed quite independently of motion in galactic orbits, and is so separate in treatment that it has been placed by itself at the end of this account of the motions of the nearby stars.

If Φ_z is the gravitational potential of the component of gravitational attraction perpendicular to the galactic plane, and if $\nu(w, \Phi_z)dw$ is the number of stars per unit volume with velocities perpendicular to the galactic plane between w and $w + dw$, then if the motion of the stars is in a steady state we have Jeans' relation,

$$\nu(w, \Phi_z) = f(w^2 - 2\Phi_z),\qquad(8)$$

the form of the function f being arbitrary. If there are n classes of stars, each of which has a Gaussian distribution of w velocities, that of the pth class being proportional to $\exp -j_p^2 w^2$, then Jeans' relation gives

$$\nu_p(w, \Phi_z) = f_p(w^2 - 2\Phi_z) = A_p \exp[-j_p^2(w^2 - 2\Phi_z)].$$

Consider the simple case where j_p has the same value j for all classes of stars, and let Φ_0 be the value of Φ_z when $z = 0$. Write $2j^2(\Phi_z - \Phi_0) = -\Psi$. Then

$$\nu(w, \Phi_z) = \text{const} \exp(-j^2 w^2 - \Psi).$$

By integration with respect to w, $\nu(\Phi_z) = \text{const} \times e^{-\Psi}$. If ρ is the density and $\rho/\rho_0 = \eta$, then $\eta = e^{-\Psi}$. We now suppose that if there is any appreciable attracting mass not concentrated in stars, its distribution is similar to that of the stars. Then Poisson's equation $\nabla^2\Phi = -4\pi\Gamma\rho$ gives

$$\frac{d^2\Phi_z}{dz^2} = -4\pi\Gamma\rho_0 e^{-\Psi}.$$

Then if we set $l = (8\pi\Gamma\rho_0 j^2)^{-1/2}$ and set $x = z/l$, we have

$$\frac{d^2\Psi}{dx^2} = e^{-\Psi},$$

subject to the boundary conditions $\psi = 0$ and $\dot{\psi} = 0$ at $x = 0$. The solution first given by Camm (1949) is

$$\Psi = 2 \ln \cosh \left(\frac{x}{\sqrt{2}} \right),$$

$$\eta = e^{-\Psi} = \mathrm{sech}^2 \left(\frac{x}{\sqrt{2}} \right).$$

(9)

This special case corresponds to the equation of the isothermal gas sphere in three dimensions. The solution does not give an infinite mass in a cylinder of finite cross-section, in fact,

$$\int_{-\infty}^{+\infty} \rho \, dz = 2 \sqrt{2} \, l\rho_0 ,$$

but of course the solution is doubly infinite in the (x, y) plane. If, however, both j^2 and l could be observed, in such a distribution, from observations of velocity and of density gradient, the central density could be computed from

$$8\pi \Gamma \rho_0 = (j^2 l^2)^{-1} .$$

Attempts have been made (Lindblad 1926a; Oort 1932, 1960; Woolley 1957; Hill 1960; Jones 1962) to compute the total density in the solar neighborhood by analyzing stellar velocities and stellar density gradients perpendicular to the galactic plane, using in effect equation (8) but abandoning the simplifications which lead to equation (9). If, following Oort, we suppose that there are n classes of stars and that for the pth class the w velocity is distributed as $\exp (-j_p^2 w^2)$; that the mass of each star in the pth class is m_p, and the abundance, at $z = 0$, is $\theta_0(p)$, subject to

$$\sum_1^n \theta_0(p) = 1 ,$$

then, by (8),

$$\nu_p(w, \Phi_z) = \mathrm{const} \, \exp [- j_p^2 (w^2 - 2\Phi_z)]$$

and

$$\eta = \frac{\rho}{\rho_0} = \frac{\displaystyle\sum_{p=1}^n m_p \theta_0(p) \exp[2 j_p^2 (\Phi_z - \Phi_0)]}{\displaystyle\sum_{p=1}^n m_p \theta_0(p)}$$

$$= \sum_{p=1}^n A_p \exp [2 j_p^2 (\Phi_z - \Phi_0)],$$

subject to

$$\sum_1^n A_p = 1 .$$

Select a suitable value of j_p^2, namely J^2, and set

$$a_p = \frac{j_p^2}{J^2}, \qquad \Psi = 2J^2(\Phi_0 - \Phi_z),$$

$$l = (8\pi\Gamma\rho_0 J^2)^{-1/2}, \qquad x = \frac{z}{l}.$$

Then Poisson's equation becomes

$$\frac{d^2\Psi}{dx^2} = \sum_{p=1}^{n} A_p \exp(-a_p\psi), \qquad (10)$$

and we may impose the condition

$$\sum_{1}^{n} A_p a_p = 1,$$

which merely defines J^2. In setting up this equation we suppose that Φ_z is a function of z alone, that is, that the matter is uniformly distributed in planes normal to the axis of z over distances large in comparison with the values of z with which we propose to deal. We also assume that dust and gas, if present, are distributed as if they formed a class or classes of stars. The solution in series of (10) is

$$\Psi = \tfrac{1}{2}x^2 - \tfrac{1}{24}x^4 + \ldots, \qquad (11)$$

$$\eta = 1 - \tfrac{1}{2}x^2 + x^4\tfrac{1}{8}\sum_{1}^{n} A_p a_p^2 + \ldots. \qquad (12)$$

The distribution of the pth class of stars is

$$\eta_p = A_p \exp(-a_p\psi)$$

or

$$\ln \eta_p = \text{const} - a_p\psi. \qquad (13)$$

For small values of x, this is, by (11),

$$\ln \eta_p = \text{const} - \tfrac{1}{2}a_p x^2 + \tfrac{1}{24}a_p x^4 \ldots,$$

or

$$\ln \eta_p = \text{const} - \tfrac{1}{2}a_p \frac{z^2}{l^2} + \tfrac{1}{24}a_p \frac{z^4}{l^4} \ldots. \qquad (14)$$

Hence if we can isolate any class of star (for example, by its spectral class) and observe its distribution with height z above the galactic plane, we can determine the product

$$\tfrac{1}{2}a_p \frac{z^2}{l^2}.$$

But $a_p = j_p^2/J^2$ and $l^2 = (8\pi\Gamma\rho_0 J^2)^{-1}$, so that

$$\tfrac{1}{2}a_p \frac{z^2}{l^2} = 4\pi\Gamma\rho_0 j_p^2 z^2; \qquad (15)$$

thus, if we observe a_p/l^2 from the observations of density and j_p^2 from (radial) velocities, we can determine ρ_0—the integrated density for all stars—though the observations were only conducted on the p stars. However, if the density distribution with height is such that it is necessary to include the term involving z^4 in order to determine the coefficient of z^2 in $\ln \eta_p$, then it is necessary to determine (or, at least, to estimate) a_p. For distances within ± 200 pc of the galactic plane the correction due to the term in z^4 is, however, small. It is assumed that the distribution of the velocities is in each case Gaussian.

The classical researches into this subject are those of Oort (1932), who investigated the behavior of stars of all spectral types. In 1957 Woolley followed up the work of Lindblad (1926b) by investigating the behavior of a restricted class of stars (those of spectral type A) and this has been carried further by other Greenwich workers (Wayman 1961, Jones 1962). Wayman made a special study of the velocities of stars of type A0 in the *Henry Draper Catalogue* and determined a number of new radial velocities of stars in the southern galactic cap. Considering the material in both N and S galactic caps he finds

$$\langle \, |w| \, \rangle = 7.4 \pm 0.8 \text{ km/sec} .$$

This gives $j_p = 0.076$ (km/sec)$^{-1}$. Further, Jones counted the number of A0 stars in a cylinder perpendicular to the galactic plane (and centered on the sun). To do this he made use of Alexander's analysis, which we have already referred to in Section 3; Alexander compared the radial velocities of A0 stars with their proper motions and came to the conclusion that these stars had an average absolute visual magnitude of $+0.14$. If it is assumed that the spread in absolute magnitude is small, this figure, combined with the star's apparent visual magnitude, gives the star's distance, which, with its galactic coordinates, locates it within or without the cylinder, and also gives the height above or below the sun in the z coordinate. Discussing the results, Jones finds

$$\sqrt{\frac{2l^2}{a_p}} = 146 \text{ pc} .$$

Inserting this, and Wayman's value of j_p, in (14), we find

$$\rho_0 = 0.15 \text{ solar masses per cubic parsec} .$$

In developing equation (15) it was assumed that the attracting material was stratified in infinite parallel planes. It is apparent from examination of other galaxies and from the evidence of 21-cm radiation concerning the distribution of hydrogen in the Galaxy that this condition is not really met on a large scale. What matters is whether the diameter of the area over which the density is reasonably uniform is or is not large in comparison with the height perpendicular to the galactic plane under discussion. Woolley (1957) and Jones (1962) consider that the run of A0 stellar density at distances greater than 200 pc from the galactic plane shows that the attraction is due to material irregularly dis-

tributed in the galactic plane. As a consequence of this it is necessary to suppose
that the local value of ρ_0 in the sun's immediate neighborhood is *greater* than
that given by equation (15).

Figure 2 shows the distribution of the logarithm of the density of A stars,
taken from a number of sources, plotted against distance from the galactic
plane. Now if the velocity function of the A stars is Gaussian, this curve represents, by equation (13), the potential Ψ as a function of height. The potential
is, of course, multiplied by an unknown coefficient, but this does not alter the

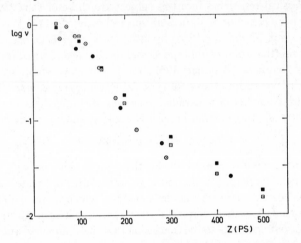

FIG. 2.—Relative densities of A stars as a function of galactic height z. *Open circles:* Lindblad; *filled circles:* counts in *Henry Draper Catalogue; open squares:* van Rhijn north-galactic
polar cap; *filled squares:* van Rhijn south-galactic polar cap.

fact that there is a well marked point of inflexion, at which $d^2\Psi/dx^2$ (and $d^2\Phi/dz^2$)
must change sign. But if Φ is a function of z alone,

$$\frac{d^2\Phi}{dz^2} = \nabla^2\Phi,$$

and this cannot change sign, since $\nabla^2\Phi = -4\pi\Gamma\rho$.

Oort (1932) accounted for the point of inflexion in the log density-height
curve by assuming a velocity function

$$\nu(w) = A_1 \exp(-j_1^2 w^2) + A_2 \exp(-j_2^2 w^2),$$

that is to say a double Gaussian distribution. If this equation is valid, the log
density is no longer proportional to the potential; but if it is valid, the velocity
dispersion must, by Jeans' theorem, increase with distance from the plane. Accordingly, near the galactic caps radial velocity dispersion should increase with
stellar magnitude. Wayman (1961) took special observations of radial velocities
of A stars near the S galactic pole to test this point, and found no such increase.

On the other hand, it is clear in principle that if Φ is a function of x and y as well as of z the relation

$$\frac{d^2\Phi}{dz^2} = \nabla^2\Phi$$

is destroyed, and that in this case it is possible for $d^2\Phi/dz^2$ to be negative. A model developed by Woolley (1957) shows that if the density is doubled in a (square section) arm of side 300 parsecs, a curve of the type shown in Figure 2 is obtained. While the model is crude, one may suppose, even a priori, that the material is not uniformly distributed in x and y, and one might well expect irregularities in the x, y to have important effects on the potential.

The motion and distribution of stars perpendicular to the galactic plane seem to demand recognition of local structure in the Galaxy, as does the tilt in the velocity ellipse of the A stars discussed in Section 3, although the effects are not due to precisely the same causes, if our analysis has been correct. The A-star velocity ellipse is tilted because the A stars themselves are distributed along an arm, but the vertical motion is affected by the gravitational effect of the arm itself, and a great deal of the mass is most probably not in the stars themselves at all, but in the form of dust and gas. Better information, some supplied perhaps by radio astronomical observations, is required before a completely satisfactory theoretical discussion can be given.

REFERENCES

ALEXANDER, J. B.   1958   M.N., 118, 161.

Boss, B.   1937   General Catalogue of 33342 Stars for the Epoch 1950 (Washington, D.C.: Carnegie Institution of Washington).

BUEREN, H. G. VAN   1952   B.A.N., 11, 385.

BURBIDGE, G. R.   1960   Die Entstehung von Sternen (Berlin: Springer), p. 1.

CAMM, G. L.   1949   M.N., 110, 309.

EDDINGTON, A. S.   1914   Stellar Movements and the Structure of the Universe (London: Macmillan & Co.).

EGGEN, O. J.   1958a   M.N., 118, 65.
                        1958b   Ibid., p. 154.
                        1960   Ibid., 120, 448.

GLIESE, W.   1956   Zs. f. Ap., 39, 1.
                        1957   Heidelberg Astr. Rechen-Inst., Mitt., Ser. A, No. 8.

HILL, E. R.   1960   B.A.N., 15, 1.

HULST, H. C. VAN DE, MULLER, C. A., and OORT, J. H.   1954   B.A.N., 12, 117.

JONES, D. H. P.   1962   Roy. Obs. Bull., No. 52.

LINDBLAD, B.   1926a   Uppsala Medd., No. 11, p. 30.
                        1926b   Arkiv f. Mat. Astr. o. Fysik., Ser. B, 19, No. 15.

McCUSKEY, S. W.   1956   Ap. J., 123, 458.

MORGAN, H. R.   1952   *Catalogue of 5268 Standard Stars, 1950.0* (Astr. Papers of the American Ephemeris, **13**, Pt. 3).

OORT, J. H.   1932   *B.A.N.*, **6**, 249.

     1960   *Ibid.*, **15**, 45.

SMART, W. M.   1938   *Stellar Dynamics* (Cambridge: Cambridge University Press).

STROMBERG, G.   1946   *Ap. J.*, **104**, 12.

TRUMPLER, R. J., and

     WEAVER, H. F.   1953   *Statistical Astronomy* (Berkeley: University of California Press) (2d Edition, Dover, 1962).

VYSSOTSKY, A. N.   1946   *Ap. J.*, **104**, 239.

WAYMAN, P. A.   1961   *Roy. Obs. Bull.*, No. 36.

WILSON, R. E.   1953   *General Catalogue of Radial Velocities* (Washington, D.C.: Carnegie Institution of Washington, Pub. No. 601).

WOOLLEY, R. v. d. R.   1957   *M.N.*, **117**, 198.

     1958   *Ibid.*, **118**, 45.

     1960   *Vistas in Astronomy* (London and New York: Pergamon Press), **3**, 3.

     1961   *Observatory*, **81**, 203.

     1964   *Astrophysica Norvegica*, **9**, No. 26.

WOOLLEY, R. v. d. R., and

     EGGEN, O. J.   1958   *M.N.*, **118**, 57.

WOOLLEY, R. v. d. R.,

JONES, D. H. P., and

     MATHER, L. M.   1960   *Roy. Obs. Bull.*, No. 23.

CHAPTER 6

Moving Groups of Stars

OLIN J. EGGEN*

Mount Wilson and Palomar Observatories
Carnegie Institution of Washington, California Institute of Technology

§ 1. INTRODUCTION

THERE is little evidence for believing that the formation of a star is an isolated event in either space or time. On the contrary, there is evidence, e.g., the
existence of clusters and multiple star systems, indicating that many stars were
formed in batches. Furthermore, the forces often suggested as capable of
breaking up these stellar batches once they are formed can not always be effective because of the great ages now assigned to many of the clusters and multiple systems. If the majority of the stars were produced in a few batches, and
if the disrupting forces are not greatly effective, might not the individual stars
of a batch still be identifiable by their motion? If so, the space motions of the
stars near the sun should be distributed in a non-random way. It is usual in
applying the various statistical procedures used in the study of stellar motions
to assume that these motions are randomly distributed with, at most, only minor
variations. If in fact the observed motions are dominated by those of a relatively
few stellar groups, then many of these procedures may be invalid. Furthermore,
if the now widely spread members of an original batch of stars can be identified
by their motion, a large sample of coeval stars could be examined for chemical
constitution and distribution in the color-luminosity array and the possibility
of catching stars in such interesting, rapid stages of their evolution as the Hertzsprung gap would be greatly increased.

Proctor (1869) was probably the first to note that community of proper
motion seemed to exist for stars located in several regions of the sky. For example, he mentioned stars spread over a 15° area centered on the Hyades cluster and also remarked that five of the "Dipper" stars in Ursa Major were moving together. While compiling the *Preliminary General Catalogue*, Lewis Boss
(1908) developed the now well known convergent-point method for discussing

* Present address: Royal Greenwich Observatory.

such widely spread groups of stars. Applying this method to the Hyades, using the proper motions of 40 stars and the radial velocities of only three, he derived a distance and space motion that have been little changed in the intervening half century. In 1909 Hertzsprung applied the same technique to the five "Dipper" stars, comprising what is now known as the Ursa Major cluster, with equal success. Hertzsprung went even further and demonstrated that (a) several widely separated bright stars, including Sirius, also shared the motion of the Dipper stars, and (b) a half-dozen widely scattered objects shared the space motion of Boss's Hyades cluster.

The success of the convergent-point method depends upon the assumption that the motions of the individual stars in these moving clusters are precisely the same. If we separate the space motion of an individual star, relative to the the sun, into components U directed away from the galactic center, V in the

TABLE 1

STARS ORIGINALLY ASSIGNED TO THE "61 CYGNI CLUSTER"

GC	V_E	$B-V$	Sp.	$m-M$	U	V	W
92..........	5^m59	$+0^m52$	G1 V	3^m00	$+90$	-55	-18
588..........	6.21	0.84	K0 IV	4.10	$+91$	-51	-16
7161..........	5.64	0.60	G3 IV	1.50	$+92$	-51	0
9523..........	5.14	1.24	gK4	4.70	$+92$	-52	$+6$
16149..........	4.90	0.64	G5 V	0.70	$+94$	-49	$+4$
29509..........	5.19	1.19	K5 V	-2.43	$+91$	-53	-8
32342..........	7.59	$+0.56$	F9 V	2.90	$+90$	-56	-12

direction of galactic rotation, and W toward the north galactic pole, then, if the convergent-point method is to be successful, these components for all of the group stars must be precisely the same.

Subsequent to Boss's and Hertzsprung's success in applying the convergent-point method, several investigations were made of other possible moving groups; the Vela moving cluster (Kapteyn 1914), the Perseus moving cluster (now called the α Persei association, Eddington 1910), the Corona Borealis moving cluster (Rasmuson 1921), the Scorpio-Centaurus moving cluster (Plummer 1913), and the 61 Cygni cluster (Boss 1911, Russell 1912). Aside from the α Persei and Scorpio-Centaurus associations, both of which may only be segments of a large local association of B-type stars (Eggen 1961), all of these moving clusters have subsequently been regarded as non-existent. For example, Rasmuson (1921) and Chaudhuri (1940) concluded that cluster motion was not present in the stars assigned by Boss and Russell to the 61 Cygni cluster; by this conclusion they meant that the stars did not meet the test of common convergent point and appropriate radial velocity for parallel motion. It is of interest to examine the (U, V, W) vectors for some of the stars originally assigned to this 61 Cygni cluster. Seven of these objects are listed in Table 1, where the distances have been adjusted to yield values of (U, V) that best match the well-determined values for 61 Cygni (*GC* 29509) with the resulting moduli, $m - M$. The array formed by these stars in the $(B - V, M_V)$ plane is very similar to that for M67 (Eggen 1962). The first three, and possibly the last, star in the table would appear to have common motion, even by the convergent-point test, but their values of W differ enough from that for 61 Cygni, and from those for the rest of the stars in the table, to give a quite different convergent point, and for this reason the stars would not appear to form a group moving with 61 Cygni when the convergent-point test was applied.

Attempts to find members of Hertzsprung's extended Hyades and Ursa Major moving clusters met with better success. The extensive literature of these "streams" has been summarized by Roman (1949: UMa) and by Wilson and Raymond (1932: Hyades). There has been a tendency in many investigations of the extended clusters to give larger and larger tolerances to the required accuracy with which a star has to meet the convergent-point test before being accepted as a cluster member. These extended tolerances admitted more members but, of course, at the same time greatly increased the probability that spurious members would be accepted. In the case of the 61 Cygni group members in Table 1, if the requirements on the convergent test had been loosened to the point where the observed value for a star only had to fall within 20° of that for 61 Cygni, most of the stars would have been regarded as members. However, loosening the tolerances on the convergent point not only admits stars whose W motion alone differs from the group mean, but it also admits those, probably non-members, whose U or V motions deviate by an equal amount.

The question of the reality of the Hyades group was re-examined in 1957 (Eggen 1958, 1959). The convergent-point method, with suitable modification to allow for errors in both the observed proper motions and in the convergent point itself, was used. That is, the same severe requirements of closely parallel motion that this method places on cluster members were also applied to the widely scattered members of the group. The results left little doubt that far more stars showed the space motion of the Hyades than would be expected from chance alone. Delhaye (1948) using a different procedure, had arrived earlier at a similar conclusion concerning the Ursa Major stream. However, because of (1) the relatively low space motions of the Hyades, and especially, the Ursa Major stream, (2) the very large number of low velocity stars, and (3) the large systematic and accidental errors occurring in much of the available motion data, spurious group members are difficult to eliminate from a consideration of the observed motions alone.

There are at least two objections to the use of the convergent-point method in isolating group members; (1) the W-motions may be uncoupled from those in (U, V), which would limit the group members found by this method to those that happened to have W values near that of the defining stars, and (2) by working with the observed equatorial components of the motions, instead of components that have some galactic significance, the physical situation is ob-

scured. Both of these objections are overcome if we work directly with the
(U, V, W) components of the space motion. The dependence of the values of
(U, V, W) on the assumed distance of the star is a linear one so that (U, V) loci
generated by varying the assumed distances are straight lines in the (U, V)
plane. Therefore, for members of a cluster the location of the intersection point
of these loci is a two-dimensional equivalent of finding the convergent point of
the observed proper motions. Furthermore, because some estimate of the
luminosity exists for nearly all stars for which accurate observed motions are
available, probable limits to the lengths of the (U, V) loci can be pre-assigned
and obviously spurious group members eliminated from consideration. This
method has been applied to the Hyades group (Eggen 1960b), and approximately 200 stars and binary systems, in addition to the known members of the
Hyades and Praesepe clusters, were selected as members. A similar procedure
applied to the Ursa Major group (renamed the Sirius group) isolated 100 members (Eggen 1960c).

§ 2. YOUNG GROUPS

To assist in the search for moving groups among the brighter stars a catalogue containing the objects for which the presently available motion data are
of the highest accuracy has been formed (Eggen 1962). The basis of this catalogue was a list of all stars for which radial velocities of quality a or b in the
GCRV were available and (a) of spectral type later than B8, (b) are in the GC,
and (c) have a probable luminosity fainter than -1^m; the limitation on the
luminosity was dropped for the K- and M-type stars. A mean position, on the
system of the GC, was then formed for all of these stars also occurring in at
least two post-1925 position catalogues, and a post-1900 proper motion determined by comparison with the GC position, which has a mean epoch near
1900. These new proper motions were then compared with the pre-1900 values
given in the GC, and the catalogue was formed of those stars for which the pre-
and post-1900 values agree well enough to insure that, if the available luminosity
estimates are nearly correct, the combined values of the proper motions will
lead to space velocities with an accidental error of only about 5 km/sec. The
catalogue contains all of the information necessary to construct the (U, V) loci
for the some 4000 stars comprising it, i.e., the values of (U, V, W) based on
the "best" luminosity derived from all available estimates, and the changes in
these velocity components (dU, dV, dW) per 1000 parsec change in the distance.

One method of detecting the presence of moving groups is to examine the
distribution of a large number of stars in the (U, V) plane. To do this requires
a homogeneously accurate set of luminosity estimates, preferably for members
of a relatively pure population sample. Such a sample is represented by the
A-type stars which are most probably less than some 5×10^8 years old and
populate a restricted region in the $(M_V, B - V)$ plane. The lower envelope of
the Pleiades main sequence, obtained by fitting the F- and G-type cluster stars

to the main sequence of the Hyades stars, is shown in Figure 1. Also, the luminosities of the metallic line (Am) and the peculiar (Ap) A-type stars in galactic clusters (Table 2) or in wide double and multiple systems (Eggen 1963*b*) are
shown in Figure 1 as filled and open circles, respectively. The luminosities of
the Ap and Am stars show little dispersion about a mean relation, $M_V = 0.35 +
7.8 (B - V)$. The few A-type stars with known luminosity of MK luminosity
class V fall in the region of Figure 1 that is enclosed by the Pleiades main sequence and the Ap and Am stars. Accurate (U, B, V) photometry is available
for most of the A-type stars brighter than visual magnitude 5.5 (Eggen 1963*c*).

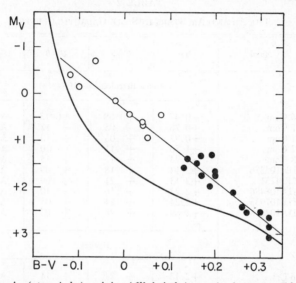

Fig. 1.—The Ap (*open circles*) and Am (*filled circles*) stars in clusters or wide binary systems. The mean $(M_V, B - V)$ relation is $M_V = 0^m35 + 7.8(B - V)$. The Pleiades main
sequence is also shown.

The (U, V) diagram for the Ap-, Am-, and A-type stars with known luminosity
class V, omitting a dozen known members of the Hyades *cluster*, is shown in
Figure 2.

Several features usually found in a discussion of the motions of A-type stars
are apparent in Figure 2. The (U, V) distribution is roughly elliptical with the
major axis of the ellipse showing a definite tilt from the direction toward the
galactic center (the deviation of the vertex). The median values for the 240
stars are $(U, V) = (+9, -9)$. From a discussion of nearly 700 A0–A9 stars
Vyssotsky and Janssen (1951) found median values of $(U, V) = (+10, -9)$,
which they use to define the "basic" solar motion. However, another obvious
feature of Figure 2 is the clumpiness in the distribution of (U, V) values. If each
of these clumps represents a kinematically related group of stars, the median
values of U, and especially of V, upon which the "basic" solar motion is based,

is determined from a statistically inadequate sample of only a half-dozen independent vectors. The bulk of the A-type stars in Figure 2 can be assigned to
a half-dozen groups: the Hyades group (Eggen 1960b), the Sirius group (Eggen
1960c), the Coma Berenices group (Eggen 1963c), and two anonymous groups
near $(U, V) = (+18, -18)$ and $(-5, +5)$ (Eggen 1963c). The Hyades, Pleiades,
and the Sirius groups are the easiest to recognize because they lie near the
extremities of the (U, V) distribution of the A-type stars.

From evolutionary consideration the age of the stars in Figure 2 can be esti-

TABLE 2

THE Ap AND Am STARS IN SOME GALACTIC CLUSTERS

Name	M_V	$B - V$	$U - B$	Sp.
		Coma Berenices $(m - M = 4^m53)$		
16 Com.........	$+0^m47$	$+0^m08$	$+0^m13$	Ap
17 Com.........	$+0.76$	$- .05$	$- .12$	Ap
21 Com.........	$+0.93$	$+ .05$	$+ .10$	Ap
22 Com.........	$+1.76$	$+ .11$	$+ .10$	Am
8 Com.........	$+1.74$	$+ .17$	$+ .15$	Am
HD 107276......	$+2.14$	$+ .18$	$+ .09$	Am
HR 4751........	$+2.13$	$+ .21$	$+ .09$	Am
HD 108486......	$+2.23$	$+ .16$	$+ .10$	Am
HD 107935......	$+2.24$	$+ .24$	$+ .05$	Am
HD 107513......	$+2.89$	$+ .28$	$+ .03$	Am
		Hyades		
16 Ori..........	$+2.13$	$+ .24$	$+ .14$	Am
81 Tau..........	$+2.42$	$+ .26$	$+ .10$	Am
60 Tau..........	$+2.88$	$+ .32$	$+ .10$	Am
63 Tau..........	$+2.54$	$+ .30$	$+ .14$	Am
HD 28226.......	$+2.55$	$+ .27$	$+ .10$	Am
		Praesepe $(m - M = 6^m04)$		
HD 73618.......	$+1.28$	$+ .19$	$+ .14$	Am
HD 73711.......	$+1.50$	$+ .16$	$+ .13$	Am
HD 73709.......	$+1.66$	$+ .20$	$+ .15$	Am
HD 73730.......	$+1.98$	$+ .19$	$+ .13$	Am
HD 73818.......	$+2.67$	$+ .32$	$+ .11$	Am
		M 39 $(m - M = 7^m20)$		
E5..............	$+0.65$	$+ .04$	$- .01$	Ap
HD 205117......	$+0.45$	$+ .01$	$+ .03$	Ap
$+47°3452.......$	$+1.68$	$+ .17$	$+ .14$	Am
E45.............	$+1.87$	$+0.22$	$+0.10$	Am

mated as probably not more than about 5×10^8 years. It may be possible to further subdivide this sample by considering the Ap (Morgan 1933) stars only. Figure 3 shows, as filled circles, the (U, V) distribution for the bluest (and there-fore, presumably the youngest) Ap stars, with $B - V < -0^m10$. All of these objects have spectral peculiarities characterized by "Si-λ 4200" or "Mn." The redder Ap stars, which are of the "Eu-Cr" or "Eu-Cr-Sr" types, are indi-cated in the figure by open circles. Also, four galactic clusters with relatively well-determined space velocities are shown as crosses. The Ap stars in Figure 3 show the same general distribution as all of the A stars in Figure 2, but a sharp

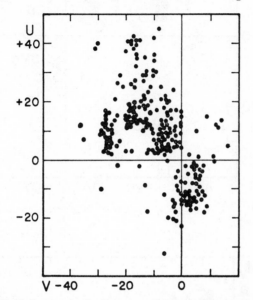

Fig. 2.—The (U, V) diagram for the A-type stars brighter than visual magnitude 5^m5 and of luminosity class V.

demarcation appears in Figure 3 between the bluest (Si-λ 4200, Mn) stars and the Eu-Cr-Sr stars. The color-luminosity arrays for the clusters Ursa Major, Coma Berenices, and M39, which are distributed in Figure 3 like the Eu-Cr-Sr stars, are shown in Figure 4. All three clusters are apparently of similar age, and each contains Ap stars of the Eu-Cr-Sr variety which are indicated in Figure 4 by arrows. Furthermore, the F- and G-type main-sequence stars in the Ursa Majoris and Coma Berenices clusters show an ultraviolet excess of about $+0^m05$ with respect to those in the Hyades cluster (Sandage and Eggen 1959); no cer-tain cluster member of type later than about F0 is known in M39. The Hyades and Pleiades clusters, on the other hand, which have the same intrinsic $(U - B, B - V)$ relation and therefore, presumably, the same abundance of heavy ele-ments, fall in Figure 3 among the bluest Ap stars. Neither of these clusters con-tain Ap stars, but the clusters NGC 2516 and IC 2602, which have motions

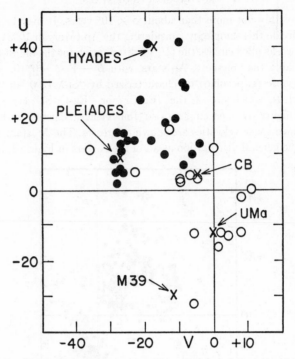

Fig. 3.—The (U, V) diagram for Ap stars bluer (*filled circles*) and redder (*open circles*) than $B - V = -0^m10$.

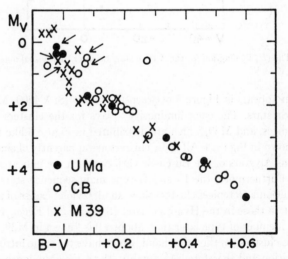

Fig. 4.—$(M_V, B - V)$ diagram for three clusters with Ap stars (*arrows*) of the "Eu-Cr-Sr" type.

similar to that of the Pleiades, do contain at least one Ap star each of the Si type. The (U, V, W) vectors of these clusters, based on the distance moduli and reddening values shown in the figure, are given in Figure 5, which also contains the color-luminosity arrays; the Ap stars in NGC 2516 and IC 2602 and the peculiar shell star Pleione in the Pleiades are indicated by arrows.

Figure 3 indicates that most of the clumpings in the (U, V) distribution of Figure 2 are associated with clusters. This distribution may be affected by further parameters involving the chemical composition of the stars. Unfortunately, the ultraviolet excess, as an indicator of the abundance of heavy elements, is not very effective for the A-type stars. There are available, however, many wide binary and multiple systems containing an early-type component and one or more F- or G-type main-sequence stars. If the components of these systems are

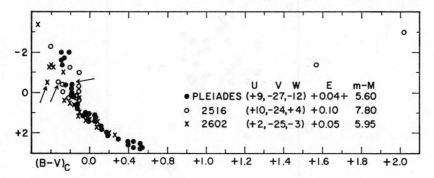

	U	V	W	E	m−M
● PLEIADES	(+9,	−27,	−12)	+0.04+	5.60
○ 2516	(+10,	−24,	+4)	+0.10	7.80
× 2602	(+2,	−25,	−3)	+0.05	5.95

Fɪɢ. 5.—Clusters probably belonging to the Pleiades group and containing Ap stars (*arrows*) of the "Si" type.

coeval, the ultraviolet excess, and therefore the abundance of heavy elements, can be obtained from members of late type which also serve to give a photometric parallax for the system. The necessary photometric observations have been made for several of these systems (Eggen 1963*b* and unpublished), and the results for those containing one component bluer than $B - V = +0^{m}40$ are shown in Figure 6. The systems in which the fainter components show an ultraviolet excess of $+0^{m}04$ or more are indicated by crosses and those with smaller excess by filled circles. When the difficulty involved in the photometry of relatively faint stars in the vicinity of brighter and bluer objects, and the uncertainty of the reddening corrections for some systems, is taken into account, it can be concluded from Figure 6 that probably all of the systems showing little or no ultraviolet excess with respect to the Hyades cluster main-sequence stars have positive values of U and have a distribution in the (U, V) plane that is similar to that of the Ap (Si-λ 4200, Mn) stars in Figure 3. The systems with an excess of $+0^{m}04$ or more have a distribution in Figure 6 that shows the same concentration near $U = -10$ as the Ap (Eu-Cr-Sr) stars in Figure 3, but there are also conspicuous groupings near $(U, V) = (+19, -19)$

and $(+14, -7)$. In addition to the evidence from Figures 3 and 6 that there is a correlation between the abundance of heavy elements and the galactic orbits of the A-type stars, there is also some indication that the ratio of hydrogen to helium may be similarly correlated with the kinematic properties. Stars showing no ultraviolet excess with respect to the Hyades cluster main sequence populate one ("Hyades-Pleiades") mass-luminosity relation, whereas those showing an excess populate another ("Sun-Sirius") relation and the differences between the two relations can be understood if the Hyades-Pleiades stars have a He/H ratio twice that of the Sun-Sirius stars (Eggen 1963a).

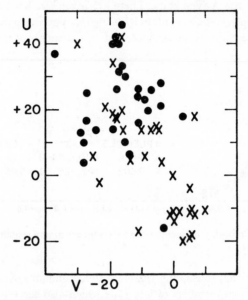

FIG. 6.—(U, V) diagram for wide binaries with the brighter component bluer than $B - V = +0^{m}4$. The filled circles and crosses represent systems with an ultraviolet excess smaller or larger, respectively, than $+0^{m}03$.

Additional evidence of the kind described above is needed, but that already available strongly suggests that at least two kinds of objects make up the young stars near the sun:

Kind	$\delta(U-B)$	He/H	Z/H	U	V
Hyades-Pleiades...	$\leq +0^{m}03$	$(3/2)$:	$(1.5-2\odot)$:	$+ 5$ to $+40$	$- 5$ to -30
Sun-Sirius........	$> +0.03$	$2/3$	$\odot$	$+20$ to -20	$+10$ to -20

The values of Z/H, which are here equated to Fe/H as measured in the spectra, depend upon the spectroscopic and photometric comparisons between the sun and the Hyades and are subject to considerable uncertainty. It seems clear that, because of the presence of groups and an imperfect understanding of the relation between the chemical constitution and the kinematics of the stars, the sun's galactic orbit cannot now be obtained from the solar motion with respect to the A stars as a whole.

Most of the groups have a considerably larger dispersion in U than in V, which may result from an effect described by Woolley (1961). If a batch of stars with a common origin in time, and in place within a kiloparsec or so, is overtaken by the sun sometime later, we would see only a selection of the original batch because of the dispersive effect of whatever velocity dispersion the stars had at origin. This selection yields those stars with a V velocity that would place them at the time and place of rendezvous with the sun. The sharpness of the V selection would depend upon both the volume surveyed and on the age of the stars, and could range from the total, original dispersion in V, if the batch is overtaken near the time of its origin, to well within 1 km/sec, if the stars had made 4 or more complete orbits about the galactic center. The U velocities of the group stars, on the other hand, may indicate the original dispersion in U, unless the dispersions in U and V are correlated for some reason. The youngest stars in the Pleiades group are probably near 5×10^7 years old, so we might expect 4 or 5 km/sec dispersion in the V velocity, whereas the older Hyades group may represent more highly selected members of the original batch with a range of perhaps only 2 km/sec in V.

It is difficult, even in the case of the relatively high-velocity groups like the Pleiades and Hyades to be certain of the membership of some individual stars; the groups of lowest velocity, such as the Coma Berenices group, are only detected when highly accurate data such as that used in constructing Figure 2 is available. However, additional tests of the group hypothesis are to be had in the consistency of the resulting color-luminosity arrays. A full discussion of this point, as well as of the new information the groups may provide for refining the theories of stellar evolution, would be out of place here. Discussions of this type are given in the references cited above for the individual groups.

§ 3. OLDER GROUPS

It would appear that the tendency of young stars to occur in groups is well established. Because of the limitations of the available observational data it cannot now be determined how strong this tendency is among the older stars. The effect of the V selection discussed above becomes sharper with time but of course the number of stars meeting the stricter tolerance on V will be smaller, so that the remnants of an old group in the solar neighborhood at any moment will decrease as the age of the group increases.

Also, it is more difficult to isolate a pure sample of old stars. As we move down the main sequence from the A stars to the F and G dwarfs we will find older stars but always mixed with young objects, so that the total age spread of our sample will increase with increasing spectral type. The subgiants, of type later than about G5, probably represent a relatively pure sample of stars older than some 5×10^9 years. The available data have been collected (Eggen 1960a), but it is difficult to obtain accurate space motions because of the lack of accurate luminosities. Several of these objects occur in wide binaries together with a main-sequence component, but not enough photometric and spectroscopic data are yet available to make a useful analysis of the space motions.

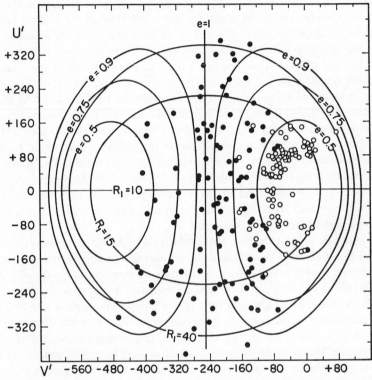

Fig. 7.—Bottlinger diagram for stars with total space velocity over 100 km/sec. The filled circles indicate objects with an ultraviolet excess greater than $+0^m15$ and the open circles those with smaller excess. Curves of equal eccentricity, e, and apogalactic distance, R_1, have been computed from a galactic model by Lynden-Bell.

The total space motion and the abundance of heavy elements may be useful indicators of stellar age. The lowest abundances of heavy elements (the largest ultraviolet excesses) are associated with the oldest stars, such as those occurring in globular clusters, and these stars also have the largest space motions in galactic orbits characterized by large eccentricities (Eggen, Lynden-Bell, and Sandage 1962). A catalogue has been formed of stars whose space motions referred to the sun probably exceed 100 km/sec (Eggen 1964). Velocity components $U' = U - 10$ and $V' = V + 15$, corrected to the local standard of rest, for the some 200 of these objects that are probably dwarfs, are shown in Figure 7, where the open and filled circles represent those with ultraviolet excesses smaller and larger, respectively, than $+0^m15$. The loci of equal eccentricity, $e = (R_1 - R_2)/(R_1 + R_2)$, and equal apogalactic distance, R_1, shown in the figure are valid for the model galaxy contributed by Lynden-Bell (Eggen *et al.* 1962).

The space motions of the stars represented in Figure 7 are based on photometric parallaxes obtained from a force-fit to the Hyades main sequence after the observed colors were corrected for line-blanketing effects. These stars are probably all quite old and in various stages of evolution, so that considerable error can be introduced into photometric parallaxes obtained in this way, and the presence of stellar groups could be obscured in the figure. Also, the estimated distances of many of these stars are such that the cosecant law of interstellar reddening would predict values of $E(B - V) = +0^m02$ or $+0^m03$, which, if allowed for, would increase the estimated distances and, therefore, also the space motions.

Examination on a larger scale, of the space-motion vectors of the stars represented in Figure 7 by open circles, reveals several clumpings in their distribution. Some of these clumpings, which include stars with well-determined parallaxes such as ζ Herculis, 61 Cygni, and η Cephei, are discussed elsewhere (e.g., Eggen 1964). Probable members of one of these groups, the 61 Cygni group, are listed in Table 3. If the space motions are correct, all of these stars are moving in isoperiodic galactic orbits with a spread of ± 10 km/sec about the value of $U = +91$ km/sec for 61 Cygni. The color-luminosity array is shown in Figure 8. The Hyades main sequence (Sandage and Eggen 1959) and the subgiant sequence of M67 (Sandage 1962) are also shown. The color-luminosity array of the 61 Cygni group is very similar to that for M67. The mean value of $\delta(U - B)$ for the main-sequence stars with $B - V$ between $+0^m6$ and $+0^m8$ is $+0^m07$. The main sequence shows a small displacement from that of the Hyades which, for the fainter stars, cannot be entirely explained as an evolutionary effect. Because the few binaries in this group populate the "Sun-Sirius" mass-luminosity relation mentioned in Section 2, one explanation of this displacement is that it results from the different He/H ratio in the Hyades and in the 61 Cygni group.

The stars in Figure 8 were selected on the basis of their motion, and it is desirable to have some independent test of the resulting group parallaxes. Figure 9 contains the correlation between the absolute magnitudes obtained from the group parallaxes, $M_V(G)$, and those obtained from spectroscopic luminosity criteria (filled circles) and trigonometric parallaxes larger than $0''035$ (open circles). It appears from this correlation that the luminosities obtained from the group parallaxes agree well with the spectroscopic and trigonometric luminosities. However, it must be stressed that the small displacement of main sequences in Figure 8 cannot be confirmed by these data.

Groombridge 1830 (HD 103095) and Kapteyn's star (HD 33793) are the only extremely high-velocity stars for which space motions are known with high

TABLE 3

Probable Members of the 61 Cygni Group

HD/BD	V_E	$B-V$	$U-B$*	E†	$\delta(U-B)$	$m-M$	U	V	W	Sp.
61 Cyg A	5^m19	1^m19	1^m10	.....	.....	-2^m43	$+91$	-53	-8	K5 V
B	6.02	1.38	1.23	.....	.....					K7 V
142.....	5.69	$+0.52$	(1.65)	.....	$+0^m02$	2.90	$+88$	-53	-18	G1 IV
2589.....	6.21	0.84	$+0.55$	$+0^m02$	$(-.05)$	4.00	$+94$	-53	-17	K0 IV
Wolf 1056.....	11.02	1.53	(1.08)	.....	.....	1.05	$+103$	-53	-9	dM4
3443 AB.....	5.56	0.71	(1.79)	.....	.....	0.95	$+88$	-53	-22	G5 V
4550.....	6.89	1.08	$+0.94$	$+.02$	$+.06$	6.75	$+91$	-53	$+11$	K0 III
10145.....	7.66	0.69	$+0.19$	.....	$+.02$	2.50	$+97$	-53	-17	G5 V
13530.....	5.32	0.93	$+0.62$	.....	$+.05$	3.70	$+88$	-53	-18	K0 III
14680.....	8.81	0.93	(2.03)	.....	$+.08$	2.40	$+88$	-53	-22	K3 V
22254.....	8.32	0.58	$+0.16$	.....	.00	4.70	$+85$	-53	$+6$	gF8
23183.....	6.14	1.01	$+0.74$	$+.03$	$(-.06)$	5.30	$+90$	-53	-15	K0 III
30604.....	8.85	0.57	$+0.03$	$+.03$	$+.08$	4.45	$+100$	-53	-3	G0 V
$+0°873$.....	10.10	0.52	0.00	$+.02$	$+.06$	5.60	$+103$	-53	-1	dF8
$+31°769$.....	9.06	0.49	-0.03	$+.03$	$+.04$	5.80	$+94$	-53	-13	{dF6
$+31°846$.....	9.22	0.61	$+0.04$	$+.04$	$+.06$			-53		dG0
35783.....	7.69	0.46	-0.02	$+.04$	$+.03$	4.45	$+88$	-53	-9	G6 V
39091.....	5.64	0.60	(1.66)	$+.02$	$+.09$	1.60	$+96$	-53	$+1$	G3 IV
39425.....	3.12	1.18	(2.26)	.....	.....	2.35	$+88$	-54	-22	gK1
55526.....	5.14	1.24	.....	.....	.....	5.30	$+90$	-53	$+5$	gK4
95272.....	4.09	1.10	$+0.99$	$+.03$	(.00)	3.30	$+100$	-53	$+6$	K0 III
100030.....	6.42	0.88	$+0.51$	$+.02$	$+.06$	4.45	$+80$	-53	$+19$	G8 IV
106849.....	4.2 var.	1.56	.....	$+.03$	.....	4.90	$+85$	-53	-24	gM6
110313.....	7.87	0.61	$+0.06$	.....	$+.08$	3.45	$+90$	-53	-13	dG1
120467.....	8.14	1.27	(2.35)	.....	.....	0.40	$+82$	-53	-21	dK6
$+34°2451$.....	9.61	1.25	$+1.17$	.....	.....	1.95	$+87$	-53	-1	dM0
130092.....	7.82	1.02	(2.15)	.....	$(-.03)$	1.25	$+92$	-53	-24	dK4
132142.....	7.76	0.79	$+0.32$	.....	$+.08$	1.75	$+100$	-53	$+18$	K1 V
149324.....	4.26	1.07	$+0.94$	.....	$+.02$	3.50	$+95$	-53	$+12$	K0 III
162756 AB.....	7.63	0.61	$+0.06$	.....	$+.08$	2.55	$+101$	-53	-25	G0 IV–V
207692.....	6.90	0.48	-0.03	.....	$+.05$	3.95	$+99$	-53	-32	dF5
210905.....	6.30	1.12	$+1.05$	$+.05$	$(-.12)$	5.85	$+97$	-53	-2	K0
$+57°2480$.....	9.74	0.58	-0.02	$+0.05$	$+.09$	3.35	$+99$	-53	-33	G0
216777.....	8.00	0.64	$+0.09$	.....	$+.09$			-53		G6 V
219175 A.....	7.59	0.56	-0.02	.....	$+.12$			-53		F9 V
219175 B.....	8.22	$+0.68$	$+0.11$	.....	$+0.12$	2.70	$+83$	-53	-7	G3 V

* The values in parentheses are on the Cape $(U-B)c$ system (Cousins, Eggen, and Stoy 1961).

† Computed from $E(B-V) = 0^m057\,\csc b\,[1 - \exp(-r\sin b/187)]$.

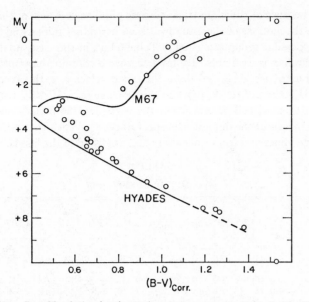

FIG. 8.—$(M_V, B - V)$ relation for the 61 Cygni group stars in Table 3. The Hyades main sequence and the M67 subgiant sequence are also shown.

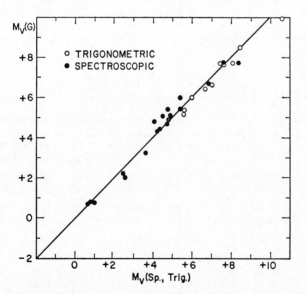

FIG. 9.—Correlation between the luminosities of the 61 Cygni group stars obtained from the group motion with the luminosities from spectroscopic (*filled circles*) or trigonometric (*open circles*) parallaxes.

125

accuracy, because of the large trigonometric parallaxes. A few of the stars that may share the motions of these subdwarfs are listed in Tables 4 and 5. Members of a third, possible group are listed in Table 6 but, in this case, no defining star of large parallax is available. Tables 4, 5, and 6 contain the photometric (U, B, V) and astrometric (μ_α, μ_δ) data, the radial velocity, ρ, the assigned modulus, $m - M$, values of (U, V, W), and their change (dU, dV, dW) per 100 parsec *increase* in the assumed distance. For the variables, the periods and values of ΔS, which measures the difference in spectral type between that estimated from the hydrogen lines and from the metal lines, are listed in the last columns of the

TABLE 4
GROOMBRIDGE 1830 GROUP

Name/Sp	$\dfrac{V_E/}{B-V}$	$U-B/\delta$	μ_α/μ_δ	$\rho/m-M$	U/dU	V/dV	W/dW	Remarks
+72°94......	9ᵐ94	−0ᵐ20	−0ˢ0492	−268.0	− 258	− 143	+ 8	$E=+0^m03$
sdF2........	+0.41	+ .22	+0″164	5ᵐ20	− 98	+ 61	+ 54	....
Gmb 1830....	6.49	+ .15	−0.3386	− 98.3	− 267	− 150	− 17	$\pi_t=0''115$
G8 Vp.......	+0.75	+ .19	−5.798	− 0.30	+2754	−1664	+888	....
ADS10938....	9.62	− .06	−0.0322	+191.0	− 240	− 161	+ 34	$\pi_t=0''020$
sdF8........	+0.61	+ .20	−0.695	3.70	− 101	− 383	+ 29	$m=0.5$
RR Lyr*.....	7.81	+0.05	−0.0110	− 72.4	− 253	− 145	+ 2	$E=+0^m07$
A–F........	+0.38	......	−0.205	7.00	− 108	− 108	+ 7	$\Delta S=6$

* Photometric data are median values.

TABLE 5
KAPTEYN'S STAR GROUP

Name/Sp	$\dfrac{V_E/}{B-V}$	$U-B/\delta$	μ_α/μ_δ	$\rho/m-M$	U/dU	V/dV	W/dW	Remarks
Kapt.*.....	8ᵐ81	+1ᵐ20:	+0ˢ6190	+244.0	− 22	− 289	− 50	$\pi_t=0''250$
M0 V......	+ 1.59	....	−5″722	− 2ᵐ00	−2201	−2594	+2342	....
LTT12271..	10.97	−0.12	0:	− 5.0	− 10	− 281	− 38	$E=+0^m03$
sdF8.......	+ 0.58	+0.22	−0.430	5.70	− 4	− 201	− 24	....
SU Dra*...	9.70	....	−0.0062	−161.0	− 19	− 282	− 22	$E=+0^m07$
A–F.......	+ 0.33	....	−0.074	8.90	+ 9	− 34	+ 16	$\Delta S=6$
ST Leo*....	11.3	....	−0.0010	+150.0	− 19	− 285	+ 45	$\Delta S=7$
A–F.......			−0.041	10.50	− 3	− 19	− 8	
HD106038..	10.18	−0.18	−0.0128	+ 96.0	− 28	− 284	+ 18	$E=+0^m03$
F6 IV–V...	+ 0.48	+0.20	−0.434	5.40	− 25	− 213	− 63	....
−13°3834..	10.68	−0.10	−0.0239	+123.5	− 33	− 286	+ 3	$E=+0^m02$
sdF7.......	+ 0.60	+0.22	−0.440	5.00	+ 44	− 248	− 85	....

* Photometric data are median values.

TABLE 6
GROUP WITH (U, V) NEAR $(-160, -320)$

Name/Sp	$V_E/B-V$	$U-B/\delta$	μ_α/μ_δ	$\rho/m-M$	U/dU	V/dV	W/dW	Remarks
HD74000.....	9m65	−0m20	+0s0205	+206.0	−166	− 317	+ 62	E=+0m03
sdF1.........	+ 0.41	+0.22	−0″482	5m10	−250	− 137	+ 8	....
+29°2091....	10.24	−0.20	+0.0141	+ 74.0	−156	− 326	+ 88	π_t=0″021
sdF5.........	+ 0.49	+0.22	−0.790	4.90	−197	− 329	+ 24	E=+0m02
Ross 451.....	12.23	+1.16	+0.0595	−118.0	−152	− 335	+152	LFT834
sdM0........	+ 1.45	....	−3.180	2.00	−393	−1107	+956	....
Ross 453.....	11.08	−0.20	−0.0027	+ 98.0	−156	− 332	− 81	LTT13387
sdF2.........	+ 0.43	+0.22	−0.415	6.30	− 80	− 156	− 91	E=+0m03
HD108177....	9.68	−0.23	−0.0018	+158.5	−170	− 332	− 8	π_t=0″031
sdF4.........	+ 0.43	+0.25	−0.476	5.00	− 99	− 177	−100	E=+0m02
−35°14849...	10.52	−0.22	−0.0076	+110.0	−163	− 332	− 49	E=+0m03
sdF.........	+ 0.40	+0.25	−0.475	5.95	− 58	− 222	+ 20	....

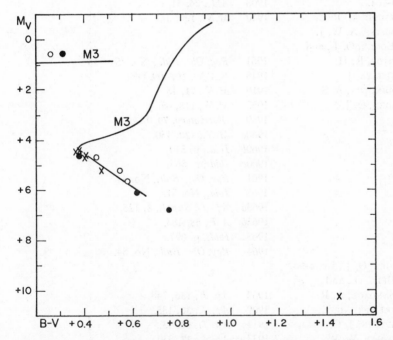

FIG. 10.—The $(M_V, B - V)$ diagram for the high-velocity stars in Tables 4 (*filled circles*), 5 (*open circles*), and 6 (*crosses*). The sequences shown schematically are for M3 with $E = +0^m04$ and $m - M$, corrected, of 14m50.

tables; this column also contains the trigonometric parallaxes for a few stars and the values of the reddening, $E(B - V)$, obtained from the cosecant law.

The colors, corrected only for reddening, and the luminosities of the group stars are shown in Figure 10, with filled circles, open circles, and crosses representing those in Tables 4, 5, and 6, respectively. Accurate photometric data are not available for ST Leonis, but the median value of M_V is near $+0^m\!.6$. The mean color-luminosity array for M3 (Sandage 1962) with $E(B - V) = +0^m\!.04$ and corrected $(m - M) = 14^m\!.50$ is also shown in the figure. From the ultraviolet excess and the size of the space motions, we can identify these stars with those in globular clusters. The ratio of three cluster variables to only 13 subdwarfs appears high compared to an estimate of approximately 1 variable per 10^5 stars in a globular cluster. However, recent surveys indicate that the 100 or so field subdwarfs now known represent only a small fraction of those near the sun, whereas the census of RR Lyrae variables to, say, magnitude 10 is probably nearly complete.

REFERENCES

Boss, B.	1911	*A.J.*, **27**, 33.
Boss, L.	1908	*A.J.*, **26**, 31.
Chaudhuri, P. C.	1940	*M.N.*, **100**, 574.
Cousins, A. W. J., Eggen, O. J., and Stoy, R. H.	1961	*Roy. Obs. Bull.*, No. 25.
Delhaye, J.	1948	*B.A.N.*, **10**, 409.
Eddington, A. S.	1910	*M.N.*, **71**, 43.
Eggen, O. J.	1958	*M.N.*, **118**, 65.
	1959	*Observatory*, **79**, 143.
	1960a	*M.N.*, **120**, 430.
	1960b	*Ibid.*, p. 540.
	1960c	*Ibid.*, p. 563.
	1961	*Roy. Obs. Bull.*, No. 41.
	1962	*Ibid.*, No. 51.
	1963a	*Ap. J.*, *Suppl.*, **8**, 125.
	1963b	*A.J.*, **68**, 483.
	1963c	*Ibid.*, p. 697.
	1964	*Roy. Obs. Bull.*, No. 84.
Eggen, O. J., Lynden-Bell, D., and Sandage, A. R.	1962	*Ap. J.*, **136**, 748.
Hertzsprung, E.	1909	*Ap. J.*, **30**, 135.
Kapteyn, J. C.	1914	*Ap. J.*, **40**, 43.
Morgan, W. W.	1933	*Ap. J.*, **77**, 330.
Plummer, H. C.	1913	*M.N.*, **73**, 492.
Proctor, R. A.	1869	*Proc. R. Soc., London*, **18**, 169.
Rasmuson, N. H.	1921	*Medd. Lunds. Obs.*, Ser. II, No. 26.

ROMAN, N. G.	1949	*Ap. J.*, **110**, 205.
RUSSELL, H. N.	1912	*A.J.*, **27**, 96.
SANDAGE, A. R.	1962	*Ap. J.*, **135**, 349.
SANDAGE, A. R., and EGGEN, O. J.	1959	*M.N.*, **119**, 278.
VYSSOTSKY, A. N., and JANSSEN, E.	1951	*A.J.*, **56**, 58.
WILSON, R. E., and RAYMOND, H.	1932	*A.J.*, **47**, 49.
WOOLLEY, R. v. d. R.	1961	*Observatory*, **81**, 203.

CHAPTER 7

Distribution of Associations, Emission Regions, Galactic Clusters, and Supergiants

STEWART SHARPLESS*

U.S. Naval Observatory, Washington, D.C.

§ 1. INTRODUCTION

O NE of the earliest attempts at deducing the structural details of our Galaxy was made by Proctor in 1869 in order to explain the apparent irregularities of the Milky Way. This represented a radical departure from the statistical methods of William Herschel. The statistical approach, which assumes a smoothed-out distribution of stars, is by its very nature not capable of revealing much of the detailed structure of our galactic system. Proctor's model of our Galaxy consisted of spiral "streams" of stars, thus suggesting the similarity of our Galaxy to the "spiral nebulae" which had been described a decade earlier by the Earl of Rosse. Proctor's method consisted in attempting to infer the distribution of stars along the line of sight on the basis of their apparent distribution as seen projected against the celestial sphere. This method is neither foolproof nor unique, but it can still be used effectively as a basis for speculation and the formation of working hypotheses.

More recently, Wilhelm Becker (1956) has used a similar approach. He has shown that if the inner part (with respect to the sun) of the Galaxy has a spiral structure, an ideal Milky Way should contain a short, bright portion asymmetrically placed with respect to the galactic center. The limits of this portion are the tangents to the spiral arm inside the one near which the sun is located. Becker identifies this ideal bright inner portion with the bright part of the Milky Way which extends from the Scutum star cloud to Carina. The asymmetrical position of this part of the Milky Way with respect to the galactic cen-

* Dr. Sharpless is now at the University of Rochester, Rochester, N.Y.

ter is such as to suggest that the spiral arms of our Galaxy trail in the galactic rotation. The boundaries of the inner portion indicate that the inner arm is at about one-sixth the distance between the sun and the galactic center, i.e., about 1.4 kpc. Plate I shows the spiral galaxy M51 with an assumed position of the sun and the corresponding tangents to the inner spiral arm. While Proctor was innocent of any knowledge of interstellar absorption, Becker, on the other hand, emphasized that his result depends on the unproven assumption that the distribution of stars, rather than interstellar absorption, is the decisive factor influencing the over-all appearance of the Milky Way.

The influence of interstellar absorption on the appearance of the Milky Way is less in the infrared on account of the greater space-penetrating property of infrared light. A wide-angle infrared photograph of the Milky Way taken by Code and Houck (1955) is shown in Plate II. The segment of the Milky Way shown on the photograph extends from $l^{II} = 58°$ through the galactic center to $l^{II} = 278°$. The inner portions of the Galaxy as shown on the photograph, present the appearance of a typical edge-on spiral of approximate type Sb. The nuclear bulge is clearly visible as well as the equatorial belt of obscuring material. A rapid decrease in surface brightness in both directions away from the galactic center is well marked. The bright inner portion of our Galaxy as shown on the infrared photograph extends from $l^{II} = 38°$ to $l^{II} = 283°$. These limits agree well with those determined by Becker, and thus tend to confirm the idea that this portion of the Milky Way may indeed represent a bright inner spiral arm which trails off in perspective in the direction of Scutum on one side of the galactic center, and in the direction of Carina on the other side. We may conclude that both the visual and infrared appearance of the Milky Way tend to suggest that our Galaxy is a typical spiral of relatively early type.

The detailed structural features of our Galaxy can be further investigated through a study of the distances of individual stars presumed to be associated with the spiral arms. This method requires a spectral datum for each star from which its absolute magnitude can be inferred, as well as photometric data sufficient for the determination of the apparent magnitude of the star corrected for interstellar absorption. Spectroscopic parallaxes can thus be derived. One of the earliest studies of this type was made by Pannekoek (1929), and was based on the material contained in the *Henry Draper Catalogue*. The tendency of early-type stars to occur in aggregates was recognized, and approximate distances of a number of these aggregates were determined. More recently the distribution of early-type stars associated with the nearer H II regions was studied by Morgan and his associates (1952). Here, for the first time, traces of a spiral pattern in our Galaxy were established. Segments of two spiral arms were delineated: one through the sun, and one at a distance of approximately 2 kpc in the direction of the anticenter. Some evidence of an inner spiral arm was also found.

A totally different approach to the study of the spiral organization of our Galaxy came through the discovery of 21-centimeter radiation from neutral hydrogen in interstellar space. This method requires observations of the Doppler displacements of the 21-cm line which, when combined with knowledge of the velocity field in the Galaxy, make it possible to investigate the distribution of neutral hydrogen. A number of spiral features have been mapped in this way (Oort *et al.* 1958). A detailed discussion of the 21-cm results will be found in chapter 9 of this volume.

These methods—radio and optical—of studying the structural details of our Galaxy tend to complement each other. It is important to correlate the results of these two methods and to study their similarities and discrepancies. There is no guarantee that the two approaches will ultimately produce identical pictures of our Galaxy. On the basis of our present knowledge, a spiral arm defined by observations of neutral hydrogen need not necessarily contain recently formed hot stars which would be accessible to optical observation. Also, if the motion of neutral hydrogen about the galactic center is constrained by forces which are not purely gravitational, then stars formed from this material need not subsequently move in exactly the same path about the galactic center. Such differences could result in a displacement of the spiral arms defined by neutral hydrogen relative to those defined optically. The radio method has the advantage that the entire Galaxy can be surveyed in considerable detail, whereas optical methods are limited by interstellar absorption to distances of a few kiloparsecs from the sun. The radio method suffers, on the other hand, from the fact that assumptions must be made regarding the velocity field of the Galaxy which may still not be completely understood.

In the optical investigation of our Galaxy, studies of extragalactic objects can serve as a guide. The close association of H II regions with the spiral arms of a galaxy was first recognized by Baade and Mayall (1951) in their study of the H II regions in M31. We know in general that objects to be investigated in connection with spiral structure in our Galaxy must necessarily be quite young, hence recently formed from the interstellar material. Since stars of population I have mean peculiar speeds of the order of 10 km/sec, such stars can diffuse from their respective points of origin to distances of about 1 kpc in 10^8 years. Obviously, optical investigations of spiral structure in our Galaxy must concern themselves with objects considerably younger than this.

In Sections 2 to 5 of this article, the distribution of O-associations, H II regions, galactic clusters, and supergiant stars will be considered. These groups cannot be considered to be mutually exclusive, therefore the following sections cannot be completely independent of one another. Galactic clusters as well as supergiants and H II regions are often connected with O-associations. Supergiant stars in the field may represent associations which have recently dispersed to the point of having lost their respective identities, whereas O-type clusters may represent an early evolutionary stage in the life of an association in which the star density is still higher than that of the field. In the final section (Sec. 6) the relevance of the space distribution of these objects to our knowledge of the structural details of our Galaxy will be considered.

§ 2. O-ASSOCIATIONS

One of the important results following the publication of the *Henry Draper Catalogue* was the recognition of the tendency of early-type stars to occur in aggregates (Charlier 1926, Struve 1927, Pannekoek 1929). The approximate distances of a number of these aggregates were determined on the basis of the apparent magnitudes of the member stars and mean absolute magnitudes corresponding to the *Henry Draper* spectral types. The significance of these aggregates of early-type stars in respect to stellar evolution has been discussed more recently by Ambarzumian (1949, 1955, 1959) who has pointed out that these O-*associations* are fundamentally different from star clusters. A cluster has a density at least an order of magnitude greater than that of the field and is thus held together by the mutual gravitation of its member stars. An association, on the other hand, has a star density considerably less than that of the field and is thus subject to rapid tidal disruption in a time of the order of 10^7 years. One might expect this disruption to be accompanied by a rapid elongation of the association owing to the shearing effect of differential galactic rotation. However, since associations appear to be spherical, or almost so, Ambarzumian reasoned that the tendency for associations to elongate must be masked by another effect, namely, expansion. From the observed sizes and shapes of associations Ambarzumian predicted an expansional motion of the order of 10 km/sec. The observational confirmation of expanding motions in associations has been discussed by Blaauw (1952), Blaauw and Morgan (1953), and van Herk (1959). The transitory nature of associations leads to the conclusion that star formation is still taking place in our Galaxy.

The rate of formation of stars in O-associations has been estimated by Ambarzumian. Assuming that there are 10^4 associations in our Galaxy and that their average age is 3×10^7 years, he finds that 10^6 associations have existed during the age of the Galaxy. If each association contains between 100 and 1000 stars, then the total number of stars which have been produced by associations is between 10^8 and 10^9. A similar type of computation was made by Roberts (1957) who found that all of the O- and B-type stars in our Galaxy can be accounted for as having originated in O-associations. One must conclude that B-type stars which occur in the field are probably the product of associations which have already disintegrated.

The star density of an O-association is considerably less than that of the field in which it is immersed, and, from the viewpoint of the observer, is further hidden by foreground stars. The existence of an O-association can thus generally be established only through a study of the actual space distribution of early-type stars. In principle, an association can be detected as a concentration of points in a three-dimensional plot of galactic longitude versus galactic latitude versus distance modulus for early-type stars. A number of O-associations have been discovered in essentially this way.

Once the probable members of an association have been identified, their individual spectroscopic parallaxes can be determined and the best distance of the association is thus the mean of these. The major study of this type was made by Morgan, Whitford, and Code (1953) in which the distances of twenty-seven associations were determined on the basis of spectral and luminosity classifications

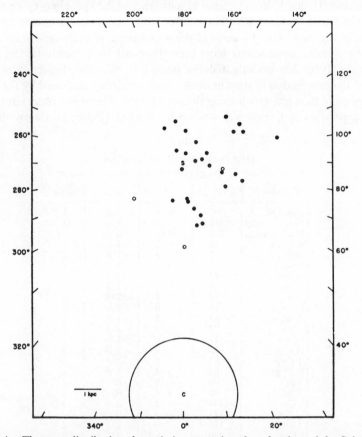

FIG. 1.—The space distribution of associations as projected on the plane of the Galaxy

and two-color photometry of some of the member stars. The resulting distribution of associations, as seen projected on the galactic plane, is represented by the solid circles in Figure 1. The two spiral arms, Orion and Perseus, which had been found in the distribution of H II regions (cf. Sec. 3) are better defined here. A bifurcation of the Orion arm is indicated between longitudes 103° and 213°, the nearer branch extending into negative latitudes. In addition, evidence for an inner (Sagittarius) spiral arm is evident between longitudes 344° and 19°. The latter is located at about 1.4 kpc from the sun at its nearest point. These associations are listed in Table 1 along with several others for which reliable distances have since been obtained. The association in the direction of the galactic center was investigated by Hiltner (1954) who found it to be situated beyond the Sagittarius arm at a distance of 3.0 kpc. Two highly obscured associations are also listed in Table 1: the VI Cygni association, studied by Johnson and Morgan (1954) who derived the distance modulus given here, and the I Crucis association (Houck 1956) which lies at a distance of 2.2 kpc, almost directly behind the Southern Coalsack. These three associations are indicated by open circles in Figure 1. The distances of other groupings of early-type stars which may be genuine associations have been discussed by Schmidt (1958), while Kopylov (1958) has investigated the possibility that the dispersion of individual distance moduli of stars in some associations may be caused by the existence of more than one group along the line of sight. The heavy concentration of early-type stars in Carina was studied by Hoffleit (1956); no clearly defined

TABLE 1

DISTANCES OF O-ASSOCIATIONS

Name	l^{II}	b^{II}	r (kpc)	Notes
I Cru........	305	+ 5	2.2	1
I Sco........	344	0	1.4	2
II Sco........	351	+17	0.21	2
Anon........	1	− 2	3.0	3
I Sgr.........	7	− 3	1.3	2
II Sgr........	8	− 2	1.4	2
III Sgr.......	13	− 2	2.3	2
IV Sgr.......	14	− 1	1.7	2
I Ser.........	18	− 1	2.3	2
II Ser........	19	0	2.0	2
I Vul........	61	− 1	1.8	2
I Cyg........	73	+ 1	2.3	2
II Cyg.......	77	0	1.5	2
III Cyg......	78	0	2.0	2
VI Cyg......	81	0	1.5	4
IV Cyg.......	84	− 8	1.0	2
I Lac........	98	−18	0.46	2
I Cep........	99	+ 5	0.72	2
II Cep.......	104	− 2	3.6	2
III Cep......	111	+ 3	0.96	2
I Cas........	116	0	2.5	2
II Cas.......	120	0	2.2	2
III Cas......	124	+ 2	2.5	2
I Per........	135	− 3	2.3	2
I Cam.......	147	+ 1	0.9	2
II Per.......	161	−15	0.36	2
I Aur........	174	0	1.15	2
I Gem.......	190	+ 3	1.5	2
I Ori........	207	−18	0.5	2
I Mon.......	209	0	1.4	2

Notes to Table 1

1. Distance derived by Houck (1956).
2. Distance derived by Morgan, Whitford, and Code (1953).
3. Distance derived by Hiltner (1954).
4. Distance derived by Johnson and Morgan (1954).

O-associations in this direction are discernible, although Hoffleit's observations indicate some degree of clumping of the stars. Since it seems probable that in the direction of Carina one views part of an inner spiral arm almost length-wise, there may be several associations and early-type clusters as well as numerous B-type stars belonging to the field scattered along the line of sight.

The clear-cut evidence in Figure 1 for the existence of spiral structure in the vicinity of the sun attests to the usefulness of associations in delineating the structural features of our Galaxy. The relatively low accidental errors of the distance determinations derive from the fact that the distance obtained for an association is based on a number of individual distance determinations for member stars. The systematic accuracy derives, in part, from the fact that the O-associations constitute a group of objects which are relatively homogeneous in respect to age, and thus evolutionary differences make only a minor contribution to systematic effects in the distance determinations as compared, say, with galactic clusters.

Further study of the space distribution of associations requires that additional associations be discovered. The numerous surveys for high-luminosity early-type stars, which have been carried out at the Warner and Swasey, Tonantzintla, and Hamburg Observatories, contribute a considerable body of material which can form the basis for investigations of more distant associations. The techniques devised by Morgan (1958) for the segregation of very faint blue stars of high luminosity will be useful in the study of still more distant groups.

§ 3. H II REGIONS

The requisite conditions for the existence of an H II region were first outlined by Strömgren (1939, 1948). Generally, the combination of a hot star (O5 to B0) and an interstellar density of the order of 1 to 10 hydrogen atoms per cubic centimeter is necessary to produce observable emission. A number of large areas of faint hydrogen emission in the Milky Way were first found by Struve and his collaborators (1939) working with the McDonald 150-foot slit spectrograph. These regions were found at low galactic latitudes, but did not appear to be particularly concentrated toward stars of early type. Subsequent spectroscopic work by Johnson (1953) has shown that regions of hydrogen emission are nearly always present near O-type stars within 250 parsecs of the galactic plane, but almost never present at greater distances above or below the plane.

The distribution of H II regions in M31 was first investigated by Baade (Baade and Mayall 1951) by means of narrow band filter photography which isolated the H-alpha line. A partial coverage of M31 revealed about 300 discrete emission regions. In almost all cases these regions were found to be associated with the spiral arms except in the inner portion of M31 where both bright stars and emission regions appear to thin out, leaving only dust lanes which approach the nucleus as continuations of the spiral arms.

Using a wide-angle camera and a photographic technique similar to that of Baade, Sharpless and Osterbrock (1952) made a survey of the nearest H II regions in our own Galaxy. Sixteen discrete regions were found which, on the basis of spectroscopic parallaxes of the associated stars, proved to be similar in size to those found by Baade in M31. Further study of the distances of these regions (Morgan *et al.* 1952) led to the first detection of spiral structure in our Galaxy. The H II regions north of $-10°$ declination were found to occur in two long, narrow belts. The first of these was found to extend from $l^{II} = 73°$ to $l^{II} = 223°$, passing near the sun in the direction of the anticenter and having among its constituents the P Cygni and North America nebulae, the ξ Persei nebulosity, the Orion nebula and loop, and the H II regions near λ Orionis and S Monocerotis. The other belt, at a distance of about 2000 parsecs in the direction of the anticenter, was traced from $l^{II} = 103°$ to $l^{II} = 173°$. Fragmentary evidence for the existence of a third arm, interior to the sun, was also given. These data indicated a tilt of the arms of about 25° with respect to the direction of galactic rotation which led to the conclusion that the Galaxy rotates with the spiral arms trailing.

Since 1952 a number of photographic surveys in Hα have been made. Bok, Bester, and Wade (1955) and Gum (1955) surveyed the part of the Milky Way visible from the southern hemisphere. H. M. Johnson (1955) searched specifically for elliptical emission regions. Hase and Shajn (1955) and Sharpless (1959) compiled catalogues of H II regions visible from the northern hemisphere, the latter survey being based on the National Geographic Society–Palomar Observatory Sky Atlas. The inter-agreement of these surveys indicates that the H II regions in our Galaxy are recognizable as discrete entities as are the H II regions observed by Baade in M31.

The distribution of H II regions as seen projected on the celestial sphere is shown in Figure 2. The data are from the work of Gum (1955) and Sharpless (1959). Approximately 400 regions are represented here. Most of these are probably within a radius of about 2 kpc from the sun, indicating that at least 10,000 such objects would be found if the entire Galaxy could be surveyed in a similar manner. Since about 300 H II regions were found by Baade in his survey of a major portion of M31, one must conclude that many more H II regions per unit volume have been found in our Galaxy as compared with M31. This discrepancy is undoubtedly due to the presence of rather small H II regions which can be found in our Galaxy and which are probably associated with stars of somewhat later type than B0.

The apparent distribution of H II regions as shown in Figure 2 has several features which may bear on the real distribution of these objects in space. The region toward the galactic center between $l^{II} = 333°$ and $l^{II} = 23°$ is thickly populated with H II regions. A gap in the distribution is present in the interval which contains the Southern Coalsack, i.e., between $l^{II} = 298°$ and $l^{II} = 333°$, with another concentration between $l^{II} = 283°$ and $l^{II} = 298°$. These two concentrations, taken together, correspond closely to the bright inner portion of the Milky Way described by Becker (1956) and thus probably belong to the inner (Sagittarius) arm defined by the O-associations. Bok (1959) has shown that the segment of the Milky Way between $l^{II} = 283°$ and $l^{II} = 298°$ is rich also in OB stars, cepheids, and other objects of population I, and has suggested that in this direction we look lengthwise along a spiral arm. The gap between $l^{II} = 298°$ and $l^{II} = 333°$ has been found to contain some OB stars (Hoffleit 1956) and O-associations (Houck 1956) at distances of the order of 2 kpc. This suggests that the two concentrations of H II regions and other population I objects ($l^{II} = 333°$ to 23° and $l^{II} = 283°$ to 298°) are parts of a continuous inner

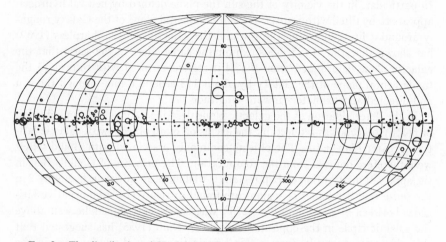

FIG. 2.—The distribution of H II regions in galactic coordinates. New longitudes are indicated.

spiral arm. The region between $l^{II} = 23°$ and $l^{II} = 58°$ contains relatively few H II regions, and those that do occur here have rather small angular dimensions. This suggests that they may be either intrinsically small objects in our own spiral arm, or else very distant objects. In either case it appears that this region of the Milky Way corresponds to a gap between two spiral arms, i.e., the Orion and Sagittarius arms. Between $l^{II} = 58°$ and $l^{II} = 73°$ there are a number of H II regions of moderate angular size, while between $l^{II} = 73°$ and $l^{II} = 93°$ some rather large regions are found. This would suggest that the Orion arm curves off in perspective in the direction of Cygnus, the more distant objects appearing at somewhat lower galactic longitudes (Sharpless 1953). The region near the galactic circle from $l^{II} = 98°$ through the anticenter to longitude 273° is more or less uniformly populated with H II regions belonging either to the Orion or Perseus arms. Between longitudes 83° and 273° a curious branch occurs which contains several dozen H II regions having an average latitude of about −15°. This coincides with the nearer branch of the Orion arm as defined by the

O-associations IV Cygni, I Lacertae, II Persei, and I Orionis (Morgan *et al.* 1953, Helfer and Tatel 1955), and contains H II regions which are excited by members of these associations.

The galactic pole, as determined from the known H II regions, can give us information concerning the over-all distribution of ionized hydrogen within several kiloparsecs of the sun. On the basis of 21-cm radio observations, Gum and Kerr (1958) have shown that the neutral hydrogen interior to the sun, from which the fundamental plane of the Galaxy can be determined, is characterized by a high degree of flattening, whereas Burke (1957) and Westerhout (1957) have shown that there exist distortions in the outer parts of the Galaxy. In particular, in the vicinity of the sun the plane defined by neutral hydrogen appears to be tilted with respect to the fundamental plane of the Galaxy roughly around a line connecting the sun and the galactic center. Sharpless (1959) has shown that the H II regions exhibit the same effect in the sense that the galactic plane determined from the H II regions is tilted with respect to the fundamental plane of the Galaxy by about $1°.3$ around a line through the sun and directed approximately toward longitude 173°.

In the determination of the galactic plane described above, the contribution of nearby objects was reduced by the exclusion of all objects with galactic latitude greater than $\pm 10°$. The objects commonly associated with Gould's Belt were therefore omitted from the computation. The presence of Gould's Belt in the apparent distribution of H II regions is well marked, however, in Figure 2 in the sense that a number of regions are found at relatively large negative latitudes between $l^{II} = 83°$ and $l^{II} = 273°$, whereas several objects lie well above the galactic circle in the opposite hemisphere. Gum (1955) has suggested that this phenomenon results from a "fin" projecting from the Orion arm in the vicinity of the sun similar to the "fins" or "spurs" which can be seen projecting outward from the spiral arms of M51 (see Pl. I). It has been noted above that the H II regions at negative latitudes between $l^{II} = 83°$ and $l^{II} = 273°$ can be identified with the nearer branch of the Orion arm as defined by the O-associations (Morgan *et al.* 1953). It appears, therefore, that the phenomenon of Gould's Belt can be explained in terms of a local non-uniformity in the spiral structure near the sun. A second, though less well defined, fin was also identified by Gum. This projects above the galactic plane between longitudes 98° and 123° and is well marked in the apparent distribution of H II regions shown in Figure 2. An inter-arm structure in this range of galactic longitudes was also detected by Weaver (1953). A more detailed discussion of the nature of these local peculiarities in the structure of our Galaxy cannot be made until more information is available on the individual distances of H II regions near the sun.

Table 2 contains a list of H II regions with reliably known distances based on spectroscopic parallaxes of associated stars. Most of the regions listed are those which belong to the O-associations listed by Morgan, Whitford, and Code

PLATE I.—The spiral nebula M51 with an assumed position of the sun, and the tangents to the inner spiral arm (after W. Becker).

PLATE II.—The Milky Way from Aquila to Carina in the infrared

(1953), and the distances given here are taken from their work. In addition, the distances of IC 1805–48 and IC 410 were determined by the author on the basis of data given by Hiltner (1956). The distances of the three southern H II regions were similarly determined on the basis of data given by Hoffleit (1956) after a transformation of her photometric data to the $B - V$ system had been made. The positions of the H II regions listed in Table 2 are plotted as solid circles in

TABLE 2

DISTANCES OF H II REGIONS

Region	l^{II}	b^{II}	Association	r (kpc)	Notes
NGC 6823	60	− 1	I Vul	1.8	2
10 Lac	97	−17	I Lac	0.46	2
129, 131	99	+ 6	I Cep	0.72	1, 2
132, 142	106	− 1	II Cep	3.6	1, 2
155	111	+ 3	III Cep	0.96	1, 2
IC 1805–48	137	+ 2	....	2.1	3
205	149	+ 1	I Cam	0.9	1, 2
NGC 1499	161	−11	II Per	0.36	2
230	174	0	I Aur	1.15	1, 2
IC 410	174	0	....	3.8	3
NGC 2174–5	191	+ 2	I Gem	1.5	2
NGC 2244	207	− 1	I Mon	1.4	2
NGC 1976–82	210	−18	I Ori	0.5	2
26 Hα	286	0	....	3.3	4, 5
η Car	288	0	....	1.9	4, 5
68 Hα	295	− 1	....	2.8	4, 5
NGC 6231	344	0	I Sco	1.4	2
M 8	7	− 3	I Sgr	1.3	2
M 20	8	− 2	II Sgr	1.4	2
41	13	− 2	III Sgr	2.3	1, 2
M 16	18	− 1	I Ser	2.3	2
NGC 6604	19	+ 1	II Ser	2.0	2

Notes to Table 2

1. Designation from catalogue of Sharpless (1959).
2. Parallax from Morgan, Whitford, and Code (1953).
3. Parallax based on data of Hiltner (1956).
4. Parallax based on data of Hoffleit (1956).
5. Designation from Hoffleit (1953).

Figure 3 with respect to the sun and galactic center. The space distribution of H II regions as shown here is not independent of the distribution of O-associations since many of the data used in the distance determinations are the same in both cases. The Vela-Puppis region ($l^{II} = 233°$ to $283°$) has received the least attention by observers and still remains a crucial region in connection with our understanding of spiral structure near the sun. The apparent edge of the population I concentration at $l^{II} = 283°$, however, is probably real (Bok and van Wijk 1952) and not caused by either a deficiency of observations at longitudes less than 283° or by overlying obscurations. The solid line in Figure 3 has been drawn to represent the inner spiral arm according to Becker's (1956) analysis, i.e., tangent to longitudes 288° and 28° and 1.4 kpc from the sun at its nearest point. The agreement with the plotted points is such as to suggest that Becker's analysis is correct and that an inner spiral arm reaching from Carina to Sagittarius does indeed exist in spite of an apparent discontinuity in the region of the Southern Coalsack. A segment of the Orion arm is also visible in Figure 3. The regions marked with plus and minus signs lie significantly above and below the galactic plane, respectively, and correspond to the two fins identified by Gum. Three H II regions beyond the Orion arm appear in Figure 3: IC 1805–48, IC 410, and NGC 7380. These three points do not clearly define a spiral feature, but they are undoubtedly associated with a spiral arm or arms more distant from the galactic center than the one containing the sun.

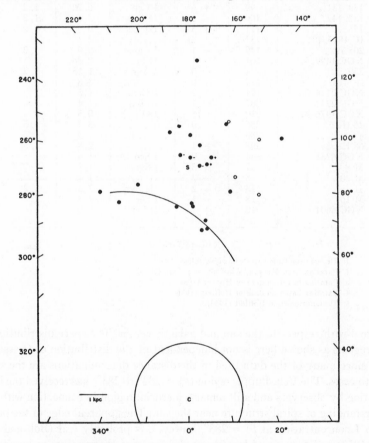

FIG. 3.—The space distribution of H II regions (*solid circles*) and M-type supergiants (*open circles*) as projected on the plane of the Galaxy.

§ 4. GALACTIC CLUSTERS

The study of the space distribution of galactic clusters can provide us with much useful information bearing on the structure of our Galaxy. Photometric parallaxes of clusters can be obtained with low accidental errors by fitting the observed cluster main sequence to a standard main sequence which has been calibrated on the basis of fundamental observations of nearby stars and moving clusters (Johnson 1957, and Vol. IV, this series, in preparation; cf. Blaauw's chap. 20 in Vol. III, this series). Evolutionary differences among clusters must be taken into account, otherwise the distance determinations would be affected by systematic errors depending on age. The fact that clusters exhibit considerable differences in age, however, can allow us, in principle, to study the evolution of structural features in our Galaxy as well as their present form. Knowledge of a cluster's age, distance, and velocity is necessary for considerations of this type.

The early work of Trumpler (1930) established that the galactic clusters form a highly flattened system approximately 1000 parsecs thick. A study of their linear diameters led to the discovery of the absorption of light in space, an effect that must be carefully accounted for in the photometric determination of cluster distances. A catalogue of 334 galactic clusters was given by Trumpler; this listed positions, diameters, classifications, and distances and has served as the standard reference for a number of years.

A more recent catalogue, compiled by Mrs. Hogg (1959, p. 194; see also Vol. IV, this series, in preparation), lists positions, descriptions, and distances of 514 galactic clusters. Counts of these clusters in various distance intervals, when corrected for incompleteness, yield a surface density of approximately 100 clusters per kpc^2 as seen projected on the galactic plane. In the z-direction, a dispersion of 60 parsecs is found under the assumption that the distribution of clusters perpendicular to the galactic plane is Gaussian. From these data one finds that the density of clusters at $z = 0$ is approximately 700 per kpc^3 near the sun and that the total number of clusters in the Galaxy is of the order of 10^4 to 10^5.

The distribution of clusters as seen projected against the celestial sphere is shown in Figure 4. The bright inner portion of the Milky Way, discussed by Becker, is well marked by the concentration of clusters between longitudes 283° and 28°. In this longitude interval the surface density of clusters is greater than elsewhere in the sky and their dispersion in latitude is smaller, suggesting that many of these form part of an inner structure which may be identified with a spiral arm. The relative frequency of clusters at intermediate galactic latitudes between longitudes 103° and 233° suggests that in this longitude interval there occur numerous nearby clusters. Outside of the concentration of clusters in the inner portion of the Milky Way there are two other major groups: one between $l^{II} = 118°$ and $l^{II} = 138°$ and the other between $l^{II} = 203°$ and $l^{II} = 213°$.

These may correspond to exceptionally rich segments of spiral arms, whereas the gap in the apparent distribution between $l^{II} = 33°$ and $l^{II} = 53°$ would, on the basis of Becker's model, correspond to the direction between two spiral arms. If Becker's model is correct, a similar gap in the apparent distribution between longitudes 243° and 283° would be expected, and indeed, a marked density minimum occurs in this interval.

The details of the space distribution of clusters must be investigated by means of distance determinations of individual clusters. The investigation of spiral structure through a study of the space distribution of galactic clusters must of necessity restrict itself to relatively young clusters, i.e., those containing O- or early B-type stars. A study of the space distribution of older clusters

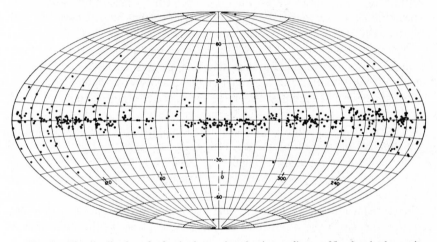

FIG. 4.—The distribution of galactic clusters in galactic coordinates. New longitudes are indicated.

may provide some information on the extent to which earlier structural features of our Galaxy may have evolved since their time of origin.

The distances of 43 galactic clusters which had been classified 1B2 or earlier by Trumpler were investigated by Weaver (1953). Weaver concluded that these clusters show a strong tendency to concentrate in regions of maximum density of neutral hydrogen, although their distribution along these spiral arms seemed rather spotty. Some evidence was found for an inter-arm structure in the approximate direction of $l^{II} = 108°$.

The distances of 82 open clusters were subsequently discussed by Becker (1961) using the method of three-color photometry. A comparison of the positions of these clusters with those of the H II regions and O-associations indicated that the three classes of objects occupy approximately the same regions in space.

More recently, the distances of 70 galactic clusters have been studied by

Johnson *et al.* (1961) using the three-color photometric method which involves a fitting of the cluster main sequence to a standard "zero-age" main sequence (Johnson and Iriarte 1958). The resulting distribution of clusters as seen projected on the galactic plane is shown in Figure 5. The open circles represent clusters for which the turn-up point of the main sequence occurs at $B - V = -0.28$ or less. These clusters thus contain stars of type B0 or earlier. Older

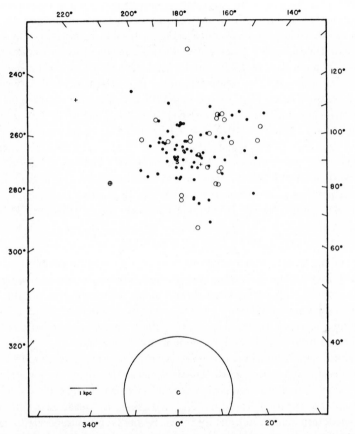

FIG. 5.—The space distribution of galactic clusters as projected on the plane of the Galaxy

clusters, having turn-up points at larger values of $B - V$, are indicated by solid dots. The crosses in Figure 5 represent additional clusters whose distances were taken from other sources. The cross at $l^{II} = 239°$ and $r = 4.4$ kpc represents the distant clusters studied by Haffner (1957). The early-type cluster NGC 3293 ($l^{II} = 287°$, $r = 2.6$ kpc) was investigated by Feast (1958) who suggested that it may be associated with the η Carinae complex of nebulae. Data for NGC 6811 ($l^{II} = 80°$, $r = 0.9$ kpc) and NGC 7243 ($l^{II} = 100°$, $r = 0.875$ kpc) were taken from Becker (1961).

The early-type clusters represented by open circles in Figure 5 appear to follow roughly the spiral pattern described in Section 1. The clusters which lie toward the galactic center appear to be associated with the inner spiral structure and conform to the pattern suggested by Becker although they are too few in number to outline it. The early-type clusters nearest the sun follow approximately the pattern of the nearer H II regions in forming a belt which extends from the direction of $l^{II} = 58°$, through a point near the sun in the direction of the anticenter, and outward toward $l^{II} = 238°$. The clusters toward the outer portion of the Galaxy show a considerable dispersion in distance and do not appear to outline a single spiral feature. A concentration of clusters appears near $l^{II} = 133°$ at a distance of 2.2 kpc and includes h and χ Persei. This can probably be identified with the concentration at this longitude which is visible in the surface distribution (Fig. 4) and undoubtedly represents an extremely rich portion of the outer spiral arm. The two clusters NGC 654 ($l^{II} = 129°$, $r = 1.55$ kpc) and NGC 7380 ($l^{II} = 107°$, $r = 2.1$ kpc) appear to be somewhat nearer than the concentration of clusters at $l^{II} = 133°$ and may thus represent an inter-arm structure as suggested by Weaver (1953). The clusters whose main sequences do not reach B0, i.e., those represented by solid dots in Figure 5, show no correlation with spiral structure and thus are apparently of sufficient age that their peculiar motions have carried them significant distances from their respective points of origin.

§ 5. SUPERGIANTS

Most of the structural features which we readily see in a photograph of an external galaxy are due to the supergiant stars. Many of these are members of associations which appear as large clumps along the spiral arms (see Pl. I). A number of supergiants, however, appear singly as members of the population I field. Some, or all, of these are probably the remnants of associations which have diffused into the field and are no longer recognizable.

Individual supergiants in our own Galaxy cannot be expected to reveal structural details as sharply as, e.g., the O-associations. First of all, the spectroscopic parallax of an individual supergiant does not have as low an accidental error as that of an O-association whose parallax represents the mean of a number of individual determinations for member stars. Secondly, many supergiants cannot be expected to have essentially zero age, hence they may have diffused a significant distance away from their respective points of origin. Although the space distribution of supergiants is a difficult observational problem, it has an important bearing on our understanding of the motions of young stars subsequent to their formation from the interstellar medium.

5.1. THE OB STARS

The "OB" classification (Morgan 1951) has proved useful in the segregation of high-luminosity stars of early type by means of objective prism spectra. Although the OB group is defined purely on the basis of the visibility of spectral features, it is an interesting fact that the boundaries of the OB group in the spectrum-luminosity diagram resemble the boundaries of the upper end of the HR diagram of an evolved association, such as I Persei. OB stars in the field may thus contain, as a large percentage, stars which have formed in associations but have recently dispersed into the field to the extent that the parent association is no longer recognizable as such.

The first survey of OB stars was made by Nassau and Morgan (1951a). Other, more recent, surveys have been made with the Tonantzintla and Hamburg Schmidt cameras and the results appear in the publications of these observatories. Several thousand OB stars have been found from these surveys, most of them probably within 2 or 3 kpc of the sun. Spectral classifications based on slit spectrograms of a number of these stars, as well as two- or three-color photometry, have been published by Morgan, Code, and Whitford (1955) and Hiltner (1956).

The surface distribution of OB stars brighter than the tenth magnitude has been studied by Nassau and Morgan (1951b). The region from longitude 8° to 23° is rich in OB stars, most of which lie several degrees south of the galactic equator. The region from $l^{II} = 23°$ to $l^{II} = 60°$, on the other hand, is relatively free of OB stars. It has been pointed out above that in these longitude intervals the H II regions show a similar surface distribution. A small group of OB stars is found in Vulpecula ($l^{II} = 60°$ to 68°) and a heavy concentration around P Cygni extends from longitude 73° to 81°. From the Cygnus concentration to a longitude of about 133° a more or less uniform distribution is found, while between 132° and 139° is found the heavy concentration associated with h and χ Persei. Beyond 139°, the distribution appears to be uniform except for the influence of the Taurus-Auriga dark nebulae. Three heavy concentrations of OB stars can be noted: the Small Sagittarius Cloud, the Cygnus Cloud, and the region of h and χ Persei. A fourth concentration of luminous O- and B-type stars occurs in Carina. From a study of the distances of early-type stars in this direction, Hoffleit (1956) has found them to be most numerous beyond a distance of about 1.2 kpc from the sun, with the highest concentration at about 2 kpc. The observations indicate a considerable spread in distance among these stars and thus suggest that in this direction we look along a spiral arm. A similar conclusion was reached by Elske Smith (1956) based on the distribution of polarization vectors in the Carina region. The three other concentrations mentioned above can be accounted for in terms of the associations III Sgr; I, II, III, and IV Cygni; and I Persei.

Twenty-seven OB stars which were found on the basis of spectroscopic parallaxes to be nearer than 400 parsecs were plotted according to galactic longitude and latitude by Nassau and Morgan (1951b), and the result is shown in Figure 6. These stars occupy a well defined plane which is inclined by about 20° to the galactic plane. The presence of a local tilted system in the distribu-

tion of nearby B-type stars is thus well established. A similar distribution of the
nearer H II regions has been noted earlier.

5.2. SUPERGIANTS OF TYPES A5–K

The space distribution of highly luminous stars having spectral types of A5
through K has been studied by Bidelman (1958) on the basis of spectroscopic
parallaxes. The individual distances determined for these stars have uncertainties of the order of 30 per cent as a result of the difficulty of assigning absolute magnitudes to the most luminous supergiants and of estimating the interstellar absorption suffered by their light. The positions of the individual supergiants studied by Bidelman as seen projected on the galactic plane are indicated
by dots in Figure 7. The crosses represent individual early-type stars observed
by Morgan, Whitford, and Code (1953) while the open circle represents the distant O-association discovered by Hiltner (1954). The curves drawn by Bidelman for the region nearest to the sun correspond to the Perseus, Orion, and

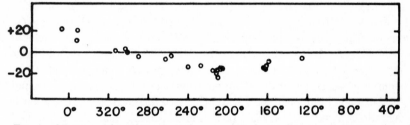

FIG. 6.—OB stars within 400 pc from the sun, plotted according to galactic latitude and
longitude.

Sagittarius arms as indicated by previous optical and 21-cm radio data. The two
curves nearest the galactic center were drawn to represent other possible, more
distant arms. Because of the large uncertainties in the individual distances,
these supergiants cannot be expected to define structural details in our Galaxy
independently of other types of observations. On the other hand, Figure 7 shows
that the supergiants plotted there do indeed tend to follow the previously suggested spiral pattern. More precise absorption and absolute magnitude data
will ultimately produce a more detailed picture of the space distribution of
these stars.

5.3. SUPERGIANTS OF TYPE M

The distribution of M-type supergiants is particularly interesting in that
some of them are known members of associations. Several hundred reddened
M-type stars have been catalogued at the Warner and Swasey Observatory
(Nassau *et al.* 1954; Blanco and Nassau 1957) on the basis of their unique appearance on infrared objective prism plates. It has been shown (Sharpless 1957)
that these lists contain a high percentage of supergiants. The surface distribution of these stars is shown in Figure 8. The most notable feature of their surface distribution is their tendency to appear in clumps which contain anywhere
from three to twenty stars. The best known of these groups is the one con-

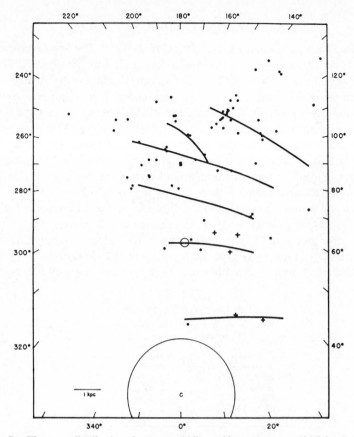

FIG. 7.—The space distribution of seventy middle- and late-type stars of high luminosity as projected on the galactic plane (after Bidelman).

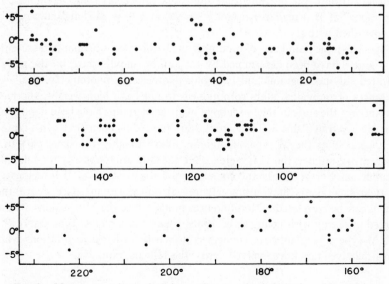

FIG. 8.—M-type supergiants plotted according to galactic latitude and longitude

nected with the association I Persei ($l^{II} = 137°$ to $140°$). Thirteen M-type super-giants in the region of h and χ Persei were first studied by Bidelman (1947) who demonstrated that they are situated at the same distance as the double cluster and undoubtedly belong to the I Persei association. Eight additional members were subsequently identified by Sharpless (1958) from the Warner and Swasey Observatory surveys. Theories of stellar evolution (Sandage 1958) suggest that associations containing late-type supergiants are in a relatively advanced evo-lutionary stage. Associations like I Persei, which contain M-type supergiant members, evidently represent a brief evolutionary stage which occurs after some of the most massive members have moved to the right-hand side of the HR diagram and before the association has diffused into the field to the extent that it is no longer recognizable as a discrete aggregate of early-type stars.

The other groups of M-type supergiants visible in Figure 8 cannot be identi-fied with any known early-type aggregates and therefore may represent as-sociations which have evolved beyond the stage represented by I Persei. The

TABLE 3

THE DISTANCES OF GROUPS OF
M-TYPE SUPERGIANTS

Group	r (kpc)	No. of stars
$l^{II} = 69°$	2.8	1
$l^{II} = 74° - 80°$	1.8	3
$l^{II} = 104° - 114°$	2.8	4
$l^{II} = 137° - 140°$	2.2	8

other main groupings in Figure 8 occur at $l^{II} = 69°$, $l^{II} = 74°$ to $l^{II} = 80°$, and $l^{II} = 104°$ to $l^{II} = 114°$. The third of these groups appears to extend into higher latitudes toward the low longitude limit and thus bears some resemblance to the "spur" of H II regions between $l^{II} = 98°$ and $l^{II} = 113°$ and may possibly be identified with it.

Spectroscopic parallaxes of a number of the M-type supergiants represented in Figure 8 have been determined by the author (unpublished) on the basis of infrared slit spectrograms and two-color photoelectric photometry. While the distances of individual stars so obtained do not have high weight, the mean distances of the stars in the four above-mentioned groups have been determined and are given in Table 3. These groups are plotted as open circles in Figure 3. It appears that the M-type supergiants follow roughly the same pattern of space distribution as the H II regions, but the data are too scanty for a detailed comparison. Further study and comparison of the distances of H II regions and M-type supergiants may ultimately reveal differences in space distribution which can be correlated with differences in age, since the H II regions are con-nected primarily with young associations (those containing O-type stars) while the M-type supergiants are connected primarily with old associations whose most massive stars have evolved across the HR diagram.

§ 6. CONCLUSION

In investigating the optical details of our Galaxy one must bear in mind that spiral structure is not, in general, simple. As an example, the structure of M51 (Pl. I) is complicated by inter-arm structures, discontinuities and occasional distortions as compared with an ideal spiral pattern. In the limited region of our Galaxy which is accessible to optical observation, there is difficulty in determining which of the observed structures are segments of main arms and which are local irregularities. An additional difficulty connected with optical studies of our Galaxy arises from the fact that the method of photometric parallaxes loses discrimination with distance. The 21-cm radio method can reveal structural details at great distances and in this respect is superior to optical methods. The optical results, on the other hand, have greater systematic reliability. In particular, they are independent of assumptions regarding the velocity field of our Galaxy. Apparently, the most reliable picture of the over-all structure of our Galaxy can be obtained only through a correlation and reconciliation of the results of the two methods.

In Figure 9 the writer has sketched a tentative optical model of our Galaxy in the vicinity of the sun based on the combined evidence contained in the preceding sections, i.e., on the known space distribution of population I objects as well as on what can be inferred from their respective surface distributions. This model is idealized, oversimplified and influenced by the optical appearance of other spiral galaxies. The nuclear bulge in Figure 9 has been drawn to a radius of 2 kpc on the basis of the infrared wide-angle photograph by Code and Houck (1955). A short segment of a spiral arm is indicated at a distance of 5 kpc from the galactic center. This is based primarily on the O-association observed by Hiltner (1954). The next spiral arm (Sagittarius arm) corresponds to the inner structure described by Becker on the basis of the visual appearance of the Milky Way. Between longitudes 343° and 23° it is well outlined by the O-associations, while at longitudes less than 343° its existence is confirmed by the early-type cluster studied by Feast (1958), three southern H II regions, and the I Crucis association (Houck 1956). The space distribution of these objects confirms Becker's suggestion of a continuous structure extending from Carina to Sagittarius.

The existence of a segment of the Orion arm at distances up to 2 kpc from the sun has been established on the basis of the space distribution of O-associations and early-type clusters. The existence of this arm as an entity distinct from the Sagittarius arm is also indicated by minima in the apparent distribution of clusters and other objects between $l^{II} = 243°$ and $l^{II} = 283°$ and $l^{II} = 33°$ and $l^{II} = 53°$. The speculative extrapolation of the Orion arm to greater longitudes, indicated by the dotted portion of the line, is based on Haffner's (1957) distant clusters. The segment of the Perseus arm between $l^{II} = 103°$ and $l^{II} = 138°$ is established on the basis of the space distribution of O-associations and early-type clusters in which a particularly concentrated region near $l^{II} = 133°$ is indicated. The existence of the Perseus arm between $l^{II} = 88°$ and $l^{II} = 158°$ as an entity separate from the Orion arm is shown most clearly in the space distribution of O-associations and is further confirmed by the work of Münch (1957) on interstellar absorption lines. The speculative extrapolation of the Perseus arm toward greater longitudes is based on the distance of the cluster NGC 1893 which is associated with the H II region IC 410. In the spiral model shown in Figure 9 no attempt has been made to include local structural irregularities although some evidence for the presence of inter-arm structures and bifurcations has been given in previous sections. The model suggested here not only gives a fair representation of the known distribution of high-luminosity objects but also appears reasonable in comparison with photographs of other spiral galaxies of intermediate type. The spiral arms indicated in Figure 9 are separated by distances of approximately 2 kpc which is a somewhat smaller separation than is found in M31. This suggests that either our Galaxy is somewhat earlier in type

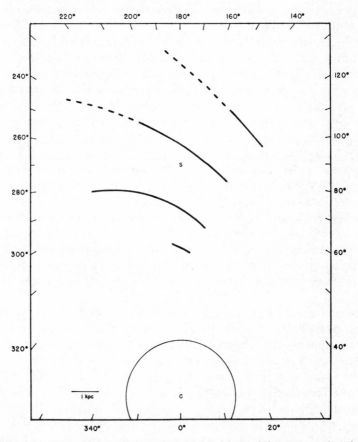

Fig. 9.—An optical model of spiral structure in the vicinity of the sun as projected on the galactic plane.

than M31, or else that one or more of the structures indicated in Figure 9 are not segments of the main spiral arms.

In Figure 10 the optical spiral model has been superposed on the isodensity contours of neutral hydrogen as derived from radio observations at 21-cm wavelength (Oort *et al.* 1958). The dashed lines correspond to a density of 0.6 atoms per cm³ while the shaded area corresponds to a density of 1.0 atoms per cm³ or more. Perfect correspondence of the two models is not to be expected. On the other hand, considerable discrepancy exists which one might hope can be reduced by future work. It is conceivable that not all of the arms indicated by the 21-cm survey need contain high-luminosity objects since the presence of neutral

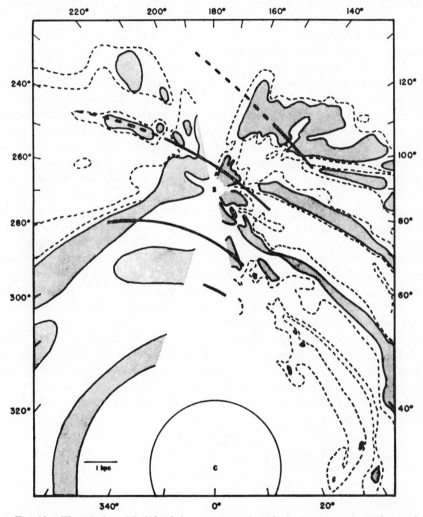

Fig. 10.—The spiral model of the Galaxy superposed on the isodensity contours of neutral hydrogen as observed at 21-cm wavelength.

hydrogen having the densities noted here is no guarantee that star formation has recently taken place. In regions where hot supergiants and H II regions are observed optically, on the other hand, one would expect to observe significant amounts of neutral hydrogen since these objects are too young to have moved significantly from their respective places of origin.

It is interesting to note that the best agreement between the two models occurs at a distance of several kiloparsecs and in directions 45° on either side of the anticenter. It is in these regions that the radial velocity effect due to differential galactic rotation is greatest. In these regions, therefore, a non-circular component in the galactic rotation will have the smallest effect on the derived distances of neutral hydrogen. Non-circularity of the motions of neutral hydrogen can arise from an expansion of the system, from random mass motions of neutral hydrogen complexes, or as the result of a force in addition to gravitation which might constrain the motion of neutral hydrogen.

Other spiral models of our Galaxy have been suggested by Elsässer and Haug (1960) on the basis of the surface distribution of color and brightness along the Milky Way, by Bok (1959) from a study of cepheids and early-type stars in Carina, and by other investigators. The model proposed by Elsässer and Haug resembles the one given here in that the arms trail in the galactic rotation; however, the two models differ considerably in the angle between the arms and the radius vector from the galactic center. The model proposed by Bok postulates a continuous, almost circular, arm extending from Carina, past the sun, and toward the direction of Cygnus. The crucial test of Bok's model will be the establishment of continuity in the distribution of young population I material between the sun and the more distant aggregates of OB stars and H II regions in Carina. The Carina region, as Bok points out, holds an important key to our understanding of local spiral structure in our Galaxy. Finally, one should not ignore the possibility that our Galaxy might be a barred spiral. Some evidence in favor of this idea has been accumulated by Johnson (1957). If this should indeed be the case, the non-circularity in the motions of the gas in the inner regions of the Galaxy should be expected.

Further study, both radio and optical, of the detailed structure of our Galaxy and its dynamics is necessary in order to shed light on such problems as the formation, the arrangement, the persistence, and the possible dissolution of spiral structure. The comparison of the radio and optical models of our Galaxy is not as much a matter of noting their similarities as it is a matter of explaining their discrepancies.

REFERENCES

AMBARZUMIAN, V. A.　　　1949　*A.J. U.S.S.R.*, **26**, 1.
　　　　　　　　　　　　1955　*Observatory*, **75**, 72.
　　　　　　　　　　　　1959　*Endeavour*, **18**, 45.

BAADE, W., and
　MAYALL, N. U.　　　　1951　*Problems of Cosmical Aerodynamics* (Dayton, Ohio: Central Air Documents Office), p. 165.

BECKER, W. 1956 *Vistas in Astronomy* (London and New York: Pergamon Press), **2**, 1515.

1961 *Zs. f. Ap.*, **51**, 151.

BIDELMAN, W. P. 1947 *Ap. J.*, **105**, 492.

1958 *I.A.U. Symposium*, No. 5, p. 54.

BLAAUW, A. 1952 *B.A.N.*, **11**, 405 and 414.

BLAAUW A., and
MORGAN, W. W. 1953 *Ap. J.*, **117**, 256.

BLANCO, V. M., and
NASSAU, J. J. 1957 *Ap. J.*, **125**, 408.

BOK, B. J. 1959 *Observatory*, **79**, 58.

BOK, B. J., BESTER, M. J.,
and WADE, C. M. 1955 *Daedalus*, **86**, 9.

BOK, B. J., and
VAN WIJK, U. 1952 *A.J.*, **57**, 213.

BURKE, B. F. 1957 *A.J.*, **62**, 90.

CHARLIER, C. V. L. 1926 *Medd. Lunds Obs.*, Ser. II, No. 34.

CODE, A. D., and
HOUCK, T. E. 1955 *Ap. J.*, **121**, 553.

ELSÄSSER, H., and
HAUG, U. 1960 *Zs. f. Ap.*, **50**, 121.

FEAST, M. W. 1958 *M.N.*, **118**, 618.

GUM, C. S. 1955 *Mem. R.A.S.*, **67**, 155.

GUM, C. S., and
KERR, F. J. 1958 *Div. of Radiophys.*, *Comm. Sci. and Ind. Res. Organiz.*, No. 138.

HAFFNER, H. 1957 *Zs. f. Ap.*, **43**, 89.

HASE, W. F., and
SHAJN, G. A. 1955 *Pub. Crimean Ap. Obs.*, **15**, 11.

HELFER, H. L., and
TATEL, H. E. 1955 *Ap. J.*, **121**, 585.

HERK, G. VAN 1959 *A.J.*, **64**, 348.

HILTNER, W. A. 1954 *Ap. J.*, **120**, 41.

1956 *Ap. J. Suppl.*, **2**, 389.

HOFFLEIT, D. 1953 *Harvard Ann.*, **119**, 37.

1956 *Ap. J.*, **124**, 61.

HOGG, H. S. 1959 *Hdb. d. Phys.*, **53**, 129.

HOUCK, T. E. 1956 Doctoral thesis, University of Wisconsin (unpublished).

JOHNSON, H. L. 1957 *Ap. J.*, **126**, 121.

JOHNSON, H. L., HOAG,
A. A., IRIARTE, B.,
MITCHELL, R. I., and
HALLAM, K. L. 1961 *Lowell Obs. Bull.*, **5**, 133.

JOHNSON, H. L., and
IRIARTE, B. 1958 *Lowell Obs. Bull.*, **4**, 47.

JOHNSON, H. L., and
MORGAN, W. W. 1954 *Ap. J.*, **119**, 344.

Johnson, H. M.	1953	*Ap. J.*, **118**, 370.
	1955	*Ibid.*, **121**, 604.
	1957	*A.J.*, **62**, 19.
Kopylov, I. M.	1958	*A.J. U.S.S.R.*, **35**, 390.
Morgan, W. W.	1951	*Mich. Pub.*, **10**, 33.
	1958	*I.A.U. Symp.*, No. 5, p. 57.
Morgan, W. W., Code, A. D., and Whitford, A. E.	1955	*Ap. J. Suppl.*, **2**, 41.
Morgan, W. W., Sharpless, S., and Osterbrock, D. E.	1952	*A.J.*, **57**, 3.
Morgan, W. W., Whitford, A. E., and Code, A. D.	1953	*Ap. J.*, **118**, 318.
Münch, G.	1957	*Ap. J.*, **125**, 42.
Nassau, J. J., Blanco, V. M., and Morgan, W. W.	1954	*Ap. J.*, **120**, 478.
Nassau, J. J., and Morgan, W. W.	1951*a*	*Ap. J.*, **113**, 141.
	1951*b*	*Mich. Pub.*, **10**, 43.
Oort, J. H., Kerr, F. J., and Westerhout, G.	1958	*M.N.*, **118**, 379.
Pannekoek, A.	1929	*Pub. Astr. Inst. Amsterdam*, No. 2.
Proctor, R. A.	1869	*M.N.*, **30**, 50.
Roberts, M. S.	1957	*Pub. A.S.P.*, **69**, 59.
Sandage, A.	1958	*Ric. Astr. Specola Vaticana*, **5**, 41 ("Stellar Populations").
Schmidt, K. H.	1958	*A.N.*, **284**, 76.
Sharpless, S.	1953	*Ap. J.*, **118**, 362.
	1957	*Pub. A.S.P.*, **69**, 397.
	1958	*Ibid.*, **70**, 392.
	1959	*Ap. J. Suppl.*, **4**, 257.
Sharpless, S., and Osterbrock, D. E.	1952	*Ap. J.*, **115**, 89.
Smith, E. van P.	1956	*Ap. J.*, **124**, 43.
Strömgren, B.	1939	*Ap. J.*, **89**, 526.
	1948	*Ibid.*, **108**, 242.
Struve, O.	1927	*A.N.*, **231**, 17.
Struve, O., Elvey, C.T., and Linke, W.	1939	*McDonald Obs. Contr.*, **1**, No. 9; *Ap. J.*, **90**, 301.
Trumpler, R. J.	1930	*Lick Obs. Bull.*, **14**, 154.
Weaver, H. F.	1953	*A.J.*, **58**, 177.
Westerhout, G.	1957	*B.A.N.*, **13**, 201.

CHAPTER 8

Distribution of Classical Cepheids

ROBERT P. KRAFT

Mount Wilson and Palomar Observatories

Carnegie Institution of Washington, California Institute of Technology

§ 1. INTRODUCTION

THE classical cepheids are generally regarded as suitable for delineating the spiral structure of the Galaxy because of their high intrinsic luminosity, and because they satisfy period-luminosity and period-color relations. Early work in this area (cf., e.g., Torgård 1956) was seriously hampered as a result of difficulties in evaluating interstellar absorption and because of inaccuracies in photographically determined magnitudes. Recently, accurate photoelectric colors and magnitudes have been determined for all cepheids within 1 kpc of the sun (Eggen, Gascoigne, and Burr 1957), for a large sample of cepheids of the southern Milky Way (Irwin 1961; Walraven, Muller, and Oosterhoff 1958), for extensive regions of the northern Milky Way (Oosterhoff 1960; Bahner, Hiltner, and Kraft 1961), and for all remaining "northern" cepheids having known radial velocities (Weaver, Steinmetz, and Mitchell 1961).

Coupled with these photometric surveys, fortunately, has come improved knowledge of intrinsic colors and absolute magnitudes resulting from the discovery that at least five cepheids are members of open clusters (reviewed by Irwin 1958). The state of the period-luminosity and period-color relations has been recently reviewed (Kraft 1961, 1963). Two possible sources of systematic error should be mentioned, however. Quite recently, a number of authors (Schmidt-Kaler 1961, Wildey 1963, Fernie 1964) have called attention to the possibility that the same quantity of interstellar dust may redden early and late-type stars somewhat differently. Prior work on cepheids in galactic clusters has assumed that the reddening appropriate to the cepheid can be interpolated directly among the B-type stars of the cluster; that assumption is continued in the present chapter. We also assume that the ratio of absorption to reddening, $A_V/E(B - V)$, has the value 3.0. If either or both of these assumptions is in error, then our distance scale is wrong. Preliminary considerations indicate, however (Kraft and Schmidt 1963, Fernie 1964), that the magnitude of the errors involved is not likely to exceed 15 per cent from these two sources and thus none of the conclusions reached in this chapter would be significantly affected.

A comprehensive review of the location of cepheids in the HR (i.e., color-magnitude) diagram and the theory of the "instability strip" advanced by Sandage (1958) have been given elsewhere (Kraft 1963). It is sufficient to state here that a cepheid of given period has a certain range of permissible colors and magnitudes available to it; thus, if Q is the pulsational constant, the period-luminosity and period-color relations can be regarded as mean traces of an equation of the form $F[(B - V)^0, M_V^0, P, Q] = 0$. Studies of cepheids in the Small Magellanic Cloud (Arp 1960) and of galactic cepheids (Kraft 1961) show that one can discriminate between cepheids near the center and cepheids near the edges of the instability strip. At a given period, the former have the largest amplitudes; small-amplitude cepheids are found near the edges of the strip. Since the amplitude discriminant is a double-valued function, however, it is not possible to decide from it alone whether a given small-amplitude cepheid is near the red or blue edge of the strip. This is possible only if spectral types are available (cf. Kraft 1960).

Kraft and Schmidt (1963) have published a list of distances to all classical cepheids for which photoelectric photometry is available. In the computation of these distances, the period-mean color and period-mean luminosity relations (Kraft 1963) were used, except in those cases where spectral types were available. For the latter, the dependence of M_V^0 on $(B - V)^0$ was explicitly taken into account.

§ 2. THE SPACE DISTRIBUTION OF GALACTIC CEPHEIDS

In Figure 1 we plot the positions of the cepheids within 5000 pc of the sun projected on the galactic plane. A few stars suspected of being type II have been omitted. The array is complete to 1500 pc except for the sector from $l^{II} = 140°$ to $l^{II} = 200°$, a portion of the winter sky for northern observers. Outside 1500 pc, the distribution is seriously affected by selection due to an apparent-magnitude limit. Thus the paucity of points toward Vela $(260° \lesssim l^{II} \lesssim 280°)$ results in part from the high obscuration in this direction. On the other hand, toward Carina $(l^{II} \sim 290°)$, we may be looking down the inside edge of a spiral arm where the obscuration is less than average. It is clear that any attempt to study spiral structure toward Carina-Vela or Cygnus, i.e., along or near an arm, will have to reach very faint magnitudes.

Figure 1 illustrates that the body of all cepheids gives little, if any, indication of spiral structure. Only a few conclusions can be reached. First, in a circle of radius 1000 pc centered on the sun, the majority of cepheids are "inside," i.e., toward the center of the Galaxy, rather than "outside" the sun. Second, in the sector from $l^{II} = 90°$ to $l^{II} = 150°$, there is an "open area" out to 1200 pc where no cepheids are found.

However, if we restrict our attention to cepheids with $\langle M_V^0 \rangle \leq -4.3$, spiral structure is quite evident, at least on the "north" side, i.e., counterclockwise from Sagittarius around to Perseus. Portions of two spiral arms are present (Figure 2); we have called these "Per-Cas" and "Cyg." The former runs from $l^{II} = 170°, r = 2000$ pc to $l^{II} = 110°, r = 3500$ pc, and the latter from the sun

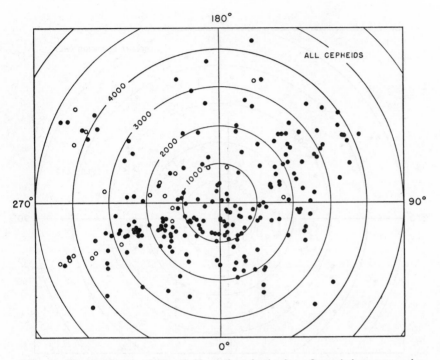

FIG. 1.—The distribution of all cepheids on the galactic plane. Open circles correspond to stars of low weight.

toward $l^{II} \sim 75°$. The placement of these arms is naturally influenced to some extent by prior studies of the distribution of early-type stars (see Sec. 3); however, their reality, if not their exact direction, is scarcely open to much doubt. On the "south" side and in the anticenter direction, the situation is more confused because of the incompleteness already cited, particularly from the anticenter around to Puppis ($l^{II} \sim 240°$), and in Vela. There is some evidence of a spiral arm running off toward Carina ($l^{II} \sim 290°$), and an inner arm directed toward $l^{II} \sim 310°$. However, the Cyg arm, near the sun, is very difficult to follow, presumably because the space density of long-period cepheids is rather low. We may ask: Does the "Cyg" arm extend down into Carina, or, following the apparent direction of the OB associations, run out into Orion-Monoceros and on into Puppis? Or does Puppis connect with "Per-Cas"? Is it possible that the "Cyg" arm has a bifurcation in the solar vicinity? Evidence of similar confusion in the interpretation of the 21-cm observations and in the apparent distribution of early-type stars will be discussed in the next section.

The reason why bright cepheids only, rather than all cepheids, outline spiral structure to some extent (Fernie 1958) may be due to the difference in average

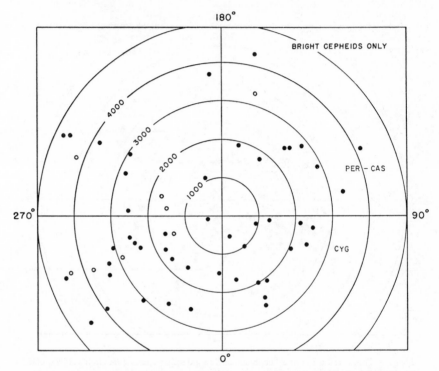

Fɪɢ. 2.—The distribution on the galactic plane of cepheids with $\langle M_V^0 \rangle \leq -4.3$. The "Per-Cas" and "Cyg" arms are indicated. Open circles correspond to stars of low weight.

age. Compared with their main-sequence progenitors, cepheids are anomalously bright because of the one-magnitude rise in the evolutionary track from the age-zero main sequence. Compared with the average, slightly evolved, main sequence, they are about $\frac{1}{2}$ mag. too bright. Thus a cepheid at $\langle M_V^0 \rangle = -5.0$ has a main-sequence progenitor of type O9V, and an age presumably about 7×10^6 years (Hoyle 1960). With a characteristic velocity of about 10 km/sec (Kraft and Schmidt 1963), it moves therefore 70 pc from its place of origin, a negligible distance. A cepheid of $\langle M_V^0 \rangle = -3.0$, however, will move about four times farther than this during its lifetime of 30×10^6 years; this is sufficient to smear the spiral structure fairly effectively.

§ 3. COMPARISON WITH OTHER "YOUNG" GALACTIC MATTER

The distribution of cepheids may be compared with that of OB associations, galactic clusters, and interstellar matter.

3.1. LONG-PERIOD CEPHEIDS AND OB ASSOCIATIONS

The positions of the latter are taken from the compilation by Schmidt (1958); these are compared with the bright cepheids of Figure 2 in Figure 3. The tentative "arms" are indicated on the north side. The distribution of OB associations on the "south" side is no doubt seriously affected by incompleteness, especially

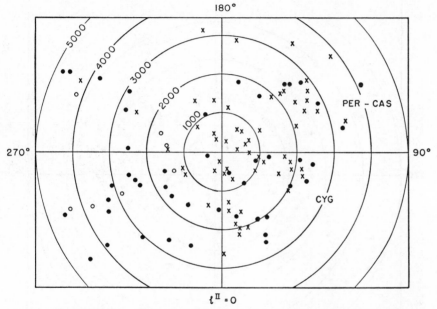

FIG. 3.—The distribution of OB associations (crosses) and bright cepheids (dots) compared

in the Carina direction. While the two distributions are remarkably similar in scale, there is a tendency for many of the OB associations to be "outside" the sun, i.e., in a direction opposite to that of the galactic center; in this region there are virtually no cepheids of long period (or of any period, as already mentioned). However, we cannot be sure that the distribution of bright cepheids within 1000 pc of the sun really differs from that of OB associations because the number of bright cepheids is very small.

3.2. LONG-PERIOD CEPHEIDS AND YOUNG GALACTIC CLUSTERS

By "young galactic clusters" we mean those which, if sufficiently rich, could contain cepheids with $\langle M_V^0 \rangle \leq -4.3$. This corresponds roughly to clusters with "bluest" spectral types of B3 or earlier. Distances for these are taken from the lists by Johnson, Hoag, Iriarte, Mitchell, and Hallam (1961) and by Becker

(1960). Comparison of these two investigations shows that the distance determinations for roughly 100 clusters do not differ systematically and are remarkably consistent except for a half-dozen highly discordant cases. We consider here only cluster distances determined from multicolor photometry.

Once again, the incompleteness of the southern clusters is apparent when the distributions of long-period cepheids and young clusters are superimposed (Fig. 4). This is clearly shown when distances to additional southern clusters based

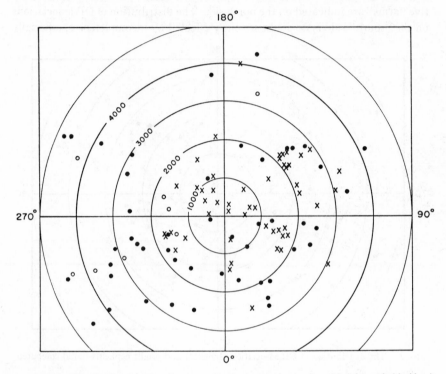

Fig. 4.—The distribution of early-type galactic clusters (crosses) and bright cepheids (dots) compared.

on a calibration of cluster diameters (Trumpler 1930, Johnson *et al.* 1961) are included. We prefer, however, to exclude non-photometric distance determinations in the present discussion.

The positions of the young clusters bear about the same relation to the bright cepheids as do the OB associations. However, the mean position of young clusters in the "Per-Cas" arm either is closer to the sun than the cepheids, or there is perhaps a narrow "inter-arm" of young clusters. The latter interpretation is favored by Johnson *et al.* (1961). Why there should be any difference in distribution between young cepheids and young clusters of presumably about the same age is not clear.

3.3. Long-Period Cepheids and Interstellar Matter

The bright cepheids of Figure 2 and the interpretation of the 21-cm observations (Oort, Kerr, and Westerhout 1958) are compared in Figure 5. As with the cepheids, there is a 21-cm arm in Puppis ($l^{\text{II}} \sim 240°$). However, it is not certain whether this connects with "Per-Cas" or "Cyg," if either. Elsewhere, the main features of the bright cepheid distribution seem reproduced by the 21-cm interpretation, including the "Per-Cas" arm and the extension into Carina. The complete absence of long-period cepheids between the "Per-Cas" and "Cyg"

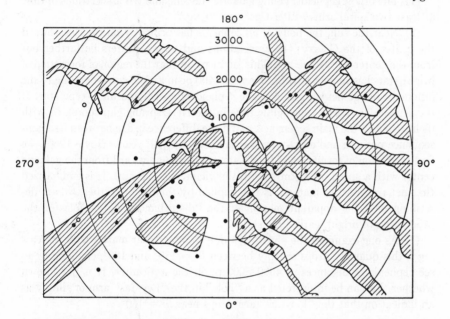

Fig. 5.—A comparison of the distribution of bright cepheids with the schematic 21-cm arms (after Oort, Kerr, and Westerhout).

21-cm arms confirms the tentative conclusion by Fernie (1958) that the long-period cepheids are found embedded essentially in the gas.

The distribution of absorbing interstellar matter, as shown by the A_V-values for cepheids, is in quite good agreement with that of the 21-cm emission, at least on the north side. (There may also be agreement on the south side, but there are not enough cepheid data in the right positions.) Consider two rectangular slabs, each with an end centered on the sun, having width 1500 pc, and extending in the direction $l^{\text{II}} = 25°$ and $l^{\text{II}} = 105°$. A plot of A_V for cepheids as a function of r, the distance from the sun, was made for each slab. For the first, the absorption on the average increases linearly with the distance; at 1000 pc, $A_V \sim 1.3$ mag. For the second, the absorption first increases to a value of $A_V \sim 1.3$ mag. at 1000 pc, then levels off from 1000 to 2600 pc, after which it increases again to $A_V \sim 3.1$ mag. at $r = 4000$ pc, the limit of the survey (rough-ly). This is in approximate agreement with the appearance of Figure 5 if it is assumed that the dust follows the 21-cm arms. The material at hand also sug-gests that the sun is approximately centrally located in the "Cyg" arm, as far as the dust is concerned.

3.4. DISCUSSION

The leading features of the distribution of young stars can be summarized as follows:

(1) The bright cepheids, young galactic clusters, and OB associations outline at least two spiral arms—"Per-Cas" and "Cyg."

(2) Near the sun, the body of *all* cepheids lies primarily on the side toward the center of the Galaxy; OB associations and young clusters lie farther out from the center on the average. This might mean that the region of formation of bright stars has moved outward by about 400 pc in a time corresponding to the difference in age between an average cepheid ($P \sim 6^d$) and an O-type star. If the cepheid has spent a negligible time in the Hertzsprung gap compared with its life time on the main seqeuence, and if the difference in age between its main-sequence position and an O-type star is about 1×10^7 years (Hoyle 1960), we find the region of formation of bright stars is moving outward from the galactic center with a speed of 40 km/sec (in the vicinity of the sun). It is emphasized that net transport of material is not implied by this result; rather, we are de-scribing only the apparent motion of the "disturbance" responsible for the production of bright, early-type stars.

(3) As one examines the absorption due to interstellar matter with increas-ing l, this quantity drops sharply between $l^{II} = 150°$ and $180°$, enabling us to see cepheids at distances of 4000–5000 pc in the anticenter. It is not known whether this can be interpreted as a "hole" in the "Per-Cas" arm or simply as an indication that the "Per-Cas" arm stops near $l^{II} = 160°$.

§ 4. THE COMPARATIVE USEFULNESS OF CEPHEIDS AND GALACTIC CLUSTERS AS DISTANCE INDICATORS

There is little question that cepheids provide a more useful tool in galactic research than is the case for individual O- and B-type stars if the latter have no more available information than MK spectral types and luminosities, and photoelectric colors and magnitudes. This is true simply because the grid of types and luminosities is too coarse to provide precision distances. It is different, however, when clusters are considered, for the cluster and cepheid moduli are comparable in accuracy.

The frequency of young clusters per unit volume of space is about twice that of cepheids with $\langle M_V^0 \rangle \leq -4.3$. If this were the only consideration, the de-lineation of spiral structure by young clusters would be markedly superior to that by bright cepheids. One sees that this is true certainly in the vicinity of the sun. However, at large distances from the sun, many clusters become so crowded that photometric separation of the stars, particularly those on which the modulus is based, becomes difficult. Moreover, consider, for example, a young cluster of "bluest" (in the Johnson *et al.* [1961] sense) type, say, B2. If it contained a cepheid, its $\langle M_V^0 \rangle$ would be around -5. Suppose such a cepheid and such a cluster are at the same distance in nearly the same direction, but the latter does not actually contain the cepheid. Let $\langle m_V \rangle$ for the cepheid be 13. To get the cepheid distance with a precision in modulus of ± 0.2 mag., we need make only about 20 measures of V and $B - V$, well distributed in phase. To get the cluster modulus with equivalent precision, we should observe stars down to $m_V \sim 18$ or 19, a not insignificant task. We may expect, therefore, that cepheids will carry much of the burden of delineating the optical spiral structure of the Galaxy at large distances. The use of O- and B-type stars in the mapping could achieve a precision greater than either that of the cepheids or galactic clusters if calibration of the luminosities by interference-filter photometry of appropriate spectral lines were carried out, in the manner of Strömgren and his associates.

Finally, a word of warning must be given. Elsewhere (Kraft 1963) it has been pointed out that the chemical composition of cepheids in the distant northern Milky Way, beyond the Perseus arm, may be different from that of cepheids in the vicinity of the sun. How this affects the P–L relation is not known. This development may provide a serious limitation on the use of cepheids as distance indicators. If the metal content of stars is, however, stratified as a function of distance from the center, and if the spiral arms are not too loosely wound, we may nevertheless be safe in using the P–L relation as far as we can see along the "Cyg" and "Per-Cas" arms.

REFERENCES

ARP, H. C.	1960	*A.J.*, **65**, 404.
BAHNER, K., HILTNER, W. A., and KRAFT, R. P.	1961	*Ap. J. Suppl.*, **6**, 319.
BECKER, W.	1960	*Zs. f. Ap.*, **49**, 168.
EGGEN, O. J., GASCOIGNE, S. C. B., and BURR, E. J.	1957	*M.N.*, **117**, 406.
FERNIE, J. D.	1958	*A.J.*, **63**, 219.
	1964	*Ibid.*, **68**, 780.
HOYLE, F.	1960	*M.N.*, **120**, 22.
IRWIN, J. B.	1958	*Trans. I.A.U.*, **10**, 680.
	1961	*Ap. J. Suppl.*, **6**, 253.
JOHNSON, H. L., HOAG, A. A., IRIARTE, B., MITCHELL, R. I., and HALLAM, K. L.	1961	*Lowell Obs. Bull.*, **5**, 133.

KRAFT, R. P.   1960   *Ap. J.*, **131**, 330.
                                    1961   *Ibid.*, **134**, 616.
                                    1963   This ser., **3**, chap. 21.
KRAFT, R. P., and
  SCHMIDT, M.   1963   *Ap. J.*, **137**, 249.
OORT, J. H., KERR, F. J.,
  and WESTERHOUT, G.   1958   *M.N.*, **118**, 379.
OOSTERHOFF, P. TH.   1960   *B.A.N.*, **15**, 199.
SANDAGE, A. R.   1958   *Ap. J.*, **127**, 513.
SCHMIDT, K. H.   1958   *A.N.*, **284**, 76.
SCHMIDT-KALER, TH.   1961   *A.N.*, **286**, 113.
TORGÅRD, I.   1956   *Medd. Lunds Obs.*, Ser. II, No. 133.
TRUMPLER, R. J.   1930   *Lick Obs. Bull.*, **14**, 154.
WALRAVEN, TH.,
  MULLER, A. B., and
  OOSTERHOFF, P. TH.   1958   *B.A.N.*, **14**, 81.
WEAVER, H. F.,
  STEINMETZ, D., and
  MITCHELL, R. I.   1961   *Lowell Obs. Bull.*, **5**, 30.
WILDEY, R. L.   1963   *A.J.*, **68**, 190.

CHAPTER 9

Distribution of Interstellar Hydrogen

F. J. KERR

Radiophysics Laboratory, C.S.I.R.O., Sydney

AND

G. WESTERHOUT

Observatory, Leiden, The Netherlands; now at University of Maryland

§ 1. OBSERVATIONS OF HYDROGEN

STUDIES of the distribution of hydrogen in the Galaxy are important in themselves, because hydrogen is the most important constituent of the interstellar gas, but they have the additional interest that hydrogen can be used as a tracer for studying basic structural features, such as the spiral arms and the galactic disk. Hydrogen is observed in the interstellar gas in both the neutral and ionized forms, and it may also be present in the molecular state.

Ionized hydrogen can be observed by both optical and radio means. Optical observations are generally concerned with individual "H II regions" or emission nebulae, which can be studied in considerable detail, but only in the immediate neighborhood of the sun. Radio observations can also detect these individual regions, but with less detail; in addition, they can provide evidence on the large-scale distribution of ionized hydrogen throughout the Galaxy.

The bulk of the atomic hydrogen is in the neutral form, which cannot be observed optically at all. Radio observations of the hyperfine transition line at 21 cm can cover the whole Galaxy, and, in fact, provide the only method available at present for tracing out the large-scale structure of the entire system. Molecular hydrogen has not yet been detected, but Gold (1961), Zwicky (1959), and others have suggested that it might be present in much larger quantities than the atomic form. This would account for the discrepancy between the known mass density near the sun, arising from stars and gas, and the density which appears to be necessary to account for the local gravitational effects. It seems more likely, however, that a significant amount of association of the atoms can

167

only occur in regions where the interstellar density is unusually high (McCrea 1960). It is expected that satellite observations will be undertaken shortly from above the atmosphere, in an attempt to detect molecular hydrogen in the far infrared.

This chapter will be concerned only with the *large-scale* distribution of hydrogen in the Galaxy. The smaller scale distribution and the properties of individual regions are treated in other places in this Compendium. Greatest attention will be given to the neutral gas, because 21-cm studies have so far provided the most information on large-scale distribution. Ionized hydrogen will also be discussed, but only as far as its large-scale properties are concerned.

§ 2. HYDROGEN VELOCITIES

The observations of the 21-cm line of neutral hydrogen have brought about a revolution in the study of galactic structure. Contrary to the optical and decameter-wave cases, radiation in the range of decimeter waves passes without hindrance through the interstellar dust and the ionized hydrogen. While observations in the continuum can only give the integrated radiation in the line of sight, the 21-cm line observations give discrimination in distance, although they cannot by themselves provide actual distances. The distance distribution in a given direction can only be inferred from radial velocities. For this we must have an accurate knowledge of the velocity distribution of the gas throughout the Galaxy. The density distribution is not homogeneous, the gas being strongly concentrated toward the spiral arms. Fortunately, the line width of the components of the line is of the same order as, or smaller than, the separation of the components due to their different radial velocities, so that they can be easily distinguished from each other.

If only gravitational forces were present, the gas in the Galaxy would be expected to move in almost exactly circular orbits, since the over-all mass distribution shows approximately radial symmetry about the galactic center; the observed velocity dispersion is in fact quite small compared with the rotational velocity. Departures from circular motion could be produced by deviations from circular symmetry in the mass distribution, or by the effect of magnetic forces, but it is clear that the gas motions are predominantly circular in most parts of the Galaxy.

The angular velocity $\omega(R)$ decreases from the center outward. For a given point P in the galactic plane (Fig. 1), let the distance to the sun be r, the distance to the center R, and the galactic longitude l^{II} (new galactic longitude, measured counterclockwise from the direction of the galactic center). A simple geometrical consideration shows that, if the average motion of the medium is everywhere perpendicular to the radius vector from the center, and if $\omega(R)$ is indeed only dependent on R and not on the position angle of this radius vector, the average radial velocity V_g of the medium near P with respect to the average of the medium near the sun is given by

$$V_g = R_0[\omega(R) - \omega_0] \sin l^{\mathrm{II}},$$

where R_0 is the distance from the sun to the center and ω_0 the angular velocity near the sun.

A convenient representation of the relation between V_g, r, R, and l^{II} is given in Figure 4. To arrive at these values, knowledge of the function $R_0 [\omega(R) - \omega_0]$ is necessary. This has been obtained from the line profiles themselves for the

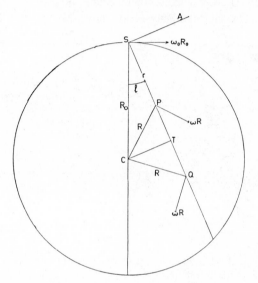

FIG. 1.—Diagram to illustrate relation between radial and rotational velocities (see text)

region $R < R_0$. For $l^{\mathrm{II}} < 90°$ the maximum velocity in the line of sight occurs at the point T closest to the center C (see Fig. 1), and near this point the velocity remains almost constant over a long path. We shall call this the "tangential point." If T lies in a spiral arm, this should result in fairly intense radiation sharply dropping to zero at the side of increasing velocities. We see this clearly illustrated by the line profiles between 45° and 65° longitude (see Fig. 6). Measurement of the radial velocity at which this sharp drop occurs, taking into account the smoothing caused by random motions, yields the value of $R_0 [\omega(R) - \omega_0]$ at T, i.e., at a distance $R = R_0 \sin l^{\mathrm{II}}$ from the center. The shape of the $\omega(R)$ curve for $R < R_0$ can thus be obtained; its scale and zero point depend on the values of R_0 and ω_0. A discussion of the derivation of these values is given in chapter 22 of this volume. In all 21-cm line work up to the present (1963), the values $R_0 = 8.2$ kpc and $\omega_0 = 26.4$ km/sec per kpc have been used. The corresponding value for the circular velocity at the sun, $\Theta_c(R_0)$, is 216 km/sec. Knowledge of these values is necessary for the construction of a model of the mass distribution in the Galaxy, from which the values of $\omega(R)$, for $R > R_0$, can be derived. Insufficient knowledge of $\omega(R)$, whether due to uncertainty in R_0 and ω_0 or to uncertainty in the mass model, will lead to a change in scale of the structure of the Galaxy, derived from 21-cm line data, but not to serious changes in shape.

The rotation curve, giving the circular velocity $\Theta_c(R) = \omega(R) \cdot R$ as a function of R, is shown in Figure 2. It was determined by Kwee, Muller, and Westerhout (1954) from northern-hemisphere data ($0° < l^{\mathrm{II}} < 90°$), and by Kerr (1962) from southern-hemisphere data ($270° < l^{\mathrm{II}} < 360°$). The two

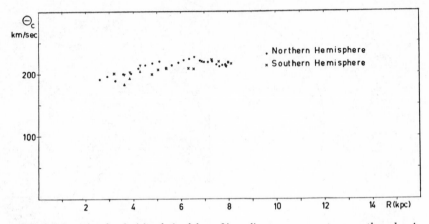

Fig. 2.—Rotational velocities derived from 21-cm line measurements: ● northern hemisphere (Leiden); ✕ southern hemisphere (Sydney).

curves agree reasonably, indicating that the assumption of circular motion, to a first approximation, is correct. There are two features worth noting.

The first is the existence of a few definite dips, showing particularly clearly in the northern curve. These are easily explained by assuming that, in the directions corresponding to the dips, the point on the line of sight nearest to the center (the tangential point, T, in Fig. 1) contains no hydrogen. The maximum radial velocity in that direction then comes from some other point on the line of sight, somewhat more distant from the center, where $\omega = \Theta_c/R$ is smaller; computing ω from the observed V_θ we then get too small a value for the supposedly maximum velocity. Therefore, the true rotation curve should run through the upper points.

The second feature is the lower value of Θ_c for the points between $R = 4.5$ and 7 kpc derived from southern-hemisphere data. Some of this could well be due to differences in the methods of observation and reduction which were used by the Leiden and Sydney groups, but the reality of the effect has been confirmed by recent Australian observations at Parkes, in which both northern and southern regions were covered with the same instrument and the same reduction procedures. If we interpret the low velocities of the points between $R = 4.5$ and 7 kpc as a "dip" in the sense described above, then this means that on the southern side of the Galaxy there is a very wide "empty" region between the arms, as is clearly illustrated in Plate I, for which a rotation curve running through the upper points was used (dotted curve in Fig. 3). A "hole" of this position and shape appears to be a result of the method of reduction, and is not likely to be real. We thus have to explain the discrepancy between the northern and southern velocities. One possibility is to assume that large portions of spiral arms at the tangential points have random tangential velocities, which for some northern points are in excess of the circular velocity, and for the low southern points happen to be below the circular velocity by 5 to 10 km/sec. Then, the true rotation curve would run somewhere between the northern and the southern points. It might also be possible that the mass distribution in the Galaxy is not quite circularly symmetric, which would give rise to real differences in circular velocity in different quadrants (dashed and dotted curves in Fig. 3).

Another possibility, which fits the data rather well, is to postulate an outward motion of the local standard of rest, with respect to which all velocities have been measured. Such an expanding motion would not seem unlikely in view of the expansion found in regions closer to the center (Sec. 5.2). If the outward velocity component of the solar neighborhood is V_e, then the radial velocity, measured in the tangential points, will be

$$V_r = V_\vartheta + V_e \cos l^{\mathrm{II}},$$

so that the northern and southern points differ in velocity by $2V_e \cos l^{\mathrm{II}}$, and the curve giving the circular velocity would run somewhere between the points in Figure 3 (middle curve). Kerr (1962) has investigated this possibility in more detail and finds that a value $V_e = 7$ km/sec fits the observed points. Although an outward motion of the surroundings of the sun is sufficient to explain the difference between northern and southern circular velocities in this way, Kerr pointed out that there are also other features of the observations which do not fit into a simple circular-orbit picture. As the available evidence is insufficient to distinguish between the various possible interpretations, Kerr considered the velocity pattern that would be indicated by the observations under one particular simplifying assumption, namely, that the Galaxy is circularly symmetric when viewed on a large scale. On this assumption, the available results could be interpreted as implying a general outward motion of the gas away from the galactic center throughout the whole Galaxy. The spiral pattern worked out on this basis becomes rather more symmetrical.

However, more recent observations in directions near the galactic center at Dwingeloo (Braes, private communication) and Parkes (Kerr, unpublished) have shown that the suggested *general* expansion is an oversimplification. Exten-

sive deviations from circular motion certainly occur, with some outward and
some inward motions, but the over-all picture is a complex one, and has not
yet been worked out in detail.

These observations near the galactic center do, however, show evidence of the
postulated outward motion of matter locally, as the profiles in this region tend
to peak at a velocity around +7 km/sec. Such a local deviation from circular
motion has yet to be reconciled with the optical solar-motion data.

It is clear that important deviations from perfect circular motion exist over
large areas of the galactic plane; this follows both from the discussion of the rotational velocities and from observations of the 21-cm line in the galactic center

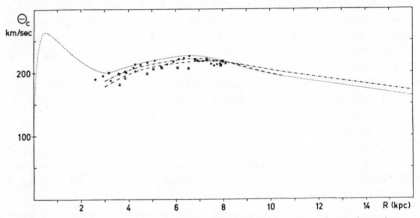

Fig. 3.—Possible rotation laws: .... ($R < 8.2$ kpc) from northern hemisphere observations; .... ($R > 8.2$ kpc) calculated from mass model (Schmidt 1956, model 2); ------ from
southern hemisphere observations; -·-·- rotation velocity if solar neighborhood is moving outward. (Also see text.)

and anticenter. The center region will be discussed in Section 5.2. In the anticenter, where the radial velocity, on the assumption of circular motion, should
be zero, individual components are detected with velocities of up to 20 km/sec.
Such deviations from a smooth velocity field for large cloud complexes are also
suspected in various other places. Some of these may be the result of an earlier
connection between such a cloud complex and an expanding stellar association.
In fact, many associations have been found to be embedded in a large mass of
hydrogen, some of which—close to the hot stars—is ionized, but most of which
is in neutral form.

A typical example is the Orion region, which has been studied by Menon
(1958) and van Woerden (1965). The association is surrounded by a complex
of hydrogen and dust clouds with a diameter of about 120 pc and a total mass of
the order of 10^5 solar masses. The velocity pattern derived from the line profiles
is consistent with a model in which the central mass is at rest, and the outer
portion is expanding with a velocity of the order of 10 km/sec.

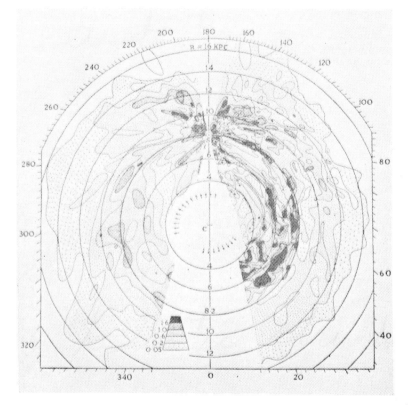

PLATE I.—Distribution of neutral hydrogen in the Galaxy (unit = atom/cm³) based on the northern hemisphere circular orbit model (Fig. 4, curve .... in Fig. 3).

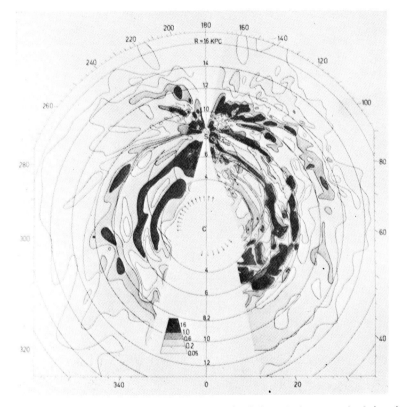

PLATE II.—Distribution of neutral hydrogen in the Galaxy (unit = atom/cm³) based on the northern hemisphere rotational velocities for $R < 8.2$ kpc, $l^{\mathrm{II}} = 0°$–$90°$, on the southern hemisphere rotational velocities for $R < 8.2$ kpc, $l^{\mathrm{II}} = 270°$–$360°$, and on the velocities from Schmidt's mass model for $R > 8.2$ kpc (in Fig. 3: curves ...., ------, and ...., respectively).

PLATE III.—Sketch of possible distribution of hydrogen in the central part of the Galaxy. The sun is at S. The arm in the upper part is the "3-kpc arm" (Rougoor and Oort 1960).

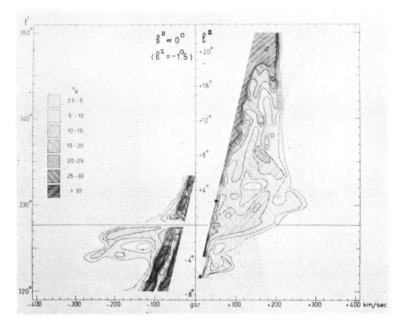

PLATE IV.—Contours of brightness temperature in the 21-cm line in the central region of the Galaxy. The radial velocities shown are corrected for the motion of the sun around the center. The central high-intensity peak has been left out (Rougoor and Oort 1960).

In view of the existence of such irregularities in the over-all velocity field of the Galaxy an attempt to derive the structure of the Galaxy from 21-cm line profiles with the aid of a generalized velocity law can only give a rough over-all picture, without detail. Details, present in the line profiles, can only be very approximately placed in the Galaxy.

The structure of the individual gas clouds which make up cloud complexes and spiral arms is still virtually unknown. There are only few cases where we can really photograph individual clouds and study them in detail, namely where the cloud is ionized by the radiation of a central or neighboring star and is smaller than the Strömgren sphere of the star. However, the interactions between the ionized gas and denser patches of neutral gas and dust change the cloud shape so completely that the picture is not at all representative of the "normal" neutral cloud. A statistical study of individual clouds, based on 21-cm line observations, has been made by Takakubo (1963). The cloud model he derives is essentially in agreement with the generally adopted values. His clouds have diameters of the order of 5 to 10 parsecs and densities of 10 to 20 atoms per cm^3. The distribution of internal velocities inside a cloud is remarkably close to a Gaussian distribution, $\exp(-v^2/2\sigma^2)$. The dispersion, σ, however, ranges from 1 km/sec in the very narrow 21-cm absorption lines to 5 or 7 km/sec. If the internal motion were entirely thermal, this would correspond to kinetic temperatures of 100 to 5000° K, completely incompatible with observed temperatures, which range from 50° K to probably at most a few 100° K. It is clear that a large part of the internal motions must be due to some kind of small-scale turbulence. The question arises as to whether a cloud is really a compact smooth structure with well-defined boundaries, or whether it is perhaps a loose collection of filaments or sheets (like the dust sheets in the Pleiades) which move with respect to one another.

Or should perhaps the cloud model be abandoned entirely, as has been suggested by various authors (see, for example, Donn 1955, 1958; also others in the latter reference). Studies of optical interstellar lines, and study of the 21-cm line profiles, show that in the solar neighborhood the individual clouds in a group or spiral arm have a velocity dispersion of 6 to 8 km/sec. The velocity and the intensity distribution of optical interstellar lines, however, can also be explained by assuming that the gas forms a more or less continuous medium with density fluctuations. These could also be described as currents of matter, since the fluctuations move through the medium. The fluctuations could have a statistical nature, although one might also conceive of a model where the density fluctuations are governed by currents induced by magnetic fields. Such a model has not been tested on 21-cm line data; it should be emphasized that a number of 21-cm absorption lines indicate the presence of small, very dense concentrations, which might be difficult to interpret on this basis. However, surveys of the 21-cm line at high galactic latitudes show surprisingly smooth variations in peak velocity, but less smooth variations in intensity. Detailed studies with high frequency and angular resolution seem to indicate that small individual clouds would cause more and stronger intensity fluctuations with position than are observed at low galactic latitudes.

As a working hypothesis, one might adopt for the present a model in which the spiral arms consist of gas, distributed in a continuous medium within the arms, with density and velocity fluctuations. The density fluctuations might take the form of rather dense concentrations in some places, perhaps more so near the centers of the arms, where the smoothed-out density is greatest and star formation with associated fluctuations most probable. Such concentrations could be described as individual clouds. The density in between the spiral arms is virtually unknown, but line profiles in some directions indicate that, at least in some places, it is extremely small. A review of the radio and optical evidence of the density and velocity distribution of the gas is given by van de Hulst in *I.A.U. Symposium* No. 8 (1958).

It is clear that the dispersion of the random gas velocities, whether these are cloud motions or disturbances in the velocity field, must increase toward the galactic center. This follows from the consideration that, in order to keep up a gas layer of constant thickness (Sec. 4.1) in the inner parts of the Galaxy, the velocity dispersion in the z-direction should increase proportionally to the derivative of the force K_z perpendicular to the galactic plane, $\delta K_z/\delta z$, near the galactic plane. This derivative increases roughly by a factor of 3 between $R = 8.2$ kpc and 2 kpc.

Finally, we come to the possible occurrence of systematic motions in directions perpendicular to the galactic plane. The extreme flatness of the gas layer for $R < 7$ kpc (deviations < 20 pc) indicates that systematic z-motions are smaller than 2 to 4 km/sec. For $R > 7$ kpc, the gas layer begins to bend upward in the northern and downward in the southern hemisphere, by an amount of up to about 600 pc at $R = 12$ kpc (Sec. 4.2). There is no way of telling whether this is due to a very large-scale z-motion, or whether we deal with a "permanent" structure, since it is too distant to measure a z-component directly.

Only in those regions where a large part of the measurable radial velocity must be a z-velocity, i.e., at high galactic latitudes, is it possible to say something more direct about this velocity. Thus, such observations are restricted to the solar neighborhood, whose properties are described in Section 5.1. The line profiles at these high latitudes are single-peaked, but their widths are larger by factors of the order of three, compared with the widths at intermediate and low latitudes (McGee and Murray 1961). This implies a higher spread of velocity in the z-direction. Most studies of 21-cm line profiles have been concentrated to the plane, and the velocity dispersion of the order of 7 km/sec mentioned before is a dispersion in directions parallel to the plane. It might be that the dispersion perpendicular to the plane is considerably larger, but, on the other hand, the observed widths might again be a local phenomenon.

There is one known case where a concentration of gas is probably situated about 500 pc below the plane; this is at about $l^{\mathrm{II}} = 135°$, at the radial velocity of the Perseus arm and below it. To reach that distance, the gas has presumably had a considerable z-velocity—it may still have that. It might be that we are dealing here with gas which was removed from the plane by the action of the expanding association, h and χ Persei (van Woerden, Hack, and Blaauw 1965). Such individual cases might occur more often. But it is safe to say that in general the z-velocities are quite small.

§ 3. LARGE-SCALE STRUCTURE

The spiral pattern of the Galaxy can be investigated by studying the space distribution of any of the constituents of extreme population I, such as neutral or ionized hydrogen, OB stars, or galactic clusters. The most extensive information is provided by 21-cm studies of neutral hydrogen, which can cover substantially the whole Galaxy; optical methods can give more detail in the solar vicinity.

The delineation of the spiral structure from observations of the 21-cm line has been based on the differential galactic rotation, which is the main cause of broadening of the line profiles. In general, radiation from the various spiral arms along a given line of sight will be received at different frequencies, because the arms will have different apparent radial velocities. Some sample line profiles for directions in the galactic plane are shown in Figure 6. They are taken from the two large-scale 21-cm line surveys, by Muller and Westerhout (1957, Leiden) and by Kerr, Hindman, and Gum (1959, Sydney). The distinct peaks are attributed to different spiral arms, and the samples in Figure 6 indicate the reliability with which the individual arms can be picked out. The line profile for a particular direction gives a relationship between brightness temperature and frequency (or velocity). To plot out the distribution of hydrogen over the galactic plane, and thus trace the spiral pattern, the basic requirement is to convert this relationship to one giving hydrogen density in terms of distance.

The total number of hydrogen atoms along the line of sight in a cylinder of unit cross-section can be obtained directly from the brightness temperature, if it is assumed that the gas temperature is known, and is constant, throughout the Galaxy. If the brightness temperature observed at a particular radial velocity is T_b, the optical depth of all the hydrogen atoms along the line of sight which move at this velocity is given by

$$\tau = -\log_e \left(1 - \frac{T_b}{T} \right),$$

where T is the kinetic temperature of the gas, generally taken as constant for simplicity. The *number* of atoms along the line of sight in a velocity interval of one centimeter per second is then

$$N(V) = 1.822 \times 10^{13} \, T\tau .$$

(The relationships between the various quantities involved are discussed in detail by Kerr in Vol. VII.) However, the *distribution* of the hydrogen along the line of sight can only be derived after a distance scale has been established. In addition, the dispersion of the velocities of the individual gas clouds, which is a secondary cause of line broadening, produces a smearing of the hydrogen distribution pattern which can only be partially allowed for.

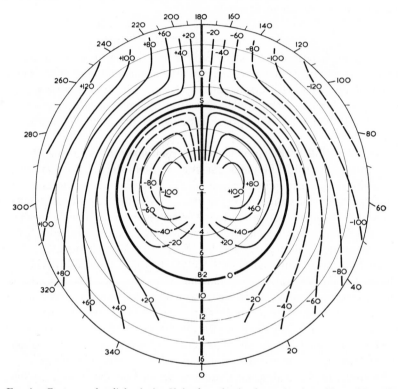

Fig. 4.—Contours of radial velocity V_ϱ in the galactic plane, circular orbit model northern hemisphere (curve .... in Fig. 3).

The major problem then is to derive a scale of distance in terms of radial velocity. The available evidence on the variation of rotational velocity with distance from the galactic center (R) has been discussed in Section 2. The distance scale depends critically on the choice of a rotational velocity model, but once a model has been chosen the relation between radial velocity and distance follows for each line of sight. A convenient representation of this relation over the whole galactic plane is shown in the contour diagram of Figure 4 for the circular orbit model (Kwee *et al.* 1954; Westerhout 1957; Schmidt 1957; top curve in Figure 3), and in Figure 5 for a model which includes the postulated 7 km/sec outward motion of the local center of rest. In the outer regions of the Galaxy, there is a unique relation between velocity and distance along each line of sight from the sun (see Fig. 1). In the inner parts, however, there is an ambiguity of distance which must be resolved before the hydrogen density can be worked out for each point separately (points P and Q in Fig. 1 have the same radial velocity with respect to S, if circular motion is assumed).

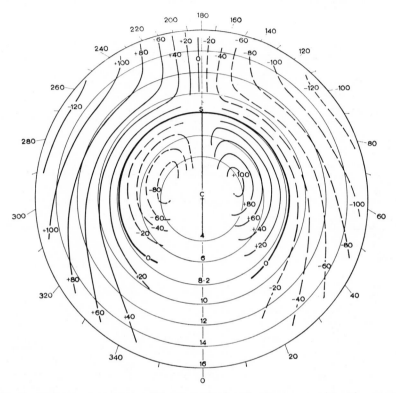

FIG. 5.—Contours of apparent radial velocity in the galactic plane, model with separate rotation curves for northern and southern sides (corresponding to an outward motion of the solar neighborhood).

Methods for deriving the hydrogen density distribution from a set of line profiles, such as those in Figure 6, have been developed by Westerhout (1957) and Schmidt (1957), who described their procedures in detail in their papers. They give considerable attention to attempts to correct for the loss of detail which results from the velocity dispersion and from the finite beamwidth and bandwidth. Schmidt tackled the problem of the distance ambiguity in the inner region by assuming that the hydrogen layer had a uniform thickness of 220 pc between half-density points, which was its measured value in the region of the tangential points (T in Fig. 1). As the "near" and "far" points corresponding to a particular velocity subtend different angles in galactic latitude, their con-

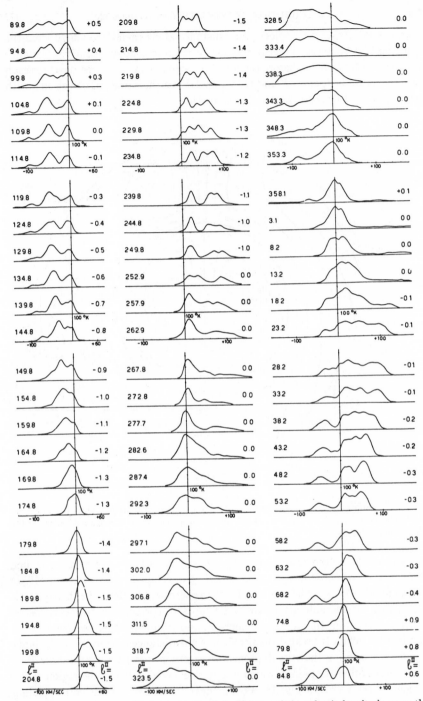

Fig. 6.—21-cm line profiles at approximately 5° intervals in galactic longitude, near the galactic plane. Antenna half-width 1°.5 to 2°.5, bandwidth 8 km/sec.

tributions can then be separated in principle by studying the variation of intensity with latitude.

Except for slight changes in the procedure used in attempting a correction for smoothing, the same methods and assumptions were followed by Kerr (1962) in his first analysis of the southern data. This made it possible to put together a composite diagram of the hydrogen distribution for the whole Galaxy on a homogeneous basis (Pl. I). A comparison of the southern and northern sides of the diagram, and the general symmetry or otherwise of the pattern, provide a good test of the circularity of the mean motion of the gas, and a check on some of the other assumptions.

As discussed in Section 2, the velocity model resulting in the diagram of Plate II seems the most plausible at the present stage. In this model different rotation curves were used for the northern and southern halves of the inner part of the Galaxy. It is assumed that either the rotational velocities on the two sides differ, or the local standard of rest has an outward velocity of 7 km/sec superposed on the circular velocity. The diagram shows a number of spiral arms, and the general spiral character of the pattern is clear. The detailed distribution should however be regarded as very tentative. In addition to the limitations set by the velocity model problem, and by the various other assumptions which are involved in the reduction, the observations have so far been made with a fairly low resolving power.

The right-hand, or northern, side of the diagram was derived from Leiden observations, and the left-hand side from the Sydney data. The somewhat different appearance of the two sides of the diagram arises from three causes: a less severe correction for the smoothing effects was applied in the Sydney case, the observing procedure in Sydney led to somewhat less detailed line profiles, and the observations in galactic longitude in the Leiden survey had a closer average spacing. The blank sectors in the directions of the center and anticenter are regions where the rotational velocity is nearly perpendicular to the line of sight, and, therefore, the normal method of inferring distance breaks down.

The Galaxy appears to be a fairly tightly wound spiral, with arms which are almost circular in form; there is no clearly marked tendency for the arms to trail or lead the direction of rotation. The pattern has many irregularities, and although all of these occur in the line profiles, their position in the galactic plane is by no means certain.

The sun lies in the inner side of an arm which has been named the Orion arm by the Dutch group (van de Hulst, Muller, and Oort 1954); Bok (1959) prefers to call it the Carina-Cygnus arm in order to stress the continuity through the sun. About 2 kpc outside the sun is the Perseus arm, so named because it contains the double cluster h and χ Persei. These two arms can be followed through a large range of galactocentric longitude. Inside the sun, and again about 2 kpc distant, lies the prominent Sagittarius arm; this arm has a curious broadening or bifurcation on each side of the line to the center, which is probably not a real feature. The next arm toward the center has been named the Scutum-Norma arm by Thackeray (1956), who found optical interstellar absorption lines which he thought originated in an inner arm. There are also indications of various spurs and interarm links.

One of the least certain features at the present time is the degree of contrast between the hydrogen density in the arms and in the interarm regions. This depends critically on the methods by which the line profiles were corrected for the smoothing effect of the random cloud velocities, on the assumptions involved in those corrections, and, in particular, on the assumption of a uniform gas temperature throughout the Galaxy.

Only the hydrogen-line method can trace out the distant spiral arms individually throughout their length. With continuous-spectrum radiation, the intensity observed in any direction is integrated along the whole line of sight. There is, however, the possibility of recognizing directions in which spiral arms are seen end-on. This method was first applied to a galactic structure study by Bolton and Westfold (1950), who suggested that the secondary maximum of 100 Mc/s intensity in the direction of Cygnus represented a spiral arm passing through the sun.

Mills (1959a, b) was able to carry the method considerably further; in his $3\frac{1}{2}$-meter survey of the Milky Way region, he found a number of "steps" in the distribution of the radiation with galactic longitude, and suggested that these might represent tangential spiral arms. This result implies emission in a direction along the arm, whereas it would be expected that the radiation, which is of synchrotron type, would show a preference for directions perpendicular to the magnetic field and hence to the spiral arms. Brown and Hazard (1960) and Ireland (1961) have shown that models can be developed, involving irregular magnetic fields, which can account for the observations.

Mills went further and suggested that a two-start regular spiral could be fitted to his pattern of steps (see Fig. 7). However, this interpretation is clearly over-idealized. South of the sun-center line, Mills's spiral-arm directions agree well with the tangential directions of the 21-cm arms, but the agreement is poor on the northern side, where the $3\frac{1}{2}$-meter steps are much less pronounced. On the other hand, the 75-cm contours of Seeger, Westerhout, Hoekema, and Conway (1965) do show well-marked steps in good agreement with the 21-cm arms.

A similar method has been applied by Elsässer and Haug (1960) to the longitude distribution of the integrated light intensity around the new galactic equator. They also interpret a number of steps or bumps as spiral arms seen tangentially. More recently, Mathewson, Healey, and Rome (1962) have found similar steps in the distribution of the thermal component of the 20-cm continuum intensity, demonstrating that ionized hydrogen too is concentrated to the spiral arms.

A diagrammatic summary of all available information on the tangential directions of spiral arms is given in Figure 8. A fair measure of agreement between the various methods is now beginning to appear, in spite of the tentative character of the results available so far. It should be noticed that all the evidence, except that of Elsässer and Haug on the integrated light intensity, refers to hydrogen in one form or another. The major conclusion to be drawn from these comparisons is that the various constituents (H I, H II, synchrotron sources, and stars) appear to be closely related in their space distribution.

So far we have been primarily concerned with the spiral pattern on a large scale. The optical evidence on the local structure (i.e., within 2 to 3 kiloparsecs) has been considered by a number of individual authors from various classes of object. There is, however, considerable disagreement among the various au-

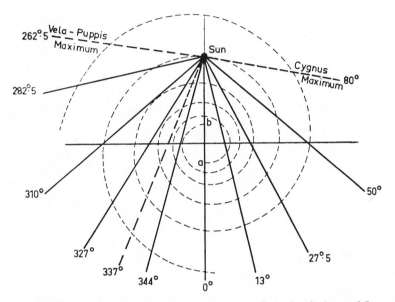

Fig. 7.—Direction of "steps" in the distribution of non-thermal radiation at 3.5 meter wavelength, and Mills' equiangular spiral fitting these steps (after Mills 1959a).

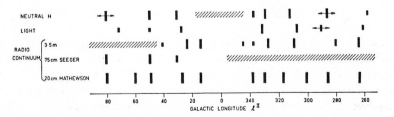

Fig. 8.—Tangential directions of spiral arms, for neutral hydrogen (Kerr 1962), light (Elsässer and Haug 1960), and radio-continuum radiation at 3.5 m (Mills 1959a), 75 cm (Seeger *et al.* 1962), and 20 cm (Mathewson *et al.* 1962). *Shaded intervals:* not covered by observations

thors on the best way to draw spiral arms through groups of optical objects. As in the 21-cm case, the principal uncertainty lies in the distance estimates.

One of the recent investigations which has collected evidence from a wide variety of sources is that of Bok (1959), whose diagram is shown in Figure 9. Bok noted the widespread disagreement, but concluded that the continuity of the Carina and Cygnus portions of the arm through the sun was an important

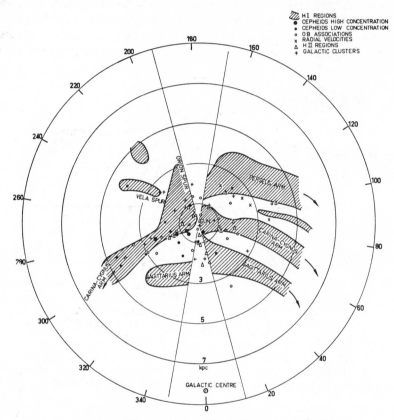

Fig. 9.—Local spiral structure of the Galaxy (after Bok 1959)

and real feature of the pattern. His interpretation also included two spurs in addition to the well-marked arms. The optical evidence on the nearby spiral structure is reviewed by Sharpless (chap. 7, this volume) and Kraft (chap. 8).

The radio and optical methods for determining spiral structure are neatly complementary in covering the Galaxy. The 21-cm method is least accurate in the solar vicinity, where local departures from the large-scale pattern of motion produce the greatest proportional errors in distance estimates. One of the great needs at the present time is to get a better overlap between the two methods in the region a few kiloparsecs from the sun—partly to extend the analysis in the best way over the whole Galaxy, and partly to see whether there is any significant difference between the distributions of the different constituents of the spiral arm population, which are observed by the two techniques. The present evidence on spiral structure, both from the radio and optical sides, must be regarded as very preliminary in character.

§ 4. THE NEUTRAL HYDROGEN LAYER

4.1. THICKNESS

In the last section, we were mainly concerned with the hydrogen distribution in the galactic plane. We now consider the distribution in the z-direction (normal to the galactic plane), which is studied by observing the variation with galactic latitude. The hydrogen is known to be confined to a very thin layer, which is almost plane. It is physically interesting to consider the variations in the thickness of the layer, and the small deviations from a plane. The most extensive information on the shape of the hydrogen layer comes again from 21-cm observations of the neutral gas.

In principle, we can find the "vertical" thickness of the hydrogen layer, at any point in the galactic disk, by scanning across the Milky Way at the appropriate galactic longitude and radial velocity. However, we are again limited by the fact that distances cannot be determined directly. Outside the sun's distance from the galactic center, estimates of layer thickness will depend on the velocity model which is being employed. Inside the sun's position, there is, in addition, a distance ambiguity, so that radiation from regions with two different layer thicknesses is observed simultaneously.

This ambiguity is only absent in the region of the tangential points. A further advantage of using these points is that a derivation of their position is, to a first order, not dependent on a velocity model, so that their distances can be found on a purely geometrical basis. The only uncertainty then is in the distance scale of the whole Galaxy, except that any departure from circular motion could cause the extreme velocity point along a line of sight to be displaced from the position of the geometrical tangential point.

There is another limitation however, which is imposed by the smearing effects of the finite aerial beamwidth and the random velocities of the gas clouds. As a result of these, the measured thickness does not refer to a single point in the galactic disk, but is averaged over a fairly substantial "area of response" (Fig. 10). Future observations with higher resolution should narrow down the region over which an average is taken, and should also make it possible to separate more definitely the "far" and "near" components, and perhaps enable the thickness (and z-distribution generally) to be determined for regions away from the tangential points.

Schmidt (1957) first obtained values for the layer thickness at a series of tangential points on the northern side of the sun-center line. He found an average value of 220 pc for the thickness between half-density points, with most of the distribution approximating a symmetrical Gaussian shape, except for the outer parts, where the distribution is wider. Also, the thickness at the tangential points appeared to be fairly constant over the range of longitude covered by his observations. He then felt justified in making the assumption of a constant layer thickness over the whole region inside the sun, which was the basis of his method for resolving the distance ambiguity. The Sydney observations for the southern half of the Galaxy gave a similar figure (220–230 pc) for the average

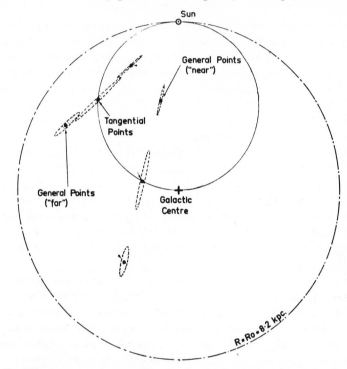

Fig. 10.—Effective "area of response" involved in the observation of general and tangential points in the region $R < R_0$. The response area is due to finite bandwidth, random cloud velocities, and aerial beamwidth.

thickness at the tangential points. The results quoted so far were obtained with beamwidths of 1°.5 to 2°. Early observations with the $\frac{1}{4}$° beam of the Australian 210-foot paraboloid indicate that the thickness should be reduced to about 160 pc.

Lower values for the thickness have been reported by Rougoor and Oort (1960) and Kerr (unpublished) for the innermost region of the Galaxy. In the arm, which is at about 3 kpc from the center, the distance between half-density points is 1°.5, or 120 pc, and about the same thickness was found for the material with high positive velocities throughout the inner region. For the small central disk (see Sec. 5.2), the half-density thickness is lower still—about 80 pc.

The layer thickness in the solar neighborhood cannot be determined directly, because of the lack of a distance scale. Indirect evidence that the 220 pc figure can be applied in the solar region has, however, been obtained by McGee and Murray (1961) from the results of their whole-sky survey. They found that the nearby gas was predominantly stratified in layers parallel to the galactic plane. A value could only be derived for the local gas density if a distance scale was introduced by assuming a value for the layer thickness. Adoption of Schmidt's thickness value led to a density near the sun of 0.46 H atoms/cm³, which is close to Westerhout's (1957) value for the mean density around a circle at the sun's distance from the galactic center. Since the latter value was derived from observations in the galactic plane, and it does not directly involve the layer thickness, the agreement between the two results supports the view that the region of approximately constant thickness extends out at least as far as the sun. Farther out, the thickness increases considerably; high-resolution observations and better knowledge of the rotation law are needed to give exact values. Recent observations at Dwingeloo (Habing, private communication) indicate that beyond $R = 12$ kpc the thickness might be many hundreds of parsecs.

It is interesting to compare the available information on the layer thickness for other constituents for extreme population I. The most detailed studies have been carried out for population I cepheids, for which two results are available. Walraven, Muller, and Oosterhoff (1958) obtained a dispersion in the z-component of ± 65 pc, for 160 cepheids whose positions were specified in terms of an early 21-cm result for the galactic pole derived by Westerhout (1957). Petit (1960) obtained a value of ± 68 pc, for a list of 191 cepheids, in terms of Ohlsson's pole. These results correspond to values for the thickness between half-density points of 153 and 160 pc, respectively. For OB stars, the observations of van Tulder (1942) lead to a figure of only 50 pc. The layer thickness for optically-observed H II regions does not appear to have been worked out with the same precision, but it is also in the region of 150 pc. Westerhout (1958) has considered the thickness of the layer of ionized hydrogen which is mainly responsible for the continuous-spectrum radiation at 22 cm. A thickness of 200 pc is consistent with the observed brightness distribution.

4.2. SHAPE

Having discussed the degree of flatness of the thin hydrogen layer, we now want to consider the position of the mean plane, and to delineate the main departures from that plane. The required picture can be built up from a series of scans across the Milky Way at sufficient frequencies and velocities to cover the whole Galaxy. A useful way to express the main results is through a "relief map," in which the z-deviations of the hydrogen layer from a plane are plotted as a function of position in the Galaxy. Figure 11 shows the relief map derived by Gum, Kerr, and Westerhout (1960) from the combined Leiden and Sydney 21-cm observations. The quantity plotted is the deviation from the new galactic plane, and refers to the point of maximum hydrogen density in each cross-section of the Galaxy. As available evidence indicates that the layer is approximately symmetrical, the point of maximum density can be taken as representing the center of mass of the layer. The distance scale in this diagram is based on the circular velocity model (Fig. 4, top curve in Fig. 3).

The main features of the relief map are the extreme flatness of the hydrogen layer in the inner region (almost out to the sun's distance from the center), and

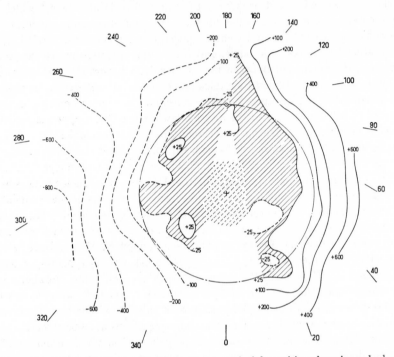

FIG. 11.—Relief map showing the height z (in parsecs) of the position of maximum hydrogen density above the new galactic plane. The distance scale is the same as that in Plate I.

the systematic distortion of the layer in the outer parts, with positive deviations of several hundred parsecs on the northern side of the sun-center line and negative deviations on the southern side. Within about 7 kpc of the galactic center (for an adopted distance to the center of 8.2 kpc), nearly all the points of maximum hydrogen density lie within 20 pc of the mean plane, i.e., the region is flat to better than 1 part in 700 of its diameter. Higher resolution observations might reveal that some of the deviations have been smoothed out, but even so this high degree of flattening must have great dynamical significance in relation to the evolution of the Galaxy. It is of interest to speculate that considerable exchange of momentum in a radial direction has taken place during the past history of the Galaxy.

Because the hydrogen layer is so flat over the inner region and can be explored over the full extent of the Galaxy, the mean plane of the hydrogen ("the principal plane of the Galaxy") provided the main evidence for the choice of the new system of galactic coordinates (Gum, Kerr, and Westerhout 1960; Blaauw, Gum, Pawsey, and Westerhout 1960).

The redefinition of the system involved a shift in the pole of $1°49$. For practical reasons the new system was defined with infinite precision, with respect to a fixed point in the sky. It is not intended that the coordinate system, although based on the position of the hydrogen layer, should be changed when later determinations give more accurate information about this layer. Instead, it now provides a very convenient reference, against which future solutions for the pole of the hydrogen (or any other constituent of the Galaxy) can be assessed. The present uncertainty in the pole of the hydrogen is $0°12$, and the height of the sun above the mean hydrogen plane is given as 4 pc ± 12 (Gum, Kerr, and

I KPC

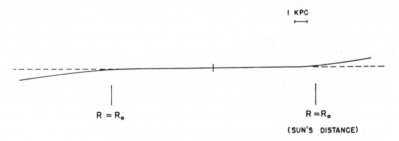

R = R$_o$ R = R$_o$

(SUN'S DISTANCE)

FIG. 12.—Cross-section of relief map, through galactic center and normal to sun-center line

Westerhout 1960). Thus, at the present time the mean plane of the hydrogen can be taken as coincident with the new galactic plane; more precise determinations can be expected to reveal slight divergences.

The studies which preceded the choice of the new coordinate system also considered all the available information on the mean plane of various optical objects. The optical solutions for a "galactic plane" were of course limited to a much smaller region of the Galaxy than the radio solutions, but it was shown that the optical and radio data agreed to within the observational uncertainties, when regions of comparable size were considered in the two cases and the large-scale distortion of the disk was properly allowed for.

This distortion starts to appear at a distance from the galactic center of 7 kpc, and increases progressively out to $R = 15$ kpc, with fairly symmetrical shapes on the northern and southern sides of the sun-center line. The form of this outer distortion (Kerr 1957; Burke 1957) can be seen best from Figure 12, which shows a section through the galactic center, perpendicular to the sun-center line (the distortion is near its maximum in this particular cross-section). The distorted region contains a number of spiral features, on each side of the Galaxy, but it seems that the distortion is a general feature of the outer regions, with the spiral-arm condensations superposed, rather than just a displacement of outer spiral arms from the mean plane.

Several alternative explanations have been considered for the outer distortion. Since the maximum downward deviation is at the galactocentric longitude of the Large Magellanic Cloud, first consideration was given to a possible tidal effect from the Clouds. Kerr (1957) and Burke (1957) both found, however, that the observed effect was one to two orders of magnitude too big to be explicable as a simple gravitational tide. If the Clouds play any part in producing the distortion, it seems that some force other than gravitation must be responsible. It is significant that the studies of interaction between galaxies by Zwicky, Vorontsov-Velyaminov, and others, have shown that gravitational effects alone cannot always account for the observed structure.

Elwert (unpublished) has recently re-examined the possibility of a gravitational interaction, and claims that a resonance effect could build up a sufficiently large distortion in the outer regions of the Galaxy after about 15 revolutions of the Large Magellanic Cloud around the Galaxy. This result has been criticized on the ground that the system is unlikely to have retained the same configuration for so long; also the calculations were carried out for point masses, which would considerably increase the effect to be expected.

An alternative interpretation involving an external influence has been proposed by Kahn and Woltjer (1959), who consider that the distortion effect can be explained in hydrodynamic terms, through the pressure on the galactic halo as the Galaxy moves through the intergalactic gas. More precise delineation of the shape of the distorted region will help to decide between the various explanations.

The relief map of Figure 11 was based on the circular-velocity model. The pattern in the outer regions shows an asymmetry, with the contours farther apart on the left of the diagram than they are on the right. Kerr (1962) showed that a model which included a general expansion would make the outer contour pattern rather more symmetrical, but the asymmetry of structure may well be a real feature.

The 21-cm line comes from a known constituent of the Galaxy but this is not so in the case of the radiation in the radio continuum, for which one of the main problems is to determine the mechanism or mechanisms responsible for its production in the Galaxy. Information on the space distribution of the continuum sources can contribute to an understanding of the mechanisms, but such information is available only in a very limited way from the continuum observations themselves, because only the integrated intensity can be measured in each direction, providing there is no discrimination between sources at different distances.

The study of the shape of the hydrogen layer has provided new evidence on the distribution of the continuum sources. Gum and Pawsey (1960) considered the position of the line of maximum brightness in several continuum surveys of the Milky Way strip, in relation to the known shape of the H I layer at various distances from the sun. They found that the continuum "ridge-lines" also exhibited the extreme flatness in directions near the galactic center, and showed the effect of the outer distortion at other longitudes, in the way that would be expected if the continuum and H I sources of the galactic disk have the same general distribution. This result applies both to the thermal and non-thermal components. The latter is believed to be due to synchrotron-type emission from relativistic electrons in interstellar magnetic fields. Gum and Pawsey, in discussing the coincidence in position of the different types of source, suggest that an increase of gas density, as evidenced by the 21-cm emission, also leads to an increase of continuum emission because it predisposes toward star formation and the release of energy in various ways, including the production of relativistic electrons and magnetic fields.

§ 5. SPECIAL REGIONS

5.1. The Solar Neighborhood

It was pointed out in Section 3 that the 21-cm method is imprecise for tracing the nearby spiral structure. Observations at middle and high latitudes can, however, reveal the general properties of the local gas. In this section we shall consider the over-all distribution and flow pattern of the local gas, relating them where possible to the large-scale situation in the whole Galaxy. The discussion will be restricted to the neutral gas, as the corresponding properties of the ionized gas are discussed in chapter 7 of this volume. Also, we shall not be concerned with the smaller-scale relationships between gas and OB associations, nor with the detailed properties of hydrogen clouds or cloud complexes, which will be considered by Kerr in Volume VII.

There have been three extensive surveys of 21-cm radiation away from the Milky Way strip. The first was carried out by the Carnegie Institution group in Washington, D.C. (Erickson, Helfer, and Tatel 1959; Erickson and Helfer 1960), the second in Sydney (McGee, Murray, and Pawsey 1961; McGee and Murray 1961), and the third at Jodrell Bank (Davies 1960).

The Carnegie and Sydney surveys were each carried out with a multichannel receiver and low aerial resolution (2°), with the object of covering all the sky which was visible from the observatory concerned. As the two observing points are in opposite hemispheres, the joint results cover the whole sky. Where comparisons have been made, the results and conclusions of the two surveys agree closely. The following discussion will be largely based on McGee and Murray's results, as they used a finer grid of points, and also their data have been analyzed in greater detail.

The area under a line profile represents the number of hydrogen atoms in the line of sight, in a column of 1 cm² cross-section (N_H), provided the gas is optically thin. Figure 13 shows the distribution of N_H over the sky, as derived by McGee and Murray (1961). The results of the Carnegie survey are very similar in the region of overlap. The variation of N_H along a number of meridians of galactic longitude is found to follow the secant of the latitude to a good approximation, indicating that the hydrogen is predominantly horizontally stratified, parallel to the galactic plane. Unfortunately there is no way of estimating the distance of the gas directly, but, as was mentioned in Section 4.1, the observed distribution is consistent with an interpretation in which the bulk of the gas is in the thin-disk layer, about 220 pc between half-density points.

The minima of the distribution are displaced from the galactic poles by about 30°. This result implies a rough connection with the plane of the local system of stars (Gould's Belt), but McGee and Murray point out that there is closer

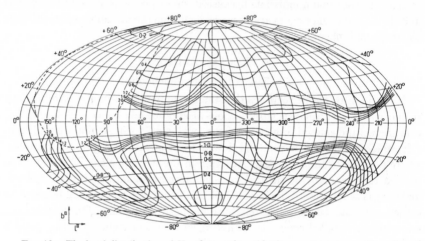

FIG. 13.—The local distribution of N_H, the number of hydrogen atoms per cm² in a line-of-sight column, over the sky. The contour interval is 0.2×10^{21} atoms/cm².

agreement with the plane of the galactic magnetic field in the solar vicinity, as derived by Shain (1957) from optical polarization measurements. However, later polarization studies by Behr (1959) do not support Shain's results. In addition to the general stratification of the hydrogen, there are some particular regions of higher density, such as a spur in Scorpius-Ophiuchus and the region of Gemini-Taurus-Orion. These are generally related to known areas of optical obscuration, and are presumably nearby cloud complexes of dust and gas.

The distribution of radial velocity over the sky is shown in Figure 14 (McGee and Murray 1961), where the quantity plotted is the peak velocity of each profile, corrected to the local center of rest. (Outside the Milky Way, the profiles are in most cases simple in form, and single-peaked.) The light and heavy gray shading indicate regions of positive and negative velocity, respectively, while the white area denotes zero velocity (0 ± 1 km/sec). The outstanding feature of the diagram is the continuity of velocities over large areas of sky, indicating the presence of a systematic flow pattern of some kind.

Both surveys show a large negative velocity area around each galactic pole, implying that hydrogen is falling in toward the galactic disk from each side, with a mean velocity of about 6 km/sec. The rate of inflow can only be worked out if a distance scale is adopted from other evidence. On the basis of Schmidt's value for the layer thickness, the inward flow amounts to 0.07 $M \odot$ per year per square kiloparsec. If this flow is general over the Galaxy, the total inflow would constitute a very significant item in the over-all circulation pattern for the whole Galaxy.

In low latitudes, differential rotation effects show up clearly in Figure 14, but there are also additional motions of a systematic character. These cannot be completely separated from differential rotation, in the absence of a distance

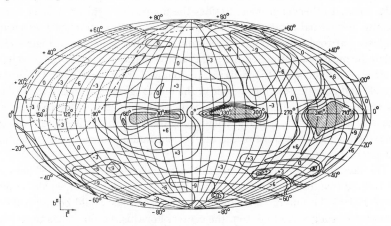

Fig. 14.—Distribution of peak radial velocity. The contour interval is 3 km/sec

scale, but the most recognizable effects, according to McGee and Murray, are an outward flow with a mean velocity of 6 km/sec in the approximate directions of the center and anticenter. Helfer (1961) has also analyzed the velocity field of the local gas, and has derived an expression for the velocity-distance relation which best fits the Carnegie observations.

The width of the line profiles in various regions of the sky gives information on the velocity dispersion of the nearby gas. Most of the profiles at middle and high latitudes have half-widths in the range 12 to 35 km/sec, but there are some large regions near the galactic poles with much wider profiles, up to 140 km/sec in half-width, with a mean width of 50 to 70 km/sec. In view of the very low intensity it is not yet clear whether these wide profiles are due to radiation in the side lobes of the antenna or to zero-line errors, or whether such a high velocity dispersion in the z-direction is a general property of the gas in the galactic plane, or a local effect. Van Woerden (1964) has made a careful study of the reality of the long wings which he observed in many profiles in the Orion region. He computed the effects which would be expected from stray radiation from other parts of the sky, received in side lobes of the antenna pattern, and obtained fair agreement between the computed and observed profile wings; he therefore concluded that the long wings were spurious. Further work will be needed, however, to determine whether or not the wide profiles reported by other observers and in other parts of the sky are all due to similar spurious effects.

5.2. Galactic Center Region

The region around the galactic center has been extensively studied by Rougoor and Oort (1960). All figures in this section are due to these authors. Theirs is the most extensive published evidence on this region of the Galaxy.

The line profiles within 15° to 20° from the center differ considerably in shape from those at other longitudes. Besides the main peak, which is rather narrow because differential rotation is small, the profiles have low-intensity extensions in places out to ±250 km/sec. Three sample profiles are given in Figure 15, in which the most interesting feature is the sharp separate peak at a radial velocity of about −50 km/sec. This peak can be followed from longitude 335° through 0° to 4° and may be described as one of the most regular features in the Galaxy. Its radial velocity changes almost linearly with longitude (Fig. 16), while its intensity and width in velocity remain roughly constant. It is seen in   absorption when it passes in front of the bright continuum source Sgr A, which is in the galactic center.

The fact that the feature disappears near galactic longitude 335° has been interpreted to indicate that it is a part of a spiral or circular arm, which becomes tangential to the line of sight at that longitude. This would correspond to a distance of roughly 3.5 kpc from the center. For this reason, it has tentatively been drawn at a radius of about 3 kpc (Pl. III), and has been referred to as the "3-kpc arm." It should be emphasized that its exact position is quite uncertain; it might spiral rapidly inward, but it must pass between the sun and the center. The arm is likely to continue past the stretch drawn in Plate III, but it becomes indistinguishable because its velocity coincides with that of other features. The density in the arm is a few atoms per cm³; it cannot be determined more accurately since the thickness of the arm in the radial direction is unknown. The number of atoms in a column of 1 cm² cross-section through the maximum of the arm is 2×10^{21}. The thickness of the arm in the z-direction is 120 pc between half-density points.

The radial velocity of the arm in the direction of the center is −53 km/sec; this indicates that at least that part of the arm is moving away from the center. Its regularity makes it probable that such expansional motion is a general property of the arm. Another curious feature is that the expansional velocity of the arm decreases by about 5 km/sec from the part farthest above the galactic plane to that farthest below; one might describe this as a "rolling" movement.

The general distribution of the 21-cm line intensity, as a function of longitude and velocity, is conveniently represented in Plate IV. The 3-kpc arm is clearly

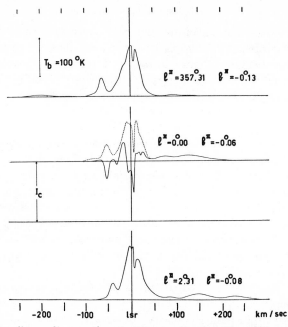

FIG. 15.—Three line profiles near the galactic center direction. The middle profile is exactly in that direction, and shows the continuum emission I_c, with the observed line profile superposed. Note the absorption effects. ...... = expected profile, if absorption had not been present (derived from neighboring profiles). The beamwidth was $0°.56$, the bandwidth 10 kc/s.

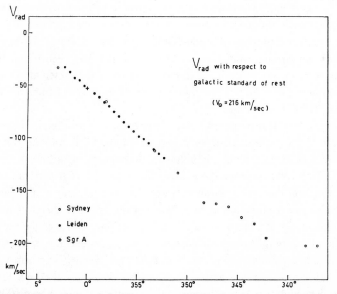

FIG. 16.—Radial velocity of the 3-kpc arm at different longitudes, corrected for the motion of the sun around the galactic center ($\Theta_{\odot} = 216$ km/sec) (Rougoor and Oort 1960).

visible on the left-hand side of the main peak. A similar structure on the other side is lacking. Instead, the hydrogen forms a low-intensity medium with a high velocity dispersion and various more or less disconnected maxima. At and just below the longitude of the center, quite considerable intensities are found between $+50$ and $+200$ km/sec. Between $+100$ and $+200$ km/sec there are no absorption features, indicating that most of this gas must lie behind the center and must, therefore, move away from it with such velocities. Farther down, there is still gas moving with velocities up to $+100$ km/sec. Rotational motion gives negative radial velocities in that direction, so that the velocity of this gas must likewise have a strong radial component. We have no way of determining whether it is in front of or behind the center, but Rougoor and Oort tentatively assume the latter, thus giving it also an expansional motion. The position of the concentrations of gas on the positive velocity side has been sketched in Plate III as a continuation of the strong arm on the far right. This is obviously a pure guess, but the line profiles indicate that at least the sketched patchiness might well be correct.

The last feature in Plate IV to be discussed is the wing at high negative velocities between $l^{II} = 356°$ and $0°$. Careful analysis shows that a similar wing is superimposed on the positive velocity side between $l^{II} = 0°$ and $4°$. It is clearly separated into two wings on the negative velocity side, one between $l^{II} = 0°$ and $358°$, and other around $l^{II} = 356°.5$. Rougoor and Oort interpret this as being due to hydrogen in a central disk with a radius of $R = 300$ or 350 pc, and a ring around it between $R = 500$ and 590 pc. The density in the ring is 1 atom per cm³. In the disk it rises from 1 at $R = 300$ pc to 3 atoms per cm³ at $R = 100$ pc. Farther inside, the density must increase very strongly. The very nucleus contains two dense patches of ionized hydrogen about 100 pc from the center. No sign of expansional motion in the ring and disk has been found, but the rotational motions are quite high, decreasing from 265 km/sec at $R = 550$ pc to 180 km/sec at $R = 70$ pc. The dynamical consequences of this are discussed in chapter 21 of this volume.

The hydrogen within 3 kpc from the center is thus distributed in the following way: a circular or spiral arm, very regular in shape, is moving out with a velocity of 50 km/sec, while partaking in the galactic rotation of about 200 km/sec. Within 600 pc from the center, the gas is concentrated in a rapidly rotating ring and disk. The region between the expanding arm and the central ring and disk is virtually empty, but diametrically opposite there seems to be a fair amount of gas scattered in small concentrations, possessing outward motions. The total amounts of gas in the expanding 3-kpc arm and in the scattered concentrations are about the same. The thickness of the 3-kpc arm is 120 pc between half-density points, that of the ring and disk is about 80 pc. The latter value is still so high that it requires internal velocities of the order of 100 km/sec in the z-coordinate in order to counteract the high values of the derivative dK_z/dz. The replenishment of the gas streaming outward from the center (at a rate of one to two solar masses per year), which might possibly stream into the central region from the halo, is discussed in chapter 23 of this volume.

5.3. The Galactic Halo

The existence of a galactic halo, with a diameter of the order of perhaps 20 to 25 kpc, is now well established. It follows from observations at radio wavelengths of the non-thermal radiation at high galactic latitudes, and similar observations of other galaxies, such as the Andromeda nebula. Moreover, the existence of a tenuous gaseous medium around the Galaxy is a basic necessity for certain theoretical arguments concerning the magnetic fields and the cosmic rays. A description of the radio halo is given in chapter 11, and the theory is reviewed in chapter 23 of this volume.

The question of the gas density in the halo is as yet unanswered, although from the observational side an upper limit to the amount of neutral hydrogen can be given. It is not known what proportion of the halo gas is in neutral form or whether it is homogeneously distributed or concentrated in clouds. As explained in Section 5.1, the reported high velocity distribution of the gas at high galactic latitudes may be a spurious sidelobe effect. Even if it is real, it is probably not a halo phenomenon, because of the concentration toward the galactic poles. At intermediate latitudes, where the line of sight through the halo must be considerably longer, the intensity of these wide profiles should be notably higher, whereas in fact they disappear. If we assume, for setting a limit, that all reported 21-cm line radiation observed near the galactic poles is halo radiation, and the line of sight through the halo is 10 kpc long, the average density is of the order of 10^{-2} cm^{-3}. This is clearly an upper limit, since the major portion of the observed radiation must be due to local gas. Recent observations at Dwingeloo (E. Raimond, private communication) indicate that at high galactic latitudes 21-cm line temperatures are certainly below 0.5° K in the range of velocities between -200 and -50 km/sec, and $+50$ and $+200$ km/sec. With a line of sight of 10 kpc, this gives again an upper limit of about 10^{-2} cm^{-3}. These figures show that very refined techniques will be necessary to detect neutral hydrogen in the halo.

Since both the above-mentioned investigations were made with fairly wide transmission bands, it might be that small individual clouds were missed. If such clouds exist, they should probably have a very low velocity dispersion in order not to evaporate. The estimates of the upper limit on the average density, however, remain valid.

§ 6. IONIZED AND NEUTRAL HYDROGEN

6.1. Distribution of Ionized Gas

In this section we shall only summarize our knowledge of the large-scale distribution of the ionized hydrogen. For a more detailed description of how this can be derived from radio observations the reader is referred to chapter 11. The distribution of H II regions is discussed in chapter 7 of this volume.

It is possible to derive the brightness distribution of the thermal radio emission on the sky from observations at short wavelengths. This has so far been done at wavelengths of 22 cm (Westerhout 1958; Mathewson, Healey, and Rome 1962), at 75 cm (Large, Mathewson, and Haslam 1961), and at 11 cm (Altenhoff, Mezger, Wendker, and Westerhout 1961). The observations by Hill, Slee, and Mills (1958) at 3.5 m, which refer mainly to the non-thermal component, have been used to subtract this component from the shortwave radiation. The thermal brightness distribution contains two constituents: a

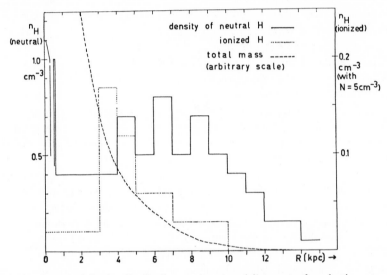

Fig. 17.—Smoothed density distribution as a function of distance to the galactic center, R, in the galactic plane, for neutral hydrogen, ionized hydrogen (assuming all ionized clouds have $N = 5$ cm^{-3}) and total mass.

number of discrete sources, most of which are identified with known H II regions, and a smooth background underlying these. This background forms a ridge with a width of about 1°.5 extending along the galactic equator. The intensity gradually increases toward the center, but shows broad maxima at $l^{II} = 25°$ and $l^{II} = 335°$, with an intensity plateau in between and much lower intensities farther away from the center. Westerhout (1958) derived a model of the density distribution of the ionized gas throughout the Galaxy from the observations by assuming this distribution to be symmetrical around the galactic axis of rotation. The distribution turned out to have a high density maximum near $R = 3.5$ kpc, and virtually zero density for $R < 3$ kpc (Fig. 17).

The quantity which can be derived from the observations is the mean-square density $\langle N_e^2 \rangle$. To derive an average density, it is necessary to have some figures on the clumpiness of the distribution. If the ionized gas is distributed in clouds with density N cm^{-3}, and if the space in between the clouds is empty, $\langle N_e^2 \rangle =$

nN, where n is the average space density in cm^{-3}. Thus, the denser the concentrations of gas, the lower the average density. A representative value for a typical H II region is $N = 10$ cm^{-3}. Many of the bright emission nebulae have values of N which are considerably higher. However, the background ridge could not be as smooth as it is if it consisted of such nebulae. In fact, if it does consist of individual H II regions, the large majority of these must have $N \leq 10$ cm^{-3}; the question of whether this is so, or whether we are dealing with a really smooth medium, can only be answered by making observations with instruments having considerably higher resolving power than the $0°.6$ to $0°.25$ used so far. Taking $N = 5$ cm^{-3}, we find that the average density n, which is zero for $R < 2$ kpc, decreases from 0.64 cm^{-3} at $R = 3.5$ kpc to 0.06 cm^{-3} at $R = 8$ kpc.

It is interesting to speculate on the reason for the occurrence of the high-density region at $R = 3.5$ kpc, in particular since this is just outside the central region and the 3-kpc expanding arm. Westerhout (1958) has suggested that the expanding gas slows down at about $R = 3$ to 3.5 kpc, thereby forming a ring where the density is higher. The inner part of this ring is still neutral, but somewhat farther out, the conditions for star formation become favorable. Expanding at the rate of 50 to 100 km/sec, the gas will take between 1 and 3×10^7 years to reach $R = 3$ kpc from the inner region. This is of the same order as the time scale proposed for star formation. The newly formed stars will then ionize part of the medium and cause the ionized ring. The mechanism also explains why there is no ionized gas within $R = 2$ kpc: the gas streaming out is too "new." Mathewson, Healey, and Rome (1962) suggest that the distribution of ionized gas is somewhat more irregular, with traces of spiral arms within $R = 3$ kpc, which might be ionized through collisional excitation by the rapid outward expansion.

The thickness of the layer of ionized gas is about 200 pc, which is comparable with the value for the neutral gas, but a precise comparison has not yet been made.

6.2. Mean Density and Mass

From the measurements described in Sections 2 and 3 it is possible to derive the average value of the density of neutral hydrogen in the galactic plane, as a function of distance from the center (Westerhout 1957; Kerr and Hindman 1957). Mean values of n_H between circles at intervals of 1 kpc in R, determined from the data of Plate II, are given in Table 1 and Figure 17. The individual values for the two sides (left and right of the sun-center line) differ somewhat, due to the different positions of the spiral arms. The three maxima at $R = 4.5$, 6.5, and 8.5 kpc reflect the main structure of the Galaxy. A fourth maximum, which is present in the northern-hemisphere data at $R = 10.5$ kpc, does not show up here because it does not exist in the southern hemisphere. The average density in the southern hemisphere tends to be some 20 per cent lower than that in the northern hemisphere. In view of the uncertainties involved, this is not considered serious.

In the original reduction of the observed intensities to hydrogen densities, a number of assumptions were made which introduce large uncertainties. The average cloud temperature was assumed to be 125° K and constant throughout the Galaxy, whereas we expect fluctuations of at least a factor of two in both directions. The clouds were supposed to be optically thin, and we know that in some cases this is not true. The correction for random cloud velocities was very uncertain. All these factors together introduce uncertainties in the density in particular regions, and thus in the over-all density and hydrogen mass.

TABLE 1

TOTAL MASS dM_H AND AVERAGE DENSITY n_H IN THE GALACTIC
PLANE IN RINGS AROUND THE GALACTIC CENTER

(dM_H and n_H [Ionized] Are Derived from Northern
Hemisphere Data Only)

R	dM_H (neutral) (northern hemisphere)	n_H (neutral)	n_H (ionized) ($N = 5$ cm^{-3})	n_H (ionized)/ n_H (neutral)
kpc	10^6 $M \odot$	cm^{-3}	cm^{-3}	
0– 3.......	55	0.4	0.02	0.05
3– 4.......	50	.4	.17	.42
4– 5.......	135	.7	.12	.17
5– 6.......	160	.5	.06	.12
6– 7.......	265	.8	.06	.08
7– 8.......	220	.5	.03	.06
8– 9.......	245	.7	.03	.04
9–10.......	330	.5	0.03	0.06
10–11.......	520	.4	....	....
11–12.......	485	.3	....	....
12–14.......	350	.15	....	....
14–15.......	30	0.05	....	....

As an example, let us consider the influence of clouds with high optical depths. Approximately 30 per cent of the 21-cm absorption lines observed in the spectra of discrete sources have optical depths $\tau > 1$. It can be shown that their average diameter cannot be very different from that of the less dense clouds. However, even with an angular resolution of 10′, very few sharp emission lines are found, whereas nearby clouds would subtend angles many times this, and thus would show up if they had $\tau > 1$. One, therefore, has to conclude that their temperature is considerably lower than the average. A spiral-arm peak in a line profile, made up of clouds of which 30 per cent have $\tau = 2$ and $T_b \approx T = 50°$ K, and 70 per cent have $\tau = 0.4$ and $T_b \approx \tau \times T = 0.4 \times 125 = 50°$ K will have a peak brightness temperature of 50° K, and the two types of cloud of which it is made up are indistinguishable. On the assumption of a constant temperature of 125° K, we would find $\tau = 0.4$. But in reality, the average optical depth, proportional to the density, is of the order of 0.9 in this model. On the basis of this example, one would estimate that our present density and mass estimates are low by a factor of two. Clearly, however, considerably better knowledge of the density and temperature distribution is needed before we can make numerical estimates. The value of 125° K used up to now for the gas temperature and based on the assumption that the average cloud has low optical depth is very uncertain due to the same cause; high-resolution observations are expected to give more insight into these problems. The indications are, as shown above, that the density and mass estimates are probably too low by as much as 50 to 100 per cent.

The density distribution has a broad maximum of 0.6 atoms per cm³ between $R = 4$ and 10 kpc, falling off on both sides. The small structures in the center do not contribute a significant amount to the total mass. This total mass may be calculated, using the values of Table 1 and taking into account the thickness of the layer. The effective width of the layer in the region with $R < 8$ kpc is 270 pc, which is larger than the half-width of 220 pc, due to the fact that the layer

TABLE 2

VALUES OF TOTAL MASS AND MASS OF NEUTRAL AND IONIZED HYDROGEN
IN THE GALAXY AND THE ANDROMEDA NEBULA

	M (total)	M_H (neutral)	M_H (ionized)	$M_H/$ M (total)	M_H (ionized)/ M_H (neutral)
	10^{10} ☉	10^{10} ☉	10^{10} ☉		
Galaxy......	7 (10?)	0.3 (0.4?)	0.004 (±50%)	0.043 (±30%)	0.013 (±50%
Andromeda..	34	0.4	?	0.012	?

is not entirely Gaussian in shape but has broader wings. In the outer parts the effective width appears to be much larger, of the order of 500 to 600 pc. Van Woerden (private communication) has recently derived the total hydrogen mass, in rings around the center, using the northern-hemisphere data ($l^{II} =$ 352° to 250°) described before (Westerhout 1957; Schmidt 1957). The rings with the largest hydrogen mass lie between $R = 10$ and 12 kpc, in the region of the Perseus arm. The Galaxy resembles the Andromeda nebula in this respect, both optically and radiowise (see van de Hulst, Raimond, and van Woerden 1957). It seems to be very asymmetrical in this region: the Perseus arm has no counterpart on the other side.

Table 1 also lists the density of ionized hydrogen as a function of R (Westerhout 1958), but derived from northern-hemisphere data only. The ratios n_H (ionized)/n_H (neutral) are, therefore, only very approximate. It should be emphasized that the density of ionized hydrogen is inversely proportional to the adopted value of the density N in individual clouds. If more dense clouds are present, n_H (ionized) might be lower by a factor of two or more.

Integration of the data in Table 1 gives the total mass of hydrogen in neutral and ionized form. In Table 2, a comparison is made between these masses and the total mass of the Galaxy, as derived by Schmidt (1956). His distribution of the total mass is given in Figure 17 for comparison. The data for the Andromeda nebula are also given in Table 2. It has been suggested that the total mass of the Galaxy is about $10 \times 10^{10}\odot$ (van de Hulst *et al.* 1957). The total mass of neutral hydrogen might have to be increased if the gas in the outer parts of the Galaxy has a wider distribution than hitherto assumed (van Woerden, private communication).

From the data on some 10 galaxies, Heidmann (1961) found that the ratio of hydrogen mass to total mass varies from somewhere between 0.1 and 0.3 for irregulars, through 0.06 to 0.01 for Sc and Sb nebulae, to a value of <0.04 for the one elliptical investigated. Additional galaxies studied by Roberts (1962) and Epstein (1962) gave rather similar figures. Our Galaxy fits well into the over-all sequence.

REFERENCES

ALTENHOFF, W., MEZGER, P. G., WENDKER, H., and WESTERHOUT, G.	1961	*Veröff. Bonn*, No. 59, p. 48.
BEHR, A.	1959	*Nach. Akad. Wissensch. Göttingen Math. Phys. Kl.*, p. 185.
BLAAUW, A., GUM, C. S., PAWSEY, J. L., and WESTERHOUT, G.	1960	*M.N.*, **121**, 123.
BOK, B. J.	1959	*Observatory*, **79**, 58.
BOLTON, J. G., and WESTFOLD, K. C.	1950	*Australian J. Sci. Res.*, Ser. A, **3**, 251.
BROWN, R. HANBURY, and HAZARD, C.	1960	*Observatory*, **80**, 137.
BURKE, B. F.	1957	*A.J.*, **62**, 90.
DAVIES, R. D.	1960	*M.N.*, **120**, 483.
DONN, B.	1955	*A.J.*, **60**, 237.
	1958	*Rev. Mod. Phys.*, **30**, 940 (*I.A.U. Symp.* No. 8).
ELSÄSSER, H., and HAUG, U.	1960	*Zs. f. Ap.*, **50**, 121.
EPSTEIN, E. E.	1962	*A.J.*, **67**, 271.
ERICKSON, W. C., and HELFER, H. L.	1960	*A.J.*, **65**, 1.
ERICKSON, W. C., HELFER, H. L., and TATEL, H. E.	1959	"Paris Symposium on Radio Astronomy," *I.A.U. Symp.*, No. 9, p. 390.
GOLD, T.	1961	*Mém. Soc. R. Sci. Liége*, Ser. 5, **4**, 476 (Tenth Liège International Colloquium).
GUM, C. S., KERR, F. J., and WESTERHOUT, G.	1960	*M.N.*, **121**, 132.
GUM, C. S., and PAWSEY, J. L.	1960	*M.N.*, **121**, 150.

HEIDMANN, J.	1961	*B.A.N.*, **15**, 314.
HELFER, H. L.	1961	*A.J.*, **66**, 160.
HILL, E. R., SLEE, O. B.,		
and MILLS, B. Y.	1958	*Australian J. Phys.*, **11**, 530.
HULST, H. C. VAN DE	1958	*Rev. Mod. Phys.*, **30**, 913 (*I.A.U. Symp.* No. 8).
HULST, H. C. VAN DE,		
MULLER, C. A., and		
OORT, J. H.	1954	*B.A.N.*, **12**, 117.
HULST, H. C. VAN DE,		
RAIMOND, E., and		
WOERDEN, H. VAN	1957	*B.A.N.*, **14**, 1.
IRELAND, J. G.	1961	*M.N.*, **122**, 461.
KAHN, F. D., and		
WOLTJER, L.	1959	*Ap. J.*, **130**, 705.
KERR, F. J.	1957	*A.J.*, **62**, 93.
	1962	*M.N.*, **123**, 327.
KERR, F. J., and		
HINDMAN, J. V.	1957	*Pub. A.S.P.*, **69**, 558.
KERR, F. J., HINDMAN,		
J. V., and GUM, C. S.	1959	*Australian J. Phys.*, **12**, 270.
KWEE, K. K.,		
MULLER, C. A., and		
WESTERHOUT, G.	1954	*B.A.N.*, **12**, 211.
LARGE, M. I.,		
MATHEWSON, D. S.,		
and HASLAM, C. G. T.	1961	*M.N.*, **123**, 113 and 123.
McCREA, W. H.	1960	*Observatory*, **80**, 90.
McGEE, R. X., and		
MURRAY, J. D.	1961	*Australian J. Phys.*, **14**, 260.
McGEE, R. X.,		
MURRAY, J. D., and		
PAWSEY, J. L.	1961	*Nature*, **189**, 957.
MATHEWSON, D. S.,		
HEALEY, J. R., and		
ROME, J. M.	1962	*Australian J. Phys.*, **15**, 354 and 369.
MENON, T. K.	1958	*Ap. J.*, **127**, 28.
MILLS, B. Y.	1959a	"Paris Symposium on Radio Astronomy," *I.A.U. Symp.* No. 9, p. 431.
	1959b	*Pub. A.S.P.*, **71**, 267.
MULLER, C. A., and		
WESTERHOUT, G.	1957	*B.A.N.*, **13**, 151.
PETIT, M.	1960	*Ann. d'ap.*, **23**, 710.
ROBERTS, M. S.	1962	*A.J.*, **67**, 437.
ROUGOOR, G. W., and		
OORT, J. H.	1960	*Proc. Nat. Acad. Sci.*, **46**, 1.
SCHMIDT, M.	1956	*B.A.N.*, **13**, 15.
	1957	*Ibid.*, p. 247.

SEEGER, C. L.,
  WESTERHOUT, G.,
  HOEKEMA, T., and
  CONWAY, R. G.   1965   *B.A.N.* (in preparation).
SHAIN, G. A.   1957   *A.J. U.S.S.R.*, **34**, 3 (*Soviet Astr.–A.J.*, **1**, 1).
TAKAKUBO, K.   1963   *Sendai Astronomiaj Raportoj* Nos. 86, 87.
THACKERAY, A. D.   1956   *Nature*, **178**, 1458.
TULDER, J. J. M. VAN   1942   *B.A.N.*, **9**, 315.
WALRAVEN, T.,
  MULLER, A. B., and
  OOSTERHOFF, P. T.   1958   *B.A.N.*, **14**, 81.
WESTERHOUT, G.   1957   *B.A.N.*, **13**, 201.
                        1958   *Ibid.*, **14**, 215 and 261.
WOERDEN, H. VAN   1965   *B.A.N.* (in preparation).
WOERDEN, H. VAN,
  HACK, M., and
  BLAAUW, A.   1965   *B.A.N.* (in preparation).
ZWICKY, F.   1959   *Pub. A.S.P.*, **71**, 468.

CHAPTER **10**

Galactic Structure and Interstellar Absorption Lines

GUIDO MÜNCH

Mount Wilson and Palomar Observatories
Carnegie Institution of Washington, California Institute of Technology

§ 1. INTRODUCTION

ALTHOUGH the extragalactic character of spiral nebulae was established nearly a half-century ago, it was quite recently, through the epoch-making observations of W. Baade, that the true nature of the phenomenon of spiral structure was understood. By comparing images of a galaxy in wavelength ranges, one containing Hα and another avoiding strong nebular emission lines, Baade (1951) and Baade and Mayall (1951) showed that the sources of emission, H II regions, are arranged along relatively well-defined lanes, imbedded in the features generally recognized as the spiral arms of the nearby galaxies. The further observation showing that distant galaxies can occasionally be seen through the interarm regions, but not in the areas covered by the arms, proved that the interarm regions were essentially devoid of interstellar dust. While on general grounds it would be expected that, as a whole, the distribution of interstellar gas follows that of the dust, after Baade's discoveries it still remained to be established that the interstellar gas was also concentrated along the arms of spiral systems.

The individuality of the star system to which the sun belongs was established simultaneously with the extragalactic nature of some systems. And already from the early estimates of dimensions and distances, it was hypothesized that our Galaxy is similar to M31. In view of Baade's results it was then natural to investigate the possible spiral nature of the Galaxy, following the same structural indicators used by Baade in M31. As described in chapter 7 of this volume, the mapping of the H II regions in our "local swimming hole"—as Baade often referred to the neighborhood of the sun accessible to the classical methods of stellar astronomy—led Morgan, Sharpless, and Osterbrock (1952) to suggest the location of the three spiral arms near to the sun. Actually, before the efforts of Morgan and collaborators had been completed, the possibility of detecting a large-scale arrangement of the interstellar neutral gas, by means of the interstellar absorption lines in distant stars, was brought to the attention of the writer by W. W. Morgan (1951). The observational material related to interstellar absorption lines, then available, gave no definite indication for such a systematic distribution. In particular, the extensive high-dispersion survey of Adams (1949) provided a picture for the distribution of interstellar gas characterized by a high degree of small-scale randomness; unfortunately it did not extend to stars as distant as could be desired for the purpose. The analysis of interstellar line intensities obtained earlier at Mount Wilson, however, led Wilson and Merrill (1937) to propose that "interstellar sodium occurs in discrete aggregations or clouds, . . . the linear dimensions of the clouds, in the galactic plane, are of the order of 700 parsecs." In my chapter in Volume VII more detailed reference to the work of Wilson and Merrill is made. It is only of importance to remark here that their main conclusion to no small extent was the result of having included in their analysis data pertaining to the distant stars in Cepheus, Cassiopeia, and Perseus. There was a reason to suspect, thus, that the structure of the interstellar lines in the northern Milky Way held the key to deciding whether the interstellar gas offered indications of spiral structure, a suspicion later confirmed by the tentative outline of the arms published by Morgan *et al.* (1952). Unfortunately, the Milky Way north of declination $+50°$ is not accessible with the coudé spectrograph of the 100-inch telescope, and the distant stars in those directions could not be observed with the necessary high dispersion at Mount Wilson. Had it not been for such a mechanical feature of the Hooker reflector, undoubtedly the large-scale arrangement of the interstellar gas clouds, now recognized as the spiral arms of the galactic system, would have been discovered by Adams at least ten years earlier. As it happened, the evidence sought after could not be obtained until the coudé spectrograph of the 200-inch telescope went into operation in the summer of 1952. Among the first few spectra taken for this purpose were those of the bright stars in h and χ Persei, which showed strikingly two well-separated components, or groups of components, quite different in structure from those observed in nearby stars.

At nearly the same time that the Palomar observations were begun, the first sweep-frequency radiometer for the 21-cm hydrogen line went into operation in Holland (van de Hulst 1953). On the basis of the first systematic survey carried out with this instrument, van de Hulst, Muller, and Oort (1954) proposed a model for the spiral structure of the outer parts of the galactic system (see also chap. 9, this volume). The region of space that may be studied by means of the interstellar absorption lines is far too small to allow an integral view of the galactic system, as it is provided by the 21-cm line. The extinction produced by interstellar dust is in all directions so large that only a few stars are known at distances larger than, say, 4 kpc, and that are bright enough to be observed at

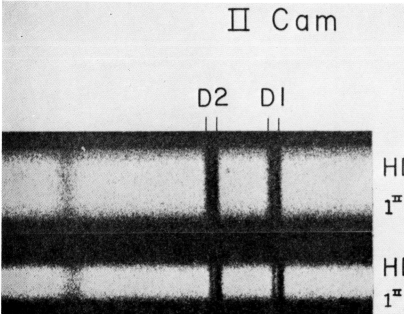

Ⅱ Cam

D2　D1

HD 25914

$1^{II} = 147°.8, b^{II} = +4°.8$

HDE 237213

$1^{II} = 147°.6, b^{II} = +2°.7$

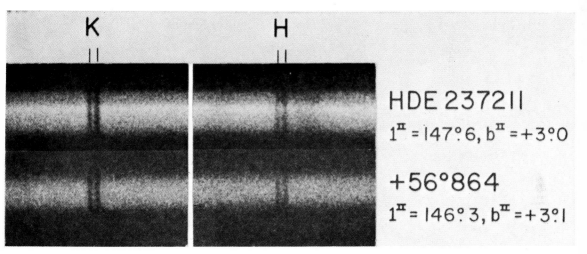

K　　　　H

HDE 237211

$1^{II} = 147°.6, b^{II} = +3°.0$

+56°864

$1^{II} = 146°.3, b^{II} = +3°.1$

PLATE I.—Interstellar Na I and Ca II lines in the spectra of stars in the association II Cam. The original plates have 13.8 A/mm in the second order (Na I) and 9.2 A/mm in the third order (Ca II).

sufficiently high resolving power. However, the interstellar absorption lines provide the means to study limited regions of the interstellar medium with very high angular resolving power, in comparison with the data provided by the 21-cm line, which refer to all the matter contained in the acceptance cone of the aerial. It is thus evident that the study of the optical interstellar absorption lines complements, indeed in a small volume of space, the information gathered in 21-cm radiation. Unfortunately, the observation of interstellar lines is a time-consuming task requiring a large telescope with a coudé spectrograph, and consequently, the amount of data available is still far smaller than it should be. In particular, the nearly total lack of data for stars accessible only from the southern hemisphere is a serious obstacle in the further development of the subject.

We propose in this chapter to summarize the results of observations of optical interstellar absorption lines, so far as they bear a relation to the large-scale structure of the galactic system. The physical processes involved in the formation of the lines, as well as the intrinsic properties of the gas clouds in which they originate, have been discussed by Münch and by Spitzer in Volume VII. We shall especially be interested in comparing the information provided by the interstellar absorption lines with that obtained from 21-cm line studies, and shall emphasize existing incompatibilities between them. No satisfactory suggestion to remove such discrepancies has yet been offered, but their mere existence should be taken as a warning against accepting the structure of the entire galactic system, as provided by 21-cm line data, as definitely established.

§ 2. OBSERVATIONAL DATA

In order to detect, within the profiles of interstellar lines, characteristics resulting from structural features on a galactic scale, a minimum spectral dispersion of 10 A/mm is required, for then the resolution of fast photographic emulsions corresponds to 15 km/sec at the wavelength of the Ca II lines. Inhomogeneities in the space distribution of absorbing gas could thus be detected by galactic rotation shifts only if they had a linear scale not less than about 1 kpc. It follows that we need to observe stars at distances greater than 2 kpc. High-luminosity stars, presumably very distant, have become available through the survey carried out with the Schmidt prismatic cameras of the Warner and Swasey, Tonantzintla, and Hamburg-Bergedorf Observatories. But as far as interstellar line work is concerned, only stars brighter than about 10^m5 (pg) matter, for an exposure time of 4–5 hours is required to obtain a usable spectrum of such a star on the fastest emulsions at the required minimum dispersion. With such exposure times, it is desirable to have some additional degree of certainty in the distance of the star, besides the OB character revealed in objective prism plates. For this purpose, the spectral-luminosity classifications and photoelectric colors published by Morgan, Code, and Whitford (1955) and Hiltner (1956) are most useful. Nevertheless, the distribution of distant stars in the various parts of the Milky Way is very irregular. The only region of the sky where a sufficient number of distant objects can be reached is that around the maximum of galactic rotation at $l^{II} = 135°$, and for this reason only this region has been so far investigated for interstellar lines with some degree of completeness. A few very distant stars around $l^{II} = 45°$ have also been studied (Münch 1960), but the information derived from their interstellar lines is yet so fragmentary that they will not be discussed here.

The interstellar lines in every star in the range $100° < l^{II} < 165°$, and at distances greater than about 2 kpc, appear to show two strong well-separated components, each of which may show evidence of further complexity (Münch 1953). The occurrence of complex interstellar lines in bright early-type stars, when observed at the highest resolving powers, is quite a common phenomenon

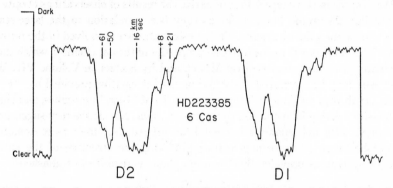

FIG. 1.—Microphotometer tracing, not in a linear intensity scale, of the interstellar lines in 6 Cas, from a spectrum at 6.8 A/mm dispersion. The width of the instrumental profile is 8 km/sec. Velocities indicated are not corrected for solar motion.

(Adams 1949). As a general rule, however, the nearer stars show one stronger component, with the least displacement from the rest wavelength, around which one or more weaker components may appear. The weak components, in general, vary quite markedly in velocity and strength from a given star to a nearby one. In the case of the distant stars of the northern Milky Way, which are spread out along an arc over 2 kpc in length, the two components are always observed, the stronger usually having a displacement not more than 10 km/sec in the local standard of rest, while the other, displaced to the violet up to 40 km/sec, shows a range in strength. For brevity we shall refer to these two features as the R and V components. As an illustration, Figure 1 reproduces a microphotometer tracing of the D lines in the star 6 Cas, obtained with a dispersion of 6.8 A/mm, corresponding to 0.34 km/sec per micron. We notice a very strong R component ($W = 0.74$ A for D2), the center of which gives a velocity of -8 km/sec (after correcting for a solar motion component of $+8$ km/sec), and a weaker V component ($W = 0.36$ A for D2), giving indications of duplicity, with subcomponents at -42 and -53 km/sec. At $+16$ and $+29$

km/sec two fainter components, with individual strengths around 0.05 A, may also be noticed but, unlike the strong V and R components, they are not present in other members of the association to which 6 Cas belongs (I Cas). The two weak components with positive displacements have the characteristics of components observed in complex interstellar lines of nearby stars (Adams 1949), and undoubtedly arise in gas clouds of dimensions not much larger than 10 pc. As an example of the degree of resolution that can be reached for the fainter stars, the interstellar lines in three stars of the distant association II Cam, at $l^{II} = 148°$, $b^{II} = +3°$, obtained recently with a dispersion of 9.2 A/mm for the Ca II lines and 13.8 A/mm for the D lines, are reproduced in Plate I. It shows the unmistakable duplicity of the lines, which can be measured for radial velocity without ambiguity, although the relative strength between the V and R components cannot be determined with high accuracy.

The velocity shifts and intensity of the interstellar line components obtained for 112 stars in the interval $87° < l^{II} < 190°$ have been published in tabular form (Münch 1957). The observational results for additional stars of special interest, including some members of the association II Cam, have appeared more recently (Münch 1964).

§ 3. INTERPRETATION

3.1. RADIAL VELOCITIES

The radial velocities of the V and R components of all stars so far observed in the northern Milky Way, referred to the local standard of rest defined by the interstellar absorption lines in nearby stars (Blaauw 1952), appear plotted against galactic longitude in Figure 2. This diagram is an up-to-date version of the one published earlier (Münch 1957), incorporating the recently obtained material. The stars represented have been entered as dots or circles, depending on whether the corresponding distance modulus is smaller or greater than 11.0. A division into such nearby and distant groups is quite natural, since very few high-luminosity early-type stars are found with distances between 1 and 2 kpc. The data pertaining to stars in recognized associations have been grouped into average values, identified in Figure 2 by larger sized symbols. Although the V components often are multiple, they have been represented by a single point referring to the mean velocity. In the case of associations, the range in velocity covered by the various components in all the members is indicated by the length of the vertical segments drawn through the mean values. For reference purposes, we have plotted the radial velocities of the distant stars, when known, or mean value for the associations, as well as the theoretical curves for the radial component of galactic rotation of points in the galactic equator at distances from the sun, $r = 1, 2, 3,$ and 4 kpc, calculated from the rotation curve used by van de Hulst et al. (1954).

The general arrangement of the points represented in Figure 2 shows clearly that the velocities of the interstellar lines in nearby stars, together with the R

components in distant ones, in the range $110° < l^{II} < 150°$, follow quite closely the galactic rotation shift of a point at a distance from the sun of about 0.5 kpc. The V components, on the other hand, correspond to galactic rotation shifts of points at distances between 2 and 3 kpc. As a whole, the separation between the R and V components appears clearly to be an effect of galactic rotation: the three stars in NGC 1893, exciting the diffuse nebula IC 410, at a distance of about 2 kpc toward the anticenter (Sharpless 1954) show strong lines at nearly zero velocity, with no trace of duplicity, while HDE 232999 at $l^{II} = 156°$ shows distinctly double lines. The separation between the R and V components

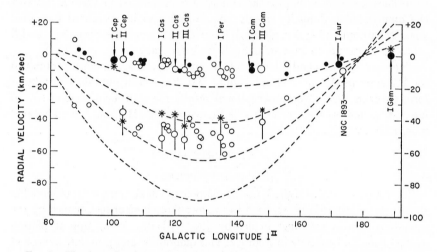

Fig. 2.—The dependence on galactic longitude of the radial velocities of the strong components of interstellar lines in the northern Milky Way. Filled circles refer to stars in the Orion arm; empty circles refer to stars in the Perseus arm. Larger symbols represent O-associations, the radial velocities of which are denoted by *. The broken-line curves represent the galactic rotation effect on the radial velocities of points at distances of 1, 2, 3, and 4 kpc from the sun.

shows a broad maximum around $l^{II} = 135°$, and then decreases again toward the direction of galactic rotation. It is noticed that the spread of the V points around a mean curve is considerably higher than that shown by the R components, and this effect is found to exist even among members of the same association, as the D lines in the two stars of II Cam illustrated in Plate I show. The R components, in comparison, vary little from one distant star to another, and have nearly the same strength and velocity as the interstellar lines observed in stars about 1 kpc distant. Finally, it is of importance to remark that the radial velocities of the distant stars are never far from those derived for their interstellar V components, although a small systematic difference seems to exist, which will be discussed in Section 4. On this basis it has been inferred that the separation between the R and V components is an effect of distance, rather than a result of a peculiar motion, with the V components arising in the neigh-

borhood of the stars in the spectra of which they are observed. It is implied also
that the line of sight to the distant stars traverses a region of space, with thickness comparable to the distance corresponding to the differential shift between
the R and V components, where the mean density of Na I or Ca II atoms is
much lower than it is nearer to the sun and to the stars.

The distances from the sun of the lanes, along which the interstellar gas
seems to be concentrated, follow from the spectroscopic distance moduli of the
individual OB stars used as background for the detection of the interstellar gas.
Since the spiral arrangement of the H II regions discovered by Morgan *et al.*
(1952) was based on the same system of spectroscopic parallaxes, it follows that
the interstellar gas clouds producing the absorption lines are arranged in space
essentially in the same fashion as the H II regions. Alternatively, we may fix the
position of the gas concentrations by interpreting the galactic rotation shifts of
the components in terms of a dynamic model for the Galaxy. This is the procedure followed to derive the spatial distribution of neutral hydrogen along a
line of sight from the study of 21-cm line profiles (cf. chap. 9). Because of the
much more extensive information available from 21-cm work, it is more convenient to compare the interstellar line velocities directly with the 21-cm data,
rather than to discuss them independently. We postpone such a comparison
until Section 4.

3.2. Line Intensities

The intensities of a component in the interstellar doublets of Ca II or Na I
provide information about the number of atoms N forming it, and their velocity distribution in the radial direction. Due to limitations in spectral resolving
power, it is possible to determine only one parameter characteristic of the
velocity distribution, which can be taken as the dispersion σ around the mean.
The curves of growth for interstellar lines, for velocity distributions either
Gaussian or simple exponential in form, have been given in my chapter in Volume VII of this Compendium. For the case of strong lines, these velocity distributions refer to the mass motions of the many clouds that may be adding up to
the entire line. It has been found that in the neighborhood of the sun, the curve
of growth for the interstellar D lines is best represented by an exponential velocity distribution with dispersion $\eta \sqrt{2}$ varying between 4.8 km/sec for log $N =$
13.0 and $\eta \sqrt{2} = 3.7$ km/sec for log $N = 14.0$ (cf. Vol. VII, my chapter, Table
6). For a Gaussian distribution, the dispersion is found to be $b/\sqrt{2} = 4.0$ km/
sec for weak lines, increasing to about $b/\sqrt{2} = 6.0$ km/sec for the strongest
lines. For the Ca II lines the corresponding parameters are larger by nearly 50
per cent.

On the basis of these curves of growth we may analyze separately the doublet
ratios for the R and V components for the distant stars. In order to average out
measurement errors, we have formed normal points from the stars in associations, with the results given in Table 1. It is noticed here that the velocity dispersions derived for the R components have essentially the same values as

quoted above for the nearby stars. For the V components, however, the dispersions are about 50 per cent higher than for the Orion arm. This result might not appear surprising, considering the tendency of the V component to show complexity. There is evidence, however, suggesting that the multiplicity of the V components is actually an effect of the velocity distribution and not of distance, because structural variations are observed from member to member of the same association, and there is no question that the linear extent of the associations is not large enough to account for the splitting in terms of galactic rotation shifts (see Fig. 4). The only exception to this argument may be the case of I Cas, the most distant association of those considered, in front of which there might be two distinct aggregations of interstellar material separated by a

TABLE 1

CURVE OF GROWTH FOR D LINES FORMED IN ORION AND PERSEUS ARMS

ASSN.	r (kpc)	l^{II} (deg)	No. OF STARS	ORION ARM		PERSEUS ARM	
				$\eta\sqrt{2}$ (km/sec)	log N (cm^{-2})	$\eta\sqrt{2}$ (km/sec)	log N (cm^{-2})
II Cep.........	3.6	100–110	3⎫	3.6	13.9	⎰6.8	13.2
I Cas..........	2.5	116	3⎭			⎱8.1	12.2
III Cas........	2.5	123	6	3.8	14.4	4.5	11.8
I Per..........	2.3	133–137	⎧4⎫ ⎨5⎬ ⎩2⎭	3.5	14.2	⎧7.4 ⎨5.7 ⎩5.7	12.3 12.5 13.0
II Cam........	3:	158–163	2	3.8	14.3	4.2	13.2

distance of the order of 1 kpc. The evidence provided by the interstellar absorption lines is in this case incomplete, as the distribution of interstellar matter in this direction appears to be very spotty.

The curve of growth analysis for the Ca II lines is more uncertain than for the Na I lines, because of the practical difficulty of obtaining reliable doublet ratios. Not only is the H line superimposed on the wing of the stellar Hε line, but also in nearly all B1–2 supergiants shallow stellar Ca II lines are present. There is concrete evidence, however, that the very large values (up to $\eta\sqrt{2} = 20$ km/sec) of the velocity dispersion derived from the V components of the Ca II lines in some stars actually refer to the interstellar matter. For example we offer the case of the supergiants HD 13854, HD 14134, and HD 14143, in the h and χ Persei cluster, which show deep and broad V components in the K line, structureless at 4.5 A/mm, and with strength quite unusual for a line stellar in origin. Stars of the same types in the extended association I Per but not in the cluster, such as HD 14818, have a K line with quite a different appearance. It is thus difficult to avoid the conclusion that the interstellar gas surrounding the h and χ Persei cluster has anomalously large turbulent velocities. The 21-cm line profiles in this region also suggest this phenomenon, as discussed below.

§ 4. COMPARISON WITH 21-CM RESULTS

While comparing the profiles of the neutral hydrogen emission line with those of the Na I or Ca II interstellar absorption lines, the completely different angular resolving power involved in each case should be kept in mind. Considered

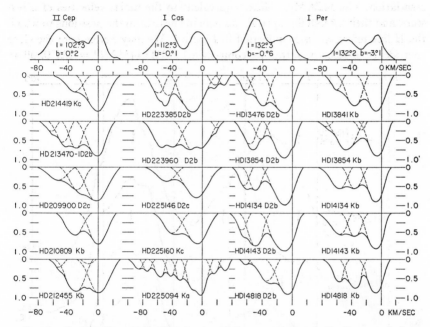

FIG. 3.—Profiles of interstellar lines in stars of three associations in the Perseus spiral arm. At the top are reproduced the profiles of the 21-cm line of hydrogen at the indicated positions, taken from van de Hulst *et al.* (1954).

as a whole, then, the maxima of the hydrogen line agree in velocity remarkably well with the absorption minima of the optical lines. This is especially the case for the components arising in the Orion arm. The optical components ascribed to the Perseus arm show considerably more variation from star to star than the 21-cm components at corresponding positions do. Most noticeable in this respect is the region around $l^{II} = 117°$ (I Cas), where the optical lines show a high degree of complexity not particularly exhibited by the 21-cm profile, as illustrated in Figure 3. The extent to which the 21-cm line agrees with the optical lines in two other OB associations may also be seen there. Considering that at the distance of the Perseus arm, the beamwidth of the Leiden 7.5-meter antenna used for obtaining the H-line profiles shown in Figure 3, is around 100 pc, the lack of detailed agreement between 21-cm profiles and optical line contours within the beam should not be surprising. Actually, when 21-cm observations obtained with the largest angular resolving power available are compared with the optical lines, the agreement is considerably improved. As an example, we reproduce in Figure 4 the 21-cm line profiles obtained with the 25-meter paraboloid at Dwingeloo, Holland (the writer is indebted to Prof. Blaauw and Dr. H. van Woerden of the Kapteyn Astronomical Laboratory for providing these profiles in advance of publication) at position intervals of one degree in the I Persei association. The 1420 Mc/s shifts equivalent to the radial velocities of a few stars, and their interstellar optical components nearest to the positions to which the H line refers, are also indicated in Figure 4. We may notice here the close coincidence in velocity of the two components in HD 14542 ($l^{II} = 135°0$, $b^{II} =$

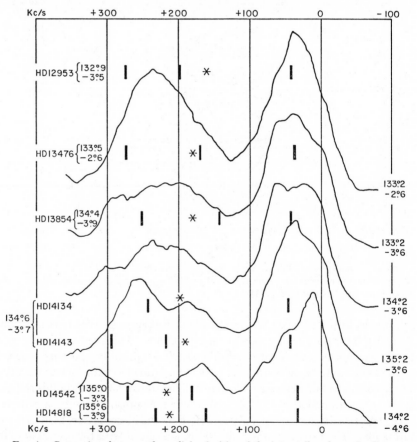

Fig. 4.—Comparison between the radial velocities of the interstellar absorption-line components (vertical bars) in stars of the association I Persei with the 21-cm line profiles at nearby positions, obtained with the 25-meter parabola at Dwingeloo, Holland. The stellar radial velocities are indicated by *.

$-3°3$) with two well-marked maxima in the 21-cm profile for $l^{II} = 135°2$, $b^{II} = -3°6$. The same agreement is apparent between the two components of HD 14143 ($l^{II} = 134°6$, $b^{II} = -3°7$) with the 21-cm line at $l^{II} = 134°2$, $b^{II} = -3°6$. Recalling that the resolving power of the optical spectra is equivalent to 80 kc/s, it becomes clear that such close agreement could be expected only in those cases where the optical lines are relatively narrow and well separated. At the same time, the considerable variation exhibited by the 21-cm line at points separated by only one degree suggests that if they referred exactly to the stars' positions, the correspondence between the optical and radio profiles would become even closer.

Paying attention now to the frequency shifts equivalent to the stars' radial velocities, we can notice that they are systematically smaller than those of the centroid of the V components. Actually, in Figure 4 the relative shift between the stars and the gas ascribed to the Perseus arm would seem to decrease steadily, from about -12 km/sec for HD 12953 to nearly zero for HD 14818. The radial velocities of other members of the same association show that this apparent monotonic variation of the relative shift is not truly related to the stars' coordinates but is a casual effect of selection. It should be emphasized that the radial velocities of the stars under discussion, having weights a and b in the *Mount Wilson Catalogue* (Wilson 1953), are of the highest accuracy, and although there are indications that all B-type supergiants have variable radial velocities of small amplitude and frequency, no reason exists to doubt that the mean of several independent wavelength measures, spread out over a long interval of time, represents the actual space motion of the star as a whole (Münch 1964). Noticing, then, that the interstellar gas, obviously in front of the star, has a radial velocity corresponding to the galactic rotation shift of a point at a greater distance from the sun than the star's, it is clear that either the stars or the gas must have a systematic non-circular component of motion. And this conclusion does not depend on the dynamical model of the Galaxy (Oort's constant A), or on possible uncertainties in the scale of spectroscopic parallaxes. The meagerness of the data available does not allow a clear-cut explanation of this important problem. Some general arguments can be given, however, favoring the idea that the interstellar gas in front of the large OB associations in the Perseus arm, or at least part of it, is expanding away from the associations.

I Persei.—Considering first the case of I Per, for which extensive data are available, we can argue that it would be extremely difficult to visualize a phenomenon through which all the members of the entire association, extending over an arc or spiral arm nearly 300 pc in length, could have formed from interstellar matter moving in nearly circular orbits, and then accelerated away from the gas arm with a speed larger than the velocity dispersion of the members, as observed some 20×10^6 years later. The velocity dispersion among the members of the association is around 4 km/sec and that of the nucleus, the h and χ Persei cluster, is only 0.4 km/sec, in comparison with the apparent relative radial motion between stars and gas, which amounts to about 10 km/sec. The alternative hypothesis, that the stars and part of the gas are, on the average, moving in circular orbits and that some gas is deviating systematically from circular motion, appears more plausible on the basis of the following evidence: it has been noticed above that the V components of the interstellar lines observed in the I Per association are clearly double with V2, the farthest displaced (average shift around -50 km/sec) varying from star to star more than V1, appearing at about -40 km/sec. If the relative shifts between these two components represented a galactic rotation effect, the distance between the two gas masses would be of the order of 1 kpc. The rather large range of variation observed in the intensity of the V2 components of the various members of the association would then imply that the extent of the association in the direction of the radius vector would also be of the order of 1 kpc, as was argued before. But such a longitudinal dimension of the association would seem ruled out by the spectroscopic distance moduli of the stars. Since other associations in the Perseus arm show the same phenomenon as discussed below, an interpretation in terms of strictly circular motions would lead to the unlikely picture that all associations in the Perseus arm are elongated along the line of sight. Noticing that in I Per the mean velocity of the V1 components (-39 km/sec) agrees quite well with the velocity of the association (-40 ± 3 km/sec), it would seem more logical to think that the gas giving origin to the V1 component is essentially at rest with respect to the association, while the gas giving rise to the V2 components, with mean velocity -57 km/sec, is expanding away from the association. Further independent evidence favoring this interpretation is provided by the relative strength of the V2 components in Ca II and Na I, which is similar to that in "high-velocity stars," Ca II being stronger than Na I. Before discussing possible interpretations of this shift, the evidence provided by other associations will be briefly considered.

II Cep.—The spectroscopic distance of this association is 3.6 kpc (Morgan, Code, and Whitford 1955) and its radial velocity corrected for solar motion is -41 ± 2 km/sec (Abt and Bautz 1963). The member stars HD 209900 and HD 213470 show V2 components at -46 km/sec and V1 at -27 km/sec. Two other stars, HD 210809 and HD 212455, show unresolved V components at -34 km/sec. Three additional stars, HD 214419, HD 215835, and HD 216927, at the smaller dispersion, show V components at -24, -31, and -44 km/sec. Clearly, this association may be at a larger distance than all the gas, and there is no evidence for non-circular motions.

I Cas.—The mean radial velocity of the association, from four high-weight stars, is -37.6 ± 0.7 km/sec. Two star members, HD 223385 and HD 223960, show resolved V components at -52 and -38 km/sec. In two other stars, HD 223987 and HD 224055, the V components appear unresolved at -50 km/sec. This association then is similar to I Per in the behavior of the V components.

II Cas.—The mean radial velocity of the association is -35 ± 2.5 (p.e.) km/sec, from only 4 stars of low weight. The V components are not resolved, as all stars were observed at 9.2 A/mm, but in HD 1743, HD 1810, and HD 2451, they appear at -59 km/sec, while in two others, HD 1383 and HD 1544, they show at -34 km/sec. The grouping of the mean velocities of the V components around two values, the smaller in absolute value nearly corresponding to the galactic rotation shift of the association, suggests the same situation as in I Persei.

III Cas.—The mean radial velocity of the association is -37 ± 4 (p.e.) km/sec from three stars of low weight. The stars HD 4841 and HD 5551 show V components at -57 and -33 km/sec. Two stars, HD 3940 and HD 4717, show unresolved V components at -52 km/sec, while HD 4768 shows it at -38 km/sec. This case is similar to I Cas.

II Cam.—The radial velocity of this association is -32 km/sec (Münch 1965), although a relatively large velocity dispersion seems to exist among its members. One of them, HD 237213, has type B3Ia, and its distance modulus is 12.7. Its mean radial velocity, determined from 10 plates extending over 4 years, is -5 ± 1 km/sec; it thus appears to be a high-velocity "run-away" member. The V components in all members of the association are very strong, but have not been resolved because their faintness does not allow higher dispersion observations. The mean shift of the V components is -45 km/sec, considerably in excess of the stellar radial velocities. This case, then, also conforms to the pattern established in the preceding associations.

Summarizing the evidence provided by the interstellar absorption lines in regard to departures from circular motion, we can say that part of the interstellar gas in the Perseus spiral arm, observed in front of the large OB associations with galactic longitudes between 100° and 150°, appears to be approaching along the line of sight with speeds up to 20 km/sec. Such a differential motion could be taking place either in the direction of the spiral arm or normally to it. The associations discussed above are at present rich in B-type supergiants and must have contained, some 20×10^6 years ago, parent O-type main-sequence stars in considerable numbers. At the early stages of their development there were, undoubtedly, extensive H II regions, which could have provided to the neutral surrounding gas a differential motion, with respect to the stars, in the direction observed. Near associations not deeply embedded within the Perseus spiral arm, the gas clouds moving in directions of decreasing mean density, toward the interarm medium, would not be dissipated in collisions with other clouds as quickly as those moving in the opposite direction, and could follow their characteristic epicyclical orbits for a time comparable to the age of the associations, say 20×10^6 years. And this age is so much smaller than the epicyclical period that the velocity of all the gas clouds could be in phase to give a motion away from the spiral arm.

The actual velocities that could be accounted for in terms of the thermal expansion of H ɪɪ regions depend critically on initial conditions in the neutral gas. For a nearly uniform initial density distribution one could not expect velocities in excess of the isothermal velocity of sound in H ɪɪ regions, around 10 km/sec (Spitzer's chapter in Vol. VII). But in the case of an extended H ɪɪ region near the edge of a spiral arm, conditions could be sufficiently far from uniformity as not to rule out systematic velocities twice as large. The possible existence of a magnetic field, with lines of force predominantly along the spiral arm and energy density comparable to the initial energy density of mass motion, would also affect the expansion of the H ɪ gas. On general grounds, it would be expected that the field strength increases by compression as it is carried by the gas, until it exerts a pressure sufficient to stop the motion. The net effect of the field would then be to decrease the dimensions of the epicyclical orbits in directions normal to the field, and to increase the magnitude of the velocities.

The question as to whether the thermal expansion of the H ɪɪ regions can provide sufficient energy to set the observed amount of gas in motion is impossible to settle at present. And, in fact, the same doubts arise in our case as have been expressed in regard to the Spitzer-Oort hypothesis explaining the mass motion of the interstellar gas in terms of the gas pressure gradients existing between H ɪ and H ɪɪ regions (Kahn 1954, Münch and Zirin 1961). A more specific objection arises from the recent observation at 21-cm wavelength of two large masses of interstellar gas, apparently associated with the association I Per, but at a latitude of $-10°$, or at about 400 pc from the galactic plane (van Woerden, Hack, and Blaauw 1964). These complexes have a combined mass exceeding $10^5 \odot$, and it appears difficult to understand their acceleration through purely thermal processes. An alternative tentative suggestion has been advanced to explain their motion (van Woerden *et al.* 1964) in terms of the energy derived from explosions of Type II supernovae which have taken place as a result of the evolution of the most massive stars in the association. The general acceptance of this novel idea to explain the observed facts no doubt will require extensive additional work, mostly of an observational nature. But whatever the correct explanation is for the origin of these gas complexes at large distances from the plane, it would seem likely that the expansion revealed by the interstellar absorption lines is a closely related phenomenon.

REFERENCES

ABT, H. A., and
  BAUTZ, L. P.   1963   *Ap. J.*, **138**, 1002.
ADAMS, W. S.   1949   *Ap. J.*, **109**, 354.
BAADE, W.   1951   *Pub. Obs. Univ. of Michigan*, **10**, 7.
BAADE, W., and
  MAYALL, N. U.   1951   *Problems of Cosmical Aerodynamics* (Dayton, Ohio: Central Air Documents Office), p. 165.

BLAAUW, A.   1952   *B.A.N.*, **11**, 459.
HILTNER, W. A.   1956   *Ap. J. Suppl.*, **2**, 389.
HULST, H. C. VAN DE   1953   *Observatory*, **73**, 129.
HULST, H. C. VAN DE,
    MULLER, C. A., and
    OORT, J. H.   1954   *B.A.N.*, **12**, 117.
KAHN, F. D.   1954   *B.A.N.*, **12**, 187.
MORGAN, W. W.   1951   Private communication.
MORGAN, W. W.,
    CODE, A. D., and
    WHITFORD, A. E.   1955   *Ap. J. Suppl.*, **2**, 41.
MORGAN, W. W.,
    SHARPLESS, S., and
    OSTERBROCK, D. E.   1952   *Sky and Telescope*, **11**, 138; *A.J.*, **57**, 3 (abstr.).
MÜNCH, G.   1953   *Pub. A.S.P.*, **65**, 179.
                                              1957   *Ap. J.*, **125**, 42.
                                              1960   *Ann. d'ap.*, **23**, 403.
                                              1965   In preparation.
MÜNCH, G., and ZIRIN, H. 1961   *Ap. J.*, **133**, 11.
SHARPLESS, S.   1954   *Ap. J.*, **119**, 334.
WILSON, R. E.   1953   *General Catalogue of Stellar Radial Velocities* (Washington, D.C.: Carnegie Institution of Washington).
WILSON, O. C., and
    MERRILL, P. W.   1937   *Ap. J.*, **86**, 44.
WOERDEN, H. VAN,
    HACK, M., and
    BLAAUW, A.   1965   *B.A.N.* (in preparation).

CHAPTER 11

Continuous Radio Emission in the Galaxy

J. L. PAWSEY†

C.S.I.R.O., Radiophysics Laboratory, Sydney

§ 1. INTRODUCTION

THE discovery by Jansky in the years 1931–35 of intense continuous radio emission from our Galaxy was the starting point of radio astronomy. Because the radiation was concentrated toward the directions of the Milky Way and the galactic center he concluded that its sources must lie "either in the stars themselves or in the interstellar matter distributed throughout the Milky Way" (Jansky 1935).

Subsequent observations, notably the pioneering ones of Reber (1958), have amply confirmed Jansky's conclusion on the emission of radio waves by our Galaxy and have pointed to the second of his two alternative sources, interstellar matter, as the correct one. The interest now lies in the extent to which cosmic radio waves, which is the term used to describe those from beyond the solar system, may be used to gain information about the Galaxy.

Spectroscopically, cosmic radio waves are now known to include a single spectral line, the 21-cm line of atomic hydrogen which is discussed in chapter 9, and a continuum extending over the whole wavelength range accessible to observation. Significant observations so far have been restricted to the surface of the earth and the upper wavelength limit has been set at about 100 meters by the opacity of the ionosphere and the lower, at about 1 centimeter, jointly by absorption bands in atmospheric gases and by the very low intensity of the shorter wavelength cosmic radio emission. The intensity is high at long wavelengths—Jansky observed at 15 m—and falls rapidly with decreasing wavelength. It is the purpose of this chapter to discuss the evidence available from studies of the radio continuum on the large-scale structure of our Galaxy.

† Deceased November 30, 1962. Dr. Pawsey's manuscript was submitted early in 1961.

219

The radiation is distributed over the whole sky and shows a background together with numerous bright sources of small angular size. The vast majority of these "discrete sources," originally called "radio stars," are not stars but nebulae of various kinds. The great majority, perhaps all, of those remote from the Milky Way, termed Class II sources by Mills (1952) who first recognized this distinction, appear to be external galaxies, mostly abnormal "radio galaxies" emitting vastly more radio frequency power than does our Galaxy (which is normal). A large proportion of the discrete sources near the galactic equator, Mills' Class I sources, are galactic nebulae. Those identified include remnants of supernovae, emission nebulae and a most interesting one at the galactic nucleus.

The background shows two major features: (1) a ridge of intense emission running round the galactic equator having a principal maximum in the direction of the galactic center, and (2) a general distribution, more nearly isotropic, but showing a broad maximum also in the direction of the galactic center. This distribution differs markedly from that of the stars or indeed of any known galactic objects and, following Shklovsky's suggestion (1952), it is now considered that galactic radio waves originate in two major subsystems: a strongly emitting region in the galactic disk, and a roughly spherical "corona" extending far beyond the bulk of the stars. In addition there must be an extra-galactic component, presumably isotropic, including the unresolved extra-galactic discrete sources and possible radiation from inter-galactic matter.

It is now believed that practically all radio waves originate, not in stars, but in interstellar gas. The stars must contribute a quota, the evidence being the observed emission from our own star the sun, but if the sun is a representative star, the integrated stellar radiation would be insignificant.

There are at least two emission mechanisms for the continuum. One, suggested by Reber (1940), is thermal emission from the hot ionized gas in H II regions. This mechanism, however, accounts for only a small fraction of the emission, particularly at the longer wavelengths where the observed intensity is very high. The high intensity and the form of the spectrum are both incompatible with such a thermal origin. The bulk of the emission, both of typical discrete sources and the background, is now believed to originate in electrons of relativistic energies spiraling in interstellar magnetic fields. This emission process is commonly known as "synchrotron emission" since it first came into prominence in connection with the energy lost by electrons in high-energy synchrotrons. It is of course quite possible that other, at present unknown, mechanisms may contribute to cosmic radio waves.

Owing to their great wavelength, radio waves are not appreciably absorbed by the dust which obstructs light so severely in directions near the Milky Way. The shorter radio wavelengths propagate freely throughout the whole Galaxy. The longer wavelengths, however, are heavily absorbed, not in dust, but in H II regions.

Accepting the current viewpoint on origins, radio observations contribute information about two important constituents of the Galaxy: about H II regions, and about what appears to be the electron constituent of cosmic rays in regions of appreciable magnetic field. The former is closely related to optical observations, though the radio and optical limitations are quite different. The latter is something completely new and of vital importance to an understanding of cosmic rays. In fact Shklovsky's recognition of the corona in our Galaxy from observations of the non-thermal component of cosmic radio waves is one of the outstanding astronomical discoveries of this century.

Further, neglecting questions of detailed origin, the delineation of the distribution of the galactic constituents evidenced by radio waves throughout the whole Galaxy, unhampered by the dust clouds which so seriously obstruct optical observations, gives very important evidence on the general question of galactic structure.

§ 2. AVAILABLE OBSERVATIONS

The principal radio observations relevant to our purpose consist of maps showing the distribution of radio brightness over the sky at particular wavelengths. The brightness b (surface brightness) is specified either in mks units [watts $m^{-2}(c/s)^{-1}$ (sterad)$^{-1}$] or in terms of brightness temperature T_b (degrees K), which is the temperature of a black body which would yield the observed brightness. These are related as follows:

$$b = \frac{2kT_b}{\lambda^2} = \frac{2.77 \times 10^{-23}T_b}{\lambda^2} \text{ mks units},$$

where k is Boltzmann's constant, and λ the wavelength. b includes both polarizations and is normally deduced from observations of a single polarization on the assumption that the radiation is randomly polarized.

The major limitation in these maps is due to the limited angular resolution of radio telescopes which are subject to diffraction limitations, related to the number of wavelengths in the aperture, similar to those applicable in optics. However, the million-fold greater wavelength greatly accentuates the problem. At wavelengths shorter than 1 m a few observations taken with parabolic reflectors or arrays are available with resolutions down to about half a degree. At longer wavelengths where the resolution attainable with available paraboloids is worse, special instruments have been developed, notably the Sydney Mills Cross and the Cambridge "aperture synthesis" equipment, which have given similar resolution. Substantial improvements in both types of instrument may be expected in the future but this paper is necessarily based on existing observations.

As previously mentioned the low intensity of cosmic radio waves at short wavelengths imposes a further limitation. At wavelengths shorter than 75 cm the "colder" regions remote from the Milky Way have not been observed and, at centimeter wavelengths, only exceptionally bright regions appear.

The broad distribution of continuum radiation over the whole sky is shown in Figure 1, which is the early, very low resolution (17° × 17°), map compiled by Dröge and Priester (1956) from their own (northern) and Allen and Gum's (southern) observations at 1.5 m. The ridge along the galactic equator and its central elongated maximum are obvious. Of the three subsidiary maxima near the galactic equator, that at $l^{II} \approx 110°$ coincides with the strongest of the discrete sources, Cassiopeia A, while those at 75° and 260° are probably directions in which we look along spiral arms. (That at 75° is accentuated by the presence of the strong discrete source Cygnus A, an extra-galactic source.) The origin of the prominent spur running north from the equatorial ridge at about $l^{II} = 30°$ is uncertain; it is probably a local concentration of emission. The over-all minima occur, not at the poles, but at intermediate latitudes at longitudes around 230°,

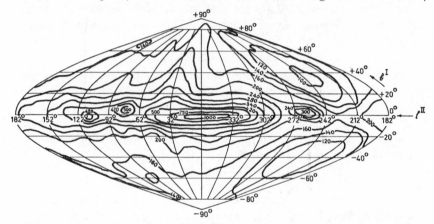

Fig. 1.—A low resolution (beam 17° × 17°) map showing the distribution of brightness temperature at 1.5 m over the whole sky (Dröge and Priester 1956). (Coordinates are old b^{I} and new l^{II}; unit ° K.)

well away from the anti-center. The resolution in this map is insufficient to show the narrowness of the disk component or the considerable degree of irregularity which exists in both corona and disk. Similarly the numerous discrete sources are lost.

Numerous more detailed surveys over parts of the sky are now available and a selection of the more recent ones is listed in Table 1 together with features of each survey. The surveys extend over a very useful wavelength range and, on a succession of maps at progressively increasing wavelengths, we should expect to be able to recognize individual features and, from possible progressive differences, derive information on the spectra of the objects concerned. This is so for the major features of the galactic ridge and the bright discrete sources, remembering that the weaker ones naturally do not appear on the wider beam surveys. But the appearance of the individual maps is surprisingly different. Some of this difference is due to the different beam shapes, ranging from a circle of 0°6 diameter to an ellipse 17° × 2°. Some also is due to genuine spectroscopic differences, which we discuss below and which are clearly established in

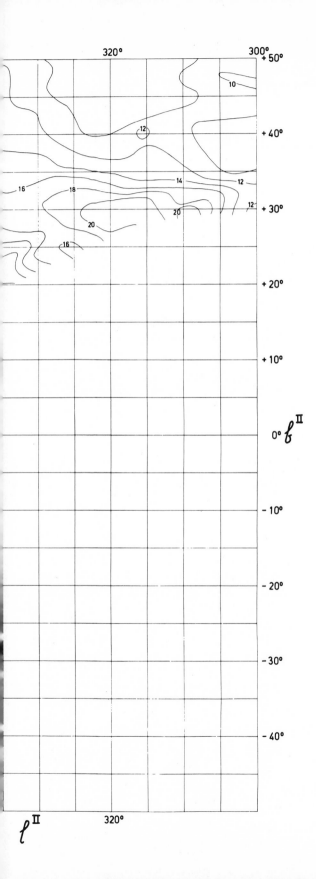

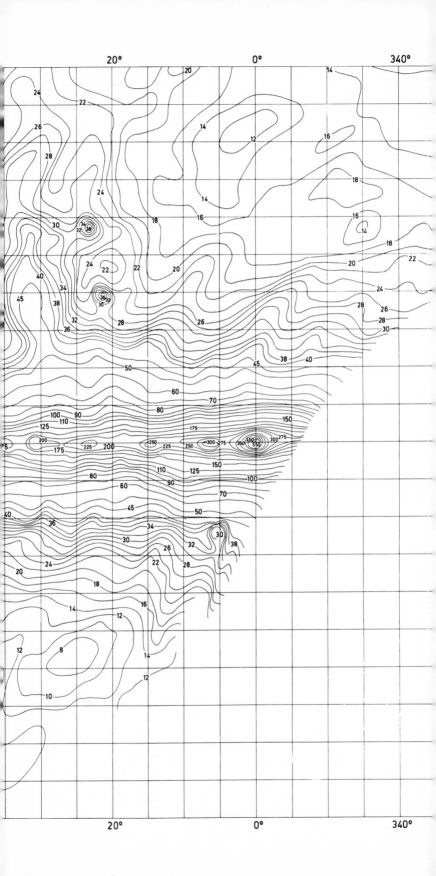

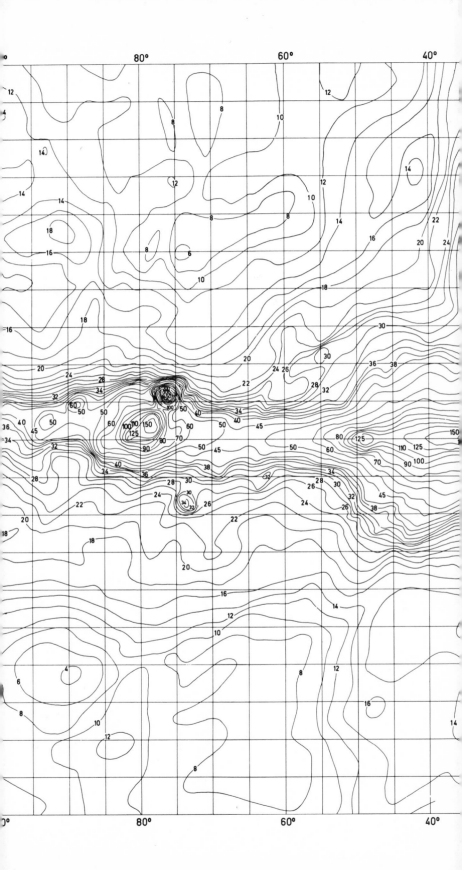

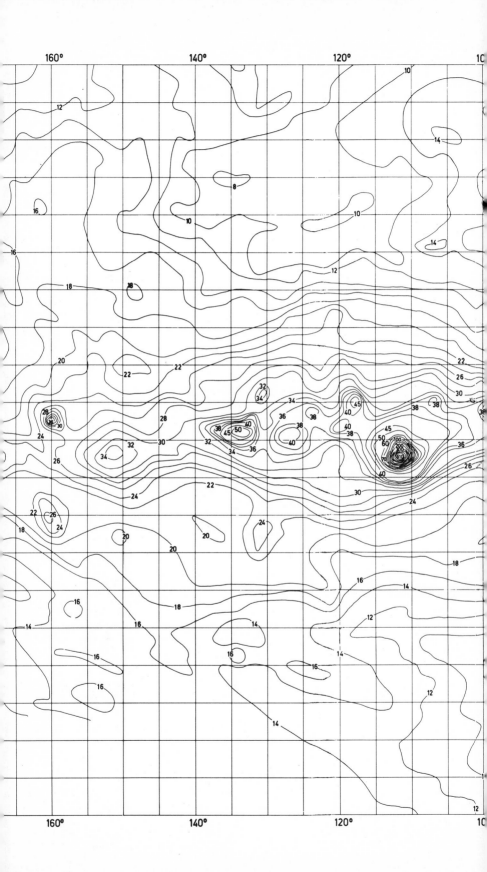

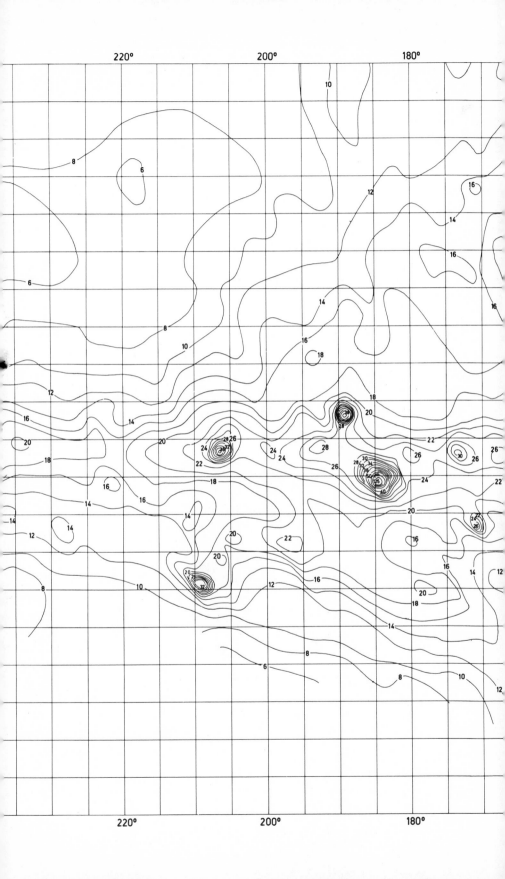

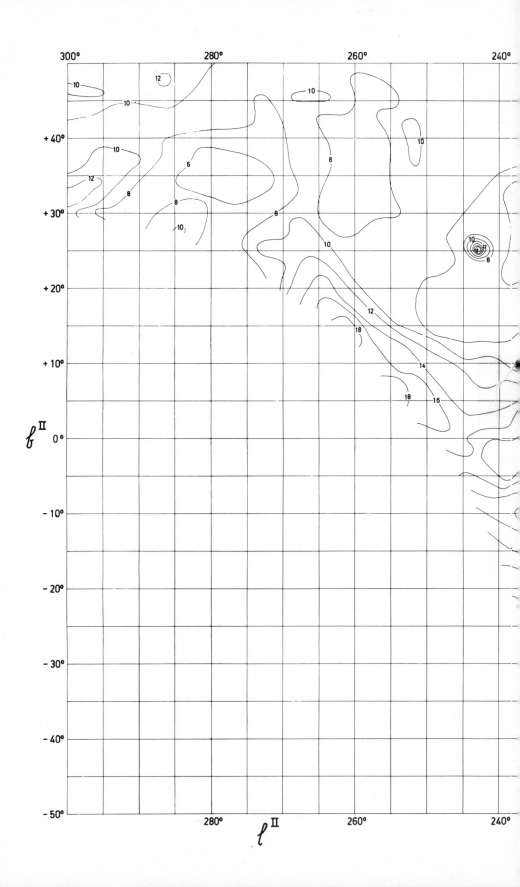

Fig. 2.—A more detailed map (beam $2° \times 2°$) of an area including the northern Milky Way. Coordinates are l^{II} and b^{II}; unit 1.3° K (Seeger, Stumpers, and van Hurck 1960; instead of the map originally presented by these authors we reproduce a redrawing in the system of new galactic coordinates, kindly made available by the director of the Leiden Observatory [Editors]).

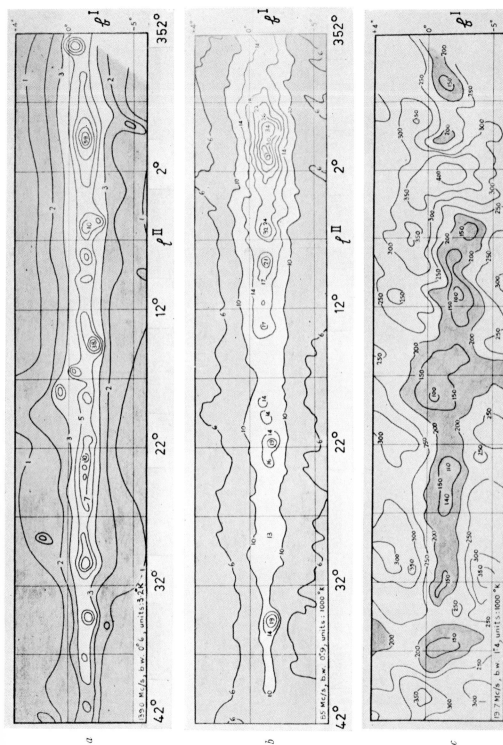

Fig. 3.—Simplified maps of a section of the Milky Way at wavelengths of (a) 22 cm, (b) 3.5 m, and (c) 15 m, illustrating absorption and emission effects of H II regions (Pawsey and Hill 1961). (Coordinates are old b^I and new l^{II}.)

the Milky Way zone. But there remains a real uncertainty about the detail of the recorded irregularities in the low intensity areas. For example Mills (1959a) comments in relation to the interpretation of his own survey,

fluctuations observed in this region (remote from the Milky Way) are of the order of one per cent of the excess-brightness temperature close to the galactic center, so that exclusion of the latter possibility (spurious instrumental response) would be a delicate matter with any instrument, particularly so with a cross-type (e.g., Mills Cross) or similar system which is rather subject to small spurious responses at large angles from the main beam. This question is best resolved by a detailed comparison between the results obtained with different instruments of comparable performance.

TABLE 1

A SELECTION OF HIGHER RESOLUTION CONTINUUM MAPS

	λ_m	Aerial Beam	Area	Coordinates*	Remarks
Shain and colleagues.	15	1°.4×1°.4	10° wide Milky Way strip $l^{\mathrm{I}}=225°$ to 15° $l^{\mathrm{II}}=257°$ to 47°	G^{I}	1
Blythe (1957)........	7.9	2°.2×2°.3 to 7°.4	$\delta=-20°$ to $+70°$ $RA=0$ to $24h$	E	2
Costain and Smith (1960)...........	7.9	0°.8×0°.8	$\delta=10°$ to 30° $RA=12\frac{1}{2}$ to $17h$	E	
Baldwin (1955)......	3.7	17°×2°	$\delta=-28°$ to $+82°$ $RA=0$ to $24h$	G^{I}	
Hill, Slee, and Mills (1958)...........	3.5	0°.8×0°.8	10° wide Milky Way strip $l^{\mathrm{I}}=223°$ to 13° $l^{\mathrm{II}}=255°$ to 45°	G^{I}	
Mills (1959a)........	3.5	0°.8×0°.8	$\delta=-80°$ to $+10°$ $RA=0$ to $24h$	G^{I}	3
Ko and Kraus (1957).	1.2	8°×1°	$\delta=-45°$ to $+65°$ $RA=0$ to $24h$	E	
Seeger, Stumpers and van Hurck (1959)..	0.75	2°×2°	Zone including Milky Way; approx. $l^{\mathrm{I}}=320°$ to 180° $l^{\mathrm{II}}=350°$ to 210° $b^{\mathrm{I}}=-50°$ to $+50°$		
Piddington and Trent (1956)...........	0.50	3°×3°	$\delta=-70°$ to $+50°$ $RA=0$ to $24h$	E	4
Wilson and Bolton (1960)...........	0.31	0°.8×0°.8	10°–25° wide Milky Way strip $l^{\mathrm{I}}=300°$ to 240° $l^{\mathrm{II}}=332°$ to 272°	E	5
Westerhout (1958)...	0.21	0°.6×0°.6	12° wide Milky Way strip $l^{\mathrm{I}}=320°$ to 56° $l^{\mathrm{II}}=352°$ to 88°	G^{I}	6

* G^{I} signifies old galactic coordinates; E, equatorial.

Remarks

1. Publication delayed by Shain's death, parts available (see Fig. 3c).
2. Some gaps due to difficulties caused by intense discrete sources.
3. Highly smoothed, based on 5° grid of sample points.
4. Sensitivity insufficient to observe sky beyond 10° to 30° from galactic equator; zero estimated.
5. Zero estimated.
6. Zero estimated.

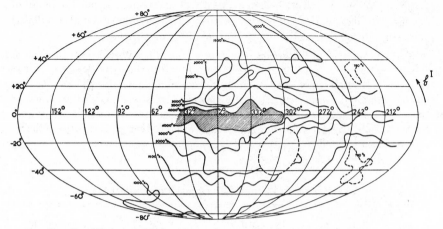

Fɪɢ. 4a.—Simplified map showing observed coronal isophotes at 3.5 m (Mills 1959a). (Co-ordinates are old b^I and new l^{II}; unit ° K.)

We strongly support this attitude and point also to the complementary diffi-culty arising in shorter wavelength surveys due to inadequate sensitivity for the weak signals often involved. We should also like to emphasize the difficulty in comparing surveys with dissimilar beams and urge some measure of standard-ization in surveys. Table 1 indicates that there are already available a number of good surveys with circular beams of diameter about 0°8 so that this is a natural first choice.

In view of the uncertainties in detail we shall present only sample maps. Figure 2 at 75 cm, due to Seeger, Stumpers, and van Hurck (1960), appears to be the most detailed and reliable of those available covering a large area both within and outside the Milky Way. Figures 3a, b, and c show simplified versions of maps of the same strip of the Milky Way, obtained using similar beamwidths at wavelengths of 0.22, 3.5, and 15 m (the area is also included in Fig. 2); it illustrates differences in spectra. Figure 4a is Mills' (1959a) "smoothed" map of the sky at 3.5 m showing detailed structure away from the Milky Way which he says needs confirmation, and Figure 4b his idealization of the mean distribu-tion after subtraction of the disk component.

Contour maps do not present a clear distinction between the Milky Way ridge, due to the disk component, and the remainder, due to the corona. This is best seen on profiles of recorded intensity on scans crossing the Milky Way. Three typical samples are given in Figure 5 and show the Milky Way ridge rising abruptly from a relatively flat distribution (Pawsey and Hill 1961).

The respective contributions from the disk and corona are estimated subjec-tively from information such as that of Figure 5. There is clearly an uncertainty as to whether the coronal contribution should be regarded as continuing through the disk, with the disk contribution as an addition, or as disappearing in the

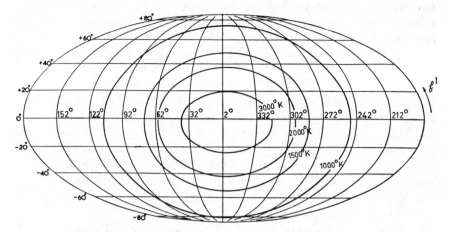

FIG. 4b.—Mills' idealization of the isophotes of (a), after subtraction of the disk component.

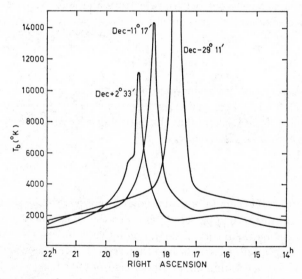

FIG. 5.—Scans across the galactic equator at a wavelength of 3.5 m at various declinations. These illustrate the way in which the disk radiation stands out above that from the corona (Pawsey and Hill 1961).

disk. The former seems the more plausible especially in view of Mills' evidence (see Sec. 4) on the concentration of the disk sources in spiral arms. The contributions from discrete sources are similarly estimated as excesses over an interpolated smooth background.

§ 3. RECOGNITION OF THE THERMAL AND NON-THERMAL COMPONENTS

As noted earlier it is now known that continuum cosmic radio waves originate in at least two processes: thermal emission from regions of fully ionized gas (H II regions), and a non-thermal process currently thought to be synchrotron emission from high-energy electrons spiraling in magnetic fields. The recognition of the existence of the non-thermal component and the determination of the individual contributions due to each is based on the study of spectra. We shall discuss the theory of thermal emission and show how it alone is inadequate to explain the observations and then proceed to a discussion of synchrotron emission and the separation of the two components. The discussion of mechanisms is a condensation of that given by Pawsey and Hill (1961).

The theory of emission from H II regions is well known. Emission, or absorption, occurs at collisions between electrons and ions, free-free transitions, and the absorption coefficient is given by

$$K = \frac{\zeta N_e^2}{f^2 T_e^{3/2}},$$
(1)

where ζ is a very slowly varying parameter approximating 0.13 cgs units for conditions of interest here and N_e = electron density, f = frequency, T_e = electron temp (° K). It follows that the optical depth τ of an isothermal region extending from x_1 to x_2 is given by

$$\tau = \frac{\zeta}{f^2 T_e^{3/2}} \int_{x_1}^{x_2} N_e^2 dx .$$
(2)

The above integral occurs in optical studies where, with N_e expressed in electrons cm^{-3} and distance in parsecs, it is called the "emission measure" (e.m.).

Studies based on the theory of excitation by very hot stars and on a limited number of observations have indicated that typical H II regions have temperatures lying in a range within about 20 per cent of 10^4 ° K and, with $T_e = 10^4$, (2) becomes

$$\tau = \frac{4.1 \times 10^{11}}{f^2} \times (\text{e.m.}).$$
(3)

It should be remembered, however, that there may well be some H II regions, such as those ionized by collisions between gas clouds, where T_e has a substantially different value.

Now τ increases rapidly with increasing wavelength (decreasing f), and numerical values are such that at the short wavelengths $\tau \ll 1$ for a path through the whole Galaxy, while at long wavelengths quite moderate H II regions have τ of the order of unity. Representative values for a typical H II region are:

T_e	N_e	Extent	e.m.	τ		
				15 m	$3\frac{1}{2}$ m	22 cm
10^4 ° K........	10 cm^{-3}	34 pc	3400 cm^{-6} pc	3.5	0.2	0.0007

In the absence of other radiation T_b is given by $T_e(1 - e^{-\tau})$. As the wavelength is increased from short wavelengths ($\tau \ll 1$) T_b at first increases as λ^2 and then levels off to the asymptotic value $T_e(\tau \gg 1)$. T_b can never increase faster than as λ^2. This last result, established here for an isothermal region, has been shown by Piddington (1951) to apply also to a region of varying temperature.

Observations of both background and discrete sources conflict with these predictions in two respects. Firstly, at the longer wavelengths, values of T_b of 10^5 to 10^6 ° K are common. These vastly exceed the expected electron temperature, 10^4 ° K, for H II regions. Secondly, the spectrum, both of the background and discrete sources, is commonly of the form $T_b \propto \lambda^a$, where $a \approx 2.5$ and definitely exceeds 2. It is therefore concluded that a further emission mechanism must exist.

The currently accepted mechanism is synchrotron emission. This mechanism was first suggested by Alfvén and Herlofson (1950) to explain the emission from discrete sources; subsequently Kiepenheuer (1950) applied the theory to the background of radiation from the Galaxy. These suggestions were developed largely by Russian theoretical workers and the development is well described by Shklovsky, a principal contributor, in his recent book (1960).

For an assembly of relativistic electrons moving in a common direction in a magnetic field having a component $H_\perp$ perpendicular to the electron velocity, and having a distribution of energies E given by

$$N(E)dE = kE^{-\beta}dE \qquad \text{for } E_1 < E < E_2,$$
$$N(E)dE = 0 \qquad \text{for } E < E_1 \text{ and } E > E_2,$$

the combined emission is a continuous spectrum of the form

$$J(f) \propto k f^{-(\beta-1)/2} H_\perp^{(\beta+1)/2} \qquad (4)$$

in a range related to E_1, E_2, and H. If we assume an *isotropic* distribution of electron directions the emission in a direction making an angle θ with the magnetic field H is given by

$$J(f) \propto k f^{-(\beta-1)/2} (H \sin \theta)^{(\beta+1)/2} . \qquad (5)$$

Observations show $T_b \propto \lambda^{2.5}$ approximately, corresponding to $J(f) \propto f^{-0.5}$ in a range of at least from 1 to 10 m. Subject to the above assumptions this implies that $\beta \approx 2$.

The theory shows that the spectrum emitted by an individual electron is concentrated in a frequency range governed jointly by the electron energy and H. Hence, if H were known, the order of magnitude of the energies of the electrons responsible for emission at particular frequencies could be deduced. For example, for $H = 10^{-6}$ oersteds, the above wavelength range involves electron energies of the order of 10^9 and 10^{10} electron volts. Similarly, given H, the total particle energy per unit volume (which depends on k and β) could be derived from the volume emissivity.

It may also be noted that equation (5) implies a directional effect, a concentration of emission perpendicular to the magnetic field. However, if the electron directions are isotropic, the degree of concentration is given by $(\sin \theta)^{(\beta+1)/2}$, or for $\beta = 2$, by $\sin^{3/2}\theta$, and is small. The emission is also substantially plane polarized at the point of origin.

In the separation of the thermal and non-thermal components we require to extrapolate the observed spectrum of the non-thermal component. The above theory indicates that simple extrapolation will be valid if the power law spectrum of the electrons can also be extrapolated. This is plausible but not proved.

The radiation from directions away from the Milky Way appears to have a consistent power law spectrum with an index of about 2.5 and is attributed to non-thermal emission from the corona. In the Milky Way, on the other hand, there are marked departures from such a law and the form of the spectrum is attributed to the presence of both non-thermal and thermal emission.

Such effects are evident on comparing the three maps of Figure 3. The two shorter wavelengths each show an irregular ridge along the Milky Way; the longest shows an initial rise toward a ridge but instead of a ridge we see an irregular trough or series of depressions. These are due to absorption in relatively near H II regions which, at 15 m, tend to have optical depths of the order of unity or more and, being at a temperature of about 10^4 °K, appear as dark patches against the background of non-thermal emission which has a brightness temperature of about 10^5 °K. At this wavelength, absorption in H II regions in the galactic disk restricts vision about as much as do dust clouds optically.

Reverting to Figure 3 we see that the 3.5 m and the 22 cm maps do not agree in detail: peaks occur on one and not on the other. This is explicable in the absence of severe absorption in terms of a mixture of H II regions and non-thermal sources of differing spectra. The brightness temperature T_b due to a region containing both H II regions and non-thermal sources is given by

$$T_b = T_T + A T_N$$

where T_T is the thermal contribution from the H II regions, T_N that which would be received from the non-thermal sources in the absence of absorption in the H II regions, and A an absorption factor to account for this absorption. It is assumed that at the low intensity levels concerned there is no appreciable absorption connected with the non-thermal emission process.

Attempts have been made by various workers, e.g., Piddington (1951) and Westerhout (1958), to separate the individual components from a study of the variation of T_b with λ. In order to make progress two hypotheses are made: (1) That the electron temperature T_e in the H II region is uniformly 10^4 ° K. (2) That the non-thermal emission varies as λ^a where $a \approx 2.5$. The evidence for the first has been discussed. That for the latter is based on observations of a power law spectrum for a limited number of areas away from the galactic equator; its application in the disk is an extrapolation. Extensive studies are necessary before either hypotheses can be considered securely established.

Accepting these hypotheses, however, for each wavelength

$$T_b = (1 - e^{-\tau})T_e + A\ T_N$$

where $\tau = \tau_1\lambda^2$ (τ_1 being the optical depth at $\lambda =$ unity), and $T_N = \lambda^a T_{N1}$ (T_{N1} being the value of T_N at $\lambda =$ unity). A is related to τ but can only be determined from it if the relative disposition of H II regions and non-thermal sources along the line of sight is known. The extreme values are: (1) $A = 1$, H II regions all beyond non-thermal sources, (2) $A = e^{-\tau}$, H II regions all this side of non-thermal sources. A more reasonable model is that in which the non-thermal sources and H II regions are distributed similarly along the line of sight. In this case $A = (1 - e^{-\tau})/\tau$. Of course for $\tau \ll 1$, applicable at short wavelengths, $A \approx 1$ independently of the relative disposition.

Thus, given T_e and a and the form of A, measurements at two wavelengths give two equations to determine the two unknowns τ_1 and T_{N1}. Westerhout used his own 22 cm and Mills' 3.5 m observations to estimate the magnitude of the respective components along the galactic ridge (see Sec. 4). At these wavelengths the attenuation is small and the value of A is not sensitive to the relative source distributions, which he assumed to be similar $[A = (1 - e^{-\tau})/\tau]$. Observations at longer wavelengths, where A is sensitive to the disposition, are capable of giving information on the relative disposition of sources.

To illustrate this process we shall consider the observations of T_b along the circle of longitude $l^{II} = 27°3$ in the vicinity of the galactic equator shown for wavelengths of 22 cm, 3.5, and 15 m in Figure 3. Westerhout's results show there is a concentration of H II regions at this longitude. We have not included the 75 cm observations of Figure 2 because the wider beam may introduce differences due to smoothing effects. Figure 6 shows values of $T_b/\lambda^{2.6}$ plotted against b^{II} for these three wavelengths; the curves would coincide for a spectrum of the form $T_b \propto \lambda^{2.6}$. The value 2.6 was chosen rather than 2.5 to improve the agreement at the edges. The close agreement of the three curves 3° or 4° from the galactic ridge indicates a power law. It is typical and supports the hypothesis that the coronal radiation is almost exclusively non-thermal. The differences near the galactic ridge are interpreted as due to the additional presence of H II regions: the depression at the center of the λ = 15 m curve as due to absorption, and the progressively taller peaks at decreasing wavelengths as due to the thermal contribution from the very thin H II layer in the disk decreasing less rapidly than the non-thermal one which originates in a thicker layer.

Quantitatively we have used the peak values at 22 cm and 3.5 m to determine the two components at the galactic ridge (taking the value of A appropriate to similar distributions). This leads to the values for T_T and T_N shown in Table 2. The observed value of T_b is in general less than the sum of T_T and T_N because

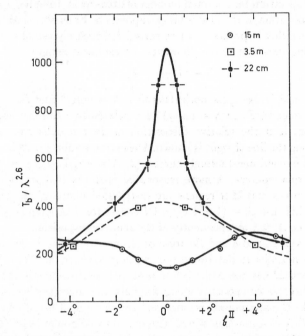

Fig. 6.—The variation of brightness across the galactic equator at $l^{II} = 27°.3$ for the three wavelengths of Figure 3. The three curves would coincide if the spectrum were of the form $T_b \propto \lambda^{2.6}$ and the differences near the center are attributed to absorption and emission by H II regions (T_b in ° K; λ in m).

TABLE 2

THERMAL AND NON-THERMAL COMPONENTS AT LONGITUDE 27°.3

λ	T_b(obs) ° K	T_T ° K	T_N ° K	A	τ
22 cm...........	20	13	7	1	1.3×10^{-3}
1 m...........	....	270	360	....	....
3.5 m..........	11,000	2800	9000	0.87	0.33
15 m...........	160,000	10000	420,000	0.36	6.0

of the attenuation, and A has been derived on the basis of this deficiency. The value of τ is also given. The values of T_{N1} and T_{T1}, the gross non-thermal and thermal components at a wavelength of 1 m, are also given as providing a convenient measure of these quantities.

The value of A of 0.36 in relation to $\tau = 6.0$ at 15 m gives significant information on the relative distribution of non-thermal sources and H II regions. It is incompatible with (1) H II regions all on the near side, $A = 0.002$ for $\tau = 6.0$, or (2) H II regions all on the far side, $A = 1$. It conforms roughly with the "similar distribution" model, computed $A = 0.17$, but the higher observed value, 0.36, indicates that, if the observations are correct, the non-thermal source density exceeds that of this model in the vicinity of the sun. This result supports Westerhout's suggestion (see Sec. 4) that the high value of the thermal contribution found at this longitude is due to a concentration of ionized hydrogen in a ring of radius 3 or 4 kpc around the galactic center and hence at a considerable distance from the sun.

Two incidental points are worthy of notice. Firstly, the successful application of this type of analysis requires accurate observations over that part of the spectrum where the thermal component is giving place to the non-thermal. They must be accurate and extend over an adequate wavelength range, because the results depend on differences between two not very dissimilar rates of variation (with λ^2 and $\lambda^{2.6}$, respectively). For this reason it is important that the observations should be made using radio telescopes of similar beamwidths.

Secondly, observations in the vicinity of 3.5 m appear to give a fair indication of the disposition of the gross non-thermal component over the sky both within and outside the Milky Way. This is due to a fortuitous combination of two circumstances: the total attenuation is, except perhaps in isolated nebulae, not great, and the non-thermal component of brightness temperature in the vicinity of the Milky Way is roughly the same as the electron temperature in H II regions, so that the net absorption or emission effects of the latter are minimized. The corresponding dominance of the thermal component is only realized in the Milky Way at wavelengths of 10 cm or shorter.

§ 4. THE GALACTIC DISK

We now discuss the information which follows from observations of continuum radiation about the disposition of its sources throughout the galactic disk. These sources include a population of intense discrete sources most of which may well be the remnants of supernovae, an extended flattened region of intense non-thermal emission, and the ionized interstellar gas responsible for the thermal component. The background due to the extended region is itself irregular and there is no clear-cut division between discrete sources of large angular size and background irregularities. Those picked out as discrete sources are simply those yielding clear-cut peaks on records. These three components show differing degrees of concentration to the galactic plane as indicated in Table 3.

The distribution of emission throughout the disk (spiral structure, etc.) appears to be different for the thermal and non-thermal components. As noted above, observations in the wavelength range about 3 m are dominated by the non-thermal component and, of these, the $3\frac{1}{2}$ m observations taken on the Sydney Mills Cross are the only ones having adequate resolution to show up possible details of spiral structure. Mills (1959*a*) (see Fig. 7*a*) has drawn the longitude distribution of brightness temperature along the galactic ridge after subtracting the recognizable discrete sources and an estimated coronal component. This distribution shows a series of steps which, Mills suggests, are associated with the line of sight becoming tangential with spiral arms. Some of these strips are well marked, other dubious, but Mills has shown that an equiangular, two-start spiral can be drawn (Fig. 7*b*) in which all the strips are tangential to spiral arms. We do not know what significance to place on this spiral but we

TABLE 3

COMPONENTS OF CONTINUUM RADIATION
IN THE GALACTIC DISK

Component	Angular Thickness in Directions of Central Region of Galaxy		Derived Thickness to Half Density of Layer	
Outstanding non-thermal discrete sources.........	1°.2	(1)	100 pc	(1)
Non-thermal background...	4°.0	(2)	500 pc	(1)
H II regions	1°.5	(2)	200 pc	(2)

(1) Mills 1959*b*.
(2) Westerhout 1958.

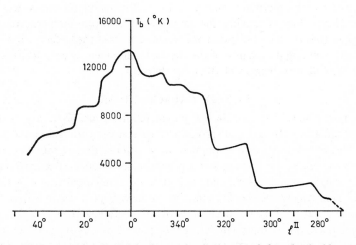

FIG. 7*a*.—The variation of the disk background radiation round the galactic ridge at 3.5 m as estimated by Mills (1959*a*).

consider the major steps, and the maxima in the Cygnus and Vela Puppis directions, to be among the most reliable of spiral arm indicators. A high proportion of them agree in position with H-line estimates of spiral arm positions but in view of current attempts to revise the latter (see chap. 9) we shall not make a comparison here.

Accepting the hypothesis that the steps are due to spiral or ring-like structure the question arises as to whether the size of the observed steps implies a major or a minor degree of concentration in the arms. Mills has deduced that the major steps imply a strong concentration, with inter-arm densities falling to 10 per cent or less of those in the arms. The arms as defined by Mills are of roughly circular section being about 500 pc in diameter. The emissivity in the bright parts of the arms is about 6×10^{10} watts $(c/s)^{-1}$ pc^{-3}.

Mills' analysis is based on the assumption that the emission from large regions is essentially isotropic. But if the emission process is the synchrotron mechanism the emission is concentrated in a direction normal to the magnetic field, and, if fields are substantially aligned in spiral arms, the emission would be concentrated in directions normal to the arms, away from the tangential directions observed by Mills. Hanbury Brown and Hazard (1960) have examined the question quantitatively and their results indicate that, if there is a moderate degree of irregularity in the field, spiral structure should be clearly recognizable. However, the degree of concentration in the arms cannot be disentangled from the degree of alignment of the field without new evidence.

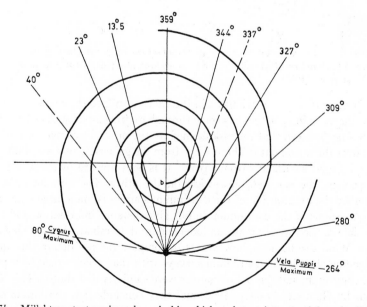

Fig. 7b.—Mills' two-start equiangular spiral in which each turn is tangential to the directions (indicated) of the steps of (a). (Dotted lines indicate minor steps.)

Westerhout (1958) has made a comparable study of the longitudinal variation along the ridge line of the thermal component which he derived by combining his own 22 cm and Mills' 3.5 m observations in the manner discussed in Section 2 (see Fig. 8a). The thermal component T_T shows somewhat similar peaks
or steps but these do not agree in position with Mills' steps. Because of the indirect derivation there is probably more uncertainty about minor features. However, there is an obviously significant maximum at $l^{II} = 25°$. This could be due
to an isolated major concentration of ionized hydrogen but Westerhout has suggested it is more likely due to a ring-shaped concentration at the appropriate
distance, 3 or 4 kpc, from the galactic center. On the hypothesis of rotational
symmetry he has derived the radial distribution of mean square density shown
in Figure 8b. This "ring" hypothesis can be checked when high-frequency southern observations become available.

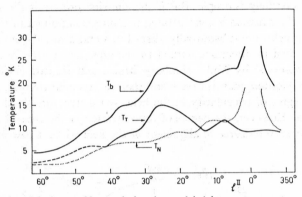

Fig. 8a.—The variation at 22 cm of the observed brightness temperature (T_b) and its
thermal (T_T) and non-thermal (T_N) components around a part of the galactic ridge as given
by Westerhout (1958).

Turning from the distribution in the galactic disk to the shape of the disk itself, the main information has come through hydrogen-line studies (see chap. 9).
It has been shown that the disk defined by the neutral hydrogen is remarkably
flat over the region out to about 7 kpc from the galactic center and that, beyond
this, it departs markedly from a plane. It is bent upward by many hundreds of
parsecs on the one side, downward on the other. The question arises as to
whether the distribution of the continuum sources is, on a large scale, similar.
Observations of the continuum do not give distance information and it is not
possible to use them to make an independent determination of the shape of the
disk. What can be done, however, is to compare the position of the equatorial
ridge-line obtained in continuum surveys with that which would be expected if
the continuum and the H-line sources were similarly distributed. This has been
done by Gum and Pawsey (1960) and they conclude that continuum observations including both thermal and non-thermal components are entirely consistent with such an hypothesis.

Thus the broad picture of the constituents of the disk revealed by continuum observations includes (1) a series of intense non-thermal discrete sources showing extreme concentration to the galactic plane, (2) a distribution of ionized hydrogen strongly concentrated to the plane and possibly showing a concentration in a ring distant 3 or 4 kpc from the galactic center, and (3) a distribution of non-thermal emission somewhat less highly concentrated to the plane than either of the former and showing marked radial concentrations strongly suggesting spiral structure. If we accept the synchrotron emission mechanism, the

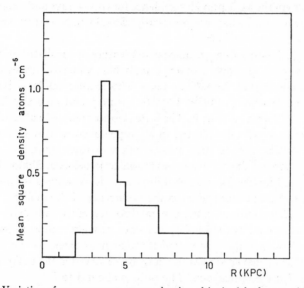

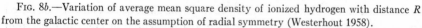

FIG. 8b.—Variation of average mean square density of ionized hydrogen with distance R from the galactic center on the assumption of radial symmetry (Westerhout 1958).

discrete sources are regions of relatively intense magnetic fields and high-energy electrons and, we presume, cosmic rays. The less intensely emitting regions in the disk must have either a lower concentration of electrons or of magnetic fields, or both. Shklovsky, see his book (1960), suggests that the non-thermal galactic discrete sources, which he considers to be supernovae remnants, are the main sources of energetic particles in the Galaxy, cosmic rays continually escaping from the edges. These give rise to further electrons through collisions. The electrons are slowed down and ultimately lost through "synchrotron" emission losses. If the flux of particles were not very different in different regions the differences in observed emissivity could be attributed to differences in magnetic field. Thus the apparent spiral arm structure in the non-thermal emission may well be indicative of magnetic field concentrations. If so, the interesting point emerges that, since this emission is less highly concentrated to the equatorial surface than is either the neutral or the ionized gas, the magnetic fields have a similar dispersion.

The distribution of H II regions has still to be fully investigated but it is now clear that radio studies of this constituent will ultimately add very greatly to our knowledge of its disposition.

§ 5 THE GALACTIC CORONA

As stated earlier the galactic corona, a vast roughly spherical radio emitting region extending far beyond the bulk of the stars, is one of the spectacular discoveries of radio astronomy. The emission is non-thermal and, accepting the synchrotron hypothesis, it provides evidence for cosmic rays and magnetic fields extending far out into what was previously thought to be empty inter-galactic space.

To the early investigators an unexpected feature of the distribution of radio brightness over the sky was the unexpectedly high values occurring in the low-intensity regions toward the galactic poles. This feature was first clearly shown by Bolton and Westfold's (1950) 100 Mc/s survey and they and Westerhout and Oort (1951) commented on it. The latter authors pointed out that this effect could be due to sources distributed in a "large spherical atmosphere" around the galactic system but preferred an alternative explanation in terms of a high isotropic background due to distant extra-galactic nebulae. Shklovsky (1952), however, argued for the former possibility and his hypothesis is now generally accepted. A most significant point is the occurrence of the minima, not at the galactic poles, but dsiplaced in the general direction of the anticenter. A further cogent argument used by Shklovsky, and since strongly reinforced by more precise observations, was the way in which the angular extent of the Andromeda Nebula (a galaxy believed similar to our own), observed in the radio continuum, greatly exceeded the optical size. The ratio is about 3 to 1.

Evidence on the distribution and extent of the galactic corona must be based on the shape of radio isophotes. These are also influenced by contributions from other regions and we must first attempt to eliminate these. Discrete sources of small angular size and the disk background component are rejected arbitrarily and there remains the wanted coronal component and an unwanted possible extra-galactic component. The background isophotes at this stage show marked irregularities (see Fig. 4a) which are presumably due mainly to the corona. The nature of these irregularities is still an unexplored field.

Estimates of the mean extra-galactic background are still very uncertain. In one method, exemplified by Baldwin (1955), a series of arbitrary models of the corona are postulated (each being a solid of rotation about the galactic axis), and their effects added to an isotropic extra-galactic component of adjustable magnitude. The results are then compared with observation. On the basis of this "plausible model" method Baldwin estimated the extra-galactic component as having, at 81.5 Mc/s, a brightness temperature $T_b < 500\,^\circ$ K. Values of T_b observed in the coldest parts of the sky were 900 $^\circ$ K.

Shain (1959), using a much lower frequency, has developed a more definite approach based on the obscuration of the extra-galactic background, but not the galactic corona, by an extensive H II region situated outside the Galaxy. For this purpose he used the giant emission region 30 Doradus in the Large Cloud of Magellan. More precise data, both radio and optical, are required for an exact determination but the available data indicate that at 20 Mc/s the contribution of the extra-galactic component is $< 22,000°$ K and possibly $\approx 7000°$ K. These figures correspond to 50 per cent and 20 per cent of the sky brightness in the colder parts and, of course, refer to a particular direction.

The best available evaluation of the spatial distribution of emissivity we believe to be that of Mills (1959a). He ignored fine structure and based his analysis on the highly idealized isophotes shown in Figure 4b and on the assumption that the large-scale distribution of emissivity is defined by a family of concentric spheroids. For the region nearer the center of the Galaxy than the sun

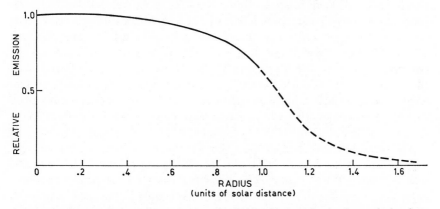

FIG. 9.—The radial distribution of coronal emissivity in the galactic plane calculated assuming radial symmetry. The dotted part of the curve is not a unique solution (Mills 1959a).

these assumptions lead to a unique solution. The derived radial distribution of emission in the galactic plane is shown by the full line of Figure 9. The solution for distances beyond the sun cannot be derived uniquely and the dotted extension in Figure 9 is one which is consistent with the data, including that concerning the uncertain extra-galactic contribution. In the inner region the spheroids were flattened, all having axial ratios of 3:2.

From the observations of brightness, Mills computed the emissivity of the corona and its total emission. At a wavelength of 3.5 m the maximum emissivity of the corona, near the galactic nucleus, is 5.4×10^9 watt $(c/s)^{-1}$ pc^{-3} and the total emission about 1×10^{22} watt $(c/s)^{-1}$. In comparison his estimate of emissivity in the center of a spiral arm, about 6×10^{10} watt $(c/s)^{-1}$ pc^{-3}, is about 10 times that of the maximum of the corona. However, the integrated emission from the disk is only about 1/10 of that from the whole corona. Baldwin, using his "plausible model" method, arrived at very similar conclusions concerning the corona except that he assumed that the emissivity was independent of radius. Mills states that this assumption is incompatible with the Sydney data.

It is clear that, especially in view of the major irregularities which are evident in radio maps (cf. Fig. 2), it will not be possible to derive precise models of the corona by methods which have to rely on assumptions as to large scale symmetry. It is thus important that the broad conclusions have been reinforced by observations of normal external galaxies, e.g., M31 and M33. The observed dimensions are each about three times the size of the corresponding optical object. In abnormal radio galaxies the emissivity is very much higher but they also show extensions far beyond the optical limits. It now seems fairly certain that a vast corona is a normal feature of late-type spiral galaxies.

One of the features of synchrotron-type radiation is that it is substantially plane polarized at the source. Observations of linear polarization might therefore supply, not only confirmation of the synchrotron hypothesis, but information on magnetic fields in space. However, owing to various depolarizing influences, the observed polarization might well be very small. It is well known that cosmic radio waves are substantially randomly polarized but one observer, Razin (1958), has reported the observation at a wavelength of 1.5 m of residual polarization of 2° to 4° K (2–4%) in all directions away from the Milky Way (i.e., in coronal radiation). This result has not been confirmed in Razin's wavelength range, the author being among those who have tried unsuccessfully to do so, but we understand that Ch. L. Seeger has obtained positive results at 75 cm (private communication). If this is correct it will be a major advance.[1]

The physical implication of the radio observations is that, throughout the vast volume of the corona, there is a distribution of energetic electrons and magnetic fields. The electrons are presumably the electron component of cosmic rays; some may be primary particles, i.e., accelerated in the same manner as the protons, others may be secondary particles formed at collisions of cosmic ray particles with interstellar atoms. The magnetic fields imply the existence of other matter, but the nature of this matter and the mechanism of field production remain purely speculative. The existence of a galactic corona has been proved; observational evidence relating to structure and physical processes in it is exceedingly sparse. The elucidation of the physics of the galactic corona is one of the most interesting challenges to present day astronomy.

I wish to thank Mr. M. M. Komesaroff and Mr. D. J. McLean for criticism of this chapter, particularly the former for extensive discussions on the separation of the thermal and non-thermal components.

REFERENCES

ALFVÉN, H., and
  HERLOFSON, N.   1950   *Phys. Rev.*, **78**, 616.
BALDWIN, J. E.   1955   *M.N.*, **115**, 684 and 690.
BLYTHE, J. H.   1957   *M.N.*, **117**, 644 and 652.

[1] For recent developments, see Westerhout, Seeger, Brouw, and Tinbergen (1962); Brouw, Muller, and Tinbergen (1962).—Eds.

BOLTON, J. G., and
  WESTFOLD, K. C.   1950   *Australian J. Sci. Res.*, Ser. A, **3**, 19.
BROUW, W. N.,
  MULLER, C. A., and
  TINBERGEN, J.   1962   *B.A.N.*, **16**, 213.
BROWN, R. HANBURY,
  and HAZARD, C.   1960   *Observatory*, **80**, 137.
COSTAIN, C. H., and
  SMITH, F. G.   1960   *M.N.*, **121**, 405.
DRÖGE, F., and
  PRIESTER, W.   1956   *Zs. f. Ap.*, **40**, 236.
GUM, C. S., and
  PAWSEY, J. L.   1960   *M.N.*, **121**, 150.
HILL, E. R., SLEE, O. B.,
  and MILLS, B. Y.   1958   *Australian J. Phys.*, **11**, 530.
JANSKY, K. G.   1935   *Proc. Inst. Rad. Eng.*, **23**, 1158.
KIEPENHEUER, K. O.   1950   *Phys. Rev.*, **79**, 738.
KO, H. C., and
  KRAUS, J. D.   1957   *Sky and Telescope*, **16**, 160.
MILLS, B. Y.   1952   *Australian J. Sci. Res.*, Ser. A, **5**, 266.
           1959a   "Paris Symposium on Radio Astronomy," *I.A.U. Symp.*, No. 9, 431.
           1959b   *Pub. A.S.P.*, **71**, 267.
PAWSEY, J. L., and
  HILL, E. R.   1961   *Reports on Progress in Physics,* **24**, 69.
PIDDINGTON, J. H.   1951   *M.N.*, **111**, 45.
PIDDINGTON, J. H., and
  TRENT, G. H.   1956   *Australian J. Phys.*, **9**, 481.
RAZIN, V. A.   1958   *A.J. U.S.S.R.*, **35**, 241.
REBER, G.   1940   *Proc. Inst. Rad. Eng.*, **28**, 68.
           1958   *Ibid.*, **46**, 15.
SEEGER, C. L.,
  STUMPERS, F. L. H. M.,
  and VAN HURCK, N.   1960   *Philips Tech. Review*, **21**, 317.
SHAIN, C. A.   1959   "Paris Symposium on Radio Astronomy," *I.A.U. Symp.*, No. 9, 328.
SHKLOVSKY, I. S.   1952   *A.J. U.S.S.R.*, **29**, 418.
           1960   *Cosmic Radio Waves* (Cambridge, Mass.: Harvard University Press).
WESTERHOUT, G.   1958   *B.A.N.*, **14**, 215.
WESTERHOUT, G., and
  OORT, J. H.   1951   *B.A.N.*, **11**, 323.
WESTERHOUT, G.,
  SEEGER, CH. L.,
  BROUW, N., and
  TINBERGEN, J.   1962   *B.A.N.*, **16**, 187.
WILSON, R. W., and
  BOLTON, J. G.   1960   *Pub. A.S.P.*, **72**, 331.

CHAPTER 12

Distribution and Motions of Late-Type Giants

VICTOR M. BLANCO

Warner and Swasey Observatory, Case Institute of Technology

§ 1. INTRODUCTION

In this chapter we consider the space distribution and motions of stars of spectral types C, S, and gM. The discussion is limited to those stars of these types that may be discovered by spectroscopic observations, regardless of whether they are variable or not. For a discussion of the galactic distribution and the space motions of red *variable* stars, the reader is referred to Plaut's chapter 13 in this volume.

The very late-type giants play an important role in evolutionary theory since they lie at the extreme right side of the HR diagram. Furthermore, they are important in studies of galactic structure because they can be observed at remote distances. Low dispersion spectroscopic observations in the near infrared region of the spectrum, following the technique pioneered by Nassau and van Albada (1949), suffice to segregate these stars in relatively clear regions to distances comparable to that of the galactic nucleus.

Due to uncertainties of the available luminosities and intrinsic colors among the C- and S-type stars, and to the relative scarcity of these objects in space, their galactic distribution is best obtained from whatever inferences one can make about their distribution in the sky and their peculiar motions. For the giant M stars, the situation is much better, and some estimates of their space-density distribution in the Galaxy are possible.

In order to review what we know about the space distribution and motions of these stars, it is convenient to first sketch the methods by which they are discovered. This is done in Section 2. Their intrinsic properties are reviewed in Section 3, and finally the space distribution and motions are described in Sections 4 and 5.

§ 2. SPECTRAL CLASSIFICATIONS; SURVEYS

The review articles by Hoffleit (1942) and Fehrenbach (1958) describe the methods of spectral classification that are used in the study of the red giants. A few words may be added with regard to small dispersion infrared classifications in the spectral region 6800 A to 8800 A. Such classifications provide the most promising methods so far developed for the discovery of faint objects of class C or M.

2.1. CARBON STARS

Carbon stars are customarily classified as C0 to C9 following the criteria of Keenan and Morgan (1941), or as R or N according to the Henry Draper system. Approximately, the R stars (R0 to R9) correspond to classes C0–C4 and the N stars (N0 to N9) to classes C5–C9. The infrared classification of carbon stars with small dispersions was developed by Nassau and Colacevich (1950) and Nassau and Blanco (1954a). A classification by individual subclasses has not proved practical, and stars of class C0, C1, and C2 are not usually detected, hence, the method favors the discovery of N stars. An important point is that the infrared spectrum of an N or a late R star can be recognized almost to the limiting magnitude of the plate. Extended lists of carbon stars discovered by infrared observations have been published by Nassau and Blanco (1954a), Blanco and Münch (1955), and Blanco (1958). References to earlier surveys may be found in these papers.

2.2. S-TYPE STARS

S-type stars sometimes show well developed LaO bands (7403 A and 7910 A) by which they can be identified on small dispersion infrared spectroscopic plates. The stars, however, are missed if these bands are weak. They are, furthermore, difficult to detect near the plate limit. A recent study by Nassau and Stephenson (1960) shows that these stars may be best searched for in the red region of the spectrum where ZrO 6474 A may be recognized with low dispersions. The results of infrared surveys for S-type stars have been published by Nassau, Blanco, and Morgan (1954), and Blanco and Nassau (1957). Other surveys for S stars as well as their classification and galactic distribution have been discussed in detail by Keenan (1954). Merrill (1952) found spectral lines of the unstable element Tc in S-type stars, a fact that suggests that this type is a short-lived phase of stellar evolution. Strong TcI lines were found in long-period variables of S type. It would be interesting to establish whether this element is present among the more constant S stars which apparently fall on the galactic spiral arms, according to Keenan (1954).

2.3. M GIANTS

In their pioneering work, Nassau and van Albada (1949) developed infrared classification criteria for M stars based on the strength of several blends of TiO bands at 7054 A, 7589 A, and 8432 A. Although an attempt was made to use the

Mt. Wilson classifications (Adams, Joy, Humason, and Brayton 1935) as standards, systematic differences exist. These are mostly due to the Nassau-van Albada definition of class M0 as that in which the TiO bands at 7054 A first appear. Keenan (1952) has found that these bands can be seen in giants as early as K4 even with small dispersions. Spectral subtypes later than M7 were not listed by the Mt. Wilson observers in order to leave available M subclasses for more advanced types, which are often observed in variable stars. A system of infrared classification with low dispersion for stars later than type M6 was developed by Cameron and Nassau (1955). Smooth gradations of the strength of TiO features and of the blends of bands of VO centered approximately at 7400 A and 7900 A were obtained for classes extending from M6 to M10. Classes M8, M9, and M10 are not based on any particular standards but represent a sequence of advancing subtypes that can be readily distinguished.

In the infrared system of classification some natural groups of subclasses among the M stars may be readily distinguished. Since a star later than M1 can be readily assigned to one of these groups with very little error, these groups are useful in galactic structure studies.

M2–M4: TiO 7054 A strong, 7589 A moderate, 8432 A absent.
M5–M6: TiO 7589 A strong, 8432 A visible, VO 7900 A absent.
M7 or later: VO 7900 A present.

The internal consistency of classification in the near infrared has been determined several times. Nassau and van Albada (1949) found the probable error of one classification to be ± 0.3 of a subclass when independent classifications were made for types M2 or later. Stars of types M0 and M1 are troublesome in this respect. Blanco and Münch (1955) found that in a group of such stars classified by memory, 20 per cent turned out to be objects of earlier classes than M. Furthermore, in two independent surveys of the same area, the percentage of M0 and M1 stars for which agreement was obtained was only 50 per cent. The corresponding percentages for classes M2 to M6 and M7 or later were 80 and 96. The source of the errors is the confusion of the atmospheric "a" band with a TiO band at λ 7126 which belongs to the λ 7054 blend of bands. Another selection effect found by Blanco and Münch is that the limiting magnitude of infrared classifications depends on the spectral subclass. Stars of type M2 must be at least 1 infrared magnitude brighter than stars of type M5 or later in order to be discovered on the same plate. Galactic surveys for M0 and M1 stars as well as for S stars are best made at present with red-sensitive plates. Classification criteria in the red region of the spectrum have been described by Lee, Gore, and Bartlett (1947), Iwanowska and Wayman (1952), and Velghe (1957), but the technique has not been extensively exploited.

The small-dispersion, infrared classification of M stars does not in general provide luminosity criteria. There are, however, a number of effects that tend to favor very strongly the segregation of giant M stars in any extended survey.

The space density of M dwarfs is sufficiently low for extremely few if any M dwarfs to be observed per square degree within the magnitude limits so far attained. It should also be mentioned that the VO 7900 band found in late giants has not been observed in dwarf stars.

A color effect that has proved useful in segregating supergiant M stars was noted by Nassau, Blanco, and Morgan (1954). The unwidened spectra of these stars often show a wedge-shape that appears to be principally caused by inter-stellar absorption. These results have been confirmed by Sharpless (1957). Supergiant M stars are also relatively rare objects and have not been found with certainty among stars of class M6 or later. Finally, no definite cases of subgiant M stars have been discovered (Moore and Paddock 1950, Eggen 1960a).

In addition to the papers mentioned so far, infrared classifications of large numbers of M stars have been published by Nassau and Blanco (1954b), Cameron and Nassau (1956), Nassau, Blanco, and Cameron (1956), Nassau and Blanco (1958), Neckel (1958), and Westerlund (1959a, b).

§ 3. INTRINSIC PROPERTIES

3.1. LUMINOSITIES AND COLORS OF C AND S STARS

According to Sanford (1944), the mean visual absolute magnitude (M_v) of N stars is -2.3 and of R stars -0.4. These values were primarily obtained from the differential galactic rotation formula. For some R stars, Sanford found evidence of marked deviations from the mean absolute magnitudes. More recently, Vandervort (1958) has determined M_v for R stars by the secular parallax method, as well as from radial velocities and τ-components of proper motion. His results are: for R0 to R2, $M_v = +0.44 \pm 0.29$; for R5 to R8, $M_v = -1.10 \pm 0.49$. Perek (1957) has shown that for a number of N stars Sanford's value of M_v, when combined with apparent magnitudes and proper motions, results in exceedingly high space velocities, even though the observed radial velocities are about 20 km/sec. Perek concludes that at least some N stars are appreciably fainter than -2.3.

For the S stars, Keenan (1954) has found that $M_v = -1.0$ with an uncertainty of "several tenths of a magnitude." The derivation is limited to 17 long-period variables and is based on secular parallaxes as well as on radial velocities and τ proper motion components. Keenan notes that about half of the known S stars are either constant in brightness or are variables of small amplitude. This group of S stars has a higher galactic concentration than the long-period S-type variables but one comparable to that of the N-type stars. Keenan and Teske (1956) measured the radial velocities of 14 S stars of small amplitude and found them similar to those of normal G and K giants. Keenan suggests a value $M_v = -1.5$ for this group of S stars, and finds a remarkable concentration of them in the nearby galactic spiral arms. This result has also been obtained by Taka-yanagi (1960). Takayanagi, however, finds $M_v = -0.1 \pm 0.6$ for the less-variable S stars and $M_v = -3.0 \pm 0.5$ for the long-period S stars at maximum brightness.

The writer is aware of only a few photoelectric determinations of the colors of N stars and none of S stars. Johnson (1955) lists $B - V$ colors for nine bright N stars. These range from 2.42 to 3.78. The $B - V$ colors for R stars have been determined by Vandervort (1958). These range from 1.22 at class R0 to 2.10 for class R8. The $R - I$ color in the photometric system developed by Kron (1956) and his collaborators is 1.0, according to Westerlund (1960), for carbon stars in the Magellanic clouds.

3.2. LUMINOSITIES AND COLORS OF M GIANTS

3.2.1. *Luminosities of Giant M Stars in General.*—Trigonometric parallaxes have not proved very useful in the determination of values of M_v for giant M

TABLE 1

VISUAL ABSOLUTE MAGNITUDES FOR GIANT M STARS

	van Rhijn	Hoffleit	Yerkes	Wilson-Bappu	Adopted
M0....	−0.2	....	−0.4	−0.3 (13)	−0.3
M1....	− .3	−0.1	−0.4	−0.5 (4)	−0.5
M2....	− .4	−0.2	−0.4	−0.8 (11)	−0.8
M3....	− .5	−0.3	−0.5	−1.1 (7)	−1.1
M4....	− .6	−0.4	−0.5	−1.0 (5)	−1.0
M5....	− .4	−1.0	−1.0	−0.9: (3)	−0.9:
M6....	−0.3	....	....	−0.9: (2)	−0.9:
M7....	....	....	−1.5	....	−0.9:

stars. The brightest M star of luminosity class III is γ Cru for which no trigonometric parallax is available. The next brightest, β And (M0 III), has a parallax of 0″.043 ± 0.006. Its visual apparent magnitude is 2.06 (Eggen 1960*b*), and its computed absolute magnitude is +0.2 ± 0.3. The trigonometric parallax of the third brightest, α Cet (M2 III) is 0″.003 ± 0.005.

The Mt. Wilson calibration of absolute magnitudes of the giant M stars due to Adams, Joy, Humason, and Brayton (1935) has been reviewed by Russell and Moore (1938), and van Rhijn (1939), who found only small adjustments to be necessary. The values of M_v computed by van Rhijn for Mt. Wilson classes are given in column 2 of Table 1. Hoffleit (1942) determined absolute magnitudes with Öpik's method and also established systematic differences existing between the Harvard and Mt. Wilson classifications of M stars. Miss Hoffleit's values of M_v are given in column 3 of Table 1 in terms of Mt. Wilson classes. Keenan and Hynek (1945) and Keenan and Morgan (1951) have presented values of M_v for M stars of luminosity class III. Their values are presented in column 4 under the "Yerkes" heading.

The foregoing determinations of M_v are based on trigonometric parallaxes, proper motions, and radial velocities. Hence, they suffer from the uncertainties in the parallaxes and proper motions. For gM stars these parameters are generally small. Wilson and Bappu (1957) and Wilson (1959) have developed a method for determining the luminosity of late-type stars from measures of the widths W_0 of the bright reversals in the H and K lines of ionized calcium. A linear relationship exists between M_v and $\log W_0$ which holds over a range of 15 magnitudes and is independent of spectral type. The relationship was calibrated with great accuracy from observations of the sun and of the K-type giants in the Hyades. The results are supported by observations of K dwarfs with reliable trigonometric parallaxes, as well as of the h and χ Persei M-type supergiants. For normal giants, absolute magnitudes with a probable error of ± 0.3 can be determined by this method. The mean luminosity for M stars of luminosity class III obtained from the work of these authors is presented in column 5 of Table 1.[1] The number of stars of each type that were used in the computation are indicated in parentheses. These absolute magnitudes do not reflect the uncertainties caused by small parallaxes and proper motions. For classes M0 and M1, the Wilson-Bappu magnitudes agree well with the older calibrations, and it is for these stars that the parallaxes and proper motions can be most trusted.

The luminosities of the semi-regular and irregular variables of type M have been investigated by Joy (1942) and Wilson (1942). These stars are mostly of type M2 or later. About 10 per cent are supergiants and the rest ordinary giants. Among the giants, no difference is found in the mean luminosities of the variables at maximum light and the normal M giants. Joy and Wilson conclude that $M_v = -0.9$ and note that this does not vary appreciably with the spectral subclass. The long-period variables of type M, on the other hand, appear to have luminosities that decrease markedly with advancing type from $M_v = -2.7$ at M1 to $+0.3$ at M8 according to Wilson and Merrill (1942) and Kukarkin (1947). It will be shown later that among the early M stars selected spectroscopically the variables of large amplitude are rare. The absolute magnitudes presented in the last column of Table 1 are adopted in the present discussion. They are based for the early M stars on the work of Wilson and Bappu, and for the late M stars on the papers by Joy and Wilson. For classes M8 or later, the long-period variables are probably dominant in any survey of M stars, and the mean absolute magnitude is appreciably less than $+0.3$ since the stars in general will not be observed at maximum light.

A number of giant M stars have been listed by Eggen (1958) as members of the extended Hyades group. Eggen's absolute magnitudes, derived from group motion, are in good agreement with those adopted here except for classes M0 and M1 where his magnitudes are somewhat brighter.

3.2.2. *Luminosity of High-Velocity M Stars and of M Giants near the Galactic Center.*—Eggen (1958) has listed 3 M-type stars as members of the ζ Herculis

---

[1] I am indebted to Dr. O. C. Wilson for making available in advance of publication a list of absolute magnitudes from which the values presented in Table 1 were derived.

group of high-velocity stars. The absolute magnitudes derived from the group motion agree with the adopted ones in Table 1. Roman (1955) listed 2 stars of type M0 III in her list of high-velocity stars for which absolute magnitudes are available from the data published by Wilson and Bappu (1957) and Wilson (1959). These magnitudes are −0.8 and +0.4. Luminosity classifications for 7 high-velocity giant M stars were published by Keenan and Keller (1953). Three stars are listed with luminosity class III−, three stars with class III, and one of class III+. It appears from these scant data that, at least among the early M giants, the high-velocity objects are not markedly different in luminosity from the normal giants.

The luminosity of giant M stars in the vicinity of the galactic nucleus as compared with the red giants in globular clusters has been studied by Arp (1959). In a small area near M22, Arp determined the apparent magnitudes and colors of 300 field stars. From the photometric data for M22, the color excess and absorption expected for the distant M giants are, respectively, $E_{B-V} = 0.4$ and $A_V = 1.4$. Hence, distant M stars will have colors in excess of $B − V = 2.0$. A negligible number of such stars with $V < 15.0$ was observed, while 19 stars with $B − V > 2.0$ were observed in the interval $15.0 < V < 16.0$, none of which may be expected to be a dwarf. The central line of sight of Arp's region approaches the galactic nucleus within a distance of 2.3 kpc, being then 1.4 kpc above the galactic plane. If the red stars observed by Arp are between the sun and the galactic nuclear bulge, their absolute magnitude is fainter than that of M giants near the sun, and this is in contradiction with the observed absence of field subgiants of M type in the solar vicinity. On the other hand, if the stars are appreciably more luminous than normal M giants, we must conclude that very luminous M stars exist far above the galactic plane on the other side of the Galaxy. This is in contradiction with observations of M stars located on the solar side. These arguments indicate that the red stars observed by Arp are similar in luminosity to those in the solar neighborhood. A similar result has been obtained by Pik Sin The (unpublished) for a relatively clear region near NGC 6530. The studies of Arp and The suggest a scarcity in our Galaxy of the bright red giants resolved by Baade (1944) in M31, M32, and NGC 205, or else that the counterparts of these stars in our Galaxy are very distant from the galactic center. We may note also that the M stars responsible for the TiO bands observed in the integrated spectrum of the nuclear region of M31, according to Morgan and Mayall (1957), very probably are normal giants.

3.2.3. *M Giants in Galactic Clusters.*—Some giant M stars have been suspected to be members of galactic clusters. Table 2 contains a list of the cases known to the writer. In addition to the stars listed in Table 2, Cox (1955) has listed his star No. 110 in NGC 2516 as of class M0 III. However, the absolute magnitude indicated by his data is −4.8. The star thus is really a supergiant, and NGC 2516 may belong to the group of clusters such as h and χ Per, and

NGC 7419, 3293, and 3766 where supergiant M stars have been observed. It is unfortunate that for the only M star in Table 2 with a definite luminosity class III no reliable apparent magnitude is available. From Table 2 one can conclude that the M giants so far suspected to be galactic cluster members are intrinsically fainter than the reddest giant stars found in globular clusters but brighter than normal giant M stars. This unexpected result is of interest in evolutionary theory, for the galactic cluster M stars are presumably younger and should have higher metallic content and lower luminosity than the field gM stars (Sandage and Wallerstein 1960).

3.2.4. *The Dispersion in Absolute Magnitudes.*—The dispersion or mean error σ of the absolute magnitudes is required in any star count analysis of giant M stars. Among the M giants the effects of variability and of spectral classification

TABLE 2

M GIANTS IN GALACTIC CLUSTERS

Cluster	Star	Spectral Type	M_v	Reference
M11.............	Küstner 143	M3 II–III	−1.3	(1)
NGC 7789........	Küstner 751	M0 : III :	−1.4	(1)
NGC 6087........	Cordoba 73	M1 III	....	(2)
NGC 7789........	Küstner 971	M1 II–III	−1.2	(3)
NGC 7790........	Sandage F	M3	−1.5:	(3)
NGC 6940........	Walker 120	M5 II	....	(4)
Anon. δ Lyr......	δ² Lyr	M4 II	−2.2	(5)

References

(1) Walker and Bidelman (1960), (2) Feast (1957), (3) Mavridis (1959), (4) Walker (1958), (5) Stephenson (1959).

errors must be taken into account when estimating σ. Among the later-type giant M stars, due to the small variation of M_v with spectral type, the effects of spectral class errors are small. A group of 190 giant stars of type M was repeatedly observed by Stebbins and Huffer (1930) with a photoelectric cell with maximum sensitivity at 4600 A. Unfortunately, equally reliable data in the visual wavelengths are not available. Excluding a few known supergiants, a plot of the magnitude ranges found is shown in Figure 1. Among stars of type M5 or earlier, ranges of variability larger than 0.3 magnitude are rare. This has been confirmed for an area near the galactic center where Nassau and Blanco (1958) found that out of 117 stars of classes M2 to M5 only 9 were listed as variables in an exhaustive search to a fainter limiting magnitude than was reached in the spectral survey. The search for variables was made by Baade (1951) and the data published by Gaposchkin (1956), and in it variables with a range over 0.4 magnitude were expected to be discovered. Among the stars of type M6, about 20 per cent appeared in Baade's list of variables; and among the M7 stars, about 30 per cent.

It is difficult to ascertain what values of σ should be assigned to a group of stars that are known to vary over a small range since sufficiently precise information on how the spectral class is correlated to the apparent magnitude is lacking. For the long-period variables, Merrill (1940) has described a commonly observed "veiling" effect which leads to marked variations in apparent magnitude with little variation of the spectral features. If this effect also operates among the small-amplitude M stars, then the dispersion in luminosity can be found from data similar to those presented in Figure 1. Neglecting the slight reduction in ranges that would be observed in visual light as compared to photographic light, we may conclude: (*a*) For classes gM2 or earlier, the dispersion introduced by variability and errors in classification yield $\sigma \approx \pm 0.3$

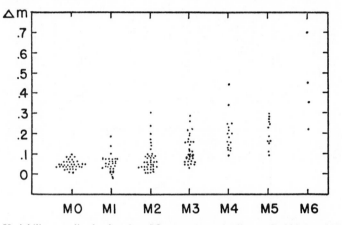

FIG. 1.—Variability amplitudes for giant M-type stars according to Stebbins and Huffer

magnitude; (*b*) for classes gM4 and gM5, $\sigma \approx \pm 0.35$ magnitude; (*c*) for gM6 or later, the dispersion effect of variability is predominant and values of σ over ± 0.4 magnitude must be used. Hoffleit (1942) has obtained a dispersion of ± 0.4 for the normal M giants, while Stephenson (1959), from a study of double stars, finds for the dispersion of the K giants the value ± 0.5.

The effect on the absolute magnitudes presented in Table 1 of the selection of stars according to apparent magnitude may be computed with Malmquist's formula (1927). Generally, the results given in Table 1 are for stars brighter than apparent magnitude 6.0. To this limit the M stars in the higher galactic latitudes cannot be assumed to preserve a constancy of space density. Malmquist's formula for computing the value of M_v per unit volume will, therefore, yield a somewhat larger correction than is valid. For $\sigma = \pm 0.3$ magnitude it may be shown that the absolute magnitudes of Table 1 should be made fainter by about 0.1 magnitude when used for space density analysis.

3.2.5. *Intrinsic Colors of gM Stars.*—Photoelectric colors in the (*U, B, V*) photometric system have been published for a moderate number of giant M stars (Eggen 1960*b*). Table 3, columns 2 and 3, summarizes the results obtained for the brighter gM stars, according to spectral classes in the Mt. Wilson system.

In studies by infrared techniques, the infrared absolute magnitudes (I) and $R - I$ colors in Kron's (1956) photometric system have proved useful. In order to derive absolute infrared magnitudes, we may employ the magnitudes adopted in Table 1 together with intrinsic $V - I$ colors. Unfortunately very few $V - I$

TABLE 3

INTRINSIC COLORS OF GIANT M STARS

	$U-B$	$B-V$	$V-I$	$R-I$	CI_i
M0......	1.82	1.53	1.47	.68	1.48
M1......	1.87	1.57	1.60	.76	1.50
M2......	1.83	1.60	1.82	.84	1.57
M3......	1.80	1.60	2.19	.9:	1.54
M4......	1.74	1.58	2.41	1.0:	1.38
M5......	....	1.56	2.95	1.1:	1.25
M6......	....	....	3.40	....	1.15

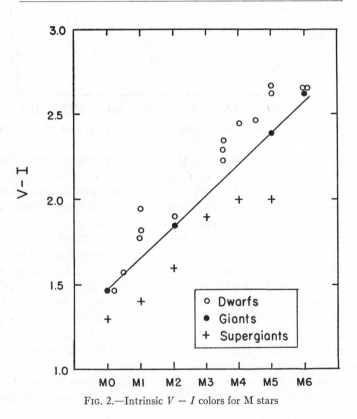

FIG. 2.—Intrinsic $V - I$ colors for M stars

and $R - I$ observations of red giants have been made, although the data published for dwarf M stars are satisfactory. Figure 2 summarizes the available information on the $V - I$ colors of dwarf, giant, and supergiant M stars. The data for dwarfs are taken from Kron (1956) and Johnson (1955). The data for supergiants refer to the M stars associated with h and χ Persei (Blanco 1955). Accurate $V - I$ colors are available for two giant M stars in the North Polar Sequence: 1r, (gM0); and 2r, (gM2). These have been published by Kron and Smith (1951). The writer has obtained $V - I$ colors corrected for absorption for over 100 giant stars of various subclasses. These colors together with those of the NPS stars were used in deriving the mean colors presented in Table 3.

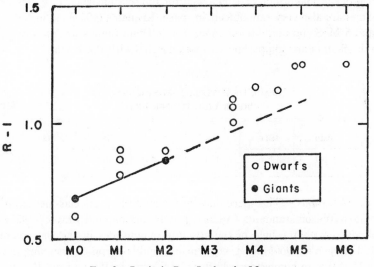

FIG. 3.—Intrinsic $R - I$ colors for M stars

The corresponding data for $R - I$ colors are summarized in Figure 3 and presented in column 5 of Table 3. Unfortunately, in this case, the colors later than class M2 are based on extrapolation. The last column of Table 3 lists the international color indices taken from the work of Nassau and van Albada (1949). These authors derived relative $m_{pg} - I$ colors for classes M0 to M4. When reduced to $V - I$ colors, their data confirm the results presented in column 4.

§ 4. SPACE DENSITY AND SURFACE DISTRIBUTION

4.1. SPACE DENSITIES IN THE SOLAR VICINITY

4.1.1. *C and S Stars.*—In the neighborhood of the sun the space density of carbon stars must be very low. Becker's analysis (1932) of the *Henry Draper Catalogue* shows only 11 N and 5 R stars brighter than visual magnitude 8.0 as compared to 1305 M stars. To this magnitude limit, the M stars are preponderantly giants. In view of our uncertainty about the luminosities of carbon stars, no accurate estimates can be made of their space densities in the solar vicinity, but the order of magnitude is 10^{-2} to 10^{-3} of that for the giant M stars. The corresponding figures for R stars are 10^{-1} to 10^{-2}. In an area of 400 square degrees about the north galactic pole, Upgren (1960) has found 54, 4 and 1 stars of type gM, R, and N brighter than $m_{pg} = 13.0$. The rapid thinning out of the red giants in the galactic pole directions makes possible an estimate of their relative space densities that is not seriously affected by the uncertainties in absolute magnitudes, assuming that the mixture of carbon to M stars does not vary with distance above the galactic plane. Upgren's results support the lower order of magnitude just indicated for the relative space densities.

S stars are also very rare objects in space. Keenan's (1954) list includes only 4 S and 5 M–S stars brighter than $m_v = 6.5$. From these scant data it appears that the S stars are comparable in space density with the R stars.

TABLE 4

SPACE DENSITIES OF gM STARS IN THE
SOLAR VICINITY PER 10^6 pc^3

M0	M1	M2	M3	M4	M5
4.1	1.6	1.4	1.1	0.5	0.2

4.1.2. *M Giants.*—The space density for giant M stars classified according to the Mt. Wilson standards (Adams, Joy, Humason, and Brayton 1935) may be obtained with the help of the absolute magnitudes in the last column of Table 1. Eggen's (1960b) list is convenient for this purpose. Assuming that the giant M stars are homogeneously distributed within 100 pc from the sun and allowing for the dispersion in absolute magnitudes indicated in Section 3.2.4, the space densities of Table 4 were derived for subclasses M0 to M5. Neckel (1958), in a study of the BD stars of M type within 6° of the old galactic equator, obtained a space density of 6.2 per 10^6 pc^3 within 430 pc from the sun for the spectral class group M2–M4, assuming an absolute visual magnitude of −0.4. Neckel's result may be adjusted for the difference in M_v between his adopted value and the ones used here by dividing by 2.3. This yields 2.7 stars of classes M2 to M4 per 10^6 pc^3 which compares well with the values of Table 4. Assuming that stars of class M5 or later have the same mean absolute magnitude as the M2 to M4 stars, Neckel's results indicate that the totality of stars later than M4 in the solar vicinity has a space density of about 0.3 stars per 10^6 pc^3.

Some idea of the density variation with distance z in the galactic north pole direction may be obtained from Upgren's (1960) list of 50 giant stars near the north galactic pole. Figure 4 presents the results (smooth line) for stars of type M2 or later. Earlier classes than these are possibly incomplete in Upgren's sur-

vey (private communication). The density value at $z = 0$ is obtained from
Table 4. The broken line in Figure 4 represents the density variation for K
giants as presented by Oort (1960). The differences between the two curves are
not significant if one considers the uncertainties in these studies. Figure 4 shows
that the M stars and the K giants have similar density distributions perpendicular to the galactic plane, and that these stars occupy a layer whose thickness at
half density points is about 500 pc.

4.2. Longitude Distributions

Nassau and Blanco (1954b) have presented the longitude distribution for
6637 stars of type M5 or later and 422 carbon stars located within 2° of the

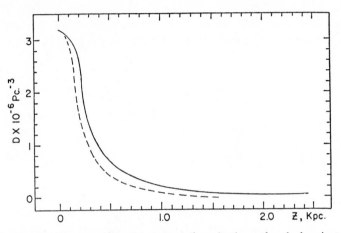

Fig. 4.—Density-distance relationship toward the galactic north pole for giant stars of
type M2 or later.

old galactic equator to the limiting apparent infrared magnitude of 10.2, and
within longitudes $l^{II} = 5°$ to 233°. A similar survey covering the longitude interval 232° to 302° has been carried out by Blanco and Münch (1955) at Tonantzintla. These two surveys are quite comparable in limiting magnitudes and
spectral classification. Smith and Smith (1956) have observed a more or less
continuous 4°-wide belt along the galactic equator which covers the southern
Milky Way and overlaps generously with the two surveys mentioned above.
The classification of M stars and the areas covered by Smith and Smith are
somewhat different than in the other surveys, but the limiting magnitudes are
similar in all three cases. From the data obtained in the overlapped regions, it
appears that the surface densities in the surveys of the Smiths should be multiplied by 2.2 for comparison with the other two surveys.

4.2.1. *Types M5 or Later.*—The longitude distribution of stars of type M5 or
later obtained from these surveys is shown in Figure 5, where the number of
M5 or later stars observed per 16 square degree areas is plotted as a function of

galactic longitude. The irregularities in this longitude distribution can be readily correlated with the presence of interstellar absorption clouds. Sanduleak (1957) has determined the longitude distribution in 25 one-square degree areas near the galactic equator selected for interstellar transparency and covering the range in $l^{II} = 24°$ to $228°$. A relatively smooth increase in numbers is found as the galactic center is approached. To the limiting infrared magnitude 10.2, Sanduleak's counts of stars of type M5 or later vary from 14 stars per square degree in the direction of the anticenter to 72 stars per square degree for an area at $l^{II} = 25°1$, $b^{II} = -3°4$ ($l^{I} = 352°8$, $b^{I} = -4°9$). The distances reached in these surveys are about 4 kpc in the clearer regions.

4.2.2. *Early M Stars.*—The longitude distribution for faint early M stars has been studied by Sanduleak (1957) and Blanco and Münch (1955). These surveys, however, cover only limited regions of the Milky Way. The stars of type M2 to M4 appear to increase in number toward the galactic center, but the

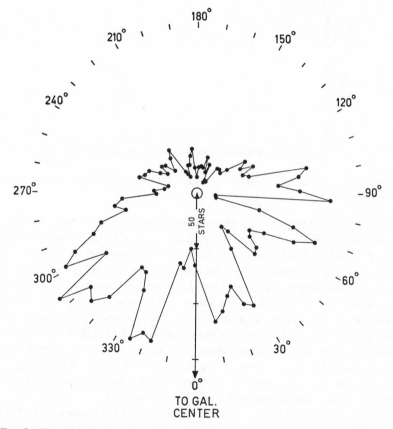

Fig. 5.—Longitude distribution of giant M stars of type M5 or later found within 2° of the Lund Galactic Equator.

effect is noticeably less pronounced than for the late M stars. The distribution also is more irregular. These effects are expected from the fainter infrared absolute magnitudes of the early M stars as compared to the late ones as well as from the differences in limiting magnitude discussed in Section 2. Among the BD early M stars, Neckel (1958) has found a pronounced maximum at $l^{II} \approx 60°$ which he interpreted as a probable concentration along the local spiral arm.

4.2.3. *Carbon Stars.*—The longitude distribution for carbon stars within 2° of the galactic equator is shown in Figure 6. The plot is based on the same infrared spectroscopic plates used in the surveys of the late M stars. The difference of this distribution and that of the late M stars is striking. From the discussion in Section 2, we may conclude that the majority of the carbon stars detected in these surveys are N stars rather than R. When observed with infrared spectroscopic techniques, these stars can be detected even when they are very faint. One may conclude that carbon stars detected in these surveys in their majority

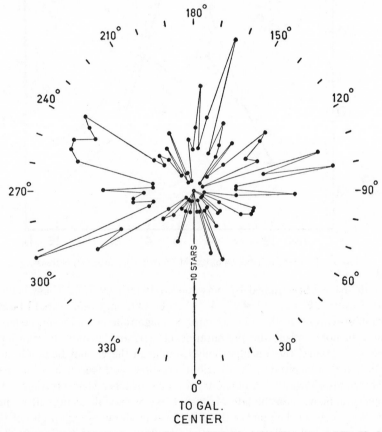

FIG. 6.—Longitude distribution of carbon stars found in infrared surveys within 2° of the Lund Galactic Equator.

do not show a preference for the galactic center. This is also indicated by detailed studies to high limiting magnitudes in relatively clear areas near the galactic center such as the one studied by Nassau and Blanco (1958), where no carbon stars were found, although the surface density of M stars was about 2000 per square degree.

4.3. Latitude Distributions

The distributions of 4235 M5 or later and 216 carbon stars located in 4°-wide belts extending in selected longitudes perpendicularly from the galactic equator

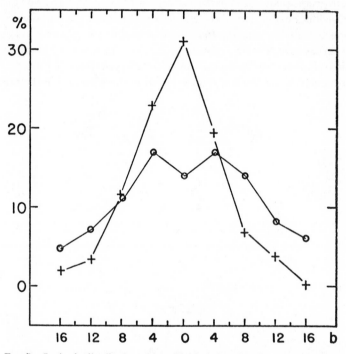

Fig. 7.—Latitude distribution of late M (circles) and carbon stars (crosses)

to ±18° have been studied by Nassau and Blanco (1954b). These belts are located every 21° from $l^{II} = 5°$ to 233°. For this purpose infrared objective prism observations to the limiting infrared magnitude of 10.2 were made. The results do not warrant the presentation of separate latitude distribution at various longitudes, these being roughly similar in the various belts. Grouping the data for all longitudes, the distributions shown in Figure 7 are obtained.

This figure shows the carbon stars to have a higher concentration toward the galactic plane than the late M stars. It is not possible at present to determine the effects on the plots of the differences in absolute magnitudes of these stars since we lack reliable information about the infrared luminosity of the carbon stars. At latitude 0°, the M star distribution shows a dip that may be explained by the effects of interstellar obscuration. The carbon stars, however, do not show the dip. This point is further discussed in the next section.

Westerlund (1959b) has studied the latitude effect for M and C stars to infrared limiting magnitude 13.0. A strongly pronounced concentration to the galactic plane is found for the carbon stars. Out of 75 objects searched in an area covering from $b^I = -2°$ to $+9°$, only four cases were found at latitudes higher than 4°.

4.4. SURFACE DISTRIBUTIONS

4.4.1. *Carbon Stars*.—Plots of the galactic distribution of the apparently bright N and R stars for the entire sky have been published by Sanford (1944). In Sanford's plots the galactic concentration of R stars is appreciably less than that of the N stars, as expected from their difference in absolute magnitudes. Sanford's plot shows a marked concentration of N stars near the galactic equator in the direction of Monoceros. This has been confirmed by the Dearborn observers (Lee, Gore, and Bartlett 1947). This nest of bright N stars may be associated with the Orion spur of the local spiral arm. It is significant that the R stars do not share in this concentration.

Nassau and Blanco (1954b) have noted that the carbon stars detected in infrared surveys seem to avoid the clearest regions of the Milky Way and often show concentrations in areas of evident interstellar obscuration. As remarked previously, these stars are preponderantly of type N. Their affinity for somewhat obscured regions may explain why the latitude distribution of carbon stars shown in Figure 7 does not show at $b^I = 0°$ a dip similar to that shown by the M stars.

4.4.2. *S-Type Stars*.—The distribution in the sky of the known S stars shows a fair amount of galactic concentration and no marked variation in frequency with longitude. The selection effects in the observations by which faint S stars have been discovered plus the fact that among the S stars two groups with distinct galactic distribution may exist (Keenan 1954; Takayanagi 1960) make it impossible to draw reliable conclusions from their surface distribution. However, a uniform search for S stars south of Dec. −25° and brighter than visual magnitude about 11.0 has been recently completed by Henize.[2] The 145 S stars detected in the survey do not show definite clusterings as would be expected for a group of stars which included spiral arm objects. According to Henize, the surface distribution of the southern S stars is similar to that of the giant M stars.

In support of the possibility of spiral arm S stars, one may mention the following suggestive coincidences. Two S stars have been found in the periphery of M8 and thus close to the young cluster NGC 6530 (The, unpublished). Four S stars have been found in the η Carinae nebulosity. Two of these are imbedded in the densest part of the nebulosity (Blanco and Münch 1955). A number of S stars have been found imbedded in obscured regions, for example, stars No. 51

---

[2] I am indebted to Dr. Karl Henize for making available his unpublished results for inclusion in this chapter.

and 52 in the list published by Blanco and Nassau (1957) are found in very small obscured regions located in otherwise relatively clear fields. These observations should not be taken as the general rule. Many S stars are found in relatively clear areas. However, the existence of these cases among a group of such rare objects supports Keenan's conclusion (1954) that among the S stars there exists a subgroup that is found in the galactic spiral arms.

4.5. Studies in Selected Clear Areas

Infrared studies based on star counts reaching M stars to about the 13th infrared magnitude have been carried out in a number of relatively clear regions. Some of the data obtained in these studies are summarized in Figure 8, where

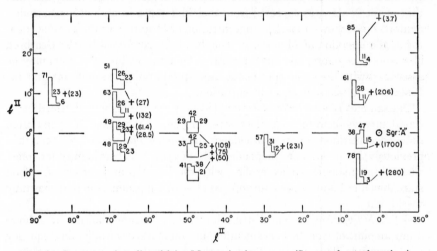

Fig. 8.—Summary of studies of faint M stars in clear areas. (See text for explanation.)

the center of each area is marked with a cross. The plot is made in the l^{II}, b^{II} system of galactic coordinates. For each region a histogram presents from left to right the percentage of stars found within the spectral class groups M2–M4, M5–M6, and M7 or later. To the right of each cross the total number, per square degree, of stars of class M2 or later is given. The area near $l^{II} = 0°.5$, $b^{II} = -3°.0$ is centered on the globular cluster NGC 6522 and was studied by Nassau and Blanco (1958). The other three areas close to $l^{II} = 0°$ were studied by Blanco and Mavridis (unpublished) who also studied the areas near $l^{II} = 81°$. The area near $l^{II} = 25°$, $b^{II} = 3°.5$ is located in the Scutum cloud and was studied by H. Albers (unpublished). The three areas at $l^{II} = 43°.5$ were studied by Westerlund (1959a). Westerlund (1959b) also studied the four areas near $l^{II} = 64°$.

Figure 8 confirms the trends found from the longitude and latitude distributions presented in Figures 5, 6, and 7. Large numbers of M stars are found in the direction of the galactic center. The concentration of M stars to the galactic plane is shown to hold also in longitudes near that of the galactic center. Furthermore, the histograms in Figure 8 suggest that the ratio of early to late-type M stars increases with galactic latitude. The increase in limiting magnitude with spectral class discussed in Section 2 and the higher infrared luminosity of the late M stars contribute to this effect. In addition, the relative numbers per unit volume of stars of different subclasses may vary with galactic position. It is difficult at present to disentangle these effects because of our uncertain knowledge of the luminosities and colors of the very late M stars.

These studies also show the higher galactic concentration of the carbon stars compared to the M stars and the fact that they are not found in large numbers in directions near that of the galactic center. This supports the conclusion that the majority of carbon stars so far discovered with infrared techniques are spiral arm objects.

Some evidence has been found by Westerlund (1959a, b), Neckel (1958), and Albers (unpublished) that the early M stars may show concentrations in galactic spiral arms. This is suggested by longitude distributions and by certain maxima in computed space densities. No general agreement, however, exists between the early M-star concentrations and the known concentrations of neutral hydrogen in the Galaxy. No such agreement must necessarily exist, however. Zwicky (1957) has shown that the red stars (presumably G, K, and M giants) in M51 are predominantly found in a nuclear bulge and also along broad, smooth spiral arms that blend into each other and which are unlike the spiral arms delineated by the blue stars and the interstellar material. On the other hand, the computed galactic space densities for early M stars are not based on a homogeneous set of assumptions as to luminosities, colors, and even spectral classification criteria. Also the selection effects on the star counts have not always been taken into account. Therefore, the intercomparison of space-density computations is difficult.

The apparent magnitude distribution for 130 stars of type M3 to M6 found by Nassau and Blanco (1958) in an area of 395 square minutes of arc near NGC 6522 is shown in Figure 9. The corresponding distribution for 85 RR Lyrae stars found by Baade (1951) in an area of 800 square minutes of arc about the same cluster is also shown. The maximum shown by the RR Lyrae star-counts at photographic magnitude 17.5 can be interpreted as caused by the high densities found as the line of sight traverses the nuclear bulge. A similar interpretation was given by Nassau and Blanco to the maximum shown by the M star-counts. In this case there were indications that the survey was essentially complete to magnitude 18.5. Newer photometric data, however, cast doubts on this limit of completeness. A check by the writer on the spectroscopic plate used by Nassau and Blanco shows that the faintest stars classified in their study have an apparent infrared magnitude of about 13.0. An estimate of 1.9 magnitudes for the total photographic absorption to NGC 6522, which is imbedded in the galactic nucleus, has been made by Kron and Mayall (1960). With the color

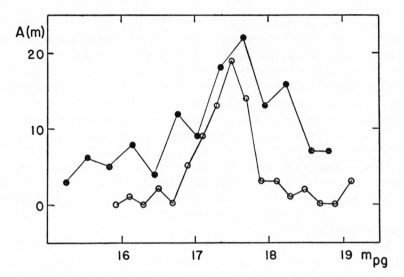

Fig. 9.—Star counts for giant M stars (dots) and for RR Lyrae stars (circles) in a clear region near the galactic center.

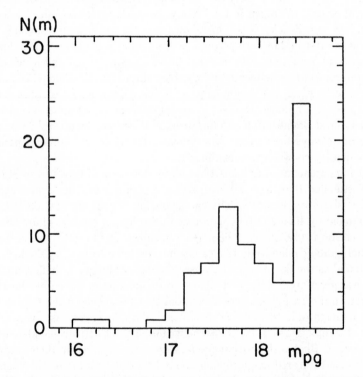

Fig. 10.—Apparent magnitude distribution of stars of class M0 or later near NGC 6522

indices presented in Table 3, allowing for absorption, it is estimated that an M5 star of infrared magnitude 13.0 will have a photographic magnitude of 17.8. This is uncomfortably close to the magnitude of the maximum of the star counts shown at 17.6.

In order to determine the reality of this maximum, the writer has studied on a pair of direct plates (blue and red sensitive) all the stars brighter than photographic magnitude 18.5 in an area of 11 square minutes adjacent to NGC 6522. Of 570 stars with $m = 18.5$ or less, 79 objects were found to have colors corresponding to about class M0 or later. The apparent magnitude distribution of these stars is shown in Figure 10. A well-defined maximum appears at photographic magnitude 17.7. This may be interpreted as formed by the red tip of the giant branch of stars concentrated in the nucleus. The rise in star-counts beyond $m = 18.2$ is probably due to a blend of foreground and background red stars. From the data in Figure 10, one may estimate that, at the closest approach to the galactic center, the line of sight encounters an M giant star density of about 30 stars per 10^6 pc^3. In this case the line of sight passes about 600 pc above the galactic nucleus. If we take $M_{pg} = +0.4$ as the absolute magnitude of the stars causing the peak at $m = 17.7$ in Figure 10, a distance of 12 kpc may be derived to the galactic nucleus.

§ 5. SPACE MOTIONS
5.1. M Giants

The solar motion with respect to the giant M stars as well as their velocity ellipsoid have been investigated by several writers. The results, which are summarized by Trumpler and Weaver (1953), show that the solar motion with respect to the giant M stars is similar to that of the K giants. There is some indication of an increase of the mean solar velocity with advancing spectral class. In a recent unpublished study, Sanduleak has subdivided the gM stars for which radial velocities are available into the spectral class groups M0–M4 (603 stars) and M5 or later (245 stars). The respective values of the solar velocity found from radial velocities are 19 and 22 km/sec. Thus the trend among the giants for the increase of this velocity with spectral class is preserved among the M stars. The galactic coordinates of the solar apex found by Sanduleak are: $l^{II} = 68°$, $b^{II} = +27°$ ($l^I = 35°$, $b^I = +26°$) for the early M stars and $l^{II} = 70°$, $b^{II} = +22°$ ($l^I = 37°$, $b^I = +21°$) for the late M stars.

The velocity ellipsoid characteristics for 603 gM0 to gM4 stars were also determined by Sanduleak. In the usual notation (Trumpler and Weaver 1953, p. 332), his values of the dispersions in km/sec are $\Sigma_1 = 26$, $\Sigma_2 = 18$, $\Sigma_3 = 24$. Compared to the values for the giant G and K stars given by Trumpler and Weaver (1953) a trend of increasing dispersions with advancing spectral class is observed.

Johnson (1957) has suggested that it may be possible to determine in an approximate manner from what part of the main sequence a group of stars, such as the giants, evolved. This may be done by looking for similarities in the peculiar motions. This method suggests an evolutionary relationship between M giants and main-sequence stars of late F or early G type. However, Roman (1952) has shown that among the G and K giants two groups may be selected spectroscopically which have different peculiar motions. No spectroscopic criteria for a similar division of the M giants are known at present. Vyssotsky (1951, 1957) finds that, among the K giants, a vertex deviation is shown only by the stars with velocity components c, perpendicular to the galactic plane, of less than 15 km/sec after correction for solar motion. These stars are interpreted as being closely related to Baade's population I. Individual space-motions for the M giants brighter than visual magnitude 5.0 have been presented by Eggen (1960b). Two possibilities for the absolute magnitudes are considered by Eggen, $M_v = 0.0$ and $M_v = -1.0$. The second of these is not far from the luminosity assumed here for stars of type M2 to M6. The writer has subdivided Eggen's data according to velocity components $c \leq 15$ and $c > 15$ km/sec. Although these groups contain, respectively, only 35 and 20 M2 or later stars, their distribution of velocity vector points projected on the galactic plane shows similarities to the plots of the gK stars presented by Vyssotsky (1951). A vertex deviation appears definite only for the group with $c \leq 15$ km/sec. Thus, if the existence of a vertex deviation is a population indicator, as suggested by Vyssotsky (1957), the giant M stars, like the K giants, include objects of different populations.

5.2. CARBON STARS

The solar motion with respect to the R stars has been studied by Vandervort (1958). The velocity ellipsoid of these stars has been investigated by McLeod (1947). A similar analysis for N stars is not known to the writer. Vandervort finds a solar motion of 34 km/sec with apex at $l^{II} = 73°$, $b^{II} = +6°$ ($l^{I} = 41°$, $b^{I} = +5°$), while McLeod finds $\Sigma_1 = 48$, $\Sigma_2 = 16$, $\Sigma_3 = 23$ km/sec. Among the main-sequence stars the peculiar motions of the R stars are best matched by dwarf G and K stars. If the R stars have evolved from this section of the main sequence, they must be older objects than the giant M stars and, at the same time, less massive stars. The R stars, as compared to N stars, show a striking preponderance among high-velocity objects (Sanford 1944). In view of this, it is interesting that, compared to the giant M stars, there is a relative scarcity of carbon stars and therefore of R stars in the Sagittarius clouds.

§ 6. SUMMARY

1. The classification criteria and observational selection effects in the discovery of the very late-type giants have been reviewed in Section 2. Infrared studies are most useful for stars of type M2 or later and for N stars. On a given plate, the very late M types and the N stars may be classified to fainter magnitudes than the early M stars.

2. The absolute magnitudes and colors of the late-type giants have been re-

viewed in Section 3. More reliable absolute magnitudes and intrinsic colors are known for the giant M and the R stars than for the N and S stars. In statistical investigations, the effects of variability among M stars earlier than M6 are not serious and may be allowed for by increasing the luminosity dispersion. There are apparently no differences in luminosity among the normal M giants in the solar neighborhood, the high-velocity gM stars, the irregular variables of M type at maximum light, and the gM stars found in great numbers near the galactic center. The giant M stars found in open clusters are more luminous than the field M giants and, at the same time, less luminous than the reddest stars found in globular clusters.

3. The space density of giant M stars in the solar neighborhood is about 9 stars per 10^6 pc^3. In a direction perpendicular to the galactic plane this density decreases to half that value at 250 pc from the plane. The space density increases toward the galactic center and decreases toward the anticenter. The rates of these variations are not reliably known. Among the gM stars, possibly half or more of the objects earlier than M5, may be concentrated in spiral arms and at the same time in the nuclear bulge of the Galaxy.

4. Among the carbon stars, the N-type objects are, in their majority, apparently concentrated in spiral arms along with other classical population I objects. The R-type stars apparently are not concentrated in the spiral arms, but so far no evidence exists of their presence in the galactic nuclear bulge.

5. The S-type stars apparently can also be divided into two groups, one belonging to the classical population I and the other having a galactic distribution similar to the long-period variables.

6. Comparisons of the velocity ellipsoids of the red giant stars with velocity ellipsoids of main-sequence stars show similarities between giant M and dwarf F stars, and between R stars and dwarf G–K stars. However, it is not clear at present that these similarities signify evolutionary relationships.

The writer wishes to thank the various investigators mentioned in the text who have made their unpublished work available for discussion here. Many of the writer's own previously unpublished results, as well as those of Mr. Sanduleak, were obtained with the support of the National Science Foundation, and this is gratefully acknowledged.

REFERENCES

ADAMS, W. S., JOY, A. H.,
  HUMASON, M. L., and
  BRAYTON, A. M.   1935   *Ap. J.*, **81**, 187.
ARP, H. C.   1959   *A.J.*, **64**, 33.
BAADE, W.   1944   *Ap. J.*, **100**, 137.
                        1951   *Pub. Obs. University of Michigan*, **10**, 7.
BECKER, F.   1932   *Hdb. d. Astrophys.*, **5**, 109.

Blanco, V. M.   1955   *Ap. J.*, **122**, 434.
    1958   *Ibid.*, **127**, 191.

Blanco, V. M., and
   Münch, L.   1955   *Bull. Obs. Tonantzintla y Tacubaya*, No. 12, p. 17.

Blanco, V. M., and
   Nassau, J. J.   1957   *Ap. J.*, **125**, 408.

Cameron, D. M., and
   Nassau, J. J.   1955   *Ap. J.*, **122**, 177.
    1956   *Ibid.*, **124**, 346.

Cox, A. N.   1955   *Ap. J.*, **121**, 628.

Eggen, O. J.   1958   *M.N.*, **118**, 154.
    1960*a*   *Ibid.*, **120**, 430.
    1960*b*   *Ibid.*, p. 448.

Feast, M. W.   1957   *M.N.*, **117**, 193.

Fehrenbach, C.   1958   *Hdb. d. Phys.*, ed. S. Flügge (Berlin: Springer-Verlag), **50**, 1 (see esp. pp. 61–63 and p. 72).

Gaposchkin, S.   1956   *Variable Stars*, Moscow, **10**, 337.

Hoffleit, D.   1942   *Harvard Obs. Circ.*, No. 448.

Iwanowska, W., and
   Wayman, P.   1952   *Ap. J.*, **115**, 129.

Johnson, H. L.   1955   *Ann. d'ap.*, **18**, 292.

Johnson, H. M.   1957   *Pub. A.S.P.*, **69**, 54.

Joy, A. H.   1942   *Ap. J.*, **96**, 344.

Keenan, P. C.   1952   *Trans. I.A.U.*, **8**, 423.
    1954   *Ap. J.*, **120**, 484.

Keenan, P. C., and
   Hynek, J. A.   1945   *Ap. J.*, **101**, 265.

Keenan, P. C., and
   Keller, G.   1953   *Ap. J.*, **117**, 241.

Keenan, P. C., and
   Morgan, W. W.   1941   *Ap. J.*, **94**, 501.
    1951   *Astrophysics*, ed. J. A. Hynek (New York: McGraw-Hill Book Co.), p. 23.

Keenan, P. C., and
   Teske, R. G.   1956   *Ap. J.*, **124**, 499.

Kron, G. E.   1956   *Proc. Third Berkeley Symp. Math. Statist. Prob.*, ed. Jerzy Neyman (Berkeley: University of California Press), **3**, 39.

Kron, G. E., and
   Mayall, N. U.   1960   *A.J.*, **65**, 581.

Kron, G. E., and
   Smith, J. L.   1951   *Ap. J.*, **113**, 324.

Kukarkin, B. V.   1947   *A.J. U.S.S.R.*, **24**, 269.

Lee, O. J., Gore, G. D.,
   and Bartlett, T. J.   1947   *Ann. Dearborn Obs.*, **5**, Pt. 6.

McLeod, N. W.   1947   *Ap. J.*, **105**, 390.

Malmquist, K. G.   1927   *Lunds Obs. Medd.*, Ser. II, No. 46.

MAVRIDIS, L. N.   1959   *Ap. J.*, **130**, 626.
MERRILL, P. W.   1940   *Spectra of Long Period Variable Stars* (Chicago:
                                   University of Chicago Press), p. 98.
                          1952   *Ap. J.*, **116**, 21.

MOORE, J. H., and
  PADDOCK, G. F.   1950   *Ap. J.*, **112**, 48.
MORGAN, W. W., and
  MAYALL, N. U.   1957   *Pub. A.S.P.*, **69**, 291.
NASSAU, J. J., and
  BLANCO, V. M.   1954a   *Ap. J.*, **120**, 129.
                          1954b   *Ibid.*, p. 118.
                          1958   *Ibid.*, **128**, 46.

NASSAU, J. J.,
  BLANCO, V. M., and
  CAMERON, D. M.   1956   *Ap. J.*, **124**, 522.
NASSAU, J. J.,
  BLANCO, V. M., and
  MORGAN, W. W.   1954   *Ap. J.*, **120**, 478.
NASSAU, J. J., and
  COLACEVICH, A.   1950   *Ap. J.*, **111**, 199.
NASSAU, J. J., and
  STEPHENSON, C. B.   1960   *Ap. J.*, **132**, 130.
NASSAU, J. J., and
  VAN ALBADA, G. B.   1949   *Ap. J.*, **109**, 391.
NECKEL, H.   1958   *Ap. J.*, **128**, 510.
OORT, J. H.   1960   *B.A.N.*, **15**, 45.
PEREK, L.   1957   *Mém. Soc. R. Sci. Liège*, Ser. 4, **18**, 270 (7th Liège
                                   Internat. Colloquium).

RHIJN, P. J. VAN   1939   *Pub. Kapteyn Astr. Lab. Groningen*, No. 49.
ROMAN, N. G.   1952   *Ap. J.*, **116**, 122.
                          1955   *Ap. J. Suppl.*, **2**, 195.

RUSSELL, H. N., and
  MOORE, C. E.   1938   *Ap. J.*, **87**, 389.
SANDAGE, A. R., and
  WALLERSTEIN, G.   1960   *Ap. J.*, **131**, 598.
SANDULEAK, N.   1957   *A.J.*, **62**, 150.
SANFORD, R. F.   1944   *Ap. J.*, **99**, 145.
SHARPLESS, S.   1957   *Pub. A.S.P.*, **69**, 397.
SMITH, E. v. P., and
  SMITH, H. J.   1956   *A.J.*, **61**, 273.
STEBBINS, J., and
  HUFFER, C. M.   1930   *Pub. Washburn Obs.*, **15**, 139.
STEPHENSON, C. B.   1959   *Pub. A.S.P.*, **71**, 145.
TAKAYANAGI, W.   1960   *Pub. Astr. Soc. Japan*, **12**, No. 3, 314.
TRUMPLER, R. J., and
  WEAVER, H. F.   1953   *Statistical Astronomy* (Berkeley: University of
                                   California Press).

UPGREN, A. R.   1960   *A.J.*, **65**, 644.

VANDERVORT, G. L.   1958   *A.J.*, **63**, 477.

VELGHE, A. G.   1957   *Ap. J.*, **125**, 728.

VYSSOTSKY, A. N.   1951   *A.J.*, **56**, 62.

                         1957   *Pub. A.S.P.*, **69**, 109.

WALKER, M. F.   1958   *Ap. J.*, **128**, 562.

WALKER, M. F., and

    BIDELMAN, W. P.   1960   *Pub. A.S.P.*, **72**, 50.

WESTERLUND, B.   1959*a*   *Ap. J.*, **130**, 178.

                        1959*b*   *Ap. J. Suppl.*, **4**, 73.

                        1960   *Nova Acta Reg. Soc. Sci. Uppsala, Ser. IV*, **17**, No. 8 (= *Uppsala Astr. Obs. Ann.*, **4**, No. 7).

WILSON, O. C.   1959   *Ap. J.*, **130**, 499.

WILSON, O. C., and

    BAPPU, M. K. V.   1957   *Ap. J.*, **125**, 661.

WILSON, R. E.   1942   *Ap. J.*, **96**, 371.

WILSON, R. E., and

    MERRILL, P. W.   1942   *Ap. J.*, **95**, 248.

ZWICKY, F.   1957   *Morphological Astronomy* (Berlin: Springer-Verlag), p. 201.

CHAPTER 13

Distribution and Motions of Variable Stars

L. PLAUT

Kapteyn Laboratory, Groningen

§ 1. INTRODUCTION

THIS chapter describes investigations of the distribution and motions of variable stars in the disk as well as in the halo of the Galaxy. The problems involved in the study of variable stars in relation to galactic structure have been thoroughly discussed by Kukarkin in *Erforschung der Struktur und Entwicklung der Sternsysteme auf der Grundlage des Studiums veränderlicher Sterne* (1954); and by Payne-Gaposchkin in *Variable Stars and Galactic Structure* (1954a).

In attempting to understand the large-scale structure of the galactic system, by means of variable stars, it is customary to investigate separately the space and velocity distributions of the different types of objects. Two conditions must then be met: the objects must be recognized at large distances, and they must constitute a homogeneous group. If we choose, for example, the RR Lyrae variables: (*a*) we investigate the absolute magnitude and intrinsic color, possibly as a function of some easily observable parameter like the period or the shape of the light curve; (*b*) we make a survey of completeness; (*c*) we determine the position, apparent magnitude, and color of each star in the group and then derive the position of all these stars in the galactic system.

This procedure will yield the spatial distribution. We can also proceed by statistical methods. Oort, in a classical paper, developed a method of deriving information on the spatial distribution from that of the velocities and, with his collaborators, applied this method to long-period variables (Oort and van Tulder 1942) and to RR Lyrae variables (Oort and van Woerkom 1941).

Several extended observational programs related to these problems are under way at present:

1. The determination of proper motions of RR Lyrae variables by van Herk at Leiden.

267

2. The determination of proper motions of variables brighter than magnitude 12.0 at maximum, by means of Carte du Ciel plates (see p. 33 of the report on *I.A.U. Symp.*, No. 1).

3. An investigation of faint variables in four regions on Palomar 48-inch Schmidt plates at Groningen (see p. 22 of the report on *I.A.U. Symp.*, No. 7).

§ 2. TYPES OF VARIABLE STARS TO BE CONSIDERED

The variable stars considered here are taken from the *Second General Catalogue of Variable Stars* (Kukarkin *et al.* 1958, henceforth denoted by *GCVS*). We shall consider the following types:

1. The *ultrashort-period stars:* These are the few classified in the *GCVS* as δ Scuti stars and those RR Lyrae stars with periods shorter than 0.200 day. This limit has been taken because the combined frequency distribution of the periods of δ Scuti and RR Lyrae variables shows a minimum at this value. A plot with the period P as abscissa and the amplitude A as ordinate (P-A diagram) shows no gap between the δ Scuti and RR Lyrae types. Eggen (1960*b*), among others, doubts whether these stars should be considered as a single group.

2. The *RR Lyrae stars:* Those classified as RR in the *GCVS* with $P > 0.200$ day.

3. The *W Virginis stars:* Stars from a list by Petit (1960*a*), who made a critical study of the criteria in order to distinguish type I cepheids (designated in the *GCVS* as Cδ) from type II cepheids (CW). Other lists (*GCVS;* Payne-Gaposchkin 1956; Walraven, Muller, and Oosterhoff 1958) show only a few discrepancies from that of Petit.

4. The *RV Tauri and the semi-regular stars* as classified in the *GCVS*, except all stars classified as SRa and a few of those classified as SRb.

5. *Long-period stars:* Stars classified as M in the *GCVS*, supplemented by the SRa stars and a few SRb stars, like U Boo and X Mon (cf. Merrill 1960).

It is well known that the divisions between these five types of variables are not clear-cut. For a number of borderline cases it is not certain to which class they belong. In fact, it may be that all the groups should be considered as one, with more or less continuously changing properties. For a further discussion, see chapter 18 in Volume III of this Compendium.

Novae and type I cepheids have been excluded because they are considered in chapters 14 and 8 in this volume; other types, either because they contain only small numbers of stars or because they have not yet been observed systematically.

§ 3. OBSERVATIONS AND INTRINSIC PROPERTIES

3.1. PHYSICAL CHARACTERISTICS

3.1.1. *Apparent magnitude.*—We shall use the following observational data: positions, proper motions, radial velocities, magnitudes, color indices, and spectral classifications.

The variety of systems used to obtain apparent magnitudes (zero point and scale) causes a certain amount of confusion. The *GCVS* quotes the magnitudes at maximum and minimum brightness reduced to the "modern photometric scales" by using the most recent and accurate observations available for each variable star (see *GCVS*, pp. 13 and 30).

In the larger surveys of variable stars (see Table 1) the magnitudes are in the system of the *Mount Wilson Catalogue of Photographic Magnitudes in Selected Areas 1–139* (Seares, Kapteyn, and van Rhijn 1930), or in that of the *Durchmusterung of Selected Areas* (Pickering, Kapteyn, and van Rhijn 1918–24). In some cases, corrections to the International System (connected with the North Polar Sequence) have been applied. For some of the Leiden-Johannesburg fields a new determination of the magnitude scale and zero point has been made by Kwee (1962). Photoelectric light curves are available for only a small number of stars, mostly those of short period. The reduction of all light curves to a uniform system like the *UBV* system of magnitudes would obviously be valuable.

3.1.2. *Period.*—The period, even if it should vary, as it does for some of the variables, can be determined more accurately than is necessary for statistical investigations. For RV Tauri stars or SR stars doubts exist, in some cases, as to whether the period should be doubled (Arp 1955).

3.1.3. *Shape of light curve.*—Many light curves have been derived from eye estimates, either visually (especially for long-period stars) or on photographic plates. The shape of a light curve obtained in this manner can be distorted because of the tendency of the observer either to prefer or to avoid estimates equal to the brightness of one of the comparison stars.

Several authors have suggested analytical expressions to describe the shape of a light curve. In most cases, however, the amplitude and one or two parameters giving a measure for the asymmetry are sufficient. Such parameters may be

$$\epsilon = \frac{(\text{phase of max.}) - (\text{phase of min.})}{\text{period}},$$

and

$$\zeta = \frac{m (\Delta \text{ phase} = .5) - \bar{m}}{\text{amplitude}},$$

where $m(\Delta \text{ phase} = .5)$ is the magnitude at which the interval between the rising and descending branches is half the period. Ludendorff (1928) and Campbell (1955) proposed similar parameters. It is well known that, in many cases, amplitude and shape vary considerably.

3.1.4. *Color index and interstellar absorption.*—Accurate color indices are available for only a relatively small number of variables, mostly for those of short period. For a statistical investigation, color indices must be relegated to a specific phase of the light variation.

Many authors have discussed the problem of intrinsic color, but a wholly satisfactory method of eliminating the interstellar absorption has not yet been obtained. For variables with $|b| > 20°$, a first approximation can be made by means of the formula

$$\text{absorption} = \frac{a_0 c}{\sin |b|}\left[1 - \exp\left(-\frac{r \sin |b|}{c}\right)\right]$$

(see Parenago 1940 and 1945; van Rhijn 1949; Geyer 1961).

3.1.5. *Spectral classification.*—In many cases, variable stars do not fit into the common sequence of spectral types. Those derived, for example, from hydrogen and from metallic lines differ from one another in extreme cases by an entire spectral class. References to investigations concerning these and other spectral peculiarities will be given below.

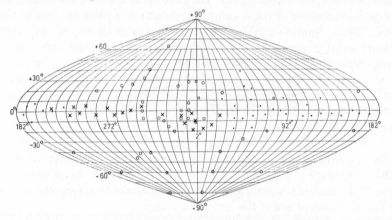

Fig. 1.—Distribution of the regions which have been extensively searched for variable stars. Open circles are Harvard fields; crosses, Leiden-Johannesburg fields; filled circles, Sonneberg fields; and squares, Palomar-Groningen fields. Longitudes are l^{II} (approximately); latitudes are b^I.

3.2. COMPLETENESS OF SURVEYS

The fact that new variables are found regularly even among rather bright stars shows that completeness has not yet been reached for the brighter stars except in the most extensively observed regions. Although this is obviously true for variables with small amplitudes, even those with a brightness range of more than half a magnitude are not by any means completely known among the brighter stars. A complete search, for example among stars brighter than magnitude 10.0, is urgently needed (see *I.A.U.* 1955).

A compilation of some of the larger survey programs is given in Table 1. References to other programs are given in the reports of the *Symposia on Coordination of Galactic Research* (*I.A.U.* 1955 and 1959) and by the author (1956). Figure 1 shows the distribution of those Harvard, Sonneberg, Leiden-Johannesburg, and Palomar fields that have been searched extensively.

The great majority of the fainter variable stars has been found by comparing a pair of photographic plates. The comparison was made by using, for example, a positive plate and a negative one, by applying either the so-called blinking method (visually or by a television technique), or a stereoscopic method, or by examining the two plates through a red and a blue filter (Plaut and Borgman 1954). The completeness of discovering variable stars by these methods has been discussed by van Gent (1933) and by Hoffmeister (1933) as well as by others. A detailed account of the problems involved is given in Appendix 1 to this chapter.

3.3. PROPER MOTIONS AND RADIAL VELOCITIES

Proper motions of the brighter variables are found in the Yale and Cape repetitions of the *AG* catalogues. More accurate values can be computed by a new reduction of the old Carte du Ciel positions combined with the Yale, Cape,

TABLE 1

SOME LARGE OBSERVATIONAL PROGRAMS

No.	Designation	Number of Fields*	Size	Limit-ing Mag-nitude	Reference to Description of Program
1........	Harvard Milky Way Fields	649 (51)	8°5	16.5	Shapley (1928)
2........	Harvard Milton Fields	54	......	10	Payne-Gaposchkin and Gaposchkin (1952a)†
3........	Sonneberg	37	9.1	16.5	Hoffmeister *et al.* (1938)†
4........	Leiden-Johannesburg	33 (26)	10	16	Leiden (1948)
5........	A.A.V.S.O.	....	......	11	Mayall (1957)†
6........	Palomar-Groningen	4	6.7	19.5	*I.A.U.* (1955, 1959)

* In parentheses: number of investigated fields.

† REMARKS TO TABLE 1

Program no. 2: Covers the whole sky; the limiting magnitude quoted is the brightness at maximum.
Program no. 3: Various instruments of different size have been used.
Program no. 5: Visual observations by amateurs of a large number, mostly long-period, variables brighter than magnitude 11.0 at maximum.

FURTHER REFERENCES TO THE LARGE OBSERVATIONAL PROGRAMS

No.	Magnitude Scale	Summary of Results	Detailed Results
1........	Pickering, Kapteyn, and van Rhijn (1918–24)	Miller (1946)	Many publications from Harvard
2........	Pg International	Payne-Gaposchkin and Gaposchkin (1952a, b)	Payne-Gaposchkin *et al.* (1943); Payne-Gaposchkin (1954b)
3........	Seares, Kapteyn, and van Rhijn (1930)	Various publications from Sonneberg and Babelsberg	Various publications from Sonneberg and Babelsberg
4........	Pickering, Kapteyn, and van Rhijn (1918–24); Kwee (1962)	Leiden (1948)	Various publications, mostly from Leiden
5........	Harvard Visual	Campbell (1955)	*A.A.V.S.O. Reports*
6........	*B, V*	....	....

and *AGK2* (Bergedorf and Bonn) positions (Heckmann, Dieckvoss, and Kox 1948). The *AGK3*, now in preparation, will yield a further improvement.

Various special programs deal with: (1) the RR Lyrae stars by Pavlovskaya (1953), by Lourens (1960), and by van Herk (in preparation); (2) long-period variables by Alden and Osvalds (1961) and Osvalds and Risley (1961); (3) the Carte du Ciel program for stars with $m_{max} < 12.0$. This is still in progress; results from the following zones are now available: Toulouse (Paloque *et al.* 1958–61), Helsinki (Ölander *et al.* 1959), San Fernando (in press), and Cape (Russo 1961).

Since the appearance of Wilson's *General Catalogue of Radial Velocities* (1953), only a few observations of radial velocities have been published, for example those of Kinman (1961), Joy (1955), and Feast (1963). Programs for long-period variables are under way at Perkins Observatory and at Radcliffe Observatory (according to communications at the Berkeley I.A.U. meeting).

§4. SOLAR MOTION AND VELOCITY DISTRIBUTION; METHODS

The equations for the solar motion are

$$4.74 \ r \ \mu_l = -X \sin l^{II} - Y \cos l^{II},$$

$$4.74 \ r \ \mu_b = -X \cos l^{II} \sin b^{II} + Y \sin l^{II} \sin b^{II} - Z \cos b^{II},$$

$$v = +X \cos l^{II} \cos b^{II} - Y \sin l^{II} \cos b^{II} - Z \sin b^{II},$$

where proper motions μ_l, μ_b are expressed in seconds of arc per year and the radial velocity, v, in km/sec; X is the component of the solar motion in the direction $l^{II} = 180°$, $b^{II} = 0°$, Y the component in the direction $l^{II} = 90°$, $b^{II} = 0°$, and Z that in the direction $b^{II} = 90°$.

For the differential galactic rotation, we have the first-order expressions

$$4.74 \ \mu_l = A \cos 2l^{II} + B,$$

$$v = rA \sin 2l^{II}.$$

It can be shown that second-order terms can be neglected for the stars considered in the present chapter.

From these equations, the solar motion with respect to the type of stars considered as well as the constants A and B of the galactic rotation can be derived, in principle. It has, however, been shown that in practice it is preferable to adopt the components X_0, Y_0, Z_0 of the solar motion relative to the circular motion, and to determine from the distant stars only the values of the asymmetrical drift $V_0 = Y - Y_0$, and of the rotational term rA. It is not yet possible to determine the orientation of the velocity ellipsoid for variable stars, since the observations, especially those of proper motions, are still neither accurate nor numerous enough.

§ 5. DERIVATION OF DENSITY DISTRIBUTION; METHODS

In principle, densities can be determined from positions and apparent and absolute magnitudes as described in the Introduction. In practice, however, the stars have to be combined into large groups, as was done by Perek (1951) in an analysis of the RR Lyrae variables. A number of extensively searched fields, with the exception of those too near the galactic plane, were considered. Completeness factors and interstellar absorption were taken into account. From the numbers of variables in each field and their distributions over the apparent magnitudes, Perek computed densities, assuming the value 0.0 for the median absolute photographic magnitude. Several groups were combined into larger regions defined by limits in the distance, R, from the axis of the galactic system and the distance, z, from the galactic plane. In this manner, the density was derived as a function of the coordinates R and z.

An indirect, but valuable, method which yields information about the local density gradient only, is based on a relation between this gradient and the velocity distribution (Oort 1928):

$$\frac{\partial \log \nu}{\partial R} = -\left[\frac{2}{\pi} \cdot \frac{V_0(2\Theta_c - V_0)}{a^2} + \left(1 - \frac{b^2}{a^2}\right)\right]\frac{\text{Mod}}{R_0}.$$

Here (1) V_0 is the systematic velocity in the direction of $l^{\mathrm{II}} = 270°$, $b^{\mathrm{II}} = 0°$ with respect to the circular velocity (the asymmetric drift); (2) Θ_c is the circular velocity at R_0; (3) a, b are the average peculiar motions in the directions $l^{\mathrm{II}} = 0°$, $b^{\mathrm{II}} = 0°$, and $l^{\mathrm{II}} = 90°$, $b^{\mathrm{II}} = 0°$, respectively; (4) ν is the space density; and (5) R_0 is the distance of the sun from the galactic center. Application of this method will be described in sections 7 to 10.

§ 6. ULTRASHORT-PERIOD VARIABLES

The GCVS contains 34 variables which can be classified as belonging to this group. In addition, two variables with periods less than 0.20 day are members of globular clusters (Sawyer 1955). If we plot these variables in a period-amplitude diagram and consider the value of the parameter ϵ (see sec. 3.1.3), we see that there is a continuous transition between Bailey's types c and a. Some of the stars, like SX Phe and AI Vel, are well known because of the varying shape of the light curve.

It is obvious that only a small fraction of the variables of this group have yet been discovered. Many of them have small amplitudes; moreover, faint stars are usually examined on plates with exposure times which are long relative to these short periods. The probability of discovering a variable with an amplitude of 1.0 magnitude and a Cepheid-type light curve from a single pair of plates is 0.054 on plates with an exposure time of 0.25 of the period, whereas this probability is 0.066 for a relatively much shorter exposure time (see Table 20).

Absolute magnitudes and colors for a few individual objects are given in

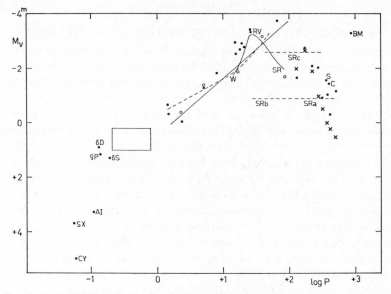

FIG. 2.—Period-luminosity diagram for various types of variables. Dots with $\log P < 0$ are ultrashort-period stars. Data by Kinman (1959a) and Eggen (1960a, c). Stars are marked by the first two letters of their names in Table 2; rectangle: RR Lyrae variables in globular clusters, see sec. 7.5; dots, circles, straight solid line, and curved broken line, $0 < \log P < 2$: variables in globular clusters, see also Fig. 9; solid curve: types W, RV, SR according to Rosino (1951); horizontal dashed lines: types SRa, b, and c according to Joy (1942), see sec. 9; dots with $\log P > 2$: long-period variables according to Osvalds and Risley (1961), see sec. 10.2; crosses with $\log P > 2$: long-period variables according to Wilson and Merrill (1942), see sec. 10.2; dot marked BM: BM Sco according to Eggen (1961a).

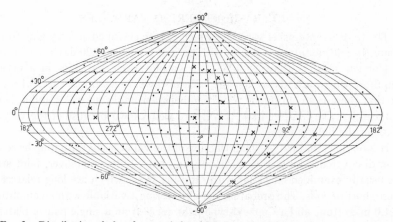

FIG. 3.—Distribution of ultrashort-period and RR Lyrae variables with mean photographic magnitude brighter than 12.0. Crosses are ultrashort-period stars, $P < 0.20$ day; filled circles are RR Lyrae variables, $P > 0.20$ day. Longitudes are l^{II} (approximately); latitudes are b^I.

Table 2. Similar values were derived by Smith (1955) and by Woltjer (1956). From these data we conclude that a period-luminosity relation exists, which at $P = 0.200$ day fades into the luminosity of the RR Lyrae stars (see Fig. 2).

The ultrashort-period variables with mean m_{pg} brighter than 12.0 are plotted in Figure 3 (crosses) in galactic coordinates. They seem to be spread rather uniformly over the sky. Their number is much too small for more detailed conclusions. It decreases rapidly with decreasing apparent brightness. At first sight, this decrease seems to be greater than would be expected from the probability of discovery. As to the motions of this class, Woltjer (1956) derived a solar motion of 47 km/sec with an apex at $l^{II} = 64°$, $b^{II} = + 14°$ and a dispersion

TABLE 2

ABSOLUTE MAGNITUDES AND COLORS OF ULTRASHORT-PERIOD VARIABLES

| STAR | PERIOD (DAYS) | M_{pg} | | | M_v | $B-V$ |
| | | Kinman (1959a) | | | Eggen (1960a, c) | McNamara and Augason (1962) |
		Pulsation Theory	Trigon Parallaxes	s.d.	Moving Groups	Narrow-Band Photometry
SX Phe......	0.056	+3.7	+4.1	±1.3	....	....
CY Aqr......	.061	....	....	....	+5	....
DQ Cep......	.079	....	....	....	....	+1.8	+0.29
AI Vel.......	.111	+2.7	+4.3	±0.6	....	....
CC And.....	.125	....	....	....	....	+2.2	+0.29
δ Del........	.135	....	....	....	+0.9	+1.6	+0.29
ρ Pup.......	.141	+2.4	+0.3	±1.5	....	+1.3	+0.39
δ Sct........	0.194	+1.4	+1.6	....	....	+1.9	+0.32

of the velocities of $±37$ km/sec in one coordinate. There are still very few observational data available for this class of stars.

§ 7. RR LYRAE VARIABLES

7.1. PERIOD-AMPLITUDE DIAGRAMS

Sixty years ago, Bailey (1902) divided the RR Lyrae variables, then called cluster-type variables, in three groups (a, b, and c) according to the shape and amplitude of their light variation. From period-amplitude diagrams we see that there is a continuous transition between groups a and b. Thus, at present, we usually combine both of them into a single group called a. In most globular clusters, the separation between groups a and c is clearly visible in a P-A diagram, although there is, in some cases, an overlap in P. The c-type stars have small amplitudes, generally smaller than 0.6 magnitude. Consequently, they are much less completely known than the type a stars, except in some rather ex-

tensively examined globular clusters. Thus, we shall restrict part of the following discussion to type a stars.

Figure 4 shows P-A diagrams for the globular clusters NGC 5904 and NGC
7078. These two clusters are extreme cases as regards the frequency distribution
of the period and the period-amplitude relation. Two types of globular clusters

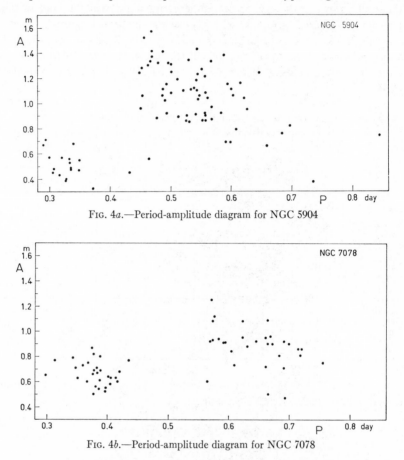

Fig. 4a.—Period-amplitude diagram for NGC 5904

Fig. 4b.—Period-amplitude diagram for NGC 7078

are commonly distinguished, one with $\langle P \rangle = 0.54$ day, the other with $\langle P \rangle = 0.64$ day for type a stars (Oosterhoff 1939; Sandage 1958). In this connection,
it is worth noticing the remarkable fact that the dwarf galaxy in Sculptor, as
far as the scarce data allow us to conclude, corresponds to the globular clusters
with $\langle P(\mathrm{RRa}) \rangle = 0.54$ day, whereas the Draco system corresponds approximately to the group with $\langle P(\mathrm{RRa}) \rangle = 0.64$ day, and that 13 out of 15 RR
Lyrae variables in the Magellanic Clouds have a mean period of .548 day. (Cf.
Thackeray 1950 for Sculptor; Baade and Swope 1961 for Draco; and Thackeray
1959 for the Magellanic Clouds.)

Figure 5 gives frequency curves of log P for the two above-mentioned globular clusters, and for field RR Lyraes from the Leiden-Johannesburg regions Nos.
25, 27, 28, and 29 (Leiden 1948) combined. The latter curve resembles the
$\langle P \rangle = 0.54$ day type of NGC 5904 rather than the $\langle P \rangle = 0.64$ day type of NGC
7078. Definitive conclusions on this matter can, however, only be made after
a detailed investigation of the completeness of the known variables (see also
van den Bergh 1957). The supposition that RRa types near the galactic nucleus
have shorter periods on the average has not been confirmed (Pavlovskaya 1957
and 1960; Alexander 1960).

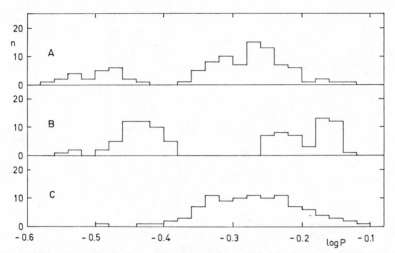

Fig. 5.—Frequency distributions of log P for short-period variables: A: for NGC 5904, B:
for NGC 7078, C: for four Leiden-Johannesburg fields.

Preston (1959) determined spectral classes separately from the hydrogen
lines and from the Ca^+ lines for a large number of RR Lyrae stars. He introduced a parameter ΔS, defined by

$$\Delta S = 10[Sp(H) - Sp(Ca^+)] .$$

Small values of ΔS correspond to strong-line stars, and large values to weak-
line stars. From his Figure 5 (which is reproduced here as Fig. 6 after adding
some recent results on southern stars by Kinman 1961), Preston concluded that
the period-amplitude relation depends on the value of ΔS and is shifted toward
longer periods for increasing values of ΔS. Consequently the mean period increases with increasing mean ΔS. Vice versa, this may mean that stars in
globular clusters with a longer average period have larger values of ΔS.

From these data we might conclude that, although the scatter in the diagram
is rather large, probably as a result of the inaccuracy of the amplitudes and
perhaps also of the ΔS values, the RR Lyrae stars of Bailey's type a should be

divided into groups according to their ΔS value, or otherwise according to their position in a period-amplitude diagram.

7.2. Colors and Absolute Magnitudes

Several investigators have tried to obtain intrinsic color indices of RR Lyrae stars. Preston and Spinrad's recent attempt (1959) to use the value of ΔS as a parameter appeared promising, but the observations were too inaccurate. The

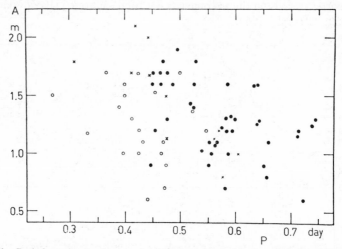

Fig. 6.—Period-amplitude diagram for RRa variables with $P < 0.75$ day. This figure is identical with Fig. 5 by Preston (1959), supplemented by observations by Kinman (1961). Open circles, crosses, and filled circles represent stars in the ΔS groups 0–2, 3–4, and 5–10, respectively.

TABLE 3

Average Color Indices for RR Lyrae Stars

	$\log P < -0.4$	$\log P > -0.4$
$(B-V)_{\min}$	$+0.27 \pm 0.05$	$+0.32 \pm 0.07$
$(B-V)_{\max}$	$+0.11 \pm 0.06$	$+0.06 \pm 0.09$

same difficulty holds for Geyer's attempt (1961) to subdivide the stars into two groups of different values of $B - V$. Using all available photoelectric measurements of $B - V$, we obtained the average values and dispersions given in Table 3. Only stars with $|b| > 20°$ were used. The colors were corrected for absorption by the formula in section 3.1.4. No significant dependence of $B - V$ on the period or on the shape of the light curve was found. We should, however, emphasize that the scatter is large, possibly because the correction for interstellar absorption and the reduction to the $B - V$ photometric system are still inadequate.

Previously, the mean absolute photographic magnitude of RR Lyrae variables was assumed to be approximately 0.0. More recently, Pavlovskaya (1954), Parenago (1954), and Notni (1957) derived different, mostly fainter, values from a discussion of proper motions and radial velocities. The first two authors included in their analyses a few stars with $P < .200$ day, which are considerably fainter than the other RR Lyraes.

Globular clusters provide another source of absolute magnitudes. Absolute magnitudes of stars in globular clusters have usually been derived by fitting either the main sequence or the horizontal branch of the color-magnitude diagram to that of clusters or of groups of stars with known absolute magnitudes. Roberts and Sandage (1955) showed that the absolute magnitude of the horizontal branch and, therefore, of the RR Lyrae stars differs from cluster to cluster.

A summary of some recent results of investigations of globular clusters is given in Table 4, in which M_v is the median absolute magnitude of RR Lyrae stars, which is taken to be also the absolute magnitude of the horizontal branch. Other properties of globular clusters, including the average period of RRa stars are given in Table 5.

Recently, Arp (1962b) rediscussed the effect of the interstellar reddening on the absolute magnitudes of RR Lyrae stars in globular clusters and in moving groups. Table 6 gives his results.

Following earlier work by Sandage (1958), Kinman (1959a) used the pulsation criterion to derive the relation

$$M_v = +3.9 \, (B - V) - 4.2 \log P + \text{const} ,$$

which yields a difference in absolute magnitude of 0.3 magnitude between RR Lyrae stars in the two kinds of clusters with mean periods for RRa stars of 0.54 and 0.64 days, respectively. The position of the RR Lyrae stars in a M_v, $\log P$ diagram is shown in Figure 2.

7.3. KINEMATICAL PROPERTIES

Recently we have redetermined the solar motion relative to various types of variable stars by the formulae in section 4 (Plaut 1963), using only radial velocities. Most of the data were taken from Wilson's catalogue (1953) with a few, recent, additional observations. The results of these computations are given in Table 7. For a discussion of the term rA of the differential galactic rotation in this table, we refer to Oort (1942). Results of two of the most recent determinations by Kinman (1959b) and by Preston (1959) are given in Table 8. Spite (1960) concluded in discussing Preston's results that there are two distinct groups of RR Lyraes, one with $\Delta S = 1$ to 4 and the other with $\Delta S = 5$ to 10 (see also Sec. 11).

7.4. DENSITY DISTRIBUTION

The distribution of the bright RR Lyraes over the sky, as represented in Figure 3 (dots), is quite uniform; the only irregularity occurs at longitudes be-

TABLE 4

Absolute Magnitude of RR Lyrae Stars in Globular Clusters

Globular Cluster	M_v	Method
NGC 6205 (M13)	$+0.4 \pm 0.15$	By adjusting 2 variables in M13 to the moving group Grb 1830 (Eggen and Sandage 1959).
NGC 7089 (M2)	$+1.0:$	By fitting C-M diagrams at the main sequence after correction for blanketing effects (Arp 1959, 1962a)
NGC 5904 (M5)	$+0.7$	
NGC 6205 (M13)	$+0.2$	
NGC 5272 (M3)	$+0.6$	By adjusting according to metal content (Sandage and Wallerstein 1960).
NGC 6341 (M92)	$+0.4$	
NGC 6356	$+0.9$	
NGC 5139 (ω Cen)	$+0.7$	By fitting of the giant-subgiant sequence (Eggen 1961b); cf. Wildey (1961).
NGC 104 (47 Tuc)	$+1.0$	

TABLE 5

Characteristics of a Number of Globular Clusters

NGC	Messier	$V*$	Deutsch	Morgan	$P_{a,b}$	No. of RR Lyrae Variables	H.B.	ΔS	Reference‡
104	(47 Tuc)	2.15	A†	High Met.†	......	2	r	5	1, 14
6356	....	2.15	......	VI	......	0	r	......	2
6838	71	2.1	......	VI	......	0	r	......	3
		2.17±0.06							
4147	....	2.45:	B	....	0.531	16	?	......	4
5272	3	2.64	AB	II	.550	201	e	......	5
5904	5	2.58	A	II	.546	99	e	0–4	6, 13, 15
6205	13	2.55	A	III	......	3	b		6, 7
6656	22	2.50	B	II	.651	19	b	4–6	8
		2.54±0.06							
5024	53	3.10	B	III	.642	45	....	......	9
5053	....	3.10	C	....	.673	10	....	......	10
5466	....	3.0	C	....	.636	18	be	......	16
5897	....	3.10	C	....	......	4	b	......	11
6254	10	2.85	B	IV	......	0	b		6
6341	92	2.92	C	I	.626	15	b	9–11	12, 13
7078	15	3.10	C	I	.645	93	be	10–11	6, 13
7089	2	2.98	B	II	0.629	13	b	8	6, 14
		3.01±0.08							

* Difference between horizontal branch and giant branch read at $(B - V)_0 = +1.4$.

† Data on spectra of individual stars from Kinman (1959a) and from Feast and Thackeray (1960).

‡ Following are the references for C-M diagrams and ΔS: 1. Wildey (1961); 2. Sandage and Wallerstein (1960); 3. Arp, preliminary, unpublished; 4. Sandage and Walker (1955); 5. Johnson and Sandage (1956); 6. Arp (1955); 7. Arp and Johnson (1955); 8. Arp and Melbourne (1959); 9. Cuffey (1958); 10. Cuffey, unpublished; 11. Sandage and Schmidt (1958); 12. Sandage and Walker (1957); 13. Preston (1961); 14. Kinman (1959b); 15. Arp (1962a); 16. Cuffey (1961),

tween 100° and 170°, and can be explained by fluctuations in the completeness of the discoveries. For the distribution of the fainter stars, we are restricted to the extensively observed areas, and correct the results derived from these for incompleteness. The areas at $|b| > 6°$ have been analyzed by Perek (1951, Tables 1 and 5), and more recently by Plaut and Soudan (1963, Table 1). No correlation of the average period with galactic latitude and longitude appears to exist.

TABLE 6

ABSOLUTE MAGNITUDES M_v OF RR LYRAE STARS IN GLOBU-
LAR CLUSTERS AND IN MOVING GROUPS ACCORDING TO A
REDISCUSSION OF INTERSTELLAR REDDENING BY ARP
(1962b).

(References to the original observations
are given in Arp's paper)

GLOBULAR CLUSTERS

| Cluster | | M_v According to | | |
M	NGC	Previously Assumed Reddening	Cosecant-Law Reddening	Reddening from Integrated Colors (Kron and Mayall 1960, Case II)
3	5272	+0.7	+0.4	+0.3
5	5904	+0.7	+0.2	+0.3
13	6205	+0.2	−0.3	+0.1
2	7089	+1.0	+0.4	+0.3

MOVING GROUPS

Star	M_v According to	
	Previously Assumed Reddening	Cosecant-Law Reddening
RR Lyr........	+0.65	+0.5
TU UMa......	+0.4	+0.2
SU Dra.......	+0.8	+0.6
X Ari.........	+0.8	+0.5
W CVn.......	+0.2	0.0

The space distribution was extensively studied by Perek (1951), and the analysis repeated by Plaut and Soudan (1963). The adopted values for some of the quantities used in the computations, which were somewhat different in these two investigations, were

	Perek	Plaut-Soudan
average absolute magnitude, M_{pg}................	0.0	+ 0.5
distance of galactic center, R_0 (kpc).............	8 and 9.5	10
lower limit of amplitude of light variation (in magnitudes)...................................	1.0	0.5

TABLE 7
VELOCITY DISTRIBUTIONS AND DENSITY GRADIENTS

Type	No. of Stars	V_0 km/sec	Ar km/sec	Dispersion km/sec	a km/sec	b km/sec	c km/sec	$\partial \log \nu/\partial R$ kpc^{-1}
RR $^d20<P\leq{}^d40$.....	30	$+\ 61\pm20$	$-\ 6\pm23$	$\pm\ 55$	$\pm\ 48$	$\pm\ 76$	±37	-0.25
RR .$40<P\leq$ .50.....	44	$+128\quad 31$	$+12\quad 41$	115	59	104	72	-0.27
RR .$50\leq P\leq$ .60.....	49	$+194\quad 29$	$+44\quad 34$	110	139	120	43	-0.09
RR .$60<P$..........	35	$+222\quad 36$	$+29\quad 42$	103	137	116	32	-0.10
RR $\Delta S=0, 1, 2$	28	$+\ 39\quad 19$	$-\ 6\quad 24$	59	22	73	12	-0.24
RR $\Delta S=3, 4, 5$	21	$+182\quad 47$	$+17\quad 64$	134	84	154	38	-0.10
RR $\Delta S\geq6$	53	$+193\quad 27$	$-20\quad 31$	96	81	106	50	-0.20
CW................	26	$+\ 6\quad 16$	$+18\quad 12$	39	13	35	57	-0.18
RV $v<70$ km/sec....	23	$-\ 2\quad 12$	$+\ 6\quad 10$	32	28	6	63	-0.01
RV $v>70$ km/sec....	15	$+247\quad 54$	$-19\quad 51$	101	131	2	9	-0.14
M $\quad P\leq150^d$....	17	$+\ 49\quad 22$	$-42\quad 28$	64	5	55	46	....
M $150^d<P\leq200$.....	25	$+132\quad 38$	$-30\quad 39$	91	95	39	43	-0.19
M $200\ <P\leq250$.....	50	$+\ 68\quad 12$	$+\ 9\quad 13$	43	44	20	33	-0.47
M $250\ <P\leq300$.....	61	$+\ 32\quad 10$	$-\ 7\quad 12$	47	48	37	22	-0.21
M $300\ <P\leq350$.....	73	$+\ 16\quad 10$	$+\ 9\quad 10$	36	39	17	23	-0.21
M $350\ <P\leq400$.....	44	$+\ 6\quad 9$	$+\ 4\quad 8$	30	36	7	15	-0.12
M $400\ <P$..........	35	$+\ 7\quad 7$	$-\ 2\quad 7$	27	32	5	23	-0.15

Results by Oort and Van Tulder (1942)

Type	No. of Stars	V_0 km/sec	Ar km/sec	Dispersion km/sec	a km/sec	b km/sec	c km/sec	$\partial \log \nu/\partial R$ kpc^{-1}
M $150^d\leq P<200^d$ ...	27	$+129\pm26$	....	$\pm\ 78$	$\pm\ 91$	$\pm\ 45$	±36	-0.26
M $\{$... $\ P<150\}$ ... $\{200\ \leq P<300\}$ ...	124	$42\quad 7$	$+\ 2\pm\ 9$	46	44	34	33	-0.40
M $300\ \leq P<350$....	75	$14\quad 8$	$+16\quad 7$	37	31	30	23	-0.26
M $350\ \leq P$.........	79	$7\quad 3$	$+\ 7\quad 5$	26	27	11	23	-0.21

TABLE 8
SOLAR MOTION FOR RR LYRAE STARS

RESULTS BY KINMAN (1959b)					RESULTS BY PRESTON (1959)			
$\langle P\rangle$ days	Type	S km/sec	Mean Res. km/sec	n	ΔS	S' km/sec	Mean Res. km/sec	n
.296	c	89	±29	14	0–2	55	±20	16
.369	a	30	27	11	3–4	115	25	10
.460	a	105	29	37	5–10	185	35	27
.548	a	167	30	46				
.666	a	205	45	21				

$S=$ the total motion found by Kinman after correcting for local solar motion. Adopted apex at $l^{II}=90°$, $b^{II}=0°$.

S' is the solar motion found by Preston from $v=S'\cos\lambda$; $\lambda=$ angular distance from apex adopted at $l^{II}=87°$, $b^{II}=+0°.6$.

The resulting density distributions (Fig. 7) agree, in general, although the values by Plaut and Soudan for the relative densities near the galactic center are lower than Perek's. This discrepancy certainly arises from the inclusion by Plaut and Soudan of the stars with amplitudes between 0.5 and 1.0 magnitude. The completeness factors adopted for the low-amplitude stars are obviously too small, especially for the fainter stars. Plaut and Soudan's data show no significant differences in the density gradients with respect to period.

From his density data Perek obtained least-squares solutions in the form,

$$\log \nu \ (R) = a - bR$$

$$\log \nu \ (z) = c - d z .$$

TABLE 9

LOGARITHMIC DENSITIES AND GRADIENTS
DERIVED BY PEREK (1951)

RANGE IN kpc		a	b
R	z		
0–15	0–2	1.83 ± 0.46	0.116 ± 0.060
0–17	2–4	1.18 ± 0.41	0.088 ± 0.044
0–17	4–6	0.94 ± 0.34	0.087 ± 0.033
0–17	6–8	0.17 ± 0.15	0.038 ± 0.014
R	z	c	d
4– 8	0–14	1.41 ± 0.19	0.192 ± 0.024
8–12	0–14	0.73 ± 0.33	0.136 ± 0.044
12–17	0–14	0.46 ± 0.51	0.139 ± 0.007

His results for $R_0 = 9.5$ are given in Table 9. Perek also made extensive comparisons with theoretical data derived from models of the mass distribution in the galactic system.

Some results by other investigators are: (a) The logarithmic density gradient perpendicular to the galactic plane as determined by Oort and van Woerkom (1941) from data by Shapley (1939):

$$\frac{\partial \log \nu}{\partial z} = -0.22 \text{ for } 1 < z < 10 \text{ kpc} .$$

(b) The number of RR Lyrae stars per 1 kpc³ at different distances from the galactic center as derived by Baade (Baade and Minkowski 1954):

$$N = 20.4 \times 10^{-.765R} \text{ for } 0.6 < R < 3.5 \text{ kpc} ,$$

$$N = 0.81 \times 10^{-.361R} \text{ for } R > 3.5 \text{ kpc} .$$

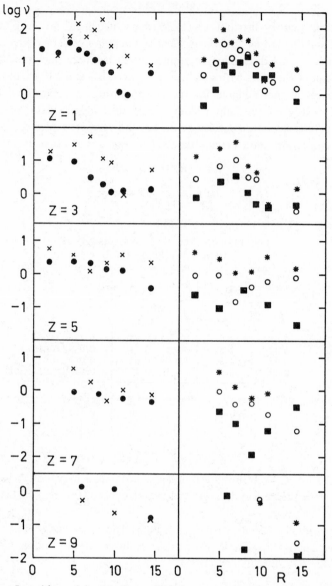

Fig. 7a.—Logarithms of densities log ν of RR Lyrae variables plotted against R, the distance from the galactic axis of rotation for different divisions of z, the distance from the galactic plane:

Left-hand figure: ● according to Perek (1951),

           × according to Plaut and Soudan (1963), all periods longer than 0.20 day;

Right-hand figure: ■ $\overset{d}{.}200 \leq P < \overset{d}{.}400$,

           ✳ $.400 \leq P < .600$,

           ○ $.600 \leq P$,

           according to Plaut and Soudan (1963).

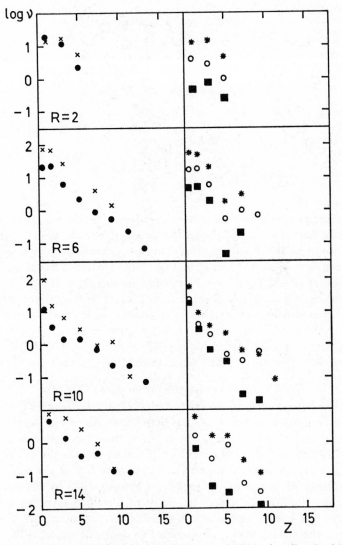

Fig. 7b.—Logarithms of densities log ν of RR Lyrae variables in the z direction for different divisions of R. Symbols as in Figure 7a.

c) The results by Kukarkin (1954) based on a statistical method proposed by Vashakidse (1937 and 1938):

$$\frac{\partial \log \nu}{\partial z} = -0.219 \pm 0.016,$$

which applies to a cylinder perpendicular on the plane of the Galaxy in the neighborhood of the sun;

$$\log \nu = 2.16 - 0.274 \, R,$$

$$\pm .30 \pm .030$$

for directions in the plane of the Galaxy; and

$$\log \nu = 1.89 - 1.058 \, (|z|)^{1/2},$$

$$\pm .09 \pm .037$$

along the z-axis.

By means of Oort's formula given in section 5, we are able to derive the logarithmic density gradient in the direction away from the galactic center by making use of the velocity distribution. The density gradients computed by this method are given in the last column of Table 7 and are from a recent publication by the author (1963). We assumed a circular velocity $\Theta_c = 217$ km/sec at the solar distance from the galactic center, $R_0 = 8.2$ kpc. In general, the agreement between these density gradients and the directly determined distributions is satisfactory. The first four rows of Table 7 show a decrease in the density gradient with increasing period for the RR Lyrae stars. This feature is not discernible in the results by Plaut and Soudan (1963), as shown in Figure 9.

7.5. RR Lyrae Variables and Globular Clusters

Relations between RR Lyrae stars in globular clusters and in the galactic field have been mentioned above. It has been known for several years that two groups of globular clusters exist, one in which the mean period of the RRa variables is 0.54 day, the other in which it is 0.64 day. In the galactic field, however, this mean period is close to 0.54 day, regardless of the region of the sky considered. It is valuable to discuss the investigations by Preston (1959) and Kinman (1959b) with respect to this point. Preston's investigations have shown that RR Lyraes with a certain value of the parameter, ΔS, which is a measure of the metal content, are confined to a specific region in the period-amplitude diagram (see Fig. 6). Moreover, the RR Lyraes in a globular cluster are limited to a similar strip in the P-A diagram, so that, presumably, all RR Lyraes in a globular cluster will have approximately the same metal content. In the general field, stars of all values of ΔS are mixed, but there are fewer stars of long period relative to the globular cluster variables. This indicates that stars with a lower metal content are less frequent in the general field than in the clusters, since there is a strong correlation between low metal content and long period (see Fig. 6). Kinman (1959b, Fig. 7) found a correlation between the integrated spectral type of a globular cluster and the mean period of the RRa variables such that clusters with a lower metal content have RR Lyraes with a longer mean period.

A comparison with other criteria for metal content is given by Sandage and Wallerstein (1960, Table 4). Their table is reproduced here (Table 5) and supplemented by a column giving ΔS as derived from a few spectra of RR Lyrae stars. It should be emphasized that there are some inconsistencies in these data. See also Kinman (1959b).

For the relation between the integrated spectral type of globular clusters and space and velocity distribution, Kinman (1959b) found the data reproduced in Table 10. In this table, $Sp(CH/H\gamma)$ is the integrated spectral type as deter-

TABLE 10

SPATIAL AND KINEMATICAL PROPERTIES OF
GLOBULAR CLUSTERS ACCORDING
TO KINMAN (1959b)

$Sp(CH/H\gamma)$	$\langle z \rangle$ (kpc)	U (km/sec)
F2–F6..........	10.3	....
F6–F9..........	5.4	162 ± 36
G0–G5..........	2.3	80 ± 82

mined from a comparison of the G-band with the $H\gamma$-line; $\langle z \rangle$ is the mean distance from the galactic plane; and U is the total motion as derived by least-squares solutions from $U \cos A = V_c$, where $\cos A = \sin l^{II} \cos b^{II}$, and V_c is the radial velocity corrected for local solar motion. When these results are compared with Tables 7 and 8, we see that, in the case of the RR Lyrae stars as well, those with higher metal content, that is with smaller value of ΔS (corresponding to later $CH/H\gamma$ spectral types for the clusters), have lower velocities relative to the local standard of rest. See also the report of a symposium on the differences among globular clusters held at Toronto (1959).

§ 8. W VIRGINIS VARIABLES

The criteria generally used to distinguish the W Virginis variables from classical or type I cepheids are: a large distance from the galactic plane, say $|z| > 250$ pc; a "peculiar" shape of the light curve; a color index increasing more slowly with increasing period than for type I cepheids; considerably earlier spectral types when compared with type I cepheids of the same period (especially at minimum light, the G-band of CH is invisible) and emission lines reaching great intensity during increasing light.

Payne-Gaposchkin (1954a) proposed to classify as W Vir stars, all stars with light curves differing more than a certain amount from those of Hertzsprung's period-shape relation (1926). By comparing light curves of type I cepheids from Hertzsprung's work with those of type II cepheids from Payne-Gaposchkin's list (1956) and from Arp's observations in globular clusters (1955), we see that the scatter in the asymmetry parameters ϵ and ζ is rather large for both categories. A significant difference is found only for periods between 12 and 20 days, where type I stars have positive values of ζ against negative ones for type II

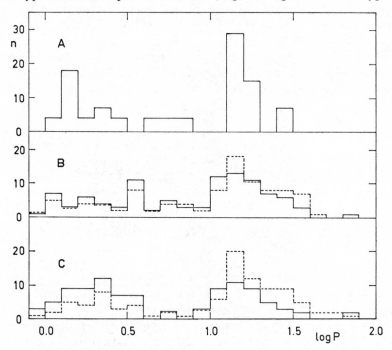

FIG. 8.—Frequency distributions of log P for W Virginis stars (P in days): A: from globular clusters according to Oosterhoff, B: according to Payne-Gaposchkin, Oosterhoff, and *GCVS*, C: according to Petit. Dashed lines are the observed frequencies; the solid lines are the frequencies reduced to unit volume; all frequencies are reduced to 100 stars.

stars (cf. Kukarkin and Kulikovsky 1951). Accurate light curves might yield more significant results, but in the present context, we are chiefly concerned with faint stars, where accurate light curves are not available. As mentioned above, we shall use the list of type II cepheids as given by Petit (1960a) who considered all available criteria.

We can make a statistical distinction between both types by means of the frequency curves of the period. Long ago Shapley recognized this fact while discussing the peculiar behavior of the "16-days Cepheids." More recently, Oosterhoff (1956) and Petit (1960b) discussed these questions. Figure 8 shows frequency curves of the period for (A) the variables in globular clusters, taken from Oosterhoff (1956); (B) for a list by Payne-Gaposchkin (1956), Walraven, Muller, and Oosterhoff (1958), and the *GCVS;* and (*C*) for the list by Petit (1960*a*). In addition, frequency curves reduced to unit volume as described by Oosterhoff are shown. There are two maxima, one at log P = 1.2 and the other at a much shorter period. These peaks are more prominent for globular-cluster stars than for those in the galactic field.

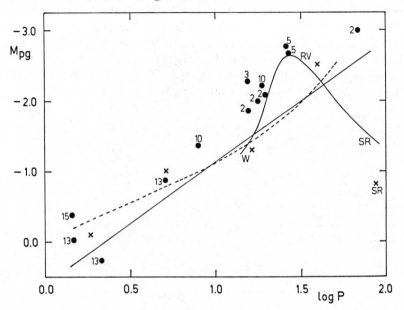

FIG. 9.—Period-luminosity relation for variables in globular clusters. Dots: according to Arp (1955), Messier numbers are added; crosses: according to Joy (1949); broken line: according to Payne-Gaposchkin (1954*a*) (above with corrected zero point); straight solid line: according to Eggen (1961*b*); solid curve: types W, RV, SR according to Rosino (1951).

For W Vir stars, absolute magnitudes can, as yet, only be derived from globular clusters. If we assume, for the median absolute magnitude of RR Lyrae stars, the following tentative values:

$$M_{pg} = +0.8 \text{ for clusters with } \bar{P} = 0.54 \text{ day,}$$
$$M_{pg} = +0.5 \text{ for clusters with } \bar{P} = 0.64 \text{ day,}$$

and corresponding values for clusters with only a few RR Lyrae stars, or none, as adjusted according to metal content, we can derive M_{pg} for the variables with longer periods by means of the difference in apparent photographic magnitude. The results are shown in Figure 9 and are incorporated also in Figure 2. The mean absolute photographic magnitude M_{pg} decreases linearly from 0.0 at log P = 0.2 to − 2.4 at log P = 1.5.

A summary of the observations of spectral-luminosity classes is given by Petit (1960*a*, Table III). It shows that these classes range from II–III for log

$P = 0.16$ to Ib at $\log P = 1.5$. No other data are known at present. Results of the computation of the kinematical properties are given in Table 7 (cf. Sec. 7.3).

The distribution over the sky has been studied by Petit (1960*b*). It is shown in Figure 10. When comparing it with the distribution of the RR Lyraes, in Figure 3, we should remember that all known W Virginis stars have been plotted irrespective of a magnitude limit. The distribution of the fainter stars is strongly biased by that of the more extensively surveyed fields. It is likely that even allowing for this bias, the concentration toward the galactic center will remain. Lack of data prevents the direct determination of the distribution in space; but a crude estimate of the density gradient may be deduced from the velocity dispersion and the solar motion (cf. Sec. 5); see also Table 7.

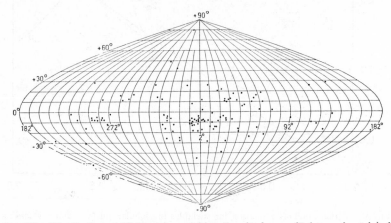

Fig. 10.—Distribution of W Virginis variables. Longitudes are l^{II} (approximately); latitudes are b^{I}.

§ 9. RV TAURI AND SEMI-REGULAR VARIABLES

The *GCVS* classifies semi-regular variables as RV when the light variation is still rather periodic and the light curve shows a double wave. In the somewhat more irregular cases, the classification is given as SR with four subgroups a, b, c, and d. In this chapter the subgroup SRa has been transferred to the long-period variables (group M in the *GCVS*). The remaining subgroups are characterized by spectral features, for example, SRb contains the red giants (types M, C, and S); SRc the red supergiants like μ Cep; and SRd the yellow (G and K type) giants and supergiants. It follows that the subgroup classification can be applied only if spectral types are known, e.g., for the brighter stars. Thus, inevitably, the group SR is a rather heterogeneous one for the fainter stars.

For discussions of the bright, semi-regular variables we refer to the following: (1) Payne-Gaposchkin, Brenton, and Gaposchkin (1943): photographic light curves for RV stars. (2) Rosino (1951): description of spectra for RV and SRd stars. (3) Joy (1952): description of spectra and radial velocities for RV

and SRd stars. If we identify these stars of Payne-Gaposchkin *et al.* (their
Table 1), of Rosino (his Table 1), and of Joy, which have radial velocities
smaller than 70 km/sec as RV stars, and the yellow semi-regulars of Rosino's
Table 2 and Joy's stars with radial velocities larger than 70 km/sec as SRd
stars, and consider furthermore the classification in the *GCVS*, we get the
statistics of the numbers of times stars have been classified as RV and SRd, respectively, given in Table 11. This indicates the ambiguousness of the classification.

TABLE 11

STATISTICS OF CLASSIFICATIONS OF RV AND SR VARIABLES

Classification	Number
Classified once as RV..	60
Classified once as SRd......................................	11
Classified twice or more times as RV......................	26
Classified twice or more times as SRd....................	11
Classified once or more times as RV and once or more times as SR..	16
Classified once as RV and once as SRa..................	1
Classified once as RV and once as EB...................	1
Classified once as RV and once as I.....................	1

TABLE 12

ABSOLUTE MAGNITUDES OF SEMI-REGULAR STARS ACCORDING
TO JOY (1942) AND WILSON (1942)

	JOY			WILSON
	$\langle M_v \rangle$	Dispersion	n	$\langle M_v \rangle$
Giants............	-0.9	± 0.4	108	-0.85
Supergiants	-3.0	± 0.8	13	$-3.4:$

In an investigation of the absolute magnitudes, Joy (1952) found, from spectroscopic criteria:

for RV Tau stars, $M_v = -3$

for yellow SR and I stars, $M_v = -1.5$.

Eggen (1961*a*) derived $M_v = -3.3$ for BM Sco (type SR, $P = 850$ days
with slow variations, $m_{pg} = 6.8 - 8.7$) assuming that the star is a member of
the open cluster NGC 6405.

Absolute magnitudes of semi-regular and some irregular stars have been investigated by Joy (1942) from spectroscopic criteria, and by Wilson (1942)

from proper motions and radial velocities. The results of both methods agree
very well. The group consists of a large number of giants with a small dispersion
in M_v and a small number of supergiants with M_v between -2.0 and -4.5; the
main properties of these two groups are given in Table 12. Dividing the stars
according to the classification of the *GCVS*, we derive from Joy's paper the
values of Table 13.

TABLE 13

ABSOLUTE MAGNITUDES OF SUBGROUPS OF SEMI-REGULAR STARS

Type	M_v	Dispersion	n	Remarks
SRa........	-0.9	±0.4	24	Excluding supergiants
SRb........	-0.9	±0.3	59	Excluding supergiants
SRc........	-2.6	±1.2	11	Including supergiants
I..........	-1.0	±0.4	6	Excluding supergiants

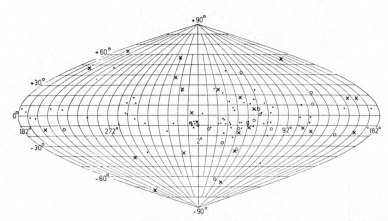

FIG. 11.—Distribution of RV Tauri and semi-regular variables. Filled circles are RV Tauri
stars; crosses are SR stars; open circles are stars of types either RV or SR. Coordinates as in
Fig. 10.

From observations in 47 Tucanae, Feast and Thackeray (1960) found M_v
(max) $= -2.1$ for three irregular and semi-regular variables. The median M_v
for two RR Lyrae stars was assumed to be $+0.5$. Data on the absolute magnitudes are assembled in Figures 2 and 15. Results of the computation of the
kinematical properties are given in Table 7 (cf. Sec. 7.3); Joy's (1952) observations were used (see Plaut 1963; the mean errors in this paper show the low
accuracy of these results).

The distribution of the RV Tau and semi-regular variables over the sky is
shown in Figure 11. The concentration toward the direction of the galactic
center is a little less than that of the W Vir stars (Fig. 10). The available data
do not permit a direct determination of the space distribution of these objects.
An estimate of the density gradient of the RV Tauri stars is given in Table 7.

§ 10. LONG-PERIOD VARIABLES

10.1. INTRODUCTION

The brighter long-period variables have been extensively observed visually by amateurs (cf. Campbell 1955); the fainter ones, almost exclusively on photographic plates. Photoelectric light curves are available for only a few stars (Eggen 1961b). Light curves have been studied by Ludendorff (1928), Campbell (1955), and Payne-Gaposchkin (1954b). Recently, Merrill (1960) published a statistical study of periods and light ranges.

Figure 12a shows the distribution in the sky of long-period variables with a photographic magnitude brighter than 11.0 at average maximum brightness. Figure 12b shows the same for maximum brightness between magnitudes 14.0

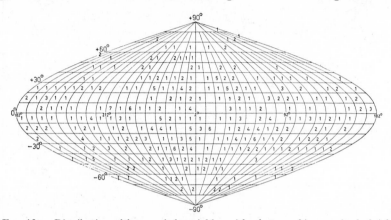

FIG. 12a.—Distribution of long-period variables with photographic magnitude brighter than 11.0 at average maximum brightness. Numbers refer to numbers of stars per square of 10 × 10 degrees. Coordinates as in Fig 10.

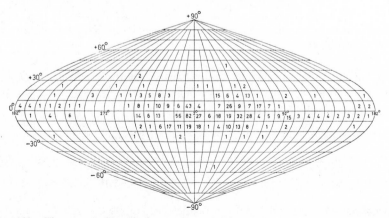

FIG. 12b.—The same as Fig. 12a for maximum brightness between 14.0 and 15.0. Coordinates as in Fig. 10.

and 15.0. The strong concentration of the fainter long-period stars to the galactic plane and to the direction of the center of the Galaxy is caused by both observational selection (see Sec. 3.2) and a real concentration to the plane and the center of the Galaxy.

A few years ago Hoffleit (1957), among others, found that the average period is smaller toward the center of the Galaxy than in the anti-center region.

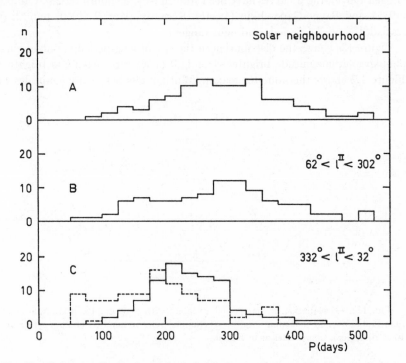

FIG. 13.—Frequency distribution of the period for long-period variables (*P* in days): A: for the solar neighborhood, B: for the anti-center direction, C: for the center direction and for Baade's field (dashed).

This conclusion is confirmed by a recent analysis of the data from the *GCVS* by Plaut (1963) as shown in Figure 13, which shows the frequency distribution of the periods for the following categories:

  a) the solar neighborhood, from all stars with $\bar{m}_{\text{max, pg}} < 11.0$,

  b) the anti-center region, viz., $\bar{m}_{\text{max, pg}} > 13.0, |b^{\text{II}}| < 10°, 62° < l^{\text{II}} < 302°$,

  c) the center region, viz., $\bar{m}_{\text{max, pg}} > 14.0, |b^{\text{II}}| < 10°, 332° < l^{\text{II}} < 32°$.

In the last plot, the variables from Baade's field at $b^{\text{II}} = -2°9, l^{\text{II}} = 359°5$ are added (Gaposchkin 1955).

10.2. COLORS AND ABSOLUTE MAGNITUDES

A comparison between Payne-Gaposchkin's photographic data and the visual as quoted in the *GCVS* yields the color indices given in Table 14. There is no significant variation from M0 to M8. Recently, Eggen (1961b) derived the mean values of $B - V$ shown in Table 15. Blanco (chap. 12, this volume) quotes $B - V = 1.57$ for types M0 to M5. Schaifers (1960, Schaifers and Wenzel 1961) observed the variation of the spectral class of X Cam ($P = 143$ days) and R UMa ($P = 302$ days) during the whole light variation.

TABLE 14

COLOR INDICES OF LATE-TYPE VARIABLES

Spectral Type	$m_{pg} - m_v$	s.d.
M..................	1.3	±0.6
N..................	3.4	1.1
R..................	2.5	....
S..................	2.0	0.6

TABLE 15

COLOR INDICES ACCORDING TO EGGEN (1961b)

	$B - V$	Spectral Class	P(days)
T Cen........	1.58	K7e–M3e	91
SX Her.......	1.52	G3e–K0(M3)	103
L² Pup.......	1.43	M5e–M6e	141
S Car........	1.65	K7e–M4e	160

The difference between the extreme maxima observed and the average maximum as derived from the data by Payne-Gaposchkin (1954b) and the *GCVS* is

$$\text{in } m_{pg}, \quad -.67 \pm .34 \text{ (s.d.)}$$

$$\text{in } m_v, \quad -.80 \pm .33 .$$

For the fainter stars, for which only the brightest observed maximum magnitude is given, we adopted a smaller value, viz., −.50 magnitude, because these stars have been observed much less frequently and, consequently, extreme maxima will have escaped attention.

Recently, Osvalds and Risley (1961) determined average absolute magnitudes from McCormick proper motions and Mount Wilson radial velocities. In Table 16 their results are compared with Wilson and Merrill's values (1942) and with values for non-variable M giants derived by Blanco (this volume, chap. 12); see also the period luminosity relation for various types of variables as shown in Figure 2.

For the early M-type stars, there is a discrepancy between the values derived from variables and from constant stars. It is an open question at which phase of the light variation we should compare the absolute magnitudes of the variables with those of the constant stars. Moreover, we do not yet know which fraction of the M-type stars, not being long-period variables, have light fluctuations with small amplitudes.

Oort and van Tulder (1942) derived $M_v = -2.1$ with a dispersion of ± 1.0 magnitude from a comparison of the density distribution in the direction perpendicular to the galactic plane and the acceleration $K(z)$ in the same direction. Keenan (1957, 1959) derived $M_v = -0.7$ for X Mon ($P = 156$ days) from a

TABLE 16

ABSOLUTE MAGNITUDES OF LONG-PERIOD VARIABLES

Group	Osvalds, Risley				Wilson, Merrill	Blanco
	$\langle P \rangle$ days	n	$\langle M_v \rangle$	$\langle Sp \rangle$	$\langle M_v \rangle$	M_v
1.......	131	14	−1.67	M 1.9	−2.0	−0.8
2.......	176	29	−2.74	M 2.7	−2.7	−1.0
3.......	223	55	−2.10	M 3.7	−1.9	−1.0
4.......	273	65	−2.03	M 4.2	−1.0	−1.0
5.......	324	73	−0.93	M 5.3	−0.5	−0.9:
6.......	376	42	−1.05	M 6.2	0.0	−0.9:
7.......	419	23	−0.31	M 6.5	+0.2	−0.9:
8.......	508	18	−1.17	M 6.0	+0.5	−0.9:
C......	404	26	−1.44	C	....	....
Se......	364	22	−1.57	Se	....	....

study of interstellar lines. From observations in 47 Tucanae, Feast and Thackeray (1960) found maximum $M_v = -3.6$ for three long-period stars with periods of approximately 200 days. The median M_v for two RR Lyrae stars was assumed to be $+0.5$.

10.3. KINEMATICAL PROPERTIES

Results of the computation of the kinematical properties by the author are given in Table 7 (cf. Sec. 7.3). Earlier results, by Oort and van Tulder (1942), are also included. Table 17 gives the results of an investigation by Osvalds and Risley (1961) kindly communicated by them in advance of publication. Space velocities are shown for groups according to period; carbon stars and Se-type stars are given separately. In general, there is good agreement among the results of the various investigators.

The agreement between the results in Tables 7 and 17 is not always satisfactory. It should, however, be mentioned that the motions in Table 7 were derived from radial velocities, whereas those in Table 17 depend on proper motions as well as radial velocities.

10.4. Density Distribution

In an application of the direct method (cf. Sec. 5), Oort and van Tulder (1942) used data by Schneller (1940). Stars with a maximum magnitude brighter than 10.0, an amplitude exceeding 2.4 magnitude and a period longer than 100 days were used. The logarithmic density gradient was found to be

TABLE 17

SPACE VELOCITIES AND THEIR DISPERSIONS OF LONG-PERIOD VARIABLES ACCORDING TO TABLE VII OF OSVALDS AND RISLEY (1961)

Subgroup or Reference	Mean Period	No. of Stars	Velocity* and M.E. in km/sec ⟨a⟩	⟨b⟩	⟨c⟩	Dispersion in km/sec a	b	c
1................	128^d	11	+22±14	−27±14	−8±14	±46	±46	±45
2................	174	24	+64 16	−104 15	−26 14	82	74	65
Safronow (1955)....	167	7	+34 84	−86 70	−7 45	136	114	72
3................	224	42	+18 14	−36 12	+8 10	83	74	64
4................	272	56	+19 10	−21 8	−6 8	82	50	51
Mean of 1+3+4 ...	239	109	+20 8	−25 6	−3 6	79	59	55
Kulikovsky (1948)†..	....	93	−4....	−13....	−2....	....	....	....
Safronow (1955)....	237	36	−9 16	−15 10	+3 10	62	43	44
5................	323	63	+10 8	−22 6	−5 4	54	42	32
6................	375	37	−4 8	−12 9	−1 6	42	52	32
7................	419	19	+15 8	−13 6	+1 3	35	22	12
8................	512	12	+16 12	−6 8	−1 6	40	23	21
Mean of 5–8.......	369	131	+8 4	−15 3	−2 2	47	40	28
Kulikovsky (1948)...	....	40	−12....	−2....	+6....	....	....	....
Safronow (1955)....	373	64	−5 10	−5 8	0 8	35	28	25
C................	405	24	+5 10	−12 9	−6 6	54	42	31
Ikauniks (1950).....	....	11	−11 6	+30 18	−2....	45	31	43
Se................	362	20	−3 8	−7 6	−12 3	29	23	15
Ikauniks (1950).....	363	17	−5....	−2....	−10....	25	17	20

* The velocity components given below are corrected for basic solar motion. Component a is directed away from the galactic center, b is in the direction of galactic rotation, and c toward the north galactic pole.

† All stars $P < 300^d$.

$\partial \log \nu / \partial R = -0.254 \pm 0.033$. The data are complete only up to magnitude 8.0; the completeness decreases rapidly for fainter stars, especially in the southern hemisphere, where at magnitude 10.0 it reaches a value of only 10 per cent.

Kukarkin (1954), however, gives certain arguments for higher values of the completeness. His density gradients are

$$\frac{\partial \log \nu}{\partial z} = -0.83 \quad \text{for} \quad |z| < 3.5 \,\text{kpc},$$

$$\frac{\partial \log \nu}{\partial z} = -0.28 \text{ for } 4 < |z| < 10 \text{ kpc},$$

$$\frac{\partial \log \nu}{\partial R} = -0.30,$$

the first two applying to a cylinder perpendicular to the galactic plane in the solar neighborhood.

Oort and van Tulder compared their above result with the density gradient computed according to the indirect method described in Section 5. The results are presented in Table 7, which also contains values of the density gradient recently computed by the author (Plaut 1963).

10.5. LONG-PERIOD VARIABLES AND M-TYPE GIANTS

Space and velocity distributions of late-type giant stars are discussed in chapter 12 of this volume by Blanco, who kindly made his manuscript available

TABLE 18

SPACE DENSITIES ACCORDING
TO BLANCO

Spectral Type	Number of Stars per 10^6 pc^3
M0+M1................	5.7
M2 to M4...............	2.8
Later than M4...........	0.3

in advance of publication, thus making it possible to compare the results for M III stars with those for long-period variables. In section 10.2 we have commented on the discrepancy between the absolute magnitudes of these two overlapping groups of stars and also on the unknown fraction of variables among the M III stars. The distribution in galactic longitude is compared in Figure 14 which is a copy, with some additional data, of Figure 5 in Blanco's paper. It shows the distribution in longitude of stars of type M5 and later near the galactic equator. The data for long-period variables with a photographic magnitude <15.0 at average maximum and with $|b| < 10°$ (Plaut 1963) were added to the diagram. If we take into account the fact that the long-period variables are still very incompletely known in the southern hemisphere (l^{II} between 210° and 30°), the two distributions agree.

The space density in the solar vicinity, according to Blanco, is given in Table 18. An estimate for long-period variables yields a value of approximately 0.1 star per 10^6 pc^3 (Oort and van Tulder 1942). The thickness of the layer parallel to the galactic plane at half-density points is 500 pc for the M giants, and approximately 1500 pc for the long-period variables.

Delhaye, in chapter 4 of this volume, gives the solar motion for all gM stars as

$$X = -5, \quad Y = +18, \quad Z = +6 \text{ km/sec},$$

with dispersions of 30, 22, and 17 km/sec, respectively. These values can be compared with those in Table 7.

Blanco suggests that M giants include objects of different populations and that "possibly half or more of the gM's earlier than M5 are concentrated in spiral arms and at the same time in the nuclear bulge of the Galaxy." According to the properties described in this section, the long-period variables, too, are in an intermediate position between the two population types (see also sec. 11).

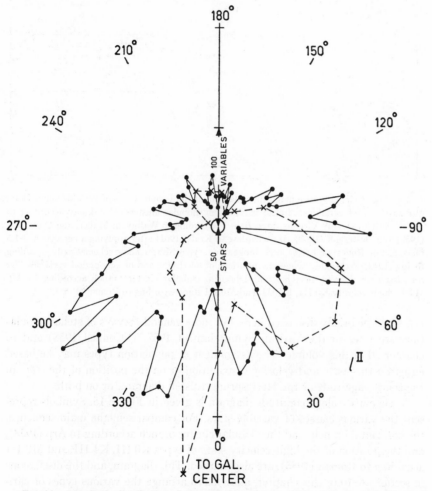

FIG. 14.—Longitude distribution of giant M stars of types M5 or later in general, and of long-period variables with average $m_{max} < 15.0$. Dots and solid line: M III stars, $|b^I| < 2°$; crosses and broken line: long-period variables, $|b^I| < 10°$.

For a discussion of stars of other late-type spectra, the reader is referred, in addition to Blanco's chapter, to recent investigations by Ikauniks (1952), Ishida (1960), and Takayanagi (1960).

§ 11. VARIABLE STARS AND STELLAR POPULATION TYPES

Since variable stars can be identified down to about one magnitude above the plate limit on celestial photographs, they easily lend themselves to studies of the properties of stellar populations throughout the Galaxy and even in extragalactic systems. The assignment of the various kinds of variables to population

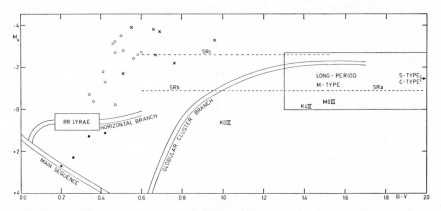

Fig. 15.—Color–absolute-magnitude diagram of the various types of variable stars. Dots: ultrashort-period variables; circles: variables in globular clusters, $P > 1$ day according to Arp (1955); crosses: W Virginis stars, $B - V$ according to Walraven, Muller, and Oosterhoff (1958) and Oosterhoff (1960), M_v according to Kraft (1961) after applying a correction $+1.5$ for reduction from type I to type II; broken line: types SRa, b, and c schematically according to Joy (1942); rectangles: schematic positions of RR Lyrae and of long-period variables. *For comparison:* main sequence, horizontal branch, globular cluster branch according to Arp (1958), high-velocity K0 III, K4 III, and M0 III stars according to Roman (1955).

types will be briefly discussed here. For more general surveys of stellar populations we refer to the Vatican Symposium of 1957 (O'Connell 1958) and to chapter 20 of this volume. The assignment of population types may be based either on the space and velocity distribution or on the position of the stars in the color-magnitude or the Hertzsprung-Russell diagram, or on both.

A schematic color-magnitude diagram is given in Figure 15. Symbols represent the various classes of variable stars. For comparison, the main sequence, the horizontal branch, and the globular cluster branch according to Arp (1958), and the position of the high-velocity stars of types K0 III, K4 III, and M0 III according to Roman (1955), are also marked. This diagram, and the discussions in sections 6–10 of this chapter, allow us to arrange the various types of variables into a sequence from population I to extreme population II:

RV Tauri stars, velocity <70 km/sec,
W Virginis stars,
long-period stars, period >300 days,
ultrashort-period stars,
RR Lyrae stars, ΔS = 0 to 4, type a,
long-period stars, period <150, and between 200 and 300 days,
RR Lyrae stars, type c,
long-period stars, period between 150 and 200 days,
RR Lyrae stars, ΔS = 5 to 10, type a,
RV Tauri stars, velocity > 70 km/sec.

In this arrangement more weight is given to the asymmetric drift velocity than to the density gradient either in the R or in the z direction.

The position of the ultrashort-period stars in this sequence seems to be clear, although there are still too few of them to provide conclusions about their distribution in space.

The RR Lyraes of type a were divided into two well-separated groups according to metal content, following Spite (1960) who showed, in a discussion of Preston's observations (1959), that there is a distinct division into two groups at a value of ΔS between 4 and 5. This division can clearly be seen in the graphs of the three velocity components for different ranges of ΔS as given by Spite.

The RR Lyraes of type c were provisionally placed near to the center of the sequence. We still have too few observations to be able to divide them into two distinct groups, although this is a possibility.

The slow-moving RV Tauri stars and the W Vir stars have the same velocity distribution. They might possibly be considered a single group, but according to their distribution in the sky (see Figs. 10 and 11) the W Vir stars should be placed much lower in the sequence.

The long-period variables are of intermediate types. They do not form a monotonous sequence as regards the correlation with the period. The group with the shortest periods is in the same position as that with periods between 200 and 300 days. These two groups have the same mean absolute magnitude, whereas the group between them, with P between 150 and 200 days, is brighter.

Some of the problems involving the relation of variable stars to population types may be nearer a solution when the observational programs of faint variables in regions close to the longitude of the galactic center are completed. Some current research programs have been mentioned in section 1; we also refer to the report of the Second Conference on Coordination of Galactic Research (*I.A.U.* 1959, pp. 22 and 28).

It is a great pleasure to thank the many colleagues who gave their valuable advice and made their unpublished material available for the preparation of this chapter.

APPENDIX 1

The Completeness of Variable Star Surveys

Several authors have discussed methods of computing completeness factors for variable star surveys. To quote van Gent (1933), for example (and replacing van Gent's symbol a by w):

Denoting by w the probability that a variable is detected by comparing one plate pair, and by N the number of variables present in the plate field, all having the same discovery chance, and by n the number of plate pairs compared, the following numbers of variables will be found $0, 1, 2, \ldots, n$ times:

$$a_0 = N(1-w)^n \qquad \text{0 times found,}$$
$$a_1 = N(1-w)^{n-1} \, w \, n \qquad \text{1 time found,}$$
$$a_2 = N(1-w)^{n-2} \, w^2 \, \frac{n(n-1)}{2!} \qquad \text{2 times found,}$$
$$\ldots\ldots\ldots\ldots\ldots\ldots\ldots \qquad \ldots\ldots\ldots$$
$$a_n = N \, w^n \qquad \text{n times found,}$$

in which: $a_0 + a_1 + a_2 + \ldots + a_n = N. \ldots$

... the discovery chance w and the total number of variables N were derived ... from the total numbers of variables found and the average number of times that each of these was found. The first quantity can be found from the observations by the formula, $A_1 = a_1 + a_2 + \ldots + a_n$, and the second quantity by the formula:

$$G_1 = \frac{a_1 + 2a_2 + \ldots + na_n}{a_1 + a_2 + \ldots + a_n}. \tag{1}$$

The average number of times that each variable, ..., including the undiscovered ones, was found is:

$$G_0 = \frac{0a_0 + 1a_1 + 2a_2 + \ldots + na_n}{a_0 + a_1 + a_2 + \ldots + a_n} = wn. \tag{2}$$

From (1) and (2) we see:

$$G_1 = wn \, \frac{N}{N - a_0} = \frac{wn}{1 - (1-w)^n}. \tag{3}$$

By this formula, w can be computed from G_1. As $N - a_0 = A_1$, the following formula for N results from (3):

$$N = \frac{A_1 G_1}{wn}. \tag{4}$$

These considerations concern of course a group of variables having the same amplitude, shape of light curve and apparent magnitude. The discovery chance w will depend on the method, the observer, and the quality of the pair of plates used. The effects of the grouping in this kind of investigation were recently considered in more detail by Kiang (1962).

If we want to determine completeness factors for small groups of variables, a more refined method which provides ratios of completeness factors for categories of variables with different kinds of light curves is preferable. As shown previously by the author (Plaut 1953) the discovery chance w of a variable by a comparison of a single pair of plates taken at random out of a number of plates uniformly distributed over all phases of the light curve is

$$w = a[1 - p(^m5)] + b[p(^m5) - p(1^m0)] + c[p(1^m0) - p(1^m5)] + d[p(1^m5)],$$

where $p(\Delta m)$ is the probability that the magnitude difference of the star on two arbitrarily chosen plates is equal to or exceeds Δm; a is the probability that a star is discovered as a variable star if the magnitude difference on the plates compared is smaller than 0.5 magnitude; b, c, d are the same probabilities if the magnitude difference is between 0.5 and 1.0, between 1.0 and 1.5, and larger than 1.5 magnitude, respectively.

TABLE 19

DISCOVERY CHANCES w FOR VARIOUS TYPES OF VARIABLES

TYPE	D	AMPLITUDE (MAGNITUDES)				
		0.6	0.8	1.0	1.5	2.0
δ Cep, RR Lyr	....	0.030	0.066	0.094	0.185	0.293
β Lyr	....	.010	.042	.051	.140	....
W UMa	....	.015	.075	.082	....	....
Algol	0.06	.006	.013	.017	.034	.052
Algol	.10	.010	.022	.028	.056	.084
Algol	.14	.014	.030	.038	.076	.114
Algol	.18	.017	.037	.048	.094	.144
Algol	0.22	0.021	0.044	0.057	0.113	0.167

The function $p(\Delta m)$ depends on the shape of the light curve and on the amplitude of light variation. It has been derived for various shapes and amplitudes by dividing the period P in n equal sections $P:n$. The brightness of the star is assumed to be constant within each section. The value of $p(\Delta m)$ equals the ratio of the number of pairs of sections for which the magnitude difference is equal to or exceeds Δm and the total number of pairs of sections.

The values of $a, b, c,$ and d depend on the method used, the plate material available, and the observer. They can be defined as the ratio of the number of differences Δm discovered to the total number occurring on the pairs of plates examined during a specific extended searching program. A survey of 30 pairs of Franklin Adams plates, made by means of a visual blinking comparator, gave the values $a = 0.00, b = 0.25, c = 0.50,$ and $d = 0.75$. Assuming these values for $a, b, c,$ and d, the discovery chances $w_n = 1 - (1 - w)^n$, expressed as a fraction of all variables, found by examining n pairs of plates, are those given in Tables 19 and 20. They refer to a cepheid light curve with a rising branch of duration ϵ and an amplitude A.

In a search for long-period variables, the condition that the pairs of plates are chosen at random from a number of plates uniformly distributed over all phases of the light curve, will not always be fulfilled. For a sinusoidal light curve with an amplitude A and a period which equals to x times the interval between the dates at which the two plates to be compared were taken, we obtain the discovery chances w given in Table 21. Ferwerda (1943) and Borgman (1956) have also made contributions to this problem. Similar investigations concerning stars with variable radial velocity have been made by Schlesinger (1915), Scott (1951), and Heard (1949, 1956).

TABLE 20

DISCOVERY CHANCES w FOR VARIOUS SHAPES OF
CEPHEID-LIKE LIGHT CURVES

$\epsilon = 0.30$ PERIOD

n	Amplitude in Magnitudes				
	0.6	0.8	1.0	1.5	2.0
1.........	0.030	0.066	0.094	0.185	0.293
10.........	.262	.495	.628	.871	0.969
30.........	0.598	0.871	0.948	0.998	1.000

$A = 1.0$ MAGNITUDE

n	Asymmetry of Light Curve (Unit Is Period)			
	0.30	0.10*	0.10†	0.10‡
1.........	0.094	0.083	0.066	0.054
10.........	.628	.580	.495	.426
30.........	0.948	0.926	0.874	0.813

* Slow decrease.
† Extremely fast decrease.
‡ *Ibidem*, exposure = 0.25 period.

TABLE 21

DISCOVERY CHANCES w FOR LONG-PERIOD VARIABLES

TIME BETWEEN TWO PLATES COMPARED, EXPRESSED IN THE PERIOD AS A UNIT			AMPLITUDE (MAGNITUDES)			
			1.0	2.0	3.0	4.0
1.5	0.5	.....	0.164	0.494	0.676	0.766
1.375	0.625	0.375	.158	.463	.638	.736
1.25	0.75	0.25	.125	.318	.511	.642
1.125	0.875	0.125	.000	.139	.241	.352
1.00	.....	.....	0.000	0.000	0.000	0.000

REFERENCES

ALDEN, H. L., and OSVALDS, V.	1961	*McCormick Pub.*, **11**, Part 20.
ALEXANDER, J. B.	1960	*Observatory*, **80**, 110.
ARP, H. C.	1955	*A.J.*, **60**, 1.
	1958	*Hdb. d. Phys.*, ed. S. FLÜGGE (Berlin: Springer-Verlag), **51**, 78, Fig. 38.
	1959	*A.J.*, **64**, 441.
	1962*a*	*Ap. J.*, **135**, 311.
	1962*b*	*Ibid.*, p. 971.
ARP, H. C., and JOHNSON, H. L.	1955	*Ap. J.*, **122**, 171.
ARP, H. C., and MELBOURNE, W. G.	1959	*A.J.*, **64**, 28.
BAADE, W., and MINKOWSKI, R.	1954	*Ap. J.*, **119**, 215.
BAADE, W., and SWOPE, H. H.	1961	*A.J.*, **66**, 300.
BAILEY, S. I.	1902	*Harvard Ann.*, **38**, 1.
BERGH, S. VAN DEN	1957	*A.J.*, **62**, 334; *Perkins Cont.*, **II**, 9.
BORGMAN, J.	1956	*Pub. Kapteyn Astr. Lab. Groningen*, No. 58.
CAMPBELL, L.	1955	*Studies of Long-Period Variables* (Cambridge, Mass.: Amer. Assoc. of Variable Star Observers).
CUFFEY, J.	1958	*Ap. J.*, **128**, 219.
	1961	*A.J.*, **66**, 71.
EGGEN, O. J.	1960*a*	*M.N.*, **120**, 430.
	1960*b*	*Ibid.*, p. 540.
	1960*c*	*Ibid.*, p. 563.
	1961*a*	*Roy. Obs. Bull.*, No. 27 (Greenwich and Cape Obs.).
	1961*b*	*Ibid.*, No. 29.
EGGEN, O. J., and SANDAGE, A. R.	1959	*M.N.*, **119**, 255.
FEAST, M. W.	1963	*M.N.*, **125**, 367.
FEAST, M. W., and THACKERAY, A. D.	1960	*M.N.*, **120**, 463.
FERWERDA, J. G.	1943	*B.A.N.*, **9**, 337.
GAPOSCHKIN, S.	1955	*Peremenniye Zvezdy*, **10**, 337.
GENT, H. VAN	1933	*B.A.N.*, **7**, 21.
GEYER, E.	1961	*Zs. f. Ap.*, **52**, 229.
HEARD, J. F.	1949	*Ap. J.*, **109**, 185; *Comm. David Dunlap Obs.*, No. 19.
	1956	*Pub. David Dunlap Obs.*, **2**, No. 4.
HECKMANN, O., DIECKVOSS, W., and KOX, H.	1948	*Sitzungsberichte Akad. Wiss. Berlin, math. nat. Klasse*, No. 7.

HERTZSPRUNG, E. 1926 *B.A.N.*, **3**, 115.
HOFFLEIT, D. 1957 *A.J.*, **62**, 120.
HOFFMEISTER, C. 1933 *A.N.*, **250**, 397.
HOFFMEISTER, C., *et al.* 1938 *Kleinere Veröff. Berlin-Babelsberg*, No. 19.
I.A.U. 1955 *I.A.U. Symp.*, No. 1.
1959 *Ibid.*, No. 7.
IKAUNIKS, J. J. 1950 *Astr. Sektora Raksti Riga*, **2**.
1952 *Trudy Inst. Fiziki Riga*, **4**.
ISHIDA, K. 1960 *Pub. Astr. Soc. Japan*, **12**, 214.
JOHNSON, H. L., and
  SANDAGE, A. R. 1956 *Ap. J.*, **124**, 379.
JOY, A. H. 1942 *Ap. J.*, **96**, 344.
1949 *Ibid.*, **110**, 105.
1952 *Ibid.*, **115**, 24.
1955 *Pub. A.S.P.*, **67**, 420.
KEENAN, P. C. 1957 *A.J.*, **62**, 244.
1959 *Ibid.*, **64**, 336.
KIANG, T. 1962 *Observatory*, **82**, 57.
KINMAN, T. D. 1959*a* *M.N.*, **119**, 134.
1959*b* *Ibid.*, pp. 157, 538, 559.
1961 *Roy. Obs. Bull.*, No. 37 (Greenwich and Cape Obs.).
KRAFT, R. P. 1961 *Ap. J.*, **134**, 616.
KRON, G. E., and
  MAYALL, N. U. 1960 *A.J.*, **65**, 581.
KUKARKIN, B. V. 1954 *Erforschung der Struktur und Entwicklung der Sternsysteme auf der Grundlage des Studiums veränderlicher Sterne* (Berlin: Akademie-Verlag).
KUKARKIN, B. V., and
  KULIKOVSKY, P. G. 1951 *Peremenniye Zvezdy*, **8**, 1.
KUKARKIN, B. V.,
  PARENAGO, P. P.,
  EFREMOV, Y. I., and
  KHOLOPOV, P. N. 1958 *General Catalogue of Variable Stars (GCVS)*, 2d ed. (Moscow: Academy of Science).
KULIKOVSKY, P. G. 1948 *Peremenniye Zvezdy*, **6**, 225.
KWEE, K. K. 1962 *Leiden Ann.*, **22**, 1.
LEIDEN 1948 *B.A.N.*, **10**, 425.
LOURENS, J. v. B. 1960 *M.N.A.S.S.A.*, **19**, 118.
LUDENDORFF, H. 1928 *Hdb. d. Astrophys.*, **6**, 92.
MAYALL, M. W. 1957 *Manual for Observing Variable Stars* (Cambridge, Mass.: Amer. Assoc. Variable Star Observers).
MCNAMARA, D. H., and
  AUGASON, G. 1962 *Ap. J.*, **135**, 64.
MERRILL, P. W. 1960 *Ap. J.*, **131**, 385.
MILLER, W. J. 1946 *Harvard Reprint*, No. 290.

Notni, R. 1957 *Mitt. Jena*, No. 26.

O'Connell, D. J. K. (ed.) 1958 *Ric. Astr. Specola Vaticana*, **5** ("Stellar Populations").

Ölander, V. R., *et al.* 1959 *Soc. Sci. Fennicae Comm. Phys. Math.*, **22**, 37.

Oort, J. H. 1928 *B.A.N.*, **4**, 269.

    1942 *Ibid.*, **9**, 334.

Oort, J. H., and
Tulder, J. J. M. van 1942 *B.A.N.*, **9**, 327.

Oort, J. H., and
Woerkom, A. J. J. van 1941 *B.A.N.*, **9**, 185.

Oosterhoff, P. Th. 1939 *Observatory*, **62**, 104.

    1956 *B.A.N.*, **13**, 67.

    1960 *Ibid.*, **15**, 199.

Osvalds, V., and
Risley, A. M. 1961 *McCormick Pub.*, **11**, Part 21.

Paloque, E., *et al.* 1958–
61 *Ann. Toulouse*, **26**, 50; **27**, 3; and **28**, 7.

Parenago, P. P. 1940 *A.J. U.S.S.R.*, **17**, 51.

    1945 *Ibid.*, **22**, 129.

    1954 *Peremenniye Zvezdy*, **10**, 193.

Pavlovskaya, E. D. 1953 *Peremenniye Zvezdy*, **9**, 233.

    1954 *Ibid.*, p. 349.

    1957 *A.J. U.S.S.R.*, **34**, 956.

    1960 *Peremenniye Zvezdy*, **13**, 8.

Payne-Gaposchkin, C. 1954a *Variable Stars and Galactic Structure* (London: The Athlone Press).

    1954b *Harvard Ann.*, **113**, Nos. 3 and 4.

    1956 *Vistas in Astronomy*, **2**, 1142 (London and New York: Pergamon Press).

Payne-Gaposchkin, C.,
and Gaposchkin, S. 1952a *Harvard Ann.*, **115**, 1.

    1952b *Ibid.*, **118**.

Payne-Gaposchkin, C.,
Brenton, V. K., and
Gaposchkin, S. 1943 *Harvard Ann.*, **113**, 1.

Perek, L. 1951 *Brno Cont.*, **1**, No. 8.

Petit, M. 1960a *Ann. d'ap.*, **23**, 681.

    1960b *Ibid.*, p. 710.

Pickering, E. C.,
Kapteyn, J. C., and
Rhijn, P. J. van 1918–
24 Harvard Catalogue of Selected Areas, *Harvard Ann.*, **101–103**.

Plaut, L. 1953 *Pub. Kapteyn Astr. Lab. Groningen*, No. 55.

    1956 *Leaflet A.S.P.*, No. 343.

    1963 *B.A.N.*, **17**, 75, 81.

Plaut, L., and
Borgman, J. 1954 *Observatory*, **74**, 181.

PLAUT, L., and
  SOUDAN, A.   1963   *B.A.N.*, **17**, 70.
PRESTON, G. W.   1959   *Ap. J.*, **130**, 507.
                       1961   *Ibid.*, **134**, 651.

PRESTON, G. W., and
  SPINRAD, H.   1959   *Pub. A.S.P.*, **71**, 497.
RHIJN, P. J. VAN   1949   *Pub. Kapteyn Astr. Lab. Groningen*, No. 53.
ROBERTS, M. S., and
  SANDAGE, A. R.   1955   *A.J.*, **60**, 185.
ROMAN, N. G.   1955   *Ap. J. Suppl.*, **2**, 195.
ROSINO, L.   1951   *Ap. J.*, **113**, 60.
RUSSO, T. W.   1961   Private communication.
SAFRONOW, V. S.   1955   *Peremenniye Zvezdy*, **10**, 236.
SANDAGE, A. R.   1958   *Ric. Astr. Specola Vaticana*, **5**, 41 ("Stellar Popu-
                               lations").

SANDAGE, A. R., and
  SCHMIDT, M.   1958   Private communication.
SANDAGE, A. R., and
  WALKER, M. F.   1955   *A.J.*, **60**, 230.
                       1957   Private communication.

SANDAGE, A. R., and
  WALLERSTEIN, G.   1960   *Ap. J.*, **131**, 598.
SAWYER, H. B.   1955   *Pub. David Dunlap Obs.*, **2**, 33.
SCHAIFERS, K.   1960   *Zs. f. Ap.*, **49**, 266.
SCHAIFERS, K., and
  WENZEL, W.   1961   *Zs. f. Ap.*, **53**, 136.
SCHLESINGER, F.   1915   *Ap. J.*, **41**, 162.
SCHNELLER, H.   1940   *Kleinere Veröff. Berlin-Babelsberg*, No. 22.
SCOTT, E. L.   1951   *Proc. Second Berkeley Symp. Math. Statist. Prob.*,
                               p. 417 (Berkeley and Los Angeles: University
                               of California Press).

SEARES, F. H,
  KAPTEYN, J. C., and
  RHIJN, P. J. VAN   1930   *Mount Wilson Catalogue of Photographic Magni-
                               tudes in Selected Areas 1–139* (Washington,
                               D.C.: The Carnegie Institution).

SHAPLEY, H.   1928   *Harvard Reprint*, No. 51; *Proc. Nat. Acad. Sci.,
                               Washington*, **14**, 825.
                       1939   *Proc. Nat. Acad. Sci., Washington*, **25**, 423.
SMITH, H. J.   1955   Harvard thesis; *A.J.*, **60**, 179.
SPITE, F.   1960   *Cont. Astr. Lab. Lille*, **10**; *Comptes Rendus*, **251**,
                               204.

TAKAYANAGI, W.   1960   *Pub. Astr. Soc. Japan*, **12**, 314.
THACKERAY, A. D.   1950   *Observatory*, **70**, 144.
                       1959   *A.J.*, **64**, 437.

TORONTO   1959   Symp. on Differences among Globular Clusters,
                               A.J., **64**, 425.

VASHAKIDSE, M. A.   1937   *Abastumani Bull.*, **1**, 87.
                           1938   *Ibid.*, **2**, 109.
WALRAVEN, TH.,
  MULLER, A.B., and
  OOSTERHOFF, P. TH.   1958   *B.A.N.*, **14**, 81.
WILDEY, R. L.   1961   *Ap. J.*, **133**, 430.
WILSON, R. E.   1942   *Ap. J.*, **96**, 371.
                           1953   *General Catalogue of Radial Velocities* (Washington, D.C.: The Carnegie Institution).
WILSON, R. E., and
  MERRILL, P. W.   1942   *Ap. J.*, **95**, 248.
WOLTJER, L.   1956   *B.A.N.*, **13**, 62.

CHAPTER 14

Distribution of Novae in the Galaxy

L. PLAUT

Kapteyn Laboratory, Groningen

§ 1. INTRODUCTION

MANY aspects of the phenomena of galactic novae have been extensively described by Payne-Gaposchkin (*The Galactic Novae* 1957), who included, in addition, a number of valuable references to earlier work in this field. Other discussions of novae can be found in monographs on variable stars and galactic structure by Payne-Gaposchkin (1954) and by Kukarkin (1954), but very little has since been published about the distribution of novae in space.

Various difficulties in the attempt to derive the space and velocity distribution of novae arise from the temporary character of these phenomena. Neither trigonometric and secular parallaxes nor, obviously, proper motions could have, so far, been obtained with any accuracy. Radial velocities cannot be distinguished from velocities of expanding masses of gas. In addition, it is difficult to estimate the completeness of the observations.

We are not concerned, in this chapter, with supernovae.

§ 2. CLASSIFICATION

It is not always possible to classify even novae as such with certainty. There are several cases of transitions between the typical novae and the recurrent novae, and between these latter and the U Geminorum or SS Cygni stars. In addition to the explosive character of the light variation common to all of these groups, the recent discovery that many of these stars are binaries confirms their mutual relationship.

§ 3. DISTRIBUTION IN THE SKY

Catalogues of novae are given by Vorontsov-Velyaminov (1953), by Payne-Gaposchkin (1957), and in the *Second General Catalogue of Variable Stars* (Kukarkin *et al.* 1958, henceforth denoted by *GCVS*). Figure 1 shows the distribution of the novae in the sky. Data are from the *GCVS;* new galactic coordinates

311

are used. Stars of different maximum-magnitude groups are marked by different symbols. The concentration toward the galactic plane and, near it, toward the galactic center, are clearly visible.

A more detailed study shows that regions with no interstellar absorption are strongly preferred, an example of which is shown in Plate I, where the novae in a region near the galactic center are plotted on a reproduction of a photographic plate of this region.

§ 4. DISTANCES

In spite of the difficulties mentioned in the Introduction, several methods of determining distances have been used. Extensive investigations based on these methods were published by McLaughlin (1942, 1945, 1946) and by Kopylov

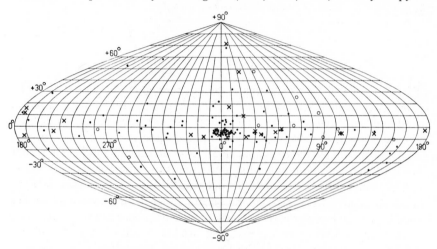

Fig. 1.—The distribution of novae in the sky. New galactic coordinates l^{II}, b^{II} are used. Circles: $m_{max} < 3.0$; crosses: $3.0 \leq m_{max} < 6.0$; dots: $6.0 \leq m_{max}$.

(1952, 1955a, b, 1957, 1958). A critical review is given by Schmidt-Kaler (1957, 1962). Payne-Gaposchkin (1957) also gives distances for a large number of novae.

A direct method of determining distances cannot be applied to most novae. Consequently, one has to look for relations between the absolute magnitude at maximum brightness, M_0, and some easily observable feature. The rate of change of the brightness (expressed in magnitudes) during the ascending or the descending branch of the light curve appears to be a usable parameter. For many novae only the descending branch has been observed extensively enough to provide a gradient. The extrapolation to the real maximum also presents difficulties.

Following Schmidt-Kaler, we can define three parameters: (a) t_2^*, the time in which the photographic brightness increases by two magnitudes just before the maximum brightness; (b) t_2, the time in which the photographic brightness decreases by two magnitudes after the maximum; (c) t_3, the time in which the

photographic brightness decreases by three magnitudes. The last two parameters are more accurately determined than t_2^*. The unit for the time is taken as
1 day.

From Arp's (1956) observations of novae in M31, Schmidt-Kaler (1957) derives

$$m_0 = + 12.7 + 3.2 \log t_2 \qquad \text{(for } 0.9 < \log t_2 < 1.7\text{)} \,;$$
$$\pm \quad .3 \pm \;\; .3 \,,$$

(1)

where m_0 is the apparent photographic magnitude at maximum brightness. He
derives other linear relations between m_0 and t_2 outside these limits of $\log t_2$,
and also finds from all available observations including novae in the Galaxy,
the Magellanic Clouds, and M31,

$$\log t_3 = \log t_2 + .3 \pm .06 \,.$$

(2)

The result is shown by the dashed line in Figure 2.

Schmidt-Kaler derives distances for eleven galactic novae by various meth-

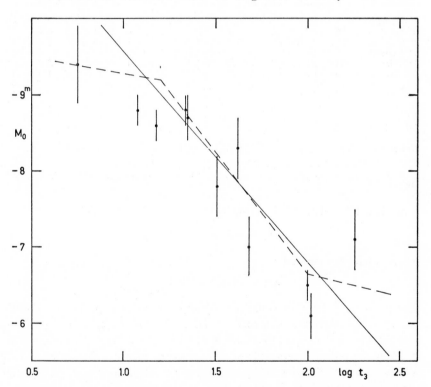

Fig. 2.—The relation between the logarithm of duration, t_3, of the decrease of brightness
from maximum to three magnitudes fainter, and the absolute photographic magnitude, M_0, at
maximum (according to Schmidt-Kaler 1957). Solid line: relation (3), derived from galactic
novae; dashed line: relation derived from objects in M31; dots: results for eleven nearby novae;
vertical lines correspond to the mean errors.

ods, based on observations of the angular and linear rates of expansion of nebular shells, of the intensity of the interstellar K line of Ca^+, of the effect of the differential galactic rotation in the radial velocity of the interstellar K line, and of the expansion of light. These eleven galactic novae follow the linear relation

$$M_0 = -11.8 + 2.5 \log t_3, \qquad (3)$$

which also holds outside the limits given for equation (1). This fact explains the lower value of the coefficient of $\log t_3$ in (3) as compared with (1). Figure 2 shows Schmidt-Kaler's data for the eleven individual novae and equation (3) (solid line).

TABLE 1

DATA FOR 11 GALACTIC NOVAE

Star	t_3 (days)		M_0 (Absolute Magnitude at Maximum Brightness)			r(kpc)			
V 603 Aql...	8	12	−8.0	−10.5	−8.8±0.2	0.22	0.36	0.2	0.34±.03
T Aur......	80	105	−5.4	− 6.8	−6.1 .2	0.50	0.71	0.8	0.33 .03
V 476 Cyg..	16	22	−8.0	− 9.7	−8.8 .2	0.78	1.66	0.8	1.15 .10
DN Gem....	37	48	−7.2	− 8.2	−7.0 .4	1.05	1.5	1.1	1.3 .3
DQ Her....	93	100	−5.4	− 6.5	−6.5 .2	0.21	0.24	0.3	0.40 .04
CP Lac.....	9	15	−8.0	−10.2	−8.6 .2	0.73	1.4	0.8	1.1 .1
DK Lac....	22	32	......	− 8.8	−7.8 .4	......	2.3	2.1	1.7 .4
GK Per.....	13	22	−8.0	− 9.7	−8.7 .3	0.38	0.4	0.4	0.6 .1
RR Pic.....	150	182	−5.4	− 7.3	−7.1 .4	0.19	0.67	0.2	1.30 .25
CP Pup.....	6	6	−8.0	−11.0	−9.4 .5	0.42	1.2	0.4	0.9 .2
EU Sct.....	42	42	......	− 7.7	−8.3 0.4	......	3.5	4.0	5.4 .6
Reference*..	(2)	(4)	(1)	(2)	(4)	(1)	(2)	(3)	(4)

* References: (1) McLaughlin (1945); (2) Kopylov (1955b); (3) Payne-Gaposchkin (1957); (4) Schmidt-Kaler (1957, 1962).

McLaughlin's data can be expressed by

$$M_0 = -10.5 + 2.2 \log t_3, \qquad (4)$$

whereas Kopylov derived

$$M_0 = -13.7 + 3.6 \log t_3. \qquad (5)$$

The discrepancy between equations (4) and (5) can be explained by the difference in the interstellar absorption as adopted by McLaughlin and by Kopylov. Schmidt-Kaler shows that the smaller amount of absorption adopted by McLaughlin probably represents a more realistic quantity. Buscombe and De Vaucouleurs (1955) arrive at the same conclusion from a comparison with the novae in the Magellanic Clouds.

The data in Table 1 are from the work of various investigators of these eleven novae and indicate the accuracy of observations of the duration of the decrease in brightness to 3 magnitudes below maximum, which can be used to compute the absolute magnitudes and the distances. A comparison between the distances of 70 novae derived from the relationships between rate of decline and absolute magnitude used by Payne-Gaposchkin and by McLaughlin yields the systematic difference, $\Delta \log r = +0.02$ with a dispersion of ± 0.12.

§ 5. SPACE DISTRIBUTION

It is difficult to estimate the completeness of the discoveries of novae. Schmidt-Kaler (1957) and Allen (1955) have concluded that only the apparently very bright novae, those with a maximum magnitude brighter than 3.0,

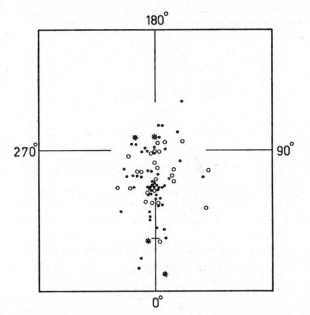

FIG. 3.—Projection of positions of novae on the galactic plane. Dots, circles, and stars denote fast, slow, and very slow novae, respectively. New galactic longitudes are shown at the margin. The short horizontal line at $l = 0°$ denotes the position of the galactic center. (From Payne-Gaposchkin 1957, Fig. 2.3.)

are known completely. From the distance distribution, Schmidt-Kaler concludes that the discoveries are complete within a distance of 800 pc. For greater distances, there is a selection of novae of high intrinsic brightness. Schmidt-Kaler (1957) derives, from the sample of eleven novae, a frequency distribution of absolute magnitudes having two sharp maxima at $M_0 = -9$ and -6.5, respectively. The same division into two groups has been found by Arp (1956) for the novae in M31.

Since we have no reliable estimate of the completeness of the known novae we are not able to determine the density distribution and can only derive a rough estimate by plotting the positions of the known objects in space. This has been done by Payne-Gaposchkin (1957) and others. Figures 3 and 4 are re-

productions of her Figures 2.3 and 2.4. They show the projected distributions
on the galactic plane and on a plane vertical to the galactic plane through the
galactic center and the sun. It is obvious that the concentration to the galactic
plane as well as to the center is high, although the latter does not fully appear
because of heavy interstellar absorption.

The mean distance from the galactic plane is 630 pc for the 93 novae listed
by Payne-Gaposchkin. This value is systematically too high because of inter-
stellar absorption. Oort (1958) gives a value $\langle |z| \rangle = 440$ pc. Kopylov (1955a),

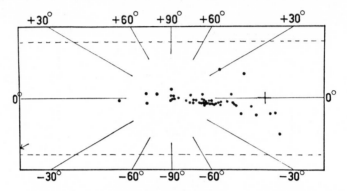

Fig. 4.—Projected distribution of novae on the plane perpendicular to the galactic plane
through sun and galactic center (short vertical line). The dotted lines are at $z = \pm 5$ kpc. Old
galactic latitudes are indicated at the margin. (From Payne-Gaposchkin 1957, Fig. 2.4.)

who assumed a much higher value for interstellar absorption than other investigators, derived density gradients per kpc as

$$\frac{\partial \log \nu}{\partial R} = -0.22 ,$$

and

$$\frac{\partial \log \nu}{\partial z} = -2.39 .$$

Similar results were derived by Kukarkin (1954); more recently Schmidt-Kaler
found

$$\frac{\partial \log \nu}{\partial R} = -0.18 ,$$

and

$$\frac{\partial \log \nu}{\partial z} = -1.5 .$$

Assuming equal density throughout the whole galactic system, Kukarkin
estimated that at least 100 novae will occur every year. Allen (1955) obtained
a similar estimate. Arp's estimate of the yearly number of novae in M31 is
26 ± 4 (1956).

PLATE I.—The distribution of novae in an area near the galactic center. The galactic equator in the new coordinate system and the direction to the center are shown by a straight line and a small line perpendicular to it. Novae are shown as white circles. The photograph was made by the late Dr. H. van Gent with the Franklin Adams camera at Johannesburg. The size is 10° × 10°. North at the top, east at the right.

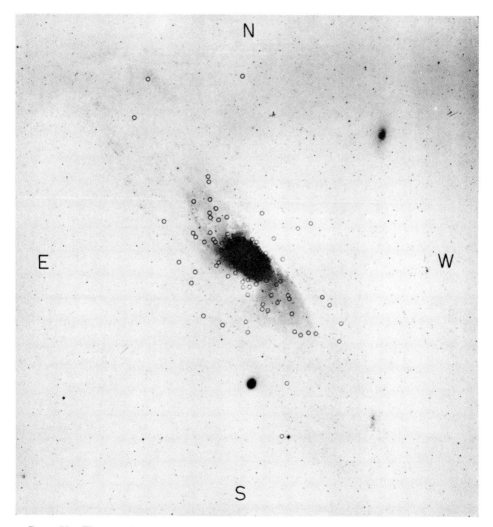

PLATE II.—The novae in the Andromeda galaxy, M31. Those listed by Hubble (1929) and Arp (1956) are shown by open circles. One degree equals 81 mm.

§ 6. NOVAE IN OTHER STELLAR SYSTEMS

The Magellanic Clouds.—Summaries on novae in the Magellanic Clouds are given by Buscombe, Gascoigne, and De Vaucouleurs (1954) and by Buscombe and De Vaucouleurs (1955). Four novae in the SMC and six in the LMC have so far been reported. Their light curves are similar to those of the galactic novae. Henize, Hoffleit, and Nail (1954) state that they are outside the dense regions of both Clouds.

The Andromeda Galaxy M31.—The novae in M31 have been studied by Hubble (1929) and more recently by Arp (1956), whose results were described above. In general, no difference appears to exist between the nova phenomena in the Galaxy and those in M31.

In Plate II the novae discussed by Hubble (1929, Table 5) and by Arp (1956, Table 1) are plotted on an enlargement of a 48″ Palomar-Schmidt plate. From the rectangular, two-dimensional coordinates given by Hubble and Arp, a root mean-square distance from the equatorial plane of 1.8 kpc is found as compared with 1.0 kpc for the galactic novae (excluding two extremely large distances). For M31 an inclination $i = 13°$ and a random distribution of longitudes was adopted (see Arp 1956).

§ 7. NOVAE AND POPULATION TYPES

Our small information with respect to space distribution indicates that novae are highly concentrated to the galactic plane and probably also to the center of the system. Classification according to the simple population I and II scheme is therefore somewhat ambiguous. Baade (1958) suggested that novae belong to type II because (*a*) nova T Sco is probably a member of the globular cluster M80 (Sawyer 1938); (*b*) there are two novae in dwarf E galaxies, one in NGC 147, the other in NGC 185; (*c*) numerous novae are found in the nuclear bulge of the Galaxy.

T Sco is very near the center of the cluster M80. Assuming it to be a member, Schmidt-Kaler (1962) finds the visual absolute magnitude -8.4, whereas from t_2 he derives -8.5. The nova V 1148 Sgr is probably a member of the globular cluster NGC 6553 (Mayall 1949, Schmidt-Kaler 1962). Recently Zwicky (1957) discovered a nova in the elliptical galaxy NGC 205.

Concerning the position of novae in the Hertzsprung-Russell diagram, Hoyle, in his summary of the discussions of the Rome symposium on stellar populations (Hoyle 1958), states:

Little, if anything, is known of the whereabouts on the HR diagram of the catastrophic stellar states. General opinion, for what it is worth, is that novae and the nuclei of planetaries may lie on a continuation of the leftward tracks of stars with masses $\sim$1.25 ⊙.

More recently, Schmidt-Kaler (1962), discussing the "normal" brightness of novae, found $+4.3$ for the photographic absolute magnitude at minimum. Together with an estimated color $B - V = -0.3$, this places the novae in the region of the HR diagram between sub-luminous B stars and the white dwarfs. In the classification of stellar populations as proposed on page 533 of the report of the concluding session of the same symposium, novae were classified as belonging to the disk population. Schmidt-Kaler estimated the velocity with respect to the sun to be about 60 km/sec, and suggested a classification as an intermediate population.

REFERENCES

ALLEN, C. W.	1955	*M.N.*, **114**, 387.
ARP, H. C.	1956	*A.J.*, **61**, 15.
BAADE, W.	1958	*Ric. Astr. Specola Vaticana*, **5**, 165 ("Stellar Populations").
BUSCOMBE, W., GASCOIGNE, S. C. B., and VAUCOULEURS, G. DE	1954	*Australian J. Sci., Suppl.*, **17**, No. 3.
BUSCOMBE, W., and VAUCOULEURS, G. DE	1955	*Observatory*, **75**, 170.
HENIZE, K. G., HOFFLEIT, D., and NAIL, V. M.	1954	*Harvard Reprint*, No. 387; *Proc. Nat. Acad. Sci.*, **40**, 365.
HOYLE, F.	1958	*Ric. Astr. Specola Vaticana*, **5**, 491 ("Stellar Populations").
HUBBLE, E. P.	1929	*Ap. J.*, **69**, 103.
KOPYLOV, I. M.	1952	*Izvestija Crimean Obs.*, **9**, 116.
	1955a	*Ibid.*, **13**, 23.
	1955b	*A.J. U.S.S.R.*, **32**, 48.
	1957	*I.A.U. Symp.*, No. 3, 71.
	1958	*Ibid.*, No. 5, 63.
KUKARKIN, B. V.	1954	*Erforschung der Struktur und Entwicklung der Sternsysteme auf der Grundlage des Studiums veränderlicher Sterne* (Berlin: Akademie-Verlag).
KUKARKIN, B. V., PARENAGO, P. P., EFREMOV, Y. I., and KHOLOPOV, P. N.	1958	*General Catalogue of Variable Stars (GCVS)* (2d ed.; Moscow: Academy of Sciences).
McLAUGHLIN, D. B.	1942	*Popular Astr.*, **50**, 233.
	1945	*Pub. A.S.P.*, **57**, 69.
	1946	*A.J.*, **51**, 136.
MAYALL, M. W.	1949	*A.J.*, **54**, 191.
OORT, J. H.	1958	*Ric. Astr. Specola Vaticana*, **5**, 415 ("Stellar Populations").

PAYNE-GAPOSCHKIN, C. 1954 *Variable Stars and Galactic Structure* (London: Athlone Press).

1957 *The Galactic Novae* (Amsterdam: North-Holland Publishing Co.).

SAWYER, H. 1938 *J.R.A.S. Canada*, **32**, 69.

SCHMIDT-KALER, TH. 1957 *Zs. f. Ap.*, **41**, 182.

1962 *Communication at the Second Bamberg Colloquium on Variable Stars; Kleine Veröffentlichungen Babelsberg*, No. 34, 109.

VORONTSOV-
VELYAMINOV, B. A. 1953 *Gasnebel und Neue Sterne* (Berlin: Verlag Kultur und Fortschritt).

ZWICKY, F. 1957 *Morphological Astronomy* (Berlin: Springer-Verlag).

CHAPTER 15

Planetary Nebulae[1]

R. MINKOWSKI

Radio Astronomy Laboratory, University of California, Berkeley

§ 1. INTRODUCTION

Planetary nebulae are objects of, at most, moderate luminosity. But since
most of their light is concentrated in a small number of strong emission lines,
they can be found on objective-prism plates even if their apparent magnitude
is well below the limiting magnitude for stars with their continuous spectrum.
For the same reason it is relatively easy to obtain slit spectrograms and to
measure the radial velocities of faint planetary nebulae. It has therefore been
possible to drive systematic searches for planetary nebulae to a stage in which
the central part of the Galaxy has been reached and in which the galactic distribution of planetary nebulae becomes directly observable. It has also been
possible to extend observations of radial velocities into the central region and
thus to obtain a picture of the kinematics of the system of planetary nebulae.
As far as these observations are concerned, planetary nebulae seem to be ideally
suited for investigations of the structure of a subsystem of the Galaxy.

It is disappointing that in many other respects the nature of planetary
nebulae is the source of difficulties that have not yet been overcome. With very
few exceptions, the distances of planetary nebulae cannot be determined
reliably. Part of the difficulty is observational, connected with the fact that the
spectrum consists of emission lines, with a considerable range of differences
between individual objects. Photographic magnitudes of planetaries with high-
excitation spectra, showing strong [O III] lines, are not comparable with those
of nebulae with low-excitation spectra which have strong [O II] lines (e.g.,
NGC 40) or with those of planetaries in which all forbidden lines in the photographic region are weak (e.g., BD 30°3639). Red magnitudes suffer from similar
difficulties caused by the wide range of the intensity ratio of the [N II] lines at

[1] The survey of the literature for this chapter was concluded in April, 1962. Some important
papers that appeared after submission of the manuscript are listed in an appendix to the references.

6548 and 6583 A relative to Hα. A spectrophotometric investigation is the only way to obtain significant values of the apparent brightness. At this time, measures of the flux density in Hβ and in the green lines of [O III] are available for a number of the brighter planetaries (Liller and Aller 1954; Liller 1955; Capriotti and Daub 1960; Collins, Daub, and O'Dell 1961; O'Dell 1962). Corrections for interstellar absorption must often be large. They cannot be established by measuring colors as for a star with a continuous spectrum. Lacking better information, investigators have used corrections derived from generalized models of the interstellar absorption or from mean values for stars in the surrounding area. The only valid way to determine the corrections would be spectrophotometric observations of the Balmer gradient (Berman 1936), which theory expects to be fairly similar in all planetaries, or of the intensity ratio of a Paschen and a Balmer line with common level (Aller and Minkowski 1956), a difficult and therefore unattractive approach.

Even if the observational problem were to be solved, the fact remains that planetary nebulae are expanding objects. Consequently, no single quantity exists that remains constant and that can be used as a distance indicator during the whole evolution of a planetary. Initially, a planetary is optically thick for the exciting radiation. If the central star is constant, the absolute magnitude of a planetary remains nearly constant while its diameter increases. In this phase, only the central ionized part of the gas is observed. The mass of the observed nebula is only a fraction of the total mass. As the nebula expands, the ionized volume increases faster than the total volume and the mass of the observed nebula increases. When the nebula becomes optically thin for the exciting radiation, the whole gas becomes observable. The observed mass now remains constant, but the absolute magnitude decreases as the optical thickness diminishes with continuing expansion. A population of planetaries in which all ages are represented equally will thus show a very large spread of absolute magnitudes, even if all of its members are strictly identical except for their ages. The luminosity function will have a maximum, which contains all optically thick objects, and will fall off gradually towards fainter absolute magnitudes.

§ 2. THE DISTANCES OF PLANETARY NEBULAE

2.1. PARALLAXES AND PROPER MOTIONS

Attempts to determine trigonometric parallaxes of planetary nebulae have only shown that the parallaxes are too small to deserve confidence. The largest parallax, $0''.040 \pm 0''.008$, was found for NGC 7293 (van Maanen 1923), which is indeed likely to be one of the nearest planetaries.

Measurements of the proper motions of 21 planetaries by van Maanen (1933) and of 33 planetaries by Anderson (1934) have been used to determine statistical parallaxes. These are still the basic data for all attempts to derive individual distances of planetaries. Results of the reduction by various authors differ somewhat. The mean parallax $\langle p \rangle = 0''.00079 \pm 0''.00011$ derived by Parenago

(1946a) is typical. The average diameter of 78″ corresponds to 0.5 pc, a value which is not characteristic and probably much too high because the material contains relatively many large nebulae of low surface brightness.

2.2. INDIVIDUAL PLANETARIES

2.2.1. *NGC 246.*—The central star of NGC 246 has a companion at a distance of about 4″. Proper motion of central star and companion (van Maanen 1929; Luyten 1961) are fairly large and so nearly equal that it is safe to assume that the stars are physically connected. The radial velocity -39 ± 7 km/sec (Mayall and Minkowski, unpublished) of the nebula also agrees satisfactorily with that of -33 ± 13 km/sec of the companion (Minkowski; cf. Bowen 1960). The velocity of the central star cannot be determined accurately. Its spectrum shows few ill-defined absorption lines of C IV, C III, N III, and O III; the measures suggest a velocity of the order -100 km/sec, a value which suggests that there is still outward flow in the atmosphere of the star.

. The spectrum of the companion, similar to τ Ceti, is of type G8 V to K0 V. If the star is a normal main-sequence star, the absolute magnitude is $M_v = 6$, but for a high-velocity object, $M_v = 6.3$. Baum (cf. Bowen 1960) has found for the nucleus, $V = 11.88$, $B - V = -0.43$; for the companion, $V = 14.28$, $B - V = 0.70$. The distance is therefore between 360 and 480 parsecs, and for the nucleus M_v is between 3.6 and 3.9.

2.2.2. *NGC 6720.*—Latypov (1955) has succeeded in measuring the expansion of NGC 6720. If the expansion of $0\rlap{.}{''}009 \pm 0\rlap{.}{''}001$ per year is combined with an expansion velocity of 19 km/sec from the observations by Campbell and Moore (1918), a distance of 450 parsecs results. A larger velocity of expansion, 30 km/sec, has been reported by Wilson (1950); this would lead to a distance of 710 parsecs. Since the velocity of expansion increases, in many planetaries, with the distance from the center of the nebula (Wilson 1950), some doubt remains as to the accuracy that can be achieved with this basically reliable method.

2.2.3. *The planetary nebula in M15.*—A planetary nebula was found by Pease (1928) in the globular cluster M15. Membership in the cluster is established by the agreement of radial velocities (Joy 1949). On a recent Hα photograph by Kinman (unpublished) with the 120-inch telescope of the Lick Observatory, the object appears elliptical with a major axis of about 1″. At the distance of M15, this corresponds to about 0.06 pc, a small diameter which is appropriate for a bright planetary nebulae. The spectrum (Joy 1949) is that of an average object; but the strength with which the continuous spectrum of the central star appears shows that the star is brighter than the nebula. Baum (unpublished) finds $M_p = -2.0$, $CI = 0.17$ for the object. If the color of the nebula is assumed to be that of a bright planetary with similar spectrum, the absolute magnitude of the nebula is $M_p = +0.7$, that of the star $M_p = -1.7$. It does not seem possible to avoid the interpretation that the central star is

unusually bright; it might be a double, however. The nebula seems to be subluminous. It is unlikely that this is the result of very low temperature of the
central star, since in that case the nebula should show a low-excitation spectrum.
More likely, the nebula is optically thin for the exciting radiation, in spite of
its small size. In that case, the mass of the nebula must be an order of magnitude
or more smaller than average.

A search for planetary nebulae in other globular clusters by Baade (unpublished) was unsuccessful. The negative result conforms to expectation. The mass
of a globular cluster is about 10^{-6} that of the Galaxy. Since the total number of
planetaries in the Galaxy is of the order 10^4, one cannot expect to find more
than one planetary in 100 globular clusters.

2.2.4. *Planetary nebulae in external galaxies.*—Baade (1955) has found, in a
field 96' south preceding the nucleus of NGC 224 (M31), five objects that are
probably planetary nebulae. The photographic magnitudes range from 21.7 to
22.2; with a distance modulus of 24.2 magnitudes, M_p is between -2.0 and
-2.5. This must be the upper limit of brightness for planetary nebulae in M31.
A revision of the photometric data by Swope (1963) gives $M_B = -2.55$ as
mean for these objects.

Lindsay (1955) and Koelbloed (1956) have reported objects assumed to be
planetary nebulae in the Small Magellanic Cloud. With a distance modulus of
19.1 magnitudes, the objects range to $M_p = -5.5$. If the objects are really
planetary nebulae, one would have to conclude that a difference exists between
planetary nebulae in M31 and in the Small Magellanic Cloud. It is much more
likely that the brightest of these objects are not planetary nebulae. They might
be small H II regions or the bright, small central regions of more extended H II
regions. Such an interpretation is supported by the fact that the bright central
parts of some galactic H II regions have been misclassified and included in catalogues of planetary nebulae, e.g., IC 1470 and NGC 7635. An investigation by
Henize and Westerlund (1963) indicates an upper limit to the photographic
absolute magnitudes of planetary nebulae in the Small Magellanic Cloud at
$M_p = -3.0$.

Planetary nebulae in the Large Magellanic Cloud have been found by Westerlund and Rodgers (1959). Photometric data are not yet available. Preliminary results suggest that no planetary is brighter than $m_p = 16$, or $M_p = -3$
(Rodgers, private communication), and that more luminous objects are not
planetaries.

2.3. STATISTICAL DISTANCES

2.3.1. *Assumption of constant absolute magnitude.*—Distances of individual
planetaries have been derived that are based on the assumption that some
simple distance indicator exists.

The assumption that the mean absolute magnitude of planetary nebulae is
a significant quantity was first introduced by Zanstra (1931). He established
a correlation between the apparent magnitude of the central stars and the mag-

nitude differences between central star (m_s) and nebula (m_n), i.e., the temperatures of the central stars. The correlation,

$$m_s = 10.4 + 0.7 \, (m_s - m_n) \, , \tag{1}$$

is interpreted as indicating that the absolute magnitudes of the stars are
given by

$$M_s = \text{const} + 0.7 \, (m_s - m_n) \, . \tag{2}$$

Equation (1) would follow immediately from equation (2) if the distances of
all planetaries involved were the same. The spread in the distances causes part
of the observed scatter with respect to Zanstra's relation. Although Zanstra
recognized that the radial velocities cannot be represented completely by differential galactic rotation, he used the radial velocities together with the assumption of differential rotation equal to that of O–B stars to determine the constant
in equation (2) and to obtain distances from the distance modulus $m_s - M_s$.
The relations (1) and (2) can be rewritten as relations for the nebular magnitudes, so that

$$M_n = M_0 - 0.3(m_s - m_n) \, . \tag{3}$$

Clearly the assumption is implied that, apart from a slight dependence on the
temperature of the central star, all nebulae have the same absolute magnitude.

This assumption was explicitly introduced by Vorontsov-Velyaminov
(1934a, b) who found a correlation between surface brightness and angular diameter which is easily understood if all nebulae have the same absolute magnitude. The correlation is actually fairly loose, partly because the dependence of
M_n on $m_s - m_n$ plays a role, partly because there must be some dispersion in
absolute magnitude, but undoubtedly also because the assumption of constant
absolute magnitude must fail for objects that are not optically thick for the
exciting radiation. To establish the absolute magnitude, the statistical parallax
of the planetaries with known proper motions was used in addition to galactic
rotation. No allowance was made for the dependence of M_n on $m_s - m_n$. Distances were obtained from the distance modulus $m_n - M_n$. Some of the nebular
magnitudes used were later found to be incorrect (Vorontsov-Velyaminov 1950).
Since no correction was made for interstellar absorption, Zanstra's and Vorontsov-Velyaminov's original distances are unrealistic and only of historical interest.

The first to take the interstellar absorption into account was Berman (1937).
The determination of M_n was based primarily on the statistical parallax of the
nebulae with known proper motions. An involved procedure of successive ap-
proximations was used to determine the value of Oort's constant A of differential rotation and the mean absolute magnitude of the nebulae. The interstellar
absorption was described by a model in which the density of an absorbing layer
depends on the distance from the galactic plane only. In the galactic plane, the
absorption is 0.55 mag/kpc. In an attempt to improve the available nebular
magnitudes, an error was committed (Vorontsov-Velyaminov 1939) which led

to the use of incorrect magnitudes for certain objects. In some cases, the error is considerable.

Parenago (1946a) determined the mean absolute nebular magnitude, disregarding the dependence on $m_s - m_n$, from the statistical parallax and from galactic rotation, using Berman's nebular magnitudes. Corrections for interstellar absorption were applied, taking into account the dependence of the absorption on the direction to the object (Parenago 1946b). Since the corrections for photographic magnitudes were used, they are probably too large for all those objects in which the [O III] lines and Hβ carry most of the intensity, probably the great majority of all planetaries. Vorontsov-Velyaminov (1950) therefore used Parenago's corrections reduced by the factor 4270/5000. The dependence of M_n on $m_n - m_s$ was taken into account. Revised magnitudes were used.

Since the basic data used are always the same, it is not very surprising that the values of M_n found by Berman, Parenago, and Vorontsov-Velyaminov (1950) are reasonably similar:

Berman................... $M_n = -0.88 - 0.32 \, (m_s - m_n)$

Parenago................. $M_n = -0.8$

Vorontsov-Velyaminov..... $M_n = 0.04 - 0.22 \, (m_s - m_n)$.

These values are derived from the small group of planetaries with measured proper motions. This group includes large nebulae with low surface brightness that may be optically thin. The resulting values of M_n, therefore, may be too faint for optically thick nebulae. The largest value of $M_s - M_n$ in the material used is 7. For the brightest nebulae one obtains thus $M_n = -3.12$ from Berman, $M_n = -1.51$ from Vorontsov-Velyaminov. These values agree not too poorly with $M_n = -2.5$ for the brightest planetary in M31 (Baade 1955) or with $M_n = -3$ for the brightest planetaries in the Small Magellanic Cloud (Henize and Westerlund 1963).

An attempt by Camm (1939) to derive distances of planetaries should be disregarded. The distances were derived with the condition that the dispersion of linear diameters of the nebulae should be minimized. For a population of expanding nebulae, this condition is quite obviously unacceptable.

2.3.2. *Assumption of constant mass.*—The derivation of distances from the assumption that all planetary nebulae have the same mass (Shklovsky 1956a) has its foundation in the basic possibility to derive distances and masses with the aid of astrophysical theory (Menzel 1931). This type of argument was first applied to NGC 3587 by Minkowski and Aller (1954). The emissivity in the light of a Balmer line is

$$E_{n2} \sim n_i n_e \, f(T_e) \, , \tag{4}$$

where n_i and n_e are the density of hydrogen ions and electrons, respectively, and where $f(T_e)$ is a function of the electron temperature, which varies only slowly with the electron temperature in the range to be considered (see, e.g., Aller 1956).

If the nebula is pictured as a homogeneous sphere with radius r, of pure completely-ionized hydrogen, the luminosity is

$$L \sim n_e^2\, r^3\, f(T_e)\,, \tag{5}$$

and if the distance of the nebula is d, the flux density is

$$F \sim \frac{n_e^2 r^3 f(T_e)}{d^2}\,. \tag{6}$$

If φ is the angular radius, the surface brightness is

$$S = \frac{F_{\!\!\!\!\cdot}}{\varphi^2}\,, \tag{7}$$

and since

$$r = \varphi\, d\,, \tag{8}$$

we have

$$S \sim n_e^2\, r\, f(T_e)\,, \tag{9}$$

and

$$d \sim n_e^{-2}\, \varphi^{-1}\, S\, f(T_e)^{-1}\,. \tag{10}$$

Introducing numerical values of the universal constants, we obtain for Hβ, assuming Menzel's case B,

$$d = 1.89 \times 10^{17} n_e^{-2} \varphi^{-1} S(\text{H}\beta)\, T_e^{3/2} \exp\left(-\frac{9800}{T_e}\right)\,, \tag{11}$$

where d is in parsecs and φ in seconds of arc. The mass of the nebula is

$$\mathfrak{M} = \frac{4\pi}{3} r^3 n_e \mu_{\text{H}}\,, \tag{12}$$

where μ_{H} is the mass of the hydrogen atom. Substituting r from (9), we have

$$\mathfrak{M} = S^3\, n_e^{-5}\, f(T_e)^{-3}\,, \tag{13}$$

or, in solar masses,

$$\mathfrak{M} = 7.0 \times 10^{35} n_e^{-5} S(\text{H}\beta)^3 T_e^{9/2} \exp\left(-\frac{29400}{T_e}\right)\,. \tag{14}$$

Substituting n_e from (11), one obtains

$$d = 1940\, \mathfrak{M}^{2/5} \varphi^{-1} S(\text{H}\beta)^{-1/5} T_e^{-3/10} \exp\left(\frac{1970}{T_e}\right)\,. \tag{15}$$

It should be noted that this relation is valid for any nebula, whether optically thin or thick, if $\mathfrak{M}$ is the mass in the ionized luminous volume.

If one plots (Fig. 1) the values of $\log n_e$ determined by Osterbrock (1950) against the values of $\log S(\text{H}\beta)$, derived from the measured flux densities and the apparent diameters, one finds a somewhat loose correlation in the sense indicated by (13). The relatively high powers which n_e and S have in (13), however, make the mass highly sensitive to the position of a nebula in this plot. A line with a slope of $\frac{5}{3}$ corresponds to a given mass; these lines have been plotted for various values of the mass with $T_e = 10^4$ degrees. The values of the mass can be seen to range from less than 10^{-5} to more than 10 solar masses. Very small masses could be understood easily for nebulae which are optically thick, so that the ionized volume is very much smaller than the total volume of the gas. Masses that are larger than 10, however, seem unacceptable for objects whose galactic distribution (see sec. 3) shows that they are part of population II

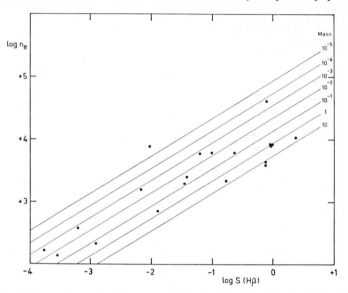

FIG. 1.—Values of log n_e for planetary nebulae determined by Osterbrock (1950), plotted against log S (Hβ).

and which should therefore not have masses very much larger than the solar mass. It can be shown that the source of the difficulty is the inadequacy of a homogeneous model for planetary nebulae.

Let ϵ be the fraction of the volume with the radius r that is filled with matter, let x be a fraction of the filled volume that has electron density N_e, and let $(1 - x)$ be the remaining fraction with the electron density aN_e. Then

$$F \sim r^3 N_e^2 \epsilon \, \frac{x + (1 - x) a^2}{d^2} , \tag{16}$$

and

$$\mathfrak{M} \sim r^3 N_e \, \epsilon[x + (1 - x)a] . \tag{17}$$

Instead of (13), one has then

$$\mathfrak{M} \sim S^3 N_e^{-5} \, \frac{x + a(1 - x)}{\epsilon^2 [\, x + a^2(1 - x)\,]^3} . \tag{18}$$

Values of a and x for a number of nebulae can be taken from data derived by Seaton (1958). It turns out that the effect of the inhomogeneity can become very large; for NGC 7027, e.g., (14) gives a mass of 1 solar mass, but the corrected mass from (18) is only 10^{-3} solar masses, assuming the filling factor ϵ to have the average value 0.7 found by O'Dell (1962). It is to be concluded that very detailed and reliable knowledge of the structure of a nebula is needed to determine its mass from (14) or its distance from the equivalent relations (11) or (15). This approach to the problem is, therefore, unlikely to lead to a satisfactory solution.

Shklovsky (1956a) uses the relation (15) with the assumption that there is a significant mean value of the mass for planetary nebulae. The adopted value of 0.2 solar masses is derived from a calibration with the aid of statistical parallaxes and of the distance of NGC 6720; T_e is assumed to be 10000°. The attractive feature of the method is its insensitivity to the interstellar absorption since S enters only as $S^{1/5}$. The angular diameter, however, is not a well-defined quantity; in many cases it is not easy to decide what the correct choice is.

The basic assumption of a constant mass can be valid, if at all, only for optically thin nebulae. If a nebula is optically thick, the mass in the luminous volume, which should be entered in (15) is smaller than the average mass. For optically thick nebulae, the distances derived under the assumption of constant mass are therefore too large, and the absolute magnitudes derived from the distances are too bright. In the derivation of absolute magnitudes, the interstellar absorption plays an important role. The absorption is represented by Shklovsky by a model consisting of an absorbing layer extending to ± 100 pc from the galactic plane with an absorption of 1.5 magnitude per kpc.

An attempt to take the filling factor ϵ into account has been made by O'Dell (1962). If there are no density fluctuations ($a = x = 1$), (18) becomes

$$\mathfrak{M} \sim S^3 \, N_e^{-5} \, \epsilon^{-2} \, , \tag{19}$$

and (15)

$$d \sim \mathfrak{M}^{2/5} \, \varphi^{-1} \, S^{-1/5} \, \epsilon^{-1/5} \, . \tag{20}$$

From Figure 1 and the relation (19), disregarding the large scatter in $\mathfrak{M}$, $\langle \mathfrak{M} \epsilon^2 \rangle$ can be determined. Using statistical parallaxes and the distance of NGC 246, $\langle \mathfrak{M}^2 \epsilon^{-1} \rangle$ can be obtained from (20). In this way, the mass $\langle \mathfrak{M} \rangle$ is found to be 0.14 solar masses, and $\langle \epsilon \rangle = 0.66$, with an assumed electron temperature of 10000°. The distances of individual planetaries are proportional to $\mathfrak{M}^{2/5} \epsilon^{-1/5}$, the value of which is 0.5 for these mean values of $\mathfrak{M}$ and ϵ. Those by Shklovsky are proportional to $\mathfrak{M}^{2/5}$, the value of which is 0.52 for the mass of 0.2 assumed by him. For the derivation of absolute magnitudes, O'Dell assumes the interstellar absorption to be 1.1 mag/kpc for objects within 9° from the galactic plane, and 0.40 csc b for objects beyond 9° from the galactic plane. This rather crude model leads to inconsistencies if the absolute magnitudes derived with its aid are compared with those from other systems of distances.

An interesting modification of Shklovsky's method has been developed by Kohoutek (1960, 1961), who shows that it is possible to derive individual masses for planetaries with observable central stars by taking into account the evolutionary changes that the central star must undergo during the lifetime of the nebula (Shklovsky 1956a). The distances derived differ for 67 per cent of the 52 objects in the final list by less than 30 per cent from those by Shklovsky; the largest deviations are +50 per cent and −100 per cent. The discussions, however, are open to objections and their main value lies in demonstrating the basic feasibility of this approach.

The observational basis of Kohoutek's analysis is a systematic increase of the absolute bolometric magnitudes M_{*bol} of the central stars with the linear radius r of the nebulae, obtained by using Shklovsky's distances and temperatures given by Vorontsov-Velyaminov (1931). Since 8 out of 64 available objects were excluded as discordant, the degree of correlation is subject to doubt. Actually a large part of the correlation may be spurious and due to systematic errors of the bolometric magnitudes. These are obtained from temperatures derived under the assumption that the nebulae are optically thick. If they are optically thin, as the analysis assumes, the temperatures are too low and the bolometric corrections too small by amounts that must increase systematically with increasing radius and therefore decreasing optical depth. The errors may be substantial, as shown by the average temperature of 31000° for nuclei of planetaries of low surface brightness and high excitation, only about half that for comparable objects of moderate surface brightness (Minkowski 1942). For large nebulae, the bolometric corrections therefore may be too small by several magnitudes. On the other hand, some of the smallest nebulae may be optically thick. Their distances derived by Shklovsky's method are then too large and their absolute magnitudes too bright.

Kohoutek's analysis is based on the arbitrary assumption that the difference between absolute magnitude M_n of the nebula and M_{*bol} remains constant from the time on when the nebula becomes optically thin. This leads to an increase of M_{*bol} with r that is too strong. The discordance is interpreted arbitrarily as due to an increase of nebular mass with time, ascribed to capture of fast particles from the evolving star. Obviously an alternate interpretation would be that the star evolves more slowly than assumed and that $M_n - M_{*bol}$ increases with increasing radius. It is not possible to differentiate between the two interpretations. The analysis of the relation between M_{*bol} and r therefore is not adequate to establish the evolution of both the nebula and the central star. A valid analysis of the nebula requires knowledge of the evolution of the central star.

2.3.3. *Comparison of distance scales.*—The distances derived from the assumption of constant absolute magnitude can be correct at most for planetaries that are optically thick for the exciting radiation. Distances derived from the assumption of constant mass, on the other hand, can be correct at best for optically thin nebulae. The best system of distances that can be obtained is therefore one in which the distances from constant mass are used for optically thin nebulae, but those from constant absolute magnitude for optically thick nebulae. If the distance scales of the two kinds are otherwise consistent, they should agree for those objects which are on the border between optically thick and optically thin. If all planetaries were identical, the absolute magnitude of a borderline object should divide all objects into two classes, one class for which the distances from constant mass are larger than those from constant absolute magnitude, the other class for which the reverse is true.

Unfortunately every author has used a different system of corrections for absorption. Repetition of the computations with a unified system of corrections is necessary before a fully valid comparison of distance scales of the two kinds can be made. It is significant that the expected picture emerges clearly even from the inhomogeneous material now available. If the planetaries are divided into one group for which, e.g., the distances by Shklovsky are larger than those by Vorontsov-Velyaminov and one in which the opposite is true, one finds that the absolute magnitudes on Shklovsky's system are brighter than zero for the first group, fainter than zero for the second group, almost without exception. If the two distance scales were otherwise consistent and if the same corrections for absorption had been used, it would be permissible to conclude that absolute magnitude zero represents the borderline object. For the first group the distances by Vorontsov-Velyaminov would be correct, for the second group those by Shklovsky. A similar situation appears if Berman's distances are compared with those of Shklovsky. The border appears, not quite as cleanly, where Berman's distance is twice that by Shklovsky.

It can be concluded that it is possible to establish a system of distances that is free from the systematic errors that arise if optically thin nebulae are treated as optically thick or optically thick nebulae as optically thin. New computations with unified corrections for interstellar absorption place the border between optically thick and optically thin planetaries between $M_n = -1.5$ and -2.0 (Minkowski, unpublished). The effects of the dispersion in mass and absolute magnitude, however, cannot be avoided.

§ 3. THE GALACTIC DISTRIBUTION OF PLANETARY NEBULAE

The classical studies of planetary nebulae by Curtis (1918), Campbell and Moore (1918), and Wright (1913) showed a total number of 78 planetaries. Even this small number of objects was adequate to give some indication of the galactic distribution. Small planetaries were found to be more concentrated toward the plane of the Milky Way than large planetaries, and a concentration of the smallest objects was in the general direction of the galactic center. The number of known planetaries increased slowly, mostly by accidental discoveries on objective prism plates. A catalogue by Vorontsov-Velyaminov (1934*b*) listed 134 objects; in 1951 the total number known was 371. From 1946 on, systematic searches increased the number of known nebulae considerably.

The first systematic search for planetary nebulae was made (Minkowski 1946, 1947, 1948, 1951) with the aid of objective-prism plates obtained in the red region with the 10-inch telescope on Mount Wilson for the survey of Be stars by Merrill. This survey covered completely a strip along the galactic equator between $+15°$ and $-15°$ latitude between longitudes $l^{II} = 319°$ and $247°$. Near the galactic center, the survey extended to latitudes $+30°$ and $-30°$. In addition, for an area of 200 square degrees surrounding the galactic center, objective-prism exposures in the red by Duncan and by Wilson with the 18-inch Schmidt telescope on Palomar Mountain were available. The 10-inch survey was completed for the southern Milky Way by Henize (unpublished) with the Mt. Wilson 10-inch telescope at the Lamont-Hussey Observatory of the University of Michigan. The central Milky Way was searched on objective-prism exposures in the red with the 24-inch Schmidt telescope at Tonantzintla by Haro (1952). The plates of the National Geographic Society–Palomar Observatory Sky Survey were searched for planetary nebulae of large apparent diameters and low surface brightness by Abell (1955). As a result of these investigations, the total number of planetary nebulae known is now 672.

Questions arise as to the reliability of the material. On objective-prism exposures in the red, a planetary nebula appears as one emission line, $H\alpha$, with little or no continuum. The dispersion is usually too small to recognize whether the [N II] lines are present or not. Near the limit of the plate, faint Be stars with moderately strong $H\alpha$ and faint peculiar stars with very strong $H\alpha$ may appear in the same way. It is therefore necessary to investigate each object individually if absolute reliability is to be achieved. A detailed investigation of this kind was carried out for the objects of the Mount Wilson and Palomar search. Direct photographs at the Newtonian focus of the 60-inch and the 100-inch served to reveal the nebular nature of the newly found planetaries. Some danger exists of classifying the bright central region of an H II region as a planetary nebula; some objects carried in published catalogues of planetaries are of this kind, e.g., IC 1470 and NGC 7635. The number of such misidentifications is not likely to exceed one per cent. Stellar objects were classified on the basis of their spectra, observed in the photographic region with low-dispersion spectrographs. A small number of misclassifications is possible, since stars with combination spectra can show at times emission spectra similar to those of planetary nebulae. The variability of these stars offers an obvious way to eliminate the misclassifications; no case of this kind has so far been reported. It seems justified to conclude that of the objects accepted after individual investigation, only a negligible fraction can have been misclassified.

The chance of a misclassification is relatively small for objects that have not been investigated in detail if the presence of forbidden lines is established. If only Hα is observed the chance depends much on the intensity of the observed line. From the experience gained on the Mount Wilson material, it seems possible that 5 to 10 per cent of the objects in the southern Milky Way are misclassified.

A plot of 686 planetaries (Minkowski and Abell 1963) in galactic coordinates l^{II}, b^{II} (Fig. 2) reveals a distribution with high concentration toward the galactic center and pronounced, but moderate, concentration toward the galactic plane. The strong concentration in the direction to the center shows that the great majority of the planetaries seen in that part of the sky are actually at the center of the Galaxy. The histograms in Figures 3 and 4 show the distribution in longitude of planetaries between $b^{II} = -10°$ and $+10°$.

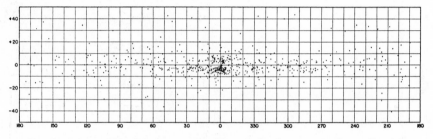

Fig. 2.—Distribution of the known planetary nebulae (in new galactic coordinates)

It is obvious that the observed distribution is greatly affected by absorbing clouds. Figure 2 shows well-defined areas of avoidance, such as that at $l^{II} = 5°$, $b^{II} = 0°$. The presence of local absorbing clouds reveals itself by minima of the area density in Figures 3 and 4. It seems probable that the marked deficiencies at positive latitudes are also due to absorbing clouds. In general, however, the clouds whose presence is suggested do not at all coincide with the known dark nebulae plotted by Khavtassi (1960). It must be assumed that the observed distribution is strongly affected by dark matter at larger distances than the obvious dark nebulae. These, of course, can be noticed: the minimum near $l^{II} = 80°$, for instance, shows clearly the effect of dark clouds in Cygnus. There is no valid way to free the observed distribution from the effects of absorption.

The strong asymmetry in latitude makes it impossible to derive reliable information on the degree of concentration toward the galactic plane. It is obvious, however, that the concentration is much less pronounced than that of the B-type stars (Minkowski 1951). With its high concentration toward the galactic center, the distribution shows clearly that planetary nebulae belong to population II. Oort (1958) places the planetary nebulae together with bright red giants and novae in the disk population. For the mean distance from the galactic plane, Parenago (1946b) and Vorontsov-Velyaminov (1950) derive values of 187 pc and 217 pc, respectively. The addition of new objects, particularly those discovered by Abell (1955), increases the mean distance; a value of about 325 pc follows from a preliminary discussion (Minkowski, unpublished).

The question remains of the extent to which the observed number and distribution are affected by observational selection. No simple limit can be stated to which objective-prism surveys are complete for objects whose apparent diameters have a large range. Since objects larger than the resolution limit of

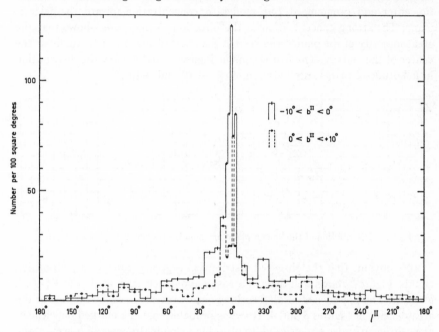

FIG. 3.—Distribution of the planetary nebulae in galactic longitude, separately for the latitude zones −10° to 0° and 0° to +10°.

the plate will be resolved, the surface brightness in the images of objects of equal apparent magnitude will be smaller for large (resolved) than for small (unresolved) objects. A selection in favor of small objects results. The visibility of the emission line which leads to the discovery of a planetary will depend on the background density and thus on star density and brightness of galactic emission in the field. This effect will discriminate most strongly against objects in the central region of the Milky Way where the star density is highest. It is difficult to assess the result of these effects, but if the central region is compared to outer regions, one should probably expect to find relatively too few faint and large objects in the central region.

The search for planetary nebulae on the *Sky Atlas* complements the objective-prism searches. It discriminates against bright and small planetaries which produce images whose true nature cannot be recognized. It is inherently a search for large planetaries of low surface brightness. The limit of the search is given by the surface brightness relative to the surface brightness of the background. The search, therefore, discriminates against the plane and the central region. The available material obviously has no well-defined limit, either in magnitude or surface brightness. Any search is probably biased against the central region. But, since the central region was searched on objective prism

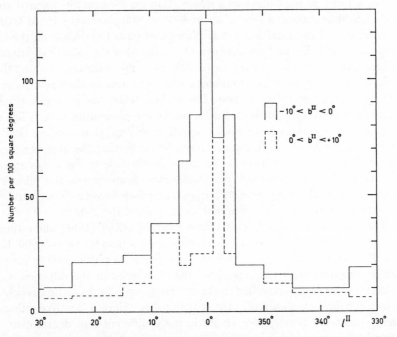

Fig. 4.—Distribution of the planetary nebulae between $l^{II} = 330°$ and 30°, separately for the latitude zones $-10°$ to 0° and 0° to $+10°$.

photographs with a larger instrument—the Tonantzintla 24-inch Schmidt telescope—than were the outer parts, it is not possible to be certain whether the central condensation is more or less pronounced than the present material shows.

Even if there were a fixed limit, say of apparent magnitude, to which the search extends, the observed distribution would have to be corrected for the effects of the large spread in absolute magnitudes which the luminosity function of planetary nebulae must show. A limiting apparent magnitude leads to a limiting absolute magnitude that becomes brighter with increasing distance or with increasing obscuration. At a given distance, and with a given obscuration, only planetaries brighter than a certain absolute magnitude will be observed. It is not possible at this time to make any reliable estimate of the corrections that

have to be applied in order to obtain from the observed distribution the distribution of planetaries that are brighter than a given absolute magnitude. No
photometric data are available for most of the known planetaries, and the luminosity function itself is quite uncertain. That the correction may be large can
be seen if the number 672 of known planetaries is compared with estimates of
the total number of planetaries in the Galaxy. Since the number 672 includes
the center of the Galaxy, one might expect it to represent a sizable fraction,
almost a third, of the Galaxy as a whole. Allowing for heavily obscured areas,
one might thus guess at a total of about 3000 or 4000 planetaries in the Galaxy.

Estimates of the total number of planetaries have been made on the basis
of distances of individual planetaries and of a model of the galactic distribution
of planetaries. Such estimates can be only very approximate, but they have
always resulted in much larger numbers. The total number of planetaries in the
Galaxy with an emission measure larger than 10000 has been estimated to
60000 by Shklovsky (1956b). Actually, the known planetaries include low sur-
face-brightness objects from Abell's search whose emission measure is of the
order of a few hundred. It seems certain, however, that the objects near the
center of the Galaxy are a selected group of bright objects. Since this group of
objects is at a large distance, it must suffer more from the selection effect than
nearer objects. The observed distribution is therefore distorted; the central condensation is actually even stronger than the present data show.

The same conclusion is reached from a result by O'Dell (1962) who estimates
the total number of planetaries with radius smaller than 0.7 pc as 50000. If the
size distribution derived by O'Dell for the planetaries within 4000 pc from the
sun is compared with that found for the planetaries in the direction of the
galactic center (Minkowski 1951), the central group is found to be strongly deficient in nebulae with a radius larger than 0.1 pc. Since it is unlikely that the
objects near the center have an intrinsically different size distribution, the
central group must be less complete. One may estimate that in the central group
not more than 10 per cent of those planetaries are observed which are within
4000 pc of the sun. It thus seems likely that the central condensation is in
reality one order of magnitude more pronounced than the observed data suggest.

At the present stage, the known planetaries are adequate to show the qualitative character of their galactic distribution. The observed distribution is distorted by selection effects; the corrections for incompleteness are probably large
and cannot be established at this time.

On the basis of the pronounced concentration toward the galactic plane, the
planetaries have been assigned to the disk population II (Oort 1958). There is
evidence, however, that planetaries occur in the extreme population II, and it
is not a foregone conclusion that planetary nebulae do not occur in population I.

One planetary nebula is known to occur in the globular cluster M 15. Membership in the cluster is established by the radial velocity of the object (Joy 1949)

which agrees with that of the cluster. A faint planetary nebula has been found near the north galactic pole by Haro (1951). To judge from the faintness of the object, about 15th magnitude, it must be at a large distance, and is likely to belong to the extreme population II. While it thus seems true that planetary nebulae occur in the extreme population II, there is no conclusive evidence at this time on the manner in which planetary nebulae are distributed into the subsystems of population II.

The frequent occurrence of stars related to Wolf-Rayet stars as central stars of planetary nebulae raises the question whether or not some of these stars are true WR stars and as such members of population I. Most of the central stars with WR-type emission bands show properties which may set them apart from the true WR stars (Swings 1942). The emission bands are relatively narrow, and bands of both C and N are present with comparable intensities. The star in BD 30°3639 (HD 184738) is in this group. Moreover, many of these objects are at relatively high galactic latitudes—e.g., NGC 6543, $b^{\mathrm{II}} = 30°$—which are not plausible for population I WR stars at the large distances indicated by the apparent magnitudes of the stars. It seems clear that, notwithstanding their similarity to WR stars, these objects do not belong to population I.

There are some planetary nebulae whose central stars mimic typical WR stars so well that they may serve as examples. The central star of NGC 6751, for instance, has a typical WC 6 spectrum with broad emission bands. The best argument that it is not a typical WC 6 star is that with $m_p = 13.3$, suggesting a distance of the order 10000 parsecs for a WR star, and with $b^{\mathrm{II}} = -5°.9$ it would be at a distance of the order 1000 parsecs below the plane of the Galaxy, which is implausibly large for a WR star. Merrill's star (1938) has a typical WN 7 spectrum; it is actually the central star of a planetary nebula (Minkowski 1946). The high radial velocity of $+200$ km/sec, confirmed by observations of the nebula, argues against membership in population I.

The stars that are considered to be typical WR stars do not show any surrounding nebulosity. The only exception seems to be HD 50896. An extremely faint shell with a diameter of about 35′ can be seen on the *Sky Atlas*. There is no evidence, however, that the star is really a typical population I star; it might well be another example of a planetary nucleus with a typical WR spectrum with broad emissions.

§ 4. THE RADIAL VELOCITIES OF PLANETARIES

To the radial velocities of 99 planetary nebulae listed by Campbell and Moore (1918) have now been added the radial velocities of 250 planetaries by Mayall and Minkowski (unpublished). Radial velocities are thus available for about half of the 672 known nebulae. The radial velocities, corrected to the local standard of rest, for the planetary nebulae with $-10° \leq b^{\mathrm{II}} \leq +10°$ are plotted in Figure 5 against the galactic longitudes l^{II}. The prevalence of negative velocities for $90° < l^{II} < 180°$ and of positive velocities for $180° < l^{II} < 270°$ is easily understood if most planetaries move in circular orbits with differential rotation. The high velocity dispersion near $l^{II} = 0°$, however, does not fit into such an interpretation and requires the presence of many objects with highly elliptical orbits.

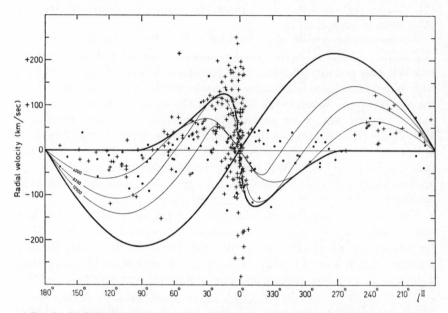

Fig. 5.—Radial velocities of planetary nebulae, reduced to the local standard of rest, plotted against galactic longitude. Heavy drawn curves represent the extremes between which the velocities should lie for circular orbits. Thin lines represent the velocities to be expected for circular orbits at the indicated distances r (parsecs) from the sun. Velocities by Campbell and Moore (1918) are plotted as points, velocities by N. U. Mayall and Minkowski (unpublished) as crosses.

To illustrate these conditions in more detail, we compare the velocities of the planetaries with the velocities to be expected for circular orbits with differential rotation. In this case, the radial velocities for $b = 0°$ are given by

$$v_r = R_0[\omega(R) - \omega_0] \sin l \,, \qquad (21)$$

where R_0 is the distance of the sun from the center, ω_0 the angular velocity of the sun, and $\omega(R)$ the angular velocity of an object at the distance R from the center. It is easy to see that for a given l there are limits between which the radial velocity must lie. In the range $90° < l < 270°$, R increases and $\omega(R)$ decreases monotonously with the distance r of an object from the sun. The limiting velocities are given by $r = 0$, $R = R_0$, $\omega = \omega_0$, and thus $v_r = 0$, and by $r = \infty$, $R = \infty$, $\omega_0 = 0$, and thus $v_r = -R_0\omega_0 \sin l$. In the range $270° < l <$

90°, R reaches a minimum and $\omega(R)$ a maximum at that distance r where the direction is tangential. The extreme velocity then is

$$v_m = R_0[\omega(R_m) - \omega_0] \sin l , \qquad (22)$$

where

$$R_m = R_0 \sin l \qquad (23)$$

is the minimum value of R. The other extreme of v_r is again $-R_0 \omega_0 \sin l$.

The limiting velocities are plotted in Figure 5 as heavy lines, using the values $R_0 = 8.2$ kpc, $\omega_0 = 26.4$ km/sec kpc, and $\omega(R)$ as given by Schmidt (1956). Also plotted as thin lines are the values of v_r for $r = 4000$ pc, 8000 pc, and 12000 pc.

It is obvious that, particularly around $l^{II} = 0°$, many objects are outside the permitted area bounded by the full lines. Substantial positive velocities for l^{II} between 355° and 360° or substantial negative velocities for l^{II} between 0° and 5° cannot be achieved by any changes in the constants of the model. The conclusion to be drawn is that the system of planetaries contains many objects on non-circular orbits and cannot be understood as a system with differential rotation in circular orbits. The presence of objects with non-circular orbits even near the anticenter must be emphasized.

As an individual object with remarkable velocity, the nebula around Merrill's star (1938) deserves to be mentioned. At $l^{II} = 55°$, it has a radial velocity of $+200$ km/sec. It is possible that this object is in a hyperbolic orbit (Perek 1956).

Away from the center, most objects have radial velocities which are not obviously inconsistent with circular orbits. This, of course, does not mean that the orbits really are circular and that a model with differential rotation is satisfactory. It is necessary to establish the proper kinematic model observationally. In particular, it is not possible to decide now whether all planetary nebulae form one kinematic subsystem or whether they are divided in a flattened, rotating system with essentially circular orbits and in a spherical system with low rotation and elliptical orbits.

To establish the proper kinematical model the individual distances of planetaries must be known. A test of the kinematic model has not been made up to now, and one may question whether any of the distances derived up to now are reliable enough to permit a valid test. As far as these distances have been derived under the assumption of differential rotation equal to that of population I, they obviously cannot be used.

It cannot be considered as a test for differential rotation that Berman (1937) was able to make a determination of the constants of differential rotation simultaneously with a determination of individual distances. Very few of the objects used by Berman are in the central region. The investigation therefore concerns the outer parts of the Galaxy only. The value of the Oort constant A thus determined is 14 km/sec per kpc. The agreement of this value with the values found for population I objects (see, e.g., Schmidt 1956; Feast and Thackeray 1958; Johnson and Svolopoulos 1961) proves nothing before it is established that the motions of planetaries can be adequately described by differential rotation.

It is also questionable whether or not values of the Oort constant A can be used to decide on the merits of different systems of distances (Psovsky 1959). To test the distance systems d_s by Shklovsky and d_v by Vorontsov-Velyaminov, the material is divided by Psovsky into one part with $d_s > d_v$, the other part with $d_s < d_v$. It is then found that d_s gives the same value of A for each part, while d_v gives a significantly larger value for the first part than for the second part. This is interpreted as proof that Shklovsky's distances are correct. Actually, the division into two parts is a division into nebulae with different absolute magnitudes. The nebulae with $d_s > d_v$ have brighter absolute magnitudes (on Shklovsky's system) than those with $d_s < d_v$. This means that the first group contains the optically thick nebulae for which Shklovsky's method gives distances that are too large. The second group contains optically thin nebulae for which Vorontsov-Velyaminov's distances are too large. One might compare the value $A = 28$ km/sec per kpc for the first group from Vorontsov-Velyaminov's distances with that of $A = 14$ km/sec per kpc for the second group from Shklovsky's distances, but since Vorontsov-Velyaminov's distances, and thus the value of A derived from them, depend on the assumed interstellar absorption, no valid conclusion can be drawn. The same objections apply to the comparison of A derived from Shklovsky's distances with A derived from Berman's distances; the curious fact needs to be mentioned that the values of A derived by Psovsky from Berman's distances are considerably smaller than those derived by Berman in establishing his distance scale.

It seems clear that the values of A derived under the assumption of differential rotation do not disagree strongly from the value for the interstellar gas and population I stars. It is not established that, apart from those in the central region and in the direction of the anticenter where radial motions are obvious, there is a system with pure differential rotation. If such a system exists, the rotation does not differ much from that of gas and population I.

If the Galaxy has central symmetry and if the sun moves in a circular orbit, the average radial velocity of objects seen in the direction of the center should be zero. For a test, a linear relation between v_r and l^{II} was fitted by least squares to the radial velocities of the 136 planetaries within 10° of the galactic plane between $l^{II} = 353°$ and 9°. The resulting relation is

$$v_r = 12.6 \ (\pm \ 9.3) + 7.0 \ (\pm \ 2.1) \Delta l^{II} \ \text{km/sec} , \qquad (24)$$

where Δl^{II} is the algebraic distance from the center. The stated errors are standard errors that include the error arising from the uncertainty of the position of the galactic center. With the low confidence of 80 per cent, the result indicates an outward motion of the sun relative to the galactic center, and supports the suggestion by Kerr (1960) that the sun moves outward with a velocity of seven km/sec. The standard deviation of an individual velocity is 91.3 km/sec. This value for the velocity dispersion should be smaller than the velocity dispersion at the center of the Galaxy since the objects included in the analysis are distributed over the whole range from the sun to the center. The value therefore is not necessarily inconsistent with a velocity dispersion in the center of the Galaxy comparable to that of 225 km/sec which has been observed in M31 (Minkowski 1962).

REFERENCES

ABELL, G. O.	1955	*Pub. A.S.P.*, **67**, 258.
ALLER, L. H.	1956	*Gaseous Nebulae* (London: Chapman and Hall).
	1957	*Ap. J.*, **125**, 84.
ALLER, L. H., and MINKOWSKI, R.	1956	*Ap. J.*, **124**, 110.
ANDERSON, C.	1934	*Lick Obs. Bull.*, **17**, 21.
BAADE, W.	1955	*A.J.*, **60**, 151.
BERMAN, L.	1936	*M.N.*, **96**, 890.
	1937	*Lick Obs. Bull.*, **18**, 57.
BOWEN, I. S.	1960	*Carnegie Inst. Yrbk.*, **59**, 18.
CAMM, G.	1939	*M.N.*, **99**, 71.
CAMPBELL, W. W., and MOORE, J. H.	1918	*Pub. Lick Obs.*, **13**, 75.
CAPRIOTTI, E. R., and DAUB, C. T.	1960	*Ap. J.*, **132**, 677.
COLLINS, G. W., DAUB, C. T., and O'DELL, C. R.	1961	*Ap. J.*, **133**, 471.
CURTIS, H. D.	1918	*Pub. Lick Obs.*, **13**, 9.
FEAST, M. W., and THACKERAY, A. D.	1958	*M.N.*, **118**, 125.
HARO, G.	1951	*Pub. A.S.P.*, **63**, 144.
	1952	*Bull. Obs. Tonantzintla y Tacubaya*, No. 1.
HENIZE, K. G., and WESTERLUND, B. E.	1963	*Ap. J.*, **137**, 747.
JOHNSON, H. L., and SVOLOPOULOS, S. N.	1961	*Ap. J.*, **134**, 868.
JOY, A. H.	1949	*Ap. J.*, **110**, 105.
KERR, F. J.	1960	*Nature*, **188**, 216.
KHAVTASSI, D. SCH.	1960	*Atlas of Galactic Dark Nebulae* (Abastumani Astrophys. Obs.).
KOELBLOED, D.	1956	*Observatory*, **76**, 191.
KOHOUTEK, L.	1960	*B.A.C.*, **11**, 64.
	1961	*Ibid.*, **12**, 213.
LATYPOV, A.A.	1955	*Pub. Astr. Obs. Tashkent* (2), **5**, 31.
LILLER, W.	1955	*Ap. J.*, **122**, 240.

LILLER, W., and
   ALLER, L. H.   1954   *Ap. J.*, **120**, 48.
LINDSAY, E. M.   1955   *M.N.*, **115**, 248.
LUYTEN, W. J.   1961   *A Search for Faint Blue Stars*, XXI, Obs. University of Minnesota.

MAANEN, A. VAN   1923   *Mt. Wilson Contr.*, No. 270.
                 1929   *Ibid.*, No. 391.
                 1933   *Ap. J.*, **77**, 186.
MERRILL, P. W.   1938   *Pub. A.S.P.*, **50**, 350.
MENZEL, D. H.   1931   *Pub. A.S.P.*, **43**, 334.
MINKOWSKI, R.   1942   *Ap. J.*, **95**, 243.
                 1946   *Pub. A.S.P.*, **58**, 305.
                 1947   *Ibid.*, **59**, 257.
                 1948   *Ibid.*, **60**, 386.
                 1951   *Pub. Obs. Michigan*, **10**, 25.
                 1962   *I.A.U. Symp.* No. 15, 112

MINKOWSKI, R., and
   ABELL, G. O.   1963   *Pub. A.S.P.*, in press.
MINKOWSKI, R., and
   ALLER, L. H.   1954   *Ap. J.*, **120**, 261.
O'DELL, C. R.   1962   *Ap. J.*, **135**, 371.
OORT, J. H.   1958   *Ric. Astr. Specola Vaticana*, **5**, 507 ("Stellar Populations").
OSTERBROCK, D. E.   1950   *Ap. J.*, **131**, 541.
PARENAGO, P. P.   1946*a*   *A.J. U.S.S.R.*, **22**, 150.
                 1946*b*   *Ibid.*, **23**, 69.
PEASE, F. C.   1928   *Pub. A.S.P.*, **40**, 342.
PEREK, L.   1956   *A.N.*, **283**, 213.
PSOVSKY, U. P.   1959   *A.J. U.S.S.R.*, **36**, 305.
SCHMIDT, M.   1956   *B.A.N.*, **13**, 15.
SEATON, M. J.   1958   *Rev. Mod. Phys.*, **30**, 1034.
SHKLOVSKY, S.   1956*a*   *A.J. U.S.S.R.*, **33**, 222.
                 1956*b*   *Ibid.*, p. 315.
SWINGS, P.   1942   *Ap. J.*, **95**, 112.
SWOPE, H. H.   1963   *A.J.*, **68**, 470.
VORONTSOV-
   VELYAMINOV, B. A.   1931   *A.N.*, **243**, 165.
                 1934*a*   *Zs. f. Ap.*, **8**, 195.
                 1934*b*   *A.J. U.S.S.R.*, **11**, 40.
                 1939   *Observatory*, **62**, 213.
                 1950   *A.J. U.S.S.R.*, **27**, 211.

WESTERLUND, B. E., and
   RODGERS, A. W.   1959   *Observatory*, **79**, 132.
WILSON, O. C.   1950   *Ap. J.*, **111**, 279.
WRIGHT, D. H.   1913   *Pub. Lick Obs.*, **13**, 191.
ZANSTRA, H.   1931   *Zs. f. Ap.*, **2**, 329.

REFERENCES ADDED IN 1965

MINKOWSKI, R. 1964 *Pub. A.S.P.*, **76**, 197.

PEREK, L. 1963 *Bull. Astr. Inst. Czech.*, **14**, 201, 218.

1964 *I.A.U. Symp.* No. 20 (Canberra: Australian Academy of Science), p. 41.

PEREK, L., and
KOHOUTEK, L. 1965 *Catalogue of Planetary Nebulae* (in press).

WESTERLUND, B. E. 1964 *I.A.U. Symp.* No. 20 (Canberra: Australian Academy of Science), p. 316.

WESTERLUND, B. E.,
and SMITH, L. F. 1964 *M.N.*, **127**, 449.

CHAPTER 16

High-Velocity Stars

NANCY G. ROMAN

National Aeronautics and Space Administration, Washington, D.C.

§ 1. HISTORICAL SUMMARY

BARELY fifty years ago, in a paper on stellar radial velocities, Adams and Kohlschutter (1914) listed twenty stars with radial velocities greater than 50 km/sec, eight of which have radial velocities greater than 100 km/sec. These authors noted the following about these stars: three-fourths of the velocities in the list are positive, indicating a non-random distribution of space motions; most of the stars are dwarfs; and stars as early as type A are included, indicating that the high velocities are not restricted to the late-type stars which were known to have higher velocity dispersions than stars of earlier types. It was noted in particular that the four stars of highest radial velocities were of types A and F. Today we recognize that these stars are actually somewhat later in type but have extremely weak metallic lines.

In 1924, Gustaf Strömberg showed that there is a steady increase in both mean velocity with respect to the sun and velocity dispersion from the Hyades and Ursa Major streams, through the later-type stars to the high-velocity stars and, finally, the globular clusters (Strömberg 1924).

Oort (1926) took issue with the interpretation of Strömberg and others, that the high-velocity stars merely represented the tail of the velocity distribution of a group of stars with a larger dispersion in their motions and, perhaps, a mean motion appreciably offset from that of the majority of stars in the solar neighborhood, in a detailed study of these stars published in 1926. His conclusion was based on the abrupt change in the distribution of the velocity vectors between stars with velocities somewhat below 63 km/sec and those with higher velocities. Oort showed that the velocity vectors, with respect to the local centroid for stars with lower velocities, are distributed randomly in all directions, but those for stars with space velocities greater than 63 km/sec are concentrated almost entirely toward one hemisphere. In that one hemisphere, most galactic longi-

345

tudes are equally frequent. A concentration of the velocity vectors toward the galactic plane was also noted.

From an extensive catalogue of high-velocity objects, Oort summarized the following statistics: about 4 per cent of the giants of types G, K, and M and of the F stars are high-velocity stars. Among the B and A stars, the percentage of high-velocity stars is more than ten times smaller but among the dwarfs, the percentage increases rapidly from about 15 per cent of the G-type stars to nearly 50 per cent of the M-type stars. Twenty-nine per cent of the long-period variables, almost all of them early M's, 25 per cent of the planetary nebulae and of the R-type stars, 72 per cent of the RR Lyrae stars, and all of the globular clusters belong to the high-velocity class. Oort also called attention to the fact that, relatively, there are only about one-fourth as many binaries among the high-velocity stars as among the low-velocity stars of the same spectral type.

Oort suggested that the 63 km/sec limit between the high- and low-velocity stars might be the velocity of escape from the local system. In that case the high-velocity stars would be interlopers from another stellar group. Alternatively, he considered it possible, although less probable, that

we might think of a rotation of the system of these high-velocity stars. Our cloud would then move nearly in the direction of this rotation, with a somewhat higher velocity. The fact that the objects of highest peculiar velocity show a higher systematic velocity with respect to us than the other high-velocity stars would require that they do not partake at all in this rotation of the larger star system or at least partake very much less.

In 1940, Miczaika compiled a catalogue of 555 high-velocity stars (Miczaika 1940). Although the data which he had available were appreciably better than those available to Oort, the conclusions were largely the same. Because of the scarcity of early-type stars, his synthetic HR diagram for the brighter high-velocity stars is similar to that which was later recognized as characteristic of population II. Miczaika also discussed the motions of these stars in some detail. More recent catalogues of high-velocity stars by Roman (1955), and Buscombe and Morris (1958), provide improved data and extend the lists to include southern stars. These later lists are also somewhat more selective.

In 1944, in his classic paper on the resolution of the nucleus of the Andromeda nebula, Baade (1944) pointed out that the star population of the nucleus and disk region of the nebula differs markedly from that of the spiral arms. The brightest stars in the spiral arms are a few very bright blue supergiants, which increase steadily in number with decreasing magnitude. In the nucleus and disk, the brightest stars are red stars of absolute magnitude about −3. Moreover, thousands of the brightest of these stars have very nearly the same magnitude. Baade also pointed out that the stellar population of globular clusters is the same in this respect as that of the nucleus region of the Andromeda nebula and of its elliptical companions, and distinguished between the HR diagram of the spiral-arm stars and the HR diagram of the globular clusters. Thus, he divided

the stars in a spiral galaxy such as ours into two populations: population I consists of the bright blue supergiants and the related stars in the spiral arms; population II includes the stars in globular clusters, in the nucleus, and in the galactic
disk.

Baade's distinction was clear for the supergiants and for the globular clusters, but studies of the Andromeda nebula do not reach to faint enough magnitudes to provide a similar distinction for the majority of stars near the sun.
These stars have been segregated into the two populations on the basis of various criteria such as location (relation to the spiral arms), velocity with respect
to the circular galactic motion, and the occurrence of similar stars in globular
clusters. Since the blue supergiants are appreciably younger than the globular
cluster giants, age has also been used as a criterion to distinguish population I
stars from those in population II. Low metal abundance, which appears to be
characteristic of many of the high-velocity stars, has been used as another
criterion for membership in population II. It is not surprising that attempts to
assign individual stars or groups of stars to the two populations has led to
numerous puzzles. This was discussed in a *Semaine d'étude* held at the Vatican in
May, 1957 (O'Connell 1958). This "week" provided an excellent review of the
problems of stellar population and proposed the classification of stellar populations given in Table 3, chapter 20, of this volume. There was appreciable discussion as to whether the disk population is homogeneous, but there did not seem
to be enough evidence to differentiate it clearly into more than one component.[1]

§ 2. SPECTRA OF NORMAL HIGH-VELOCITY STARS

Keenan and Keller (1953) published a detailed study of the spectra of high-
velocity stars in 1953. Recognizing that the peculiarities in spectra of high-
velocity stars make their exact comparison with spectra of low-velocity stars
impossible, they used a number of line ratios which are sensitive indicators of
spectral type and luminosity but which do not appear to be affected by the high-
velocity peculiarities. A comparison of their spectroscopic parallaxes with
trigonometric parallaxes for the same stars indicates that the spectroscopic
luminosities are essentially correct. They plotted an HR diagram, based on
spectroscopic parallaxes, for eighty-three stars with space velocities higher than
85 km/sec. One star on their diagram plotted at A8 is actually an F-type subdwarf and one is brighter than absolute magnitude -1.5, but the majority of
the stars lie on the red-giant sequence or on the dwarf sequence between F5
and M0. The intrinsic faintness of the later-type dwarfs accounts for their
scarcity on this diagram.

Plate I illustrates the spectra of several high-velocity giants. Several low-

[1] It is this author's opinion that most of the weak-line stars belong with the older population I objects rather than with the RR Lyrae stars and stars in the galactic nucleus. The high-
velocity stars, with more extreme manifestations of the weak-line characteristic, do belong to
the disk or intermediate populations.

velocity standards are also illustrated for comparison. Keenan and Keller summarized the main peculiarities in the spectra of high-velocity stars as follows:
(1) the spectra of high-velocity giants and subgiants of types G6 to K4 show a
cyanogen deficiency which can be measured either by the break in the continuum at λ 4216 or by the difference between the intensity estimates of λ 4172
and λ 4216. (2) For stars in the range F5 to G5, there is a general weakening of
the atomic lines and a strengthening of the G band of CH. (3) Among stars of
the same type and luminosity, a considerable range of the cyanogen discrepancy

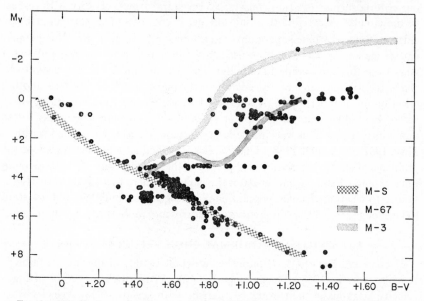

Fig. 1.—HR diagrams of various populations. The dots represent the high-velocity stars
plotted according to their spectroscopic parallaxes. The cluster and normal main sequences
(M−S) are from Sandage (1957). M67 is one of the oldest well-studied open clusters; M3 is a
typical globular cluster.

is observed. Greenstein and Keenan (1958) analyzed the abundances of metals,
carbon, and nitrogen in high-velocity giants and concluded that both metals and
nitrogen were decidedly underabundant in these stars, a result in reasonably
good agreement with those of Schwarzschild and his co-workers (M. and B.
Schwarzschild 1950; M. and B. Schwarzschild, Searle, and Meltzer 1957).
Keenan and Keller pointed out that none of the stars which they studied look
like the stars that Baum (1952) had observed in globular clusters. These differences are illustrated in Plate II. The giants are much more similar in appearance to normal K giants and are spectroscopically appreciably fainter than the
red giants in the globular clusters.

    Probably because the high-velocity stars are not members of a single homo-
geneous stellar population, it is difficult to define their relation to more clearly

defined population subgroups. The weakness of the metallic lines, the most striking spectroscopic characteristic of the high-velocity stars, ranges in degree from that in normal stars near the sun to that in globular clusters. While no high-velocity stars are included among the strong-line stars in the solar neighborhood, many are indistinguishable spectroscopically from the low-velocity weak-line stars. None of the high-velocity stars observed by the author display metallic lines as weak as those found in members of the globular cluster M92. Both the Sr II lines and the G-band region indicate that the brightest of the globular-cluster giants are of higher luminosity and, possibly, of later spectral type than the high-velocity field stars. Of the latter, BD +30°2611 probably resembles these globular-cluster stars most closely. This star has a well-established velocity perpendicular to the galactic plane of 248 km/sec (depending entirely on its radial velocity) and may well be a member of the halo population. In spite of such exceptions, the vast majority of high-velocity stars resemble, both on the basis of their HR diagram and on the basis of spectroscopic appearance, the stars in old galactic clusters such as M67 rather than globular-cluster stars. The resemblance of the high-velocity star HR diagram to that of M67, rather than to that of M3, is clearly illustrated in Figure 1.

§ 3. SUBDWARF SPECTRA

One group of high-velocity stars is sufficiently common and sufficiently easy to recognize that it is profitable to study them separately. These are the F-type subdwarfs, whose high velocities were first discussed by Adams and Joy (1922). On spectra of moderate dispersion (near 120 A/mm) these stars show sharp hydrogen lines about equal in strength to those in F-type stars; the calcium K line is approximately equal in strength to Ca H + Hε, again indicating an F-type spectrum; but the G band, Ca I, λ 4226, and the strongest of the metallic lines are either absent or present only weakly, indicating an A-type star (Roman 1954). The colors of these stars indicate that the spectral types derived from the hydrogen lines are a truer indication of their temperatures than those derived from the metallic lines, but the colors do not match those of any normal stars. Instead, these stars are as much as $0^{m}.2$ brighter in the U color than would be predicted from their B and V magnitudes.

Chamberlain and Aller (1951) showed that the metals are underabundant in these stars by at least a factor of 10. More recent work by Aller and Greenstein (1960) indicates that the metals are underabundant in HD 19445 and HD 140283, by factors of 40 and 100, respectively. These authors find not only that the mean metal abundance varies from star to star, but also that the deficiencies for different metals vary both from metal to metal within a star and, relative to the mean, from star to star.

Melbourne (1960) has made a careful study of the blanketing effect in A- and F-type stars and has shown that the metallic lines apparently redden a star like the sun by $0^{m}.43$ and $0^{m}.20$ in the $U - B$ and $B - V$ colors, respectively. He also finds that the subdwarfs HD 19445 and HD 140283 fall almost exactly on the same line in a two-color diagram as the normal main-sequence stars would occupy if their observed colors were not influenced by line blanketing. On this reasoning, the temperature of HD 19445, classified F7 according to the strength of its hydrogen lines, equals that of the sun. HD 140283, with a somewhat lower metal abundance and a hydrogen-line type of F5, is actually a G5 star on the basis of its temperature. Thus, the low metal abundance in these stars can explain both the anomalous colors and the apparently low luminosities. Further support of this interpretation is given by Wallerstein and Carlson (1960), who derived metal abundances for 23 late F- and early G-type dwarfs. They found that the logarithm of the metal-to-hydrogen ratio correlates well with the observed ultraviolet excess with $U_{ex} = 0.13 \log (M/H) +$ constant.

Chalonge and his co-workers have noted that the Balmer discontinuity is unusually small in the F-type subdwarfs, an effect which will also contribute to the ultraviolet excess (Chalonge 1957). The later spectral types will explain this small Balmer jump, but will not explain the deviation from the behavior of normal stars in Chalonge's plots of the magnitude of the Balmer jump as a function of its position. Moreover, the hydrogen lines are noticeably stronger in these stars than is normal in a G-type star. More accurate models of stellar atmospheres are needed to explain these discrepancies.

Among the brighter stars, the earliest subdwarf is HD 161817. The hydrogen lines indicate a spectral type near A7, in complete agreement with the color which can be relatively little affected by blanketing by metallic lines. The assumption that HD 161817 is a main-sequence star implies a tangential velocity of more than 350 km/sec, but, since the radial velocity of this star is 363 km/sec, this may not prove that the star lies below the main sequence.

Later members of this group are somewhat more difficult to recognize, since the relative weakening of the metallic lines is less obvious and the spectra can be approximated by those of normal stars of somewhat lower luminosity. The famous high-velocity star, Groombridge 1830 (HD 103095) is illustrated in Plate III. The spectrum matches that of a G8 dwarf fairly well except that the Sr II lines are appreciably weaker—an effect which can be explained by either lower luminosity or later spectral type. Although it has been usual to interpret this discrepancy as a luminosity effect, both the well-determined trigonometric absolute magnitude and the relative intensities of the various metallic lines are equally well explained by a spectral type near K1. Although Melbourne's line-blanketing measurements and calculations do not apply to stars later than G4, a reasonable extrapolation indicates that the color of HD 103095 is not incompatible with that of a K1 dwarf with a deficiency of metals.

Thus, the evidence has grown in recent years that the so-called subdwarfs are actually main-sequence stars, later in spectral type than is indicated by the broad appearance of their spectra. A careful study of high-dispersion spectra of these stars to determine the pressure and ionization states in their atmospheres would be desirable, but will be complicated by the fact that both lower luminosity and cooler temperature affect the majority of the lines available for study in the same way. Because of the effect of line blanketing, Melbourne points out that we should not indiscriminately compare the main sequences of globular clusters, in which the stars are probably similar to those of the subdwarfs, to the main sequences of normal galactic clusters without allowing for the effect of the difference in line intensity on the color-magnitude diagram.

Subdwarfs have also been found among the B-type stars. These stars are appreciably farther below the main sequence than the later-type subdwarfs and are probably unrelated to them. The later-type subdwarfs are almost certainly stars which were formed with a low abundance of metals, while the B-type subdwarfs or horizontal-branch B stars are probably stars which have aged to such an extent that the hydrogen has been nearly exhausted.

§ 4. A-TYPE STARS

Three per cent of the stars in the author's catalogue of high-velocity stars are late B or A stars. If the high-velocity stars are old stars, there should be no stars earlier than F0 among them. Are these early-type stars related to the A0 star in the old galactic cluster NGC 752 or to the high-velocity B stars which have been studied by Blaauw (1961) and others? The A stars in NGC 752 and in other old galactic clusters may have formed, somewhat later than the majority of the cluster stars, from residual gas and dust in the vicinity, but this explanation seems improbable for the high-velocity A stars. On the other hand, the same mechanism which produces the high-velocity, or run-away, B stars can also produce less massive stars which can appear in the vicinity of the sun as high-velocity A-type stars. Unlike the subdwarfs, these A-type high-velocity stars show no obvious spectral peculiarity on moderate dispersion spectra. Because the Yale catalogues provide proper motions and spectral types, and hence tangential motions, for a large number of 8th to 10th magnitude stars, for which no comparable source of radial velocities as yet exists, the majority of these high-velocity A stars have been selected by proper motion data and, naturally, a large percentage of their space velocities is in the tangential motion. Hence, these large space velocities may be spurious as a result of either errors in the spectroscopic parallaxes or errors in the proper motions. However, the radial velocities of some of these stars are also large, ranging up to 100 km/ sec. For many of the stars, two or more accordant determinations of proper motions are available. Finally, errors in spectral type large enough to decrease these velocities significantly are impossible if these stars are normal A-type dwarfs as they appear to be from their spectra. There is also some indication that these stars tend to be farther from the galactic plane than the high-velocity dwarfs of somewhat later spectral type.

§ 5. VARIABLE STARS

It was recognized quite early that the cluster-type variables have a mean motion with respect to the sun which is extremely high. Since, as the name implies, these stars are found frequently in globular clusters, it is not surprising that their motion is similar to that of the globular clusters. The assignment of most other types of variable stars to population II is based primarily on galactic concentration or the frequency with which they occur in globular clusters.

In a classic paper on the spectra of the brighter variables in globular clusters, Joy (1949) describes five groups among the 33 stars for which spectra were obtained. Six stars were observed with periods between one and three days. Although these stars are possibly related to the RR Lyrae stars, they are separated from the shorter period stars by a distinct gap, not only in period, but also in absolute magnitude and spectral type. The spectra, which range from A2 to F8, are definitely earlier than those of normal cepheids of the same period and have an absolute magnitude near -1. One cepheid with a period of 5.1 days was observed. Ten of the stars are W Virginis stars with absolute magnitudes near -2. These are earlier in type, but fainter than classical cepheids of similar periods. Five RV Tauri stars were observed with periods between 25 and 90 days and absolute magnitudes near -3. These stars are distinctly brighter than any others in these clusters. They show emission lines which are not quite as strong as those in W Virginis stars. Finally, eleven stars near absolute magnitude -1.5, whose periods are between 65 and 106 days, are semi-regular variables ranging in spectral type between G0 and M0 with changing magnitude. Each of these groups has also been recognized in the field population; the data which are available substantiate their assignment to the high-velocity stars. Baade (1958) lists three other classes of variable stars as definite members of population II: long-period variables of small amplitude with periods between 70 and 200 days, type I supernovae, and ordinary novae. The population II long-period variables are spectroscopically earlier than ordinary long-period variables.

Among the field variables in population II, a range of characteristics is often observed which is probably correlated with the occurrence of these stars in both the disk and the halo populations. Preston (1959) estimated the weakness of the metallic lines in 129 RR Lyrae stars by determining the difference in the spectral type at minimum light, according to the hydrogen lines and to the K line of Ca II. This parameter ranged from no difference to as much as a full spectral class (e.g., A5 and F5). Grouping the stars according to this spectral class difference, he found that the average space velocity with respect to the sun ranged from 55 km/sec for the group with the strongest lines to 185 km/sec for the stars with the weakest lines. He noted, however, that the weak-line characteristic appeared to vary continuously among the RR Lyrae stars within the uncertainties of classification, and that no sharp boundary could be placed between the strong- and weak-line groups. Both kinematically and spectroscopically, the stars with the weakest lines obviously belong to the halo population.

§ 6. SPACE VELOCITIES

As the name implies, the term "high-velocity stars" refers to a group of stars selected solely on the basis of velocity—usually a space velocity greater than about 65 km/sec. Because of this method of selection, it is difficult to derive any additional information from the space motions of these stars. To complicate such discussions, most of the stars have been chosen on the basis of either radial velocity or proper motions, not on the basis of space velocity. Since proper-motion and radial-velocity catalogues for faint stars usually contain stars only in a limited region of the sky, the selection of the high-velocity stars is also influenced by the "drift motion" of these stars in the region of the sky surveyed. Similarly, since motions of variable stars have been studied to much fainter magnitudes than the motions of normal stars, their importance among the high-velocity stars has often been overemphasized.

Nevertheless, some characteristics are worth mentioning.[2] The most striking feature of the high-velocity star motions is the asymmetric distribution of their velocity vectors. Since the circular velocity at the sun's distance from the galactic center is more than 200 km/sec, the velocity of escape must be greater than 80 km/sec, and the 63 km/sec limit to the symmetric distribution must result from a decided decrease in the density beyond twice the sun's distance from the center rather than because other stars would escape from the system. Since most stars moving in galactic orbits of low eccentricity are automatically excluded from lists of high-velocity stars by the velocity criterion, the stars included regularly cross several spiral arms in their orbits around the galactic center. With a median eccentricity of 0.55, they are probably typical representatives of the interarm region.

The velocities perpendicular to the galactic plane indicate that an overwhelming majority of the high-velocity stars remain within 500 parsecs of the plane. Thus, the galactic concentration of these stars, while probably not as great as that of the planetary nebulae, is strikingly different from the low concentration of the globular clusters. For the most part, the high-velocity stars form a true disk population. The primary exceptions are the subdwarfs and the B- and A-type stars. As mentioned above, the latter stars are probably unrelated to the majority of high-velocity stars, both in the time and in the circumstances of their formation.

The subdwarfs are so easy to recognize spectroscopically and have such high space velocities that selection effects play a relatively small role in the discus-

---

[2] The space velocities in the author's (1955) high-velocity star catalogue are in error because the solar motion was applied incorrectly. The corrections +8 km/sec and +28 km/sec should be added to U and V respectively; W is correct as published. These changes in U and V do not change e and a significantly.

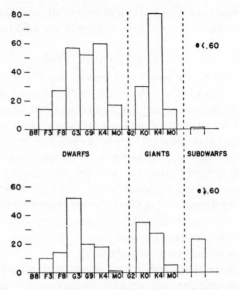

FIG. 2.—Relative frequency of spectral types among stars with high and low eccentricity. It seems apparent from this and Figure 3 that the halo and nucleus stars are earlier in type than the interarm stars near the sun.

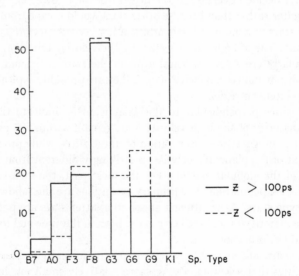

FIG. 3.—Relative frequency of spectral types among stars near and away from the galactic plane.

sion of their velocities. Although their absolute magnitudes are not well determined, it is obvious that, as a group, these stars show a smaller concentration to the galactic plane than any other group except the globular clusters and the RR Lyrae stars. Moreover, the mean eccentricity of the galactic orbits of the subdwarfs is very high and their semi-major axes rather small, so that many of these stars must penetrate the galactic nucleus. Thus, they may be representative of both the halo and the nuclear regions of our Galaxy. It may be significant that not only the subdwarfs, but also those late-type giants with high Z-velocities, have ultraviolet excesses of at least $0^m.1$. The converse is not true, however. Many stars with large ultraviolet excesses never leave the vicinity of the galactic plane.

Figures 2 and 3 compare the spectral distributions for the stars with high- and low-eccentricity orbits, and for those near and away from the galactic plane. The halo and nuclear stars seem to be somewhat earlier in type than the stars which remain nearer the sun. This may indicate that weaker metallic lines have caused these stars to be systematically classified too early.

§ 7. THE HIGH-VELOCITY STAR POPULATION

It is seldom possible to study both the space distribution and the velocity distribution for a significantly large group of stars and, hence, to determine the exact relation between the high-velocity stars and such groups, selected by other criteria, as the disk and halo populations or the oldest stars in our Galaxy. Nor are we able to settle the question, "Are the disk, halo, nucleus, and spiral-arm populations clearly distinct or do they represent merely easily recognized regions in a continuum of space motions and galactic location, age, and metal abundance?"

An inspection of the composite spectra and colors of high-velocity stars is interesting but inconclusive. Reduced to a volume of space, 48 per cent of the light of the high-velocity stars is contributed by dwarfs of spectral types F5 to G5. Only 7 per cent of the light is from stars earlier than F5, and only 7 per cent from stars brighter than luminosity class IV. Thus, in comparison with the composite types which Morgan (1958) has determined for both globular clusters and elliptical galaxies, the high-velocity stars seem to be surprisingly weak in high-luminosity stars. While nearby dwarfs may be appreciably easier to detect from their proper motions than the giants, this is compensated by the comparative ease of finding giants with high radial velocities. Hence, it seems difficult to attribute this striking deficiency of high-luminosity stars to selection effects. The composite colors of the high-velocity stars are: $B - V = +0^m.60$; $U - B = +0^m.12$, the first of which agrees surprisingly well with the value $B - V = +0^m.62$, determined by Baum for the average globular cluster, but is appreciably bluer than the color $B - V = 0^m.9$ of giant elliptical galaxies (Baum 1959).

A clue to the origin of the high-velocity stars might be derived from the fact, originally mentioned by Oort, that high-velocity stars are less frequently binaries than are normal stars near the sun. However, this suggestion no longer bears close scrutiny. Eighty of the 570 stars in the author's high-velocity catalogue are visual or spectroscopic binaries; a rapid count of pages selected at random in the Yale *Bright Star Catalogue* (Schlesinger and Jenkins 1940) indicates that this percentage is very similar to that observed among the bright stars.

§ 8. SELECTION CRITERIA

The difficulty of selecting "high-velocity stars" other than by velocity results both from their scarcity and from the often quite subtle differences which distinguish them from normal stars near the sun. Of the non-variable stars in spectral classes F0 to M0, fainter than supergiants, only about 10 per cent of the stars selected by apparent magnitude have space velocities greater than 63 km/sec and only 6 per cent have velocities as high as 80 km/sec. For stars near the sun, 30 per cent have velocities greater than 63 km/sec, but most of these stars are absolutely faint dwarfs which are exceedingly difficult to detect except by their large proper motions.

In spite of these difficulties, several methods now exist for segregating at least some of the types of high-velocity stars without using space motions. The first criterion which has been used is their spectroscopic appearance. This is satisfactory for the F-type subdwarfs and reasonably so for the later-type subdwarfs and the giants with weak cyanogen, but, as it is difficult to measure the spectroscopic peculiarity quantitatively, it is hard to use this feature to assign intermediate stars to their proper niche.

Miss Divan has shown that the subdwarfs lie below normal stars on a plot of the depth of the Balmer jump versus the position of this discontinuity (Divan 1956). She also found a small difference between the high-velocity stars and normal stars in the slope of the continuum in the region of the spectrum near λ 4800. The results indicate that these criteria can be used successfully for segregating high-velocity stars and do provide a quantitative measure of the peculiarity, but the detailed analysis of the spectra which their use requires makes them difficult to apply to large numbers of faint stars.

It was mentioned in section 3 that the underabundance of metals in the high-velocity subdwarfs makes these stars bluer than their temperatures would indicate and affects the ultraviolet-blue color more than the blue-yellow color. If this underabundance of metals is present, although less obviously, in other high-velocity stars, their colors might well reveal this. Let us define the ultraviolet excess as $U_{ex} = (U - B)_{pre} - (U - B)_{obs}$, where $(U - B)_{obs}$ is the observed color on the V, B, U system and $(U - B)_{pre}$ is the color which is predicted from the observed $(B - V)$ and the relation between $(U - B)$ and $(B - V)$ for normal stars (Morgan, Harris, and Johnson 1953). An examination of the high-velocity stars of types F0 to K0 in the author's catalogue indicates that this ultraviolet excess correlates exceedingly well with space velocity (see Fig. 4).

As a test of the usefulness of U_{ex} as a criterion for selecting high-velocity stars, a rapid survey for stars of large ultraviolet excess was made among about 300 stars in selected areas north of declination $+29°$ with photographic magnitudes between 8^m and 12^m. No spectral information was used in this test, although objective prism spectral types would normally be desirable, particularly for late-type stars for which the $U - B$ color is a function of luminosity. In the Milky Way fields, this search yielded a number of reddened A stars, but this proved no problem in the high-latitude fields and would certainly be no problem if even rough spectral types had been used. Ten stars later than F0 were selected. These include $BD + 30°2611$, which was mentioned in section 2 as

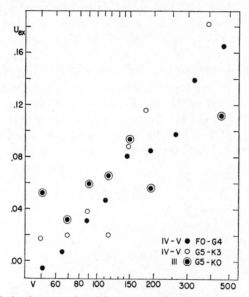

Fig. 4.—The relation between ultraviolet excess and space velocity for various classes of stars.

resembling the globular cluster stars, and two stars, BD $+30°2740$ and BD $+44°2515$ which are spectroscopically similar, a subdwarf discovered by Greenstein (private communication), BD $+44°1910$, a subdwarf near G3, BD $+29°2055$, and BD $+45°2225$, a giant with strong CH and weak CN. Two stars are probably weak-line stars but do not show extreme peculiarities. However, one of these, BD $+45°2227$, has a tangential velocity of at least 100 km/sec. The other two stars are probably reddened giants near K0 III, as they are in the same field as the reddened A stars. Thus, this superficial test shows that with even approximate spectral types to eliminate the effects of interstellar reddening in fields near the galactic plane, the color excess provides an efficient criterion for detecting the extreme high-velocity stars. Presumably, with greater care, it would be equally useful for segregating homogeneous groups from the intermediate population.

Borgman (1959) has shown that a more sensitive index of the weak-line characteristics is obtained by replacing the U filter of the VBU system by an interference filter with a bandwidth of 325 A and an effective wavelength of 3660 A.

Although the color excess is a criterion which can be applied easily to stars as faint as 16^m, the requirement of an independent determination of approximate spectral type is a drawback. A fourth color would probably suffice, however. Strömgren and his co-workers have suggested the use of narrow-band colors freed from the effect of interstellar reddening. In particular, Strömgren (1958) has shown that the index m is well correlated with U_{ex}, where $m = -2.5$ [log $I(a) + \log I(e) - 2 \log I(d)$] and $I(a)$, $I(d)$, and $I(e)$ are the intensities measured through interference filters with maximum transmissions at $\lambda\,5000$, $\lambda\,4500$, and $\lambda\,4030$, respectively. Gyldenkerne (1961) suggests that it is preferable for later-type giants to use $C = m + n + (5/4)k$, where $n = 2.5$ [log $I(4280) - \log I(4210)$] and $k = 2.5$ [log $I(3290) - \log I(4070)$] $+$ const. Both of these indexes are unaffected by interstellar reddening, and either can be combined with other narrow-band indices to provide spectral types as well.

A survey using any of these velocity-independent criteria to select at least 100 stars at large distances from the galactic plane, and a similar number in the interarm region of the disk, should appreciably clarify the presently confused population problem.

REFERENCES

ADAMS, W. S., and JOY, A. H.	1922	*Ap. J.*, **56**, 242.
ADAMS, W. S., and KOHLSCHUTTER, A.	1914	*Ap. J.*, **39**, 341.
ALLER, L. H., and GREENSTEIN, J. L.	1960	*Ap. J. Suppl.*, **5**, 139.
BAADE, W.	1944	*Ap. J.*, **100**, 137.
	1958	*Ric. Astr. Specola Vaticana*, **5**, 165 ("Stellar Populations").
BAUM, W. A.	1952	*A.J.*, **57**, 222.
	1959	*Pub. A.S.P.*, **71**, 106.
BLAAUW, A.	1961	*B.A.N.*, **15**, 265.
BORGMAN, J.	1959	*Ap. J.*, **129**, 362.
BUSCOMBE, W., and MORRIS, P. M.	1958	*Mem. Mt. Stromlo Obs.*, No. 14.
CHALONGE, D.	1957	*Ric. Astr. Specola Vaticana*, **5**, 345 ("Stellar Populations").
CHAMBERLAIN, J. W., and ALLER, L. H.	1951	*Ap. J.*, **114**, 52.
DIVAN, L.	1956	*Ann. d'ap.*, **19**, 287.
GREENSTEIN, J. L., and KEENAN, P. C.	1958	*Ap. J.*, **127**, 172.
GYLDENKERNE, K.	1961	*Ap. J.*, **134**, 657.

JOY, A. H. 1949 *Ap. J.*, **110**, 105.
KEENAN, P. C., and
KELLER, G. 1953 *Ap. J.*, **117**, 241.
MELBOURNE, W. G. 1960 *Ap. J.*, **132**, 101.
MICZAIKA, G. 1940 *A.N.*, **270**, 249.
MORGAN, W. W. 1958 *Ric. Astr. Specola Vaticana*, **5**, 325 ("Stellar Populations").

MORGAN, W. W.,
HARRIS, D. L., and
JOHNSON, H. L. 1953 *Ap. J.*, **118**, 92.
O'CONNELL, D. J. K. 1958 *Ric. Astr. Specola Vaticana*, **5** ("Stellar Populations").

OORT, J. H. 1926 *Groningen Pub.*, No. 40.
PRESTON, G. W. 1959 *Ap. J.*, **130**, 507.
ROMAN, N. G. 1954 *A.J.*, **59**, 307.
1955 *Ap. J. Suppl.*, **2**, 195.
SANDAGE, A. R. 1957 *Ap. J.*, **125**, 435.
SCHLESINGER, F., and
JENKINS, L. F. 1940 *Catalogue of Bright Stars* (New Haven: Yale University Observatory).
SCHWARZSCHILD, M. and B. 1950 *Ap. J.*, **112**, 248.
SCHWARZSCHILD, M. and B.,
SEARLE, L., and
MELTZER, A. 1957 *Ap. J.*, **125**, 123.
STRÖMBERG, G. 1924 *Ap. J.*, **59**, 228.
STRÖMGREN, B. 1958 *Ric. Astr. Specola Vaticana*, **5**, 245 ("Stellar Populations").

WALLERSTEIN, G., and
CARLSON, M. 1960 *Ap. J.*, **132**, 276.

CHAPTER 17

Subluminous Stars

JESSE L. GREENSTEIN
Mount Wilson and Palomar Observatories
Carnegie Institution of Washington, California Institute of Technology

§ 1. INTRODUCTION

MANY types of stars have apparent locations in the Hertzsprung-Russell diagram below and to the left of the main sequence, giving them the name of subdwarfs. More careful definitions of both the ordinate and abscissa are required to reduce the vagueness intrinsic in the nomenclature. Vertically, there are large and as yet unknown bolometric corrections to be applied for both hot and cool stars. Horizontally, line blanketing seriously affects the colors of F, G, and K stars, except in the infrared, while TiO affects the colors of the M stars over a wide range of wavelengths. The coordinates should be bolometric magnitude and effective temperature, and each point should be labeled by mass and chemical composition. The impracticality of such a program for subdwarfs is nearly complete. Almost no accurate parallaxes, masses (except for the K and M stars), or temperatures are known. Hot subdwarfs probably have abnormal chemical composition and partially degenerate, high-temperature cores. The so-called subdwarfs of types F, G, and K have abnormally low abundances of the metals, but probably normal interiors; a determination of their hydrogen-to-helium ratio is badly needed. The percentage of close visual binaries containing subdwarfs is small. The white dwarfs have accurately known luminosities, and radii can be estimated; a few masses have been observed.

The meaning of the word subdwarf must remain vague until more quantitative data are available. The term should ideally be applied only to a star underluminous for its mass, when compared with a main-sequence star. In practice, I will use it to denote stars whose absolute visual magnitude, M_V, is below that of main-sequence stars of approximately the same effective temperature, as indicated by color (corrected for differential blanketing) or by spectral type. Within such a sample, many types of objects can be distinguished. A diagram of these general types is given by Greenstein (1960). From the point of view of

361

galactic structure, the significance of these stars has grown as it became clear that the normal main-sequence Hertzsprung-Russell diagram of such a young group of stars as the Hyades was far from typical of all clusters, galactic, globular, or those in other galaxies. In addition, the easy recognizability of the horizontal-branch and halo blue stars has made them a valuable tool for probing the Galaxy in the z-coordinate by searches near the galactic poles. The large space motions of the F to M subdwarfs and their consequent large proper motion, together with their abnormal colors, have made them particularly easy to recognize and valuable for the study of galactic kinematics and moving groups. The total mass of white dwarfs has significance for the study of galactic dynamics and evolution.

Parenago (1946) collected data on a very mixed group of subluminous stars, including white dwarfs, F to M subdwarfs, and the apparently subluminous companion of Antares. Samples of the rarer blue stars were omitted for lack of parallax data, but the large velocity dispersion of the subdwarfs and their membership in the "spherical subsystem" was strongly emphasized in this pioneering synthesis. The Soviet astronomers have been active in the study of the correlations between the kinematical properties, spatial distribution, and physical properties of stars. For related stars, including many subgroups of the high-velocity population, extensive compilations of data are given by Kukarkin (1954), Parenago (1948a, b) and Vorontsov-Velyaminov (1953), and of dynamical theory by Ogorodnikov (1948).

The present review cannot present final results on the spatial distribution of subdwarfs or white dwarfs, although their kinematics can be studied and correlated with physical properties. Hertzsprung-Russell diagrams can be obtained, and will be emphasized, but not a Hess diagram showing the frequencies in an HR diagram. Some guide to the spatial distributions will be found in the correlation with kinematic properties given by the Soviet school; counts of faint blue stars being made by Haro and Luyten will permit study of the z-coordinate density decrease.

§ 2. THE WEAK-LINE F AND G SUBDWARFS

2.1. Correction of Photoelectric Colors

It is now clear that extreme metallic-line weakness caused two major errors in the classification of the so-called subdwarfs. Spectral types which were between one and two whole classes too early had been assigned to these stars from the absolute strength of their neutral or ionized metallic lines. In addition, since the metallic lines increase in number and strength at shorter wavelengths, a progressively increasing deficiency of radiation toward the ultraviolet affects broad-band photometry. This deficiency affects normal stars more than metal-poor stars. The subdwarfs show $B - V$ colors bluer than normal stars of the same effective temperature, and also have an apparent ultraviolet excess, i.e., a smaller $U - B$ color than normal for a given $B - V$, in the range $0^m3 < B -$

$V < 0^m8$. The ultraviolet excess, $\delta(U - B)$, reaches 0^m25 and provides a quick means for recognizing the subdwarfs.

If we use the "unevolved" Hyades main sequence as a standard, the sub-dwarfs appear to lie below the Hyades in the $(M_V, B - V)$ color-luminosity diagram. But these halo-population objects and other weak-line stars which were apparently subluminous by about one magnitude are, in fact, the true "normal" main sequence; it is the Hyades that are displaced with respect to a theoretical HR diagram plotted with coordinates $(M_{bol}, \log T_e)$. Sandage and Eggen (1959), Eggen and Sandage (1962), and Wildey, Burbidge, Sandage, and Burbidge (1962) give the most recent complete discussion of this topic. The first extensive spectral results were published by Roman (1954) and Greenstein (1956).

The $U - B$ excess of the late A and early F stars cannot be defined accurately for $B - V < 0^m3$ because of the rarity of unevolved, early-type, metal-poor stars. It also becomes smaller, but perhaps does not vanish, for $B - V > 0^m8$. The actual line weakening caused by low metal abundance diminishes in cool stars because the ratio of the concentration of neutral atoms to the H^- continuous absorption becomes nearly constant. In F and G stars this ratio is nearly proportional to the metal/hydrogen content; in K and M stars it drops to about (metal/hydrogen)$^{1/3}$. In addition, the direction in the $U - B$, $B - V$ plane in which a star is shifted by a change in metal content, the "blanketing line," becomes nearly parallel to the locus of the $U - B$, $B - V$ colors of normal stars.

The definitions of the quantities involved in correction of U, B, V, photometry are shown in Figure 1. The slope of the blanketing line is given by Wildey et al. (1962) as

$$\frac{\Delta(U - B)}{\Delta(B - V)} = 2.70(B - V)_{Hyades} + 0.62, \tag{1}$$

and the correction to the V magnitude caused by blanketing is

$$\frac{\Delta V}{\Delta(B - V)} = 0.75(B - V)_{Hyades} - 0.97. \tag{2}$$

This correction seldom exceeds 0.10 mag. Figure 2 shows the correction, $\Delta(B - V)$, to be added to the observed $B - V$ color of a star of a given $\delta(U - B)$. This correction may easily reach 0.25 mag. Since the absolute magnitude on the main sequence varies about as $6(B - V)$, a weak-line star may easily appear to lie 1.5 mag below the normal main sequence. Eggen and Sandage (1962) find that among stars in moving groups or of fairly good parallaxes ($\geq 0''035$), the stars with $\delta(U - B) > 0^m16$ appear, if uncorrected, to lie at $\Delta M_V = +1^m05 \pm 0^m04$ below the Hyades sequence. After correction for the effect of blanketing on colors, $\Delta M_V = +0^m03 \pm 0^m05$. Greenstein (1956) using proper motions as a source of distances, found $\Delta M_{pg} = +1^m8$ for stars classified as F1 to G8 sub-dwarfs, and $+2^m4$ for the few stars with parallaxes available. A large fraction of this difference arises from the spectroscopic misclassification of the weak-line stars.

Although at present still impractical, it appears that an ideal, unevolved, main sequence might be established for the halo-population stars using the nearly line-free subdwarfs of color $B - V > 0^m3$. The calibration of the distance to the weak-line globular clusters and the reduction in scatter of the main sequence of field stars are already made possible by the realization that the

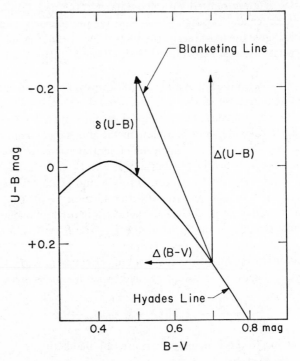

Fig. 1.—The standard Hyades $U - B$, $B - V$ relation is sketched. A star with weak metallic lines falls on the blanketing line. The observed ultraviolet excess $\delta(U - B)$ (taken as positive) yields corrections to the observed colors, $\Delta(B - V)$ and $\Delta(U - B)$, as shown.

ultraviolet excess is a sensitive method of correction of observed to line-free colors. It is probable, although not definitely proved, that no F to K subdwarf is far below such a corrected main sequence.

An interesting probability is that color systems farther to the infrared will be essentially free of differential line-blanketing effects. Unpublished infrared data by Sears and Whitford are quoted by Eggen and Sandage (1962); these observers used $(G - I)$ colors, which are nearly line free in the Hyades as well as in the extreme subdwarfs. The corrected $M_{V, \text{corr}}$ luminosities of 31 subdwarfs, with $\langle \delta(U - B) \rangle = +0^m14$, were derived by applying $\Delta(B - V)$ to their observed colors and reading $M_{V, \text{corr}}$ from the Hyades. The infrared colors of

Sears and Whitford were then used to derive M_V, without correction. The mean of the subdwarfs was found to lie $+0^m04 \pm 0^m03$ below the Hyades.

Since techniques involving U, B, and V will dominate until satisfactory red and infrared data become available, it is apparent that the blanketing-correction technique should be generally used. Low-resolution spectral scanning in the near-infrared and multicolor-infrared systems will be useful.

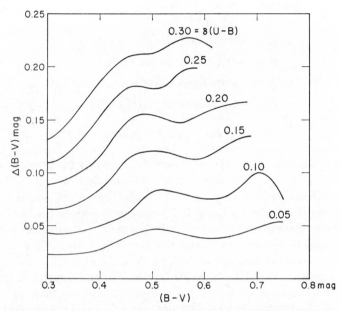

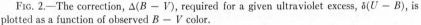

FIG. 2.—The correction, $\Delta(B - V)$, required for a given ultraviolet excess, $\delta(U - B)$, is plotted as a function of observed $B - V$ color.

2.2. SPECTRAL CLASSIFICATION OF THE SUBDWARFS

Roman (1954) measured photoelectric colors and classified some of the extremely weak-line F and G stars. She confirmed that their galactic orbits were very eccentric and inclined and noted the large spectral peculiarities. My own preliminary spectral types (1956), based on 18 A/mm plates, were still quite poor, as shown by the large ΔM_V with respect to the main sequence. I have since attempted to develop a classification based on excitation temperature independent of the degree of line weakening. Almost all normal criteria such as the strength of the hydrogen lines, the ratio $K/(H + H\epsilon)$, the CH and CN band strengths must be abandoned. I assumed that the relative abundances of the metals within the iron group, as well as of Ca, Ba, and Sr, did not change from star to star. (Actually there is some indication that Mn and V vary with respect to other metals [Wallerstein 1962], and that the heavy elements, Ba and Sr, may vary with respect to the iron group in the oldest stars.) I believe, after making three separate attempts, that it is possible, although difficult, to obtain a satisfactory type based on such an estimate of excitation temperature. After the type was assigned, an estimate was made of the absolute strength of the lines, compared with the average for the type, and note was taken of the strength of the ionized lines, of the CH band at λ 4300 (λ 4320 is used for stars with strong CH) and of λ 3883 of CN, if abnormal. Symbols used include:

sd, extr wk = extremely weak-line subdwarf,

sd = weak-line subdwarf,

id = intermediate weak-line subdwarf,

sl wk = slightly weak lines only,

ions = ions abnormally strong,

CH = CH abnormally strong.

Several arbitrary decisions were needed in order to keep the classification system parallel to the MKK system. The estimated excitation level for the extremely weak-line stars, HD 19445, 84937, and 140283 (which differ appreciably) was taken as a definition of type sdG1 and that for HD 103095 as type sdK0. HD 103095 is slightly weak-lined and has a temperature probably nearer that of a K2 or K3V star. It is almost impossible to match an early sdF star with an equivalent main-sequence F. The early subdwarfs merge into evolving "subgiant" F stars; there are very few lines visible. Thus, considerable ambiguity exists between sdF, weak-line F IV, and horizontal-branch (HB) stars, whose types are near HB A5 or F0 III–IV. The entire group of spectra was classified by this metallic-line, subjective, excitation-temperature scale, on two occasions. For extremely weak-line stars the accidental errors could reach 0.7 spectral type; for more normal stars, about 0.3 spectral type included the entire range of error.

The observed relation between type and color permits evaluation of the significance of the derived types. Figure 3 shows the results where the observed $\delta(U - B)$ has been used to give the $(B - V)_0$ corrected for differential blanketing to the Hyades. In the final correlation of corrected colors with type, there is a residual tendency for the G5 to K2 stars still to be classified too early for their colors. If HD 103095 had been changed to be sdK2, which from astrophysical investigations is more nearly the correct type, this tendency would have been reduced. However, another factor enters here—the appearance of the so-called CH stars, or subgiants. They are denoted by triangles in the figure and scatter widely from the normal relations; they become quite common at $B - V >$ 0ᵐ75. They may be evolved stars of the high-velocity population. Their line blanketing can be appreciably different both because of the presence of strong lines and of CH bands in the blue; their temperature-spectral type relation may be affected by luminosity differences.

The earliest Mount Wilson classification of an extreme subdwarf like HD

19445 was A5; my 1956 class was F2 and it is now G1, typical of the effect for extremely weak-line stars. The $(B - V)_0$ colors and the recent spectral types agree moderately well. The main conclusion is that the so-called weak-line F to K subdwarfs are very weak-line main-sequence stars of high velocity with no essential deviations from the unblanketed main sequence.

2.3. Statistical Results and Spectroscopic Peculiarities

Table 1 shows the frequency of spectral classification and degree of line weakening in the present sample. There is an excellent correlation between $\delta(U - B)$ and classification by line strengths, i.e., with the estimates "extremely weak subdwarf" to "intermediate dwarf." The id's dominate for $\delta(U - B)$ of less than 0^m17, the sd and sd extr wk for $\delta(U - B) > 0^m18$. An

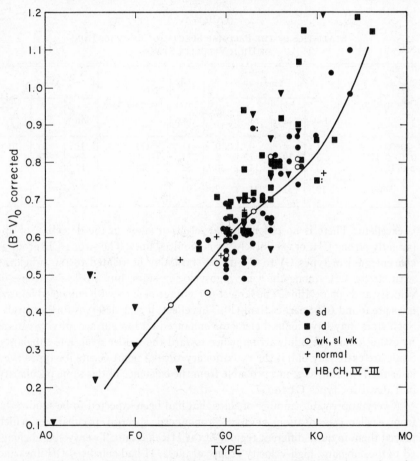

Fig. 3.—The $(B - V)_0$ colors corrected for differential line blanketing bring the subdwarfs into the normal Hyades relation shown by the solid line (colors by Eggen and others, types by Greenstein).

excellent correlation between hydrogen/metal abundance ratio and ultraviolet excess has been found by Wallerstein (1962). Only three extreme subdwarfs, with abundances taken from the work by Aller and Greenstein (1960) and Baschek (1959), are included in Wallerstein's list; his other stars with $\delta(U - B)$ up to 0^m15 would probably have been called id or sl wk in my classification.

The stars observed at Palomar were chosen as probable subdwarfs, from earlier spectroscopic classifications, from available colors, or from proper-motion catalogues. They are selected for extreme line weakness, in that the previous observers, working at low dispersion, could only recognize extreme cases. The group in Table 1 with $\delta(U - B) > 0^m18$ has 85 per cent sd and extremely weak sd stars, while for $0^m10 \le \delta(U - B) \le 0^m17$ only 29 per cent belong to these extreme groups. The correlation between line-weakness estimates and $\delta(U - B)$

TABLE 1

STATISTICS OF THE PALOMAR SPECTRAL CLASSIFICATIONS
OF HIGH-VELOCITY STARS

$\delta(U-B)$	LINES				TOTAL	SPECTRAL TYPE	LINES		
	sl wk	id	sd	sd extr wk			All	stg CH	stg ions
$\le 0^m09$......	7	4	0	0	11	$\le$ G0.......	31	3	10
0.10–0.17......	3	19	7	2	31	G1–G7......	46	7	12
>0.18........	0	8	14	30	52	$\ge$ G8.......	17	1	2
Total......	10	31	21	32	94				

is excellent. There is no observational selection effect in the detection of apparently strong CH, or excessively strong ionized lines. The strong CH group is concentrated in types G1 to G7; these stars may be related to the subgiants with strong CH among the very high-velocity stars, but are less extreme in velocity and composition. The largest percentage of stars with enhanced ionized lines are found to be earlier than G0. This effect, if real, deserves further study. Such stars may have ionized elements enhanced by low surface gravity caused by evolution off the subdwarf sequence toward the redder weak-line subgiants. Some are extremely old, if the evolutionary turnoff point occurs for types even later than the sun, as seems probable from the existence of this same peculiarity in Table 1 for types G1 to G7.

A very appreciable number of stars that had been expected to be subdwarfs, from earlier classification, showed pronounced spectral peculiarities which placed them in quite different regions of the HR diagram. Twenty stars belonged to the subgiant, high-velocity group; of these, 11 had enhanced CH lines and one was a high-velocity "barium" star. The $B - V$ colors ranged from $+0^m53$ to $+1^m26$; the cooler members of this group are probably related to globular cluster type giants. Eighteen stars were classified as "horizontal-branch" stars of types A to early F (colors $+0^m04$ to $+0^m30$), and one had a color $+0^m70$ and a type HB G0. Nineteen stars appeared to have completely normal spectra (colors $+0^m45$ to $+0^m78$), with $\langle\delta(U-B)\rangle = +0^m05$, and two had $\langle\delta(U-B)\rangle = +0^m12$, but were classified as nearly normal (μ Cas and HD 144515, a spectroscopic binary). In résumé, of 146 stars suspected as possible F or G subdwarfs, 65 per cent were subdwarfs with lines of slight to extreme weakness, 14 per cent seemed normal, but may have a small $\delta(U-B)$, 13 per cent were possible horizontal-branch stars, and 8 per cent had an enhanced CH band and were possibly subgiants. The percentage of horizontal-branch stars is abnormally high, because a special search was made for a possible blue extension of the subdwarfs. One definite velocity variable ($-3°2525$) exists among 146 subdwarfs. There are two velocity variables ($-12°2669$, $-26°16876$) out of 19 so-called horizontal-branch stars. The former may be a subdwarf; the latter is a close visual double and may be a multiple star. The percentage of visual and spectroscopic binaries is consequently extremely low. The stellar rotational velocities of the subdwarfs are also very low; only two of the 146 stars showed significant line broadening at 18 A/mm.

2.4. Space Motion and Galactic Evolution

Roman (1954) computed galactic orbits for 16 subdwarfs on two alternative assumptions as to their mean luminosity. Fifteen of her stars now have new spectra, velocities, and U, B, V colors. Correcting for differential blanketing, the $(B-V)_0$ colors give luminosities from matching to the Hyades main sequence. The $\langle M_V \rangle = +4^m7$, close to one of her assumed values of $+5^m$. Therefore, the characteristics of the osculating orbits can be rederived as: total space motion 262 km/sec, z-coordinate velocity $\langle |W| \rangle = 52$ km/sec, perigalacticon $\langle r_p \rangle = 1.4$ kpc, eccentricity $\langle e \rangle = 0.86$ (with one indeterminate and 2 retrograde orbits omitted).

A complete study of the U, V, W components of the motion of the known subdwarfs and high-velocity stars is being made by Eggen. A wide variety of brighter stars from the catalogues by Eggen (1962, 1964) is included in the analysis of the motions of the stars of high velocity by Eggen, Lynden-Bell, and Sandage (1962). These observers find that stars of $0^m15 < \delta(U-B) < 0^m30$ have eccentricities from 0.3 to 1.0, with a mean near 0.7 (Fig. 4 in Eggen *et al.*), and an excellent correlation in the maximum value of $|W|$ with increasing $\delta(U-B)$; some of the stars with large ultraviolet excess reach a maximal height above the galactic plane near 7 kpc. Stars with large $\delta(U-B)$ have apogalacticon distances from 10 to 40 kpc, with three larger values (including one of 107 kpc). No star of small $\delta(U-B)$ (<0.14 mag) has apogalacticon beyond 20 kpc. Thus, in addition to the well-known orbital characteristics of large W motion and z-coordinate height, eccentric and inclined orbits, and small perigalacticon, Eggen *et al.* indicate an excellent correlation of $U-B$ excess with high eccentricity, low angular momentum, and large apogalacticon. Their conclusion is that the metal-poor stars were formed during the collapse of the Galaxy from a much larger early configuration. The subdwarf orbits are a fossilized reminder of the motions of the gas during the initial collapse phase, having been formed from low-density, metal-poor gas far from the galactic center. The largest part of this gas collapsed into a thin disk, and by viscous energy dissipation took on circular orbits. Thenceforward, according to current theories of star formation and nucleosynthesis, later generations of stars were formed from metal-enriched material in the galactic disk and had small peculiar motions.

2.5. Solar Motions as Determined from Subdwarf Radial Velocities

In addition to 175 new Palomar radial velocities of high accuracy (Greenstein 1965; Sandage, unpublished), available data include a number of velocities

TABLE 2

Space Motion and Velocity Dispersion of the F and G Subdwarfs
(km/sec)

Group	n	U	V	W	σ	U'	V'	W'
1. Palomar, All..........	143	$+ 3\pm16$	-162 ± 20	-27 ± 16	114	$- 8$	-145	-20
2. Palomar, Normal......	18	$+40\pm16$	$- 75\pm20$	$+ 1\pm14$	40	$+29$	$- 58$	$+ 8$
3. Palomar, Slightly weak..	23	$+57\pm29$	-133 ± 40	-16 ± 32	89	$+46$	-116	$- 9$
4. Palomar, Intermediate...	34	-35 ± 29	-127 ± 40	-46 ± 30	94	-46	-110	-39
5. Palomar, Subdwarfs.....	23	-19 ± 40	-222 ± 64	-54 ± 43	116	-30	-205	-47
6. Palomar, Extreme weak..	37	-13 ± 47	-227 ± 48	-43 ± 48	159	-24	-210	-36
7. Deeming..............	103	$- 2\pm27$	-148 ± 27	$- 4\pm26$	135	-13	-131	$+ 3$
8. Palomar and Deeming...	173	$- 3\pm14$	-164 ± 18	-27 ± 15	114	-14	-147	-20

observed by Popper (1942, 1943) and others in the Wilson *Catalogue*. Some southern stars are given separately by Deeming (1962). The older spectral classifications are approximately one spectral type too early, judged from available photoelectric colors. In this analysis of solar motion, I include only stars for which I have new data on velocities and spectral classification, and 20 stars from Deeming's velocity catalogue. The new Palomar radial velocities concern a group of highly selected stars. Even the apparently spectroscopically normal stars were initially suspected as high-velocity, weak-line, or large proper-motion stars. No group solution contains normal, unselected F–K main-sequence stars. A computer program for solar motion, written by Derek Jones, was available, which allowed for galactic rotation. Since all objects had $r < 250$ pc and the mean $\langle r \rangle = 75$ pc, interstellar reddening was neglected. The distribution of the stars in longitude was uniform over the northern hemisphere; the mean galactic latitude was high, near 40°. Table 2 shows the results of seven solutions for computations of (U, V, W), the motions of the subdwarfs with respect to the sun. The (U', V', W') motions of the subdwarfs with respect to the local standard of rest can be obtained from the motion of nearby stars with respect to the sun (u_0, v_0, w_0); Woolley (1958) gives $(+11,$ $-17, -7$ km/sec) for the latter. Values of $U' = U - u_0$, $V' = V - v_0$, $W' = W - w_0$ are given in the last columns. The dispersion, σ, is a measure of the star's residual velocity from the solution for its group. As a result of the large values of σ and the small number of stars in each sample, the mean errors of the determinations of U and W are especially large; these quantities are very poorly determined except for the uninteresting groups 2 to 4. The major effect is clearly in V, i.e., the low angular momentum and galactic rotation of the subdwarfs

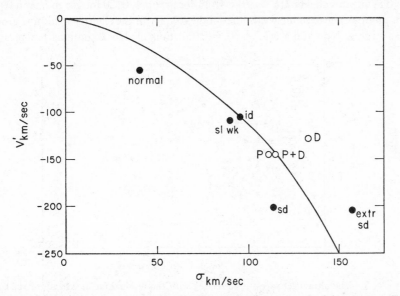

Fig. 4.—The root-mean-square residual radial velocity for groups of subdwarfs, types F to K, correlated with the V' component of space motion. The degree of line weakening is indicated.

result in a systematic lag of over 200 km/sec for groups 5 and 6, the very weak-line stars. Even though the mean error is large, V' sets a lower limit to the galactic rotation, a circular velocity of about 210 km/sec, if we assume only that the systematic motion of the extreme subdwarfs is not retrograde. If we con-sider only V', Figure 4 shows the correlation between V' and σ. The circles rep-resent the entire material (P = Palomar, D = Deeming) and the different classes of line weakening are distinguished for the Palomar material. As would be expected, there is a large increase of V' with σ, reflecting the predominantly "plunging" orbits with $e \approx 1$ and small perigalacticon. In addition, Figure 4 shows the high statistical correlation of large σ and great line weakening. Groups 3 and 4, slightly weak and intermediate (id) stars, have $\sigma = 90$ km/sec and V' near -115 km/sec; groups 6 and 7, subdwarfs (sd) and extremely weak-line sd stars, have $\sigma \approx 140$ km/sec and V' near -210 km/sec. The star $-29°2277$, with the highest known radial velocity, $+516.3$ km/sec, belongs to group 6; it has a residual radial motion of 361 km/sec. Seven of 37 stars in group 6 have residuals greater than 200 km/sec; only 2 of 23 stars in group 5, the usual "subdwarfs," have so large a residual. The correlation of degree of line weakening and random velocity is extremely close among the most metal-poor objects. This fact was pointed out by Greenstein (1956) and others; we now have sufficient detail concerning the extreme halo objects, from spectra and $U - B$ excesses, to view this as important evidence in the study of the early stages of the formation of our Galaxy.

The mean value of $\delta(U - B)$ is $0^{m}14$ for group 4, $0^{m}20$ for group 5, and $0^{m}22$ for group 6, the extreme weak-line subdwarfs. Even the slightly weak-line group has large motion and a $\delta(U - B) = 0^{m}06$; thus, Table 2 contains few normal

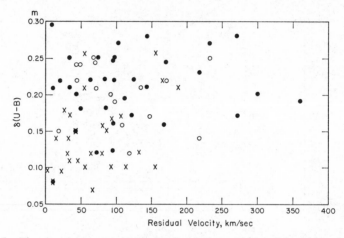

Fig. 5.—The ultraviolet excess is correlated with the residual radial velocity of the subdwarfs. Crosses are intermediate line weakening, open circles are subdwarfs, and filled circles extremely weak-line objects.

stars. Individual velocity residuals from the group motion are shown in Figure 5, as correlated with $\delta(U - B)$. Stars of a given line-weakening or $\delta(U - B)$ show a real spread of velocity residual; a few very weak-line stars of large $\delta(U - B)$ have low residuals. (Use of all three components of the space motion might remove some of these cases.) As already pointed out, however, only seven stars of the moderate line-weakening group (id) have velocity residuals >100 km/sec. The highest $\delta(U - B)$ stars have by far the largest peculiar velocities. Composition and place of origin in the halo are most clearly correlated for the stars with low angular momentum.

2.6. MOVING GROUPS CONTAINING SUBDWARFS

Eggen has suggested that stellar groupings over large volumes of space exist with common space motions, and that some have high velocity (see chap. 6, this volume). The question of their stability (and even of their existence) can be illuminated by the uniformity of their chemical composition. Eggen selected stars with $\delta(U - B) > 0^m19$, plotted their U, V loci, and isolated three possible groups of weak-line stars. One contains RR Lyr and Groombridge 1830 (Eggen and Sandage 1959), and others are the Ross 451 and Kapteyn's star group. Table 3 contains data on those stars that I have observed spectroscopically. Ross 451 is of particular interest in that it was originally classified as sdK6, then sdM0, but its colors are $+1^m45$, $+1^m16$, far too red even for this type. I find extremely strong MgH bands, so that it is probably a peculiar sdM2 star with weak TiO bands. It is interesting to find that the other members of the Ross 451 group are stars of very weak lines and large $\delta(U - B)$. The criteria for

TABLE 3

SPECTROSCOPIC AND $\delta(U - B)$ DATA FOR SUSPECTED MOVING GROUPS

Star	$\delta(U-B)$	Spectrum	Remarks
		Groombridge 1830 Group*	
$+72°94$	0^m22	sd G3	Extr. weak lines, ions strong
103095	.19	sd K3	No CN; Groom. 1830
163810	0.21	id G5	ADS 10938
R R Lyr			$\Delta S = 6$
		Kapteyn's Star Group†	
HD 33793			Kapteyn's star. Like R451 from $I-R$ colors; old type dK2 must be incorrect
CC 486	0.23		
SU Dra			$\Delta S = 6$
ST Leo			$\Delta S = 6$
$+14°2481$	.20	sd G:	Ions strong
$-13°3834$	0.25	sd G5	
		Ross 451 Group‡	
74000	0.25	sd F7	Extr. weak lines
$+29°2091$	.22	sd G0	Extr. weak lines
Ross 451		sd M2p	MgH strong, TiO weak
108177	.25	sd G0	Extr. weak lines
$-35°14849$	0.21	sd F:	Extr. weak lines

* Here the spectral classification of HD 163810 as id disagrees with the otherwise very weak-line characteristics of the group and with the large $\delta(U - B)$. It is possible that some contribution by the close companion ($\Delta m = 1$) may affect both line weakening and color. Then HD 163810 might be excluded as a non-member. Alternatively, $+72°94$ might be excluded as the discrepant star, since neither RR Lyr or Groombridge 1830 have very large metal deficiencies. Three of the four stars are similar spectroscopically.

† The spectral characteristics are fairly homogeneous and all stars have large line weakening. The M star has not been re-observed.

‡ The stars have a remarkably homogeneous appearance, all with large $\delta(U - B)$ and very weak lines.

line weakening in sdM stars are still unknown; theoretically there is a partial cancellation of metal poorness by low H⁻ opacity; molecular bands of an oxide should be weakened, while a hydride may be unchanged. For RR Lyr stars, unfortunately, we cannot use $\delta(U - B)$ as a measure of line weakness, but the difference between the spectral types indicated by the hydrogen and by the metallic lines, ΔS, is an excellent substitute. In spite of the great age and the large space motion, the Ross 451 group and to some extent the Kapteyn star group are strikingly homogeneous, spectroscopically. At the very least, we can assert that no evidence here presented contradicts the hypothesis of common origin for stars in these groups, as far as low metal content is concerned.

§ 3. WHITE DWARFS

3.1. Discovery of Individual White Dwarfs

Discovery lists, colors, and classification are given by Luyten for a very large number of stars (1949, 1952, 1953–1963) and Greenstein (1958, 1960); photoelectric colors by Harris (1956) are being supplemented by Eggen; and lists of probable white dwarfs are given in the Lowell proper-motion surveys (Giclas et al. 1959, 1961). Approximately 200 white dwarfs have been confirmed by spectra, and about 50 more stars of large proper motion by photoelectric colors. The additional known number of bright probable white dwarfs, based on photographic estimates, is about 200. Their frequency in space and their masses have been estimated by Luyten (1958, 1961); their masses from spectroscopic determinations of surface gravity are given by Greenstein (1958) and Weidemann (1963). The most recent data are given by Eggen and Greenstein (1965).

The emphasis here will be on stars for which spectra or photoelectric colors are available. The number of misidentifications of white dwarfs is far from negligible. The large ultraviolet excess of F and G subdwarfs, also stars of large proper motion, makes them easy to confuse with the yellower of the white dwarfs. Among the Lowell proper-motion stars of estimated colors -1^m and 0^m, I found 11 sdF to sdK stars and 14 white dwarfs out of 25 observed. Similarly, out of 44 Luyten proper-motion blue stars, I found 13 sdF to sdK, 3 sdB, 1 composite, and 27 white dwarfs. Among 80 supposedly blue stars, magnitude 13 to 16 (not selected by proper motion), from lists by Humason and Zwicky (1947), Feige (1958), Iriarte and Chavira (1957), and Chavira (1958), I find 25 white dwarfs, 36 sdB or sdO, and 19 normal or halo A or F stars. Thus, a simple estimate of blue color at high latitudes yields 30 per cent white dwarfs, while 60 per cent of stars examined are white dwarfs when both large proper motion and blueness are selection criteria. The 30 per cent yield among faint blue stars is not to be taken as a general statistic, since for some I had photoelectric colors and could select those stars in an interesting portion of the $U - B$, $B - V$ diagram; the majority of faint blue stars are probably halo A stars. Another source of confusion, even with U, B, V colors, arises from the existence of unresolved doubles containing a G or K star and (presumably) a subluminous blue star.

We may also question the definiteness of the spectroscopic criteria. The pressure broadening of lines of hydrogen and helium in the DA and DB stars is so characteristic that it gives clear evidence for high surface gravity. Stars without lines, DC, are found over a wide range of color; the bluest ones of this group may be confused with very hot subdwarfs, nuclei of planetary nebulae, or nova remnants, with a possible difference in M_V of 3 to 5 mag. The theoretical upper limit to the luminosity of a completely degenerate star is near $M_V = +7$.

The color surveys permit identification of possible white dwarfs without prior selection for large proper motion. We will see in Table 5 that 21 white dwarfs were confirmed by spectra from among the blue stars. Their proper motions were then found to be small. The HR diagram of white dwarfs of known parallax and photoelectric colors permits us to obtain photometric or spectroscopic parallaxes for these blue white dwarfs; their mean luminosity is $\langle M_V \rangle = +10^m0$ and their $B - V$ colors range from -0^m35 to $+0^m09$. Although their motions are small, the mean tangential velocity is well determined and is found to be near 30 km/sec. Consequently, I evaluated the individual values of the τ-component motion, and from the photometric parallaxes, the $|V_\tau|$, whose mean value is 11.4 km/sec. Errors in luminosity may occur for the *brighter* hot white dwarfs, since none have trigonometric parallaxes; the correction to log V_τ is $-0.2\ \Delta M_V$. Thus, even if the stars are two magnitudes brighter, the increase in V_τ is only by a factor of 2.5. Clearly the blue-star lists give us largely the relatively young white dwarfs of population I, since $\langle |V_\tau| \rangle$ of 11 km/sec is close to that of the B stars. Such objects should become rare at z-coordinate heights of more than 100 pc. The high velocities found statistically for white dwarfs selected from proper-motion surveys are due to selection. There is little doubt of the existence of white dwarfs in both population types.

Iwanowska and Opaska-Burnicka (1962) used the proper motions of white dwarfs of known parallax or $B - V$ color and divided the stars into two groups with $V_T \gtrless 70$ km/sec. Of 62 stars, 20 are ascribed with varying degrees of certainty to population II. An auxiliary criterion, depending on the direction of the star's motion, as compared to the motion of the high- and low-velocity stars, was studied, but gives at present no criterion for separation of the population types. In principle, it is an ingenious source of such information. Of the 62 stars in their two groups a and b, I have spectral data for 49; the so-called population I group contained 2 DB, 27 DA, 1 DApe (old nova), 2 DF, 1 DC, 1 λ 4670 (C_2 star), and 1 λ 4135 star (unidentified bands). The population II group contained 2 DB, 6 DA, 1 DG, 4 DC, and 1 λ 4670 star. Although the sample is small and the assignment of population type uncertain, it is, however, interesting that the population I group contains predominantly DA stars, i.e., relatively bright stars, while the population II group contains a wider diversity of types, including fainter objects, and a surprising number of lineless, DC, stars, possibly reflecting the low metal content of the parent stars.

3.2. Use of Reduced Proper Motions

The old lists of white dwarfs confirmed spectroscopically or by photoelectric measures provide about 70 stars; about 30 new objects can be included for which colors or spectra are available but are still unpublished. The values of $\langle H_V \rangle$, where H_V is the reduced proper motion

$$H_V = m_V + 5 + 5 \log \mu , \qquad (3)$$

are shown in Figure 6 as a function of $\langle B - V \rangle$, for stars for which all data are available. The relation is nearly linear and is fairly well defined. The DA stars

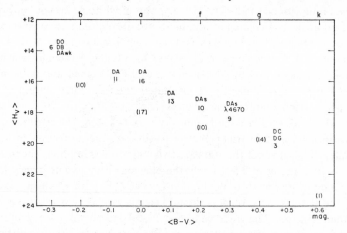

Fig. 6.—The mean reduced proper motion for single white dwarfs of known spectra and color. The numbers of stars involved in each group are shown. The main spectral types are given for each group. The bracketed figures refer to Luyten's new faint white dwarfs, with color classes given on the top scale.

should have their mean colors moved 0.2 mag to the left if the blanketing by the Balmer lines is removed, when they are compared with a line-free star. The 68 stars plotted have $\mu > 0\overset{''}{.}10/\mathrm{yr}$. A linear regression of $\langle H_V \rangle$ on $\langle B - V \rangle$ gives

$$\langle H_V \rangle = 16.2 + 8.14 \langle B - V \rangle . \qquad (4)$$

The white dwarfs of known parallax, similarly grouped, give

$$\langle M_V \rangle = 11.3 + 5.6 \langle B - V \rangle , \qquad (5)$$

which results in

$$\langle M_V \rangle = 0.687 \langle H_V \rangle + 0.2 . \qquad (6)$$

Basing their estimates on earlier material, Greenstein (1958) gave, instead of equation (6), $0.71 \langle H_V \rangle + 0.4$, and Luyten (1958) gave $0.83 \langle H_V \rangle - 2.5$. In spite of the apparent difference between these expressions, the tangential velocities, computed from the relation

$$M_V = H_V + 3.4 - 5 \log V_T , \qquad (7)$$

depend on H_V in similar fashion; V_T increases from 22 to 69 km/sec for H_V increasing from 11 to 19 from equation (6), while from Luyten's relation the run is from 35 to 66 km/sec. As would be expected, my spectroscopic list, which contains some stars first selected by blue color rather than proper motion, yields a lower mean velocity for the brighter and bluer white dwarfs.

Luyten (1963) has studied the distribution of H for faint white dwarfs and obtained the solar apex. For 256 brighter stars, he gives 18^h58^m, $+39°.3$ and, for 23 possible yellow white dwarfs, 20^h40^m, $+53°$ (with large probable errors). The difference of about 20° is probably significant. He also gives a preliminary analysis of 52 very faint, probable white dwarfs recently found in a survey on Palomar-Schmidt plates, in the range 16 to 21 mag. Only color classes and estimated μ were available. The $\langle H \rangle$ and mean color classes are shown in Figure 6; these faint stars deviate slightly from my relation based on well-determined brighter stars. The deviation is such that $\langle H \rangle$ is larger for a given color class, if my correlation of $B - V$ and color class remains correct. Another interpretation is that Luyten's colors of faint stars are somewhat too blue. It is apparent that ultraviolet excess does affect his estimates of photographic color. The agreement is close enough to suggest that the faint white dwarfs discovered with the Palomar-Schmidt are essentially the same kinds of objects as the brighter well-known stars.

3.3. BINARIES

It is generally assumed that close binary stars are rare in population II. The discovery of red-dwarf, white-dwarf pairs among the proper-motion stars is a particularly efficient means of finding white dwarfs. The majority of those pairs suspected by Luyten or Giclas, for which Eggen has photoelectric colors or I have spectra, have proved to be physically connected systems. An important advantage, moreover, is that photoelectric colors and spectra of the primaries determine metallic-line weakness and luminosities over certain ranges of spectral type. Among 22 pairs which Eggen and Greenstein (1965) have observed, five main-sequence stars have a $\langle \delta(U - B) \rangle = 0.08$ (slight line weakening). Two stars were classified spectroscopically as subdwarf M. The balance were dM stars, only one of which was a dMe; eight were clearly normal by color and spectra but three were unusually red, suggesting, perhaps, that TiO bands were weaker than normal. Therefore, approximately one-half of the stars were candidates for membership in the weak-line population. Wide binaries do exist in the old population; detailed study of the space motions will be required to establish whether any of these objects are members of the extreme, halo-population II type. A very large sample of pairs containing white dwarfs is available from Luyten, mainly in the southern hemisphere. The Lowell proper-motion survey also yields a large number of new pairs.

Luyten (1961) studied the relative orbital motion of 15 pairs containing white dwarfs as compared with 13 pairs of faint red dwarfs. He finds statistical evidence for a small, real orbital motion which is larger for the white-dwarf pairs. If the mean mass of the red dwarfs is about 0.4 $M\odot$, the mean white-dwarf mass is near 0.6 $M\odot$, i.e., like that of o^2 Eri B rather than like α CMa B, in agreement with the statistical evidence by Weidemann (1963) and Eggen and Greenstein (1965).

3.4. An Astrophysical Hertzsprung-Russell Diagram

An entirely spectroscopic analysis of the white dwarfs yields, in principle, the effective temperature, T_e, and the surface gravity; from them the bolometric and visual absolute magnitudes can be obtained. Weidemann (1963) has ana-lyzed Greenstein's (1960) line profiles and the U, B, V data, using model atmospheres and line-broadening theory. The mass is uniquely determined from the degenerate-gas mass-radius relation, if the chemical composition is known. Since He, C, O, Ne, have the same effective molecular weights, $\mu_e = 2$, the de-tails of the composition have only a small effect on the mass. Thus, spectro-scopic observations yield the bolometric correction T_e, the radius, R, and, there-fore, the luminosity, L. The results of Weidemann's analysis, as shown in Figure 7, have remarkably little scatter. The mean $R \approx 10^{-2} R\odot$, the T_e range for DO and DA stars is 45000° to 7000° K, the M_V range is +9 to +13, and the mass, 0.5 $M\odot$.

3.5. Frequency in Space

Luyten (1958) has given the most complete study of this topic and finds that white dwarfs represent about 2 per cent of the stars within 20 pc. His study is based on the distribution of proper motions as a function of apparent magnitude among the broader class of white dwarfs, for which he has proper motion and photographic estimates of color. His Table 1 contains the fraction of white dwarfs at a given m and μ. Grouping stars by their reduced proper motion, H, he finds the smoothed percentage as a function of H (from 0.4 per cent to 8.4 per cent). This is converted into the absolute number of white dwarfs; their maxi-mum frequency is at $H \approx 14$, and their number 2.1 $\pm$ 0.3 per cent of the total stars. From stars of large parallax, he finds white dwarfs to be 2.1 $\pm$ 0.7 per cent of the stars known within 10 pc.

The number of hot white dwarfs found by color and not by proper motion is appreciable. In my spectral survey of faint blue stars, 10 white dwarfs were found, as compared with a total of 53 new or newly confirmed white dwarfs in my survey of stars originally suspected from proper motions. But those stars, found by blueness only, are almost certainly the more luminous objects, near +9 or +10, judging from color and spectral type. They are found over a larger volume of space, since the mean luminosity of proper-motion white dwarfs is nearer $+13$. They change the bright end of Luyten's luminosity distribution negligibly. Presumably, such bright stars cool and evolve rapidly down the white-dwarf sequence.

The number of cool white dwarfs, however, is very uncertain and especially those with $B - V > 0^m6$ are poorly known. The theory of the HR diagram for white dwarfs (where the surface flux is maintained at the expense of internal energy only) suggests that red-degenerate stars might be among the most

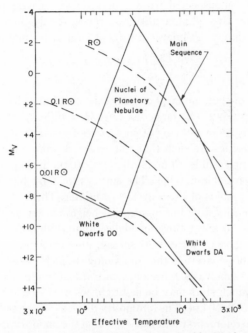

Fig. 7.—The HR diagram of the white dwarfs determined by Weidemann from line widths and broadening theory, giving the M_V, T_e relation. Curves of constant radius are shown by dashed lines. The nuclei of planetary nebulae have luminosities within the area noted. They were derived by O'Dell, using a modified Zanstra and Shklovsky method.

frequent type of stars, next to dwarf M stars. The maximum cooling time without nuclear energy sources is 4×10^9 yr for a star like vMa2, if the core is helium and the envelope is of normal stellar composition. If the core contains heavier elements and the envelope helium, the time drops to 6×10^8 yr. Discovery of red-degenerate stars is very difficult; proper-motion surveys down to $0''2/yr$ contain 10^4 stars, and it is difficult to distinguish colorimetrically between the enormously numerous K and M dwarfs and possible red-degenerate stars with nearly continuous spectra. For objects of low space motion, $\mu = 0''2/$ yr means a parallax of $0''04$, and a volume of 6×10^4 pc³. Consider the luminosity function of red-degenerate stars for stars near $M = +15$, not far from the most frequent type found by Luyten. Then 0.003 of all intrinsically faint stars are white dwarfs within ± 0.5 mag of $M = 15$. There would be 18 such stars within 25 pc of the sun, with absolute magnitudes from $+14.5$ to $+15.5$, i.e., with apparent magnitudes brighter than 17.5. This is far too small a number to be noted in the proper-motion survey of 10^4 stars. The mean distance between such stars is 10 pc; the nearest neighbor would have $m - M \approx 0$, and we would expect one such star at $m = +15$. An increase of the numbers of the faintest and reddest white dwarfs by a factor exceeding 10 might escape notice. My own spectroscopic work on suspected red-degenerate stars of large proper motion, and observations by Herbig, have until now revealed only three new faint red objects, and many late weak-line subdwarfs of large space motion.

§ 4. HOT SUBLUMINOUS STARS

4.1. TYPES

A great variety of subluminous hot stars exists, and little has yet been done to group or classify them. The range between $M = 0$ (horizontal branch) and the white dwarfs at $M = +9$ contains examples from both major population types; their luminosities are such that the expected proper motions are negligible at apparent magnitude 10 or fainter, i.e., at the magnitude where they first appear in appreciable number. The surveys for faint blue stars have revealed enormous numbers of them at 15^m or fainter. These objects will aid in the study of the density distribution at great heights in the z-coordinate when it becomes possible to select those of higher luminosities. Discovery of faint blue stars at high galactic latitude is simple; multicolor photometry offers a promising means of separating the "horizontal-branch" stars from the less luminous, hotter, O subdwarfs. Since blue stars are known to $m = 20$, and since some horizontal-branch stars may be as bright as $M \approx +1$, the survey in the galactic halo reaches to 60 kpc. The luminosity dispersion is already known to be very large. It is, therefore, first necessary to name the major types of stars to be expected and to obtain rough luminosity calibrations. Methods must be developed for recognizing what type of star is involved, without spectroscopic observation. Photoelectric observations at 15^m are rapidly executed, but a spectrum requires an hour's exposure even with the 200-inch telescope.

Objective-prism methods have not been rewarding because of the weakness of all spectral lines in hot stars. A schematic classification of types of stars is contained in Table 4. The quantitative data are very poor, and much further work will be required to refine them. The galactic-center population is conspicuous in the planetary nebulae; the horizontal-branch stars, like the RR Lyr stars, range from pure halo to old disk population. Novae belong to the old disk population, as might be expected for objects which are nearly all close binaries; the U Gem variables are also close binaries and have a large velocity dispersion. White dwarfs seem to be the end product of evolution for both populations. The lifetime of some of these stages of evolution must be short; a typical globular cluster with 10^5 stars may have 100 horizontal-branch stars and one or no B or

O star just below the main sequence. Planetary nebulae themselves have lives near 10^4 years, but isolated stars with spectra identical with planetary nuclei exist, for example, $+28°4211$, suggesting that the star survives the ejection stage nearly unchanged. The white-dwarf stage is very long-lived, and, per volume of space, the white dwarfs are the commonest. A lifetime inversely proportional to the luminosity represents the general frequency of the hot subdwarfs, except for an apparent heaping up near $M = 0$ to $+1$.

TABLE 4

MAJOR GROUPS OF SUBLUMINOUS BLUE STARS

Name*	Color	Abs. Mag.	Spectral Features
1. Globular cluster B and O....	-0^m4 to -0^m1	-2	Sharp H. He sharp and weak. Weak O II, C II
2. Nuclei of planetary nebulae...	-0.4 to -0.2	-1 to $+8$	Of among brighter stars. Very weak or no lines at faint end
3. Horizontal-branch stars......	-0.4 to $+0.1$	0 to $+3$	Sharp, strong H; large Balmer jump. Other lines weak
4. Hot subdwarfs.............	-0.4 to -0.2	$+2$ to $+5$	Broad H, He I, He II. Some have rich, sharp-lined spectrum of N, Ne, C, O; others have very weak lines
5. Blue objects in SS Cyg stars..	Composite	$+3$ to $+9$	Emission lines, nova-like variations. Binaries with red companions
6. Old novae................	-0.3 to $+0.4$	$+3$ to $+9$	Weak or no absorption; variable emission lines and light. Largely binaries
7. White dwarfs.............	-0.4 to $+1.0$	$+9$ to $+16$	Complex; highly broadened lines, some nearly continuous

* *Typical Objects*

1. Barnard 29, M13.
2. Star in NGC 7009 (bright), NGC 7293 (faint).
3. HD 161817 (many weak lines), λ Boo (few weak lines).
4. HZ 44 (rich line, $M \approx +3$), $+75°325$ (poor-lined).

5. SS Cyg, AE Aqr, U Gem.
6. DQ Her (bright), WZ Sge (faint).
7. α CMa B (pop. I); o² Eri B (old pop. I); vMa2 (pop. II).

The significance of the blue stars for galactic structure and evolution has been frequently emphasized by Vorontsov-Velyaminov (1953), although because of lack of data, his interpretation of the "blue-white" sequence as a single evolutionary track should not be considered proved. We will see that this left-hand edge of the HR diagram is not homogeneous. For example, there can be no meaningful relation between the ordinary Wolf-Rayet stars and the nuclei of planetary nebulae; their galactic distributions are very different, and there may be a 10 mag difference in luminosity. A large range of temperature, and therefore of bolometric correction, corresponds to a small change of ordinary color index. The conventional HR diagram gives a distorted impression of the existence of a nearly vertical sequence. The nuclei of planetary nebulae show a very large temperature range, indicating a variation in bolometric correction up to 7 magnitudes, within this one group of stars.

4.2. The Evolution and the Luminosity Function of the Blue Subdwarfs

Very large lists of faint blue stars have been given, based on the Minnesota and Tonantzintla surveys; the stellar statistical approach, using counts as a function of magnitude, $N(m)$ and secular parallaxes, or reduced proper motions, H, will be useful to study their galactic distribution and mean luminosity. Unfortunately, few of these objects have large motions, and almost none will have measurable trigonometric parallax.

Preliminary estimates of the mean absolute magnitude have been in the range $+1$ to $+4$. If all halo stars were like the horizontal-branch blue stars in globular clusters, their luminosity function would be quite peculiar. Star counts in clusters show a preliminary maximum near $M = 0$ to $+1$, even when the RR Lyrae stars are omitted. Arp's (1955) study of seven globular clusters gives fragmentary information concerning the first magnitude of the luminosity function of the blue stars in the "turndown" region of the HR diagram (left-hand side of the variable-star gap). While clusters differ, there is little concentration of stars per interval of M_V, i.e., $\varphi(M_V)dM_V$ is constant down to $+1.0$, and then apparently drops to nearly zero. Only M13 has stars down to $+1.5$. Measured on a bolometric scale, the bluest stars probably have nearly the same M_b as the A stars, producing an even sharper maximum in $\varphi(M_b)$. In the seven globular clusters studied by Arp, the number of blue stars from 0^m to $+1^m$, in the color range $-0^m.2$ to $+0^m.2$ is about 300, while there are 100 red giants in the top range of brightness, $-2^m.4$ to $-3^m.4$, and 250 from $-1^m.4$ to $-2^m.4$; thus, the frequency of blue stars and red giants in globular clusters is nearly the same. But a two-magnitude differential in luminosity corresponds to a factor of 16 in the volume of space observed in the galactic field. The number of blue stars in the galactic halo at a given apparent magnitude should therefore be small compared to that of red giants. Whether this is true is unknown, but seems improbable, at faint apparent magnitudes at the galactic pole. Here the density decrease in the z-direction must be a significant factor.

At some late stage in evolution, the blue stars begin a collapse that ends in the white-dwarf region. In the latter, the $\varphi(M)$ curve is determined in other ways and depends on other factors (for example, rate of surface cooling). We do not yet know from observations whether the luminosity function of the subdwarfs has a maximum, or even whether the distribution is continuous. But in the possibly nearly vertical descent in the HR diagram, some evolutionary considerations can give useful information.

Assume a loss of nuclear-energy sources in a star of high surface temperature. The high surface flux cannot be maintained, and there is a limited range of core contraction to provide potential energy. Plausible luminosity functions can be derived, dependent on the assumed lifetime at a given luminosity. Log $\varphi(M)$ can be either linear or quadratic depending on cooling rates. If all stars pass smoothly through all stages, and if the luminosity function is not a function of the z-coordinate, we predict star counts as shown in Figure 8. The quadratic forms give maxima within a reasonable range of m, that is, they permit appreciable numbers of blue stars down to $m = 16$ or fainter. These curves can be displaced vertically, and their maxima can be placed at fainter apparent

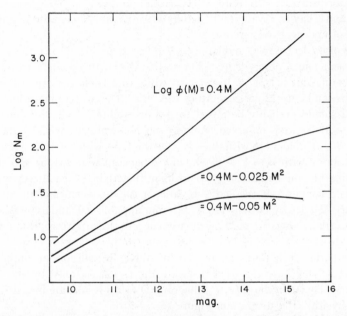

FIG. 8.—Predicted counts of stars of magnitude m at the galactic pole, shown for three assumed luminosity functions, $\varphi(M)$. The mean density of stars is assumed to vary as $10^{-z/z_0}$, where $z_0 = 1000$ pc.

magnitudes by decreasing the concentration to the galactic plane. The mean parallaxes, and therefore the mean proper motions, can be estimated for these models. They vary slowly with m, but are critically dependent on the scale height, z_0. For the value used, $z_0 = 1$ kpc, the mean parallax ranges from $0''.0027$ to $0''.0014$, typically, near 15^m. If the transverse motion is about 100 km/sec the mean expected proper motion is about 20 times the mean parallax, i.e., $0''.03$ to $0''.05$ per year. At fainter magnitudes, or for stars of lower velocity, the proper motions are barely larger than the reduction from relative to absolute proper motion. In spite of the large color difference, proper motions of blue stars at high galactic latitude should be, ideally, based on the reference frame provided by extragalactic nebulae. The stars are sufficiently faint (13–19 mag) to make this a good program for a large astrographic telescope.

4.3. HOT SUBDWARFS DISCOVERED IN COLOR SURVEYS

To obtain a statistical picture of the nature of the faint stars and yet to avoid the selection of the types of intrinsically low-luminosity stars found in proper-motion surveys, I have been making a spectroscopic survey of faint blue stars, largely halo stars near the galactic poles. My own selection within the discovery surveys was by "very blue" color, reducing the number of Ap halo stars[1] found. The major lists used were those of Humason and Zwicky (1947), Feige (1958), Iriarte and Chavira (1957), and Chavira (1958). Table 5 contains a statistical résumé of my spectroscopic results.

Stars of moderate color and large $U - B$ excess are likely to be white dwarfs and these, again, I observed first. The statistics, omitting planetary nuclei and remembering this bias, give 16 per cent white dwarfs, 49 per cent Bp or sdO, sdB stars, and only 12 per cent Ap or sdA stars. The over-all mean luminosity of $+4.2$ should probably be raised to $+3$ or brighter, if all stars bluer than $B - V = 0^m00$ were observed. Among the non-white dwarfs, 38 stars had known $B - V$ colors: 16 with $B - V < -0^m21$, 14 with $-0^m20 < B - V < -0^m01$, and 8 with $B - V > 0^m00$. Only 8 per cent were sdF or sdG stars or composite, i.e., the number of gross errors in the original color survey was low.

Table 5 contains, at the end, estimates of the luminosities of the nuclei of planetary nebulae by O'Dell (1962) and from unpublished studies by Abell and from spectra by Greenstein. My estimates concern the spectroscopic luminosity, from hydrogen line widths, of the central stars in planetaries of large diameter and low surface brightness discovered by Abell. In addition, an unpublished study by O'Dell has been used to locate the region occupied by the normal planetary nebulae in the (M_V, T_e) diagram. O'Dell's results are included in the "astrophysical" HR diagram of Figure 7.

In conclusion, we see that the faint, very blue stars at the galactic pole cover an enormous range in luminosity and have obvious spectral peculiarities. Normal B and A stars are very rare.

4.4. SPECTRA OF BLUE STARS SELECTED BY PROPER MOTIONS

In the Luyten and Lowell (Giclas *et al.* 1959, 1961) proper-motion surveys, note was taken of apparently blue stars. Naturally, the yield of white dwarfs and F subdwarfs in these surveys is higher, and the space motion of all stars larger. These stars have $\mu > 0''05$, and usually $\mu > 0''20$. Of 71 newly observed stars (omitting previously known white dwarfs) my spectra showed 21 to be white dwarfs, 13 to be halo Ap or Bp stars, 4 sdO and Bp, 26 sdF and G, 4 metallic-line or magnetic A stars, and 3 normal. The high percentage of yellow types sdF, G arises from their large space motion; the frequency of white dwarfs is doubled in this proper-motion sample when compared to those in Table 5. In this group of stars the selection by color is small, because only rough color estimates of

---

[1] Note that Ap in this paper indicates a peculiar A star, not a magnetic A star.

TABLE 5

Statistical Results for Blue Stars Found Colorimetrically

n	$\langle m_V \rangle$	$(B-V, U-B)$-Colors	Distribution of Spectra	Mean Proper Motions		
			Feige Stars			
40...	12.3	$(-0^m31, -1^m25)$ to $(+0^m05, +0^m10)$	2 DO, 1 DB, 4 DA, 7 Bp, 3 Ap, 6 sdO, 7 sdB, 2 sdF, 8 normal B	DO, DB, DA 0″.063	sdO, sdB 0″.022	Bp, Ap 0″.028
			Humason-Zwicky Stars			
32...	14.2	$(-0^m35, -1^m25)$ to $(+0^m25, -0^m41)$	2 DO, 1 DB, 8 DA, 5 Bp, 1 Ap, 4 sdO, 5 sdB, 3 normal B, 3 composite B+G	DA 0″.096	sdO, sdB 0″.017	Bp, Ap 0″.022
			Tonantzintla Stars			
22...	14.5	$(-0^m40, -1^m14)$ to $(+0^m38, -0^m10)$	2 DA, 1 DC, 1 Ap, 8 sdO, 8 sdB, 1 sdA, 1 sdF	....	....	......
			Miscellaneous Color or Spectral Discoveries			
38...	10.0	$(-0^m20, -0^m90)$ to $(+0^m30, -0^m41)$	4 Bp, 6 Ap, 8 sdO, 3 sdF, 4 sdA, 5 sdF, 8 normal	....	....	......

All Blue Stars (JLG)

Distribution of Types	Per Cent	$\langle M_V \rangle$	Estimated Range, M_V
7 DO, DB, DC.....	5 ⎫	+9.6	+7 to +13
14 DA............	10 ⎭		
16 Bp............	11 ⎫	+2.2	0 to + 3
11 Ap............	8 ⎭		
26 sdO...........	18 ⎫	+3.7	+2 to + 5
23 sdB...........	16 ⎭		
5 sdA...........	3	....	....
8 sdF, G........	6	+5	....
19 normal.........	13	....	−2 to + 2
3 composite.......	2	....	....
12 planetary nuclei...	8	+2.9	0 to + 6

proper-motion stars existed when the spectroscopic observations began. The effect of the sdF, G stars on the statistics of proper-motion stars is important, since their space motion is about four times that of even the white dwarfs. In addition, their large ultraviolet excess apparently affects their blue-visual color index, making them bluish even when refractors are used, as in the Lowell and in some of the Luyten color estimates.

4.5. Properties of Brighter Blue Stars near the Galactic Poles

Two hundred blue stars, 10^m to 12^m, have been surveyed by Klemola (1962) north of $-21°$ and within $40°$ of the galactic poles. Sixteen Op or Bp stars, six possible horizontal-branch A stars, and 30 metallic-line or magnetic stars were recognized; the rest are apparently normal, spectroscopically or colorimetrically. However, all the bluest stars ($U - B < -0^m.94$) are peculiar (hot subdwarfs or white dwarfs). Klemola gives the $U - B$, $B - V$ diagrams for groups of high-latitude blue stars, divided by apparent magnitude (see his Fig. 2). The essential conclusions are that, if $m < 10$, the stars show largely the normal galactic-plane luminosity function. His group, 10^m to 12^m, shows very blue, hot stars, normally very rare near the sun; at 12^m to $14^m.5$ the hot stars exceed the A stars in number (a conclusion somewhat affected by observational selection); for $14^m.5$ to 16^m, the hot subdwarfs and white dwarfs dominate. The compound effects of change of population type and density decrease in the z-coordinate explain most of these effects.

Analysis of proper motions depends on a knowledge of peculiar velocities, very few of which have been published for the blue stars. The dispersion in the radial component was given by Greenstein (1956) as ± 48 km/sec at $\langle m \rangle =$ 11.8 and by Berger (1963) as ± 30 km/sec at $\langle m \rangle = 11.0$. Slettebak, Bahner, and Stock (1961) give rough velocities. Those with peculiar spectra (sdO, Ap, or horizontal branch) have a dispersion of ± 60 km/sec, an unexpectedly high value, from 8 stars at $\langle m \rangle = 9.4$. If we can assume a random tangential velocity of 38 km/sec, the derived luminosities from tau components lie between $\langle M_V \rangle =$ $+1$ and $+3.5$; the upsilon components give $\langle M_V \rangle$ of $+2$ to $+3$ if the normal solar motion is used, and -1 to -3 if the high-velocity-star solar motion is adopted. The observed mean parallaxes seem to be too small to obtain reliable results. Klemola confirms the small mean proper motion of the blue stars; only 5 per cent have $\mu > 0''.1/$yr. Because of the brightness of his stars, it is, unfortunately, a particularly heterogeneous group in content.

§ 5. THE M SUBDWARFS

M dwarfs are the most common objects in the Galaxy and contribute a large fraction of its stellar mass; they are also the most common objects in proper-motion and parallax surveys. Little detailed spectroscopic work has been carried out; the U, B, V photometry of these stars gives little information. The frequency of visual, astrometric, and even spectroscopic binaries is high. Both high- and low-velocity objects are found.

5.1. The Frequency of High-Velocity M Dwarfs

Excellent résumés of statistical properties are given by Vyssotsky (1956, 1957), who initiated the program for the discovery by objective-prism surveys of dM stars. Dyer (1954, 1956) and Mumford (1956a, b) have analyzed the space motions and find, for example, a total dispersion near ±36 km/sec, corresponding to old population I stars. Vyssotsky finds $\sigma = \pm 18$ km/sec for dMe and ±30 km/sec for dM stars. Radial velocities for the proper-motion stars are given by Joy (1947), Wilson (1953), and Dyer (1954). The dispersion in radial velocity, in Joy's sample chosen from proper-motion stars, is ±27 km/sec, and, for 12 stars classified as sdM, ±133 km/sec.

Possible selection effects introduced by the choice of M stars by large proper motions affect the derived solar motion and the individual space motions. The U, V, W motions of 305 stars discovered in the McCormick spectroscopic surveys are given by Dyer (1956). We find that only seven of the stars in his diagram have $|W| > 50$ km/sec. Stars with $|W| = 50$ will not reach much above 1 kpc in the z-coordinate, and are not extreme halo members. The frequency of such (marginal) halo stars is then about 2 per cent. If we arbitrarily set another criterion for definition of a high-velocity star, such as requiring either that $|U| > 75$ or $|V| > 75$ km/sec (equivalent to eccentricities of >0.2 and >0.3, respectively), we find 14 and 8 stars, respectively. The actual total is 19 stars (since some have both large $|U|$ and $|V|$), or 6 per cent. Many of the parallaxes have been determined spectroscopically, and may be subject to systematic error if high- and low-velocity stars have a different (M_V, spectral type) HR diagram. But a reasonable estimate is that about 5 per cent of the dM stars brighter than 11.5 belong to the high-velocity population.

For the 100 stars for which Kron (1956) provides M_R and $R - I$, we have accurate parallaxes and 92 radial velocities. A computing-machine program for the U, V, W components was available and provided the coordinates for Kron's stars plotted in Figure 9. The U, V coordinates of the normal dM stars are available from the McCormick list, and the "boundary" of these unselected stars, as given by Dyer (1956), is also shown. Stars within this boundary are members of population I and have relatively low velocity. The proper-motion stars have very large space motions, ranging up to ±125 km/sec in U and to −275 km/sec in V. Seventeen percent lie outside a circle of radius 63 km/sec, and 11 per cent have $|U|$ or $|V| > 75$ km/sec. Only 4 per cent have $|W| > 50$ km/sec, so this sample also does not contain stars of large orbital inclination. It should be remembered that these stars are very close to the sun.

The dM stars in the McCormick surveys have $\langle M_V \rangle \approx +9$; the sdG stars have $\langle M_V \rangle \approx +5$, so that in a given volume of space, the sdM stars would be about 4 mag fainter. To an equal limiting apparent magnitude, there should be about $4 \times 10^{-3} \, \varphi(\text{sdM})/\varphi(\text{sdG})$, as many sdM as sdG stars, where $\varphi(\text{sdM})$ is the luminosity function of stars of type sdM. Since the normal dwarf luminosity function has $\varphi(\text{dM})/\varphi(\text{dG}) \approx 5$, few sdM stars are to be expected among the brighter stars, even if the luminosity function is similar for normal and sub-dwarf stars. The brightest sdG stars are near $m = 8$; the sdM stars should ap-pear near $m = 12$ in 5 times greater numbers, or the brightest should be near $m = 11$. Since appreciable numbers of high-velocity M stars are found with $m = 9$, it seems probable that the rise in the subdwarf luminosity function to-ward fainter stars is steeper than for the normal stars. Of the 30 nearest systems of stars within 5 pc of the sun, 70 per cent are of spectral type dM. Three of the 37 individual stars are classified as sdM, or have high velocities. If my figure of

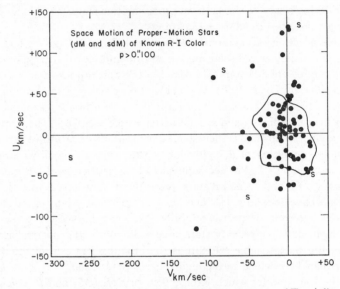

Fig. 9.—The space motions, (U, V), for the 100 proper-motion stars of Kron's list, without omissions. U is positive away from the galactic center, and V is positive in the direction of galactic rotation. The irregularly shaped boundary from Dyer (1956) includes the densest re-gion in the (U, V) plane of the brighter dM stars selected spectroscopically at McCormick Ob-servatory. The symbol, s, denotes a spectroscopic subdwarf.

5 per cent for the fraction of dM stars which are sdM is still taken as correct, there are 0.004 sdM stars in the solar neighborhood per pc^3.

5.2. The Color-Magnitude Diagram

The spectrum of TiO is the main classification criterion for dM stars. If Ti and O both have lower than normal abundances, say, by a factor of 10, the molecule will be one hundred times less abundant; the opacity is reduced only by a factor of 10 (if the hydrogen ion is still the opacity source). Thus, we may expect TiO band weakening to be greater than that of neutral metallic lines, in metal-poor stars. If the TiO bands affected the color of the star in the same way as metallic lines, we would find sdM stars bluer than dM stars at the same tem-perature. But the TiO band absorption is largest in the yellow-green, in the V and B filter regions, and only bands of high excitation occur below λ 4500. Thus, even the sign of the blanketing correction is not certain in $B - V$. It is interesting to note that a number of the red companions of the high-velocity, large proper-motion white dwarfs have quite red $B - V$ colors. This could be interpreted to mean that if the TiO bands are weakened, the star apparently becomes redder, i.e., that the blanketing is greater in V than in B.

An HR diagram where M_V is shown either as a function of $B - V$ color or of TiO band strength could be sensitive to metal composition. The M_V are measured with unusual accuracy in dM stars because of their large parallaxes. But, unfortunately, no detailed information is yet available concerning the reliability of the abscissae, i.e., the various color coordinates. Joy (1947) gave an HR diagram with M_V as ordinate and spectral type as abscissa; he classified 12 stars as sdK5 and sdM. They lie an average of 1.8 mag below the normal main sequence. On the other hand, some of his stars are clearly misclassified; one, 20 C 212, has extremely weak lines, is called sdM0, and apparently lies 5 mag below the main sequence. Another low-velocity star, ADS 246B, is called a subdwarf although its primary is a normal dM2.5.

The slope of the diagram showing the $M_V, B - V$ relation is very steep for the McCormick dwarf M stars. There are about 25 stars with parallaxes greater than $0\overset{''}{.}1$; they range in M_V from $+9$ to $+13$, but their $B - V$ range is only $0\overset{m}{.}3$, that is, the change in M_V is 13 times that in $B - V$. The HR diagram therefore shows largely observational error, and gives no clues as to population types.

An alternative approach is to use infrared color indices, as done by Kron (1956). He gives an interesting HR diagram for stars of large parallax ($>0\overset{''}{.}110$) with ($M_R, R - I$ color) coordinates. The infrared indices are also affected in an unknown way by TiO blanketing, since the TiO band system extends far into the infrared.

The spectroscopic separation of normal and subdwarf M stars is difficult, and the classifications available must be viewed as uncertain. Consequently, we must rely more heavily on velocity characteristics than on low-dispersion spectroscopy in defining a sdM. In Kron's HR diagram the isolation of the subdwarfs remains uncertain, but the high accuracy of the colors, which has not been surpassed, and the intrinsic accuracy of M_R and space motions make a reanalysis worthwhile. I reviewed the observational data, eliminating all astrometric or unresolved doubles, all suspected spectroscopic binaries, and all flare variables, reducing Kron's list from 100 stars to 62. Figure 10 shows this improved HR diagram. The solid line is a rough main sequence drawn through the normal, low-velocity dM stars. Stars classified spectroscopically as sdM, and stars whose U or V component exceeds 70 km/sec are indicated by the symbols, s (spectroscopic subdwarf), open circle (high velocity), or open triangle (marginally high velocity). The mean ΔM_R of the 22 probable members of the halo population is $+0.4$ mag, and for 16 definite sd and high-velocity stars $\langle \Delta M_R \rangle = +0.6$ mag. Since the slope of the $M_R, R - I$ sequence is about 6, this estimate is equivalent to 0.1 mag difference in $R - I$ color, with the subdwarfs being bluer. It is improbable that differences of line blanketing in the red contribute as much to color differences at a given temperature in the dM stars as do changes in TiO bands. If, as seems possible, TiO is weaker in high-velocity than in normal stars, the positive value of ΔM_R requires that TiO bands have less effect on the brightness in the I than the R region, a plausible but unproved hypothesis. The effect required is small enough to make it possible that true subdwarfs do not exist and that band (and line) blanketing differences explain the statistical faintness of the subdwarfs. But whether large

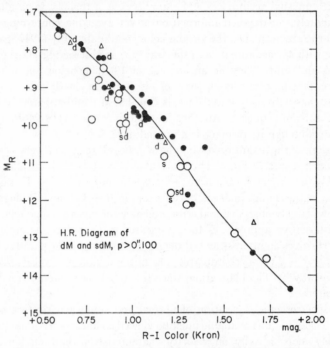

Fig. 10.—Absolute red magnitudes, M_R, and $R - I$ colors from Kron. The large open circles indicate high-velocity stars, the open triangles marginally high-velocity stars, the closed circles normal stars. Wide visual binaries are labeled d. Stars classified spectroscopically as sdM stars are labeled s. Close binaries and light and velocity variables are omitted.

deviations from the main sequence, such as are found for Kapteyn's star ($\Delta M_R = +1.6$) and Barnard's star ($\Delta M_R = +1.2$), can be explained as blanketing effects caused by very low metal abundance is not yet known. Such individual objects deserve special attention by spectroscopists.

The frequency of high-velocity objects is very high in this sample, chosen for large proper motion; 30 per cent of the stars remaining in the sample are spectroscopically subdwarfs or have marginally high velocities. Twenty per cent have definitely high velocities. Part of this high frequency arises from the elimination of flare variables (dMe stars of the young population) and of close and spectroscopic binaries (also more common in the young population).

REFERENCES

ALLER, L. H., and
GREENSTEIN, J. L.   1960   *Ap. J., Suppl.* **5**, 139.
ARP, H. C.   1955   *A. J.*.**60**, 317.
BASCHEK, B.   1959   *Zs. f. Ap.*, **48**, 95.
BERGER, J.   1963   *Pub. A.S.P.*, **75**, 393.
CHAVIRA, E.   1958   *Bull. Obs. Tonantzintla y Tacubaya*, No. 17, p. 15
DEEMING, T. J.   1962   *M.N.*, **123**, 273.
DYER, E. R.   1954   *A.J.*, **59**, 218, 221.
                       1956   *Ibid.*, **61**, 228.
EGGEN, O. J.   1962   *Roy. Obs. Bull.*, No. 51.
                       1964   *Ibid.*, No. 84.

EGGEN, O. J., and
GREENSTEIN, J. L.   1965   *Ap.J.*, **141**, 83.
EGGEN, O. J., LYNDEN-
BELL, D., and
SANDAGE, A. R.   1962   *Ap. J.*, **136**, 748.
EGGEN, O. J., and
SANDAGE, A. R.   1959   *M.N.*, **119**, 255.
                       1962   *Ap. J.*, **136**, 735.
FEIGE, J.   1958   *Ap. J.*, **128**, 267.
GICLAS, H. L.,
BURNHAM, R., and
THOMAS, N. G.   1961   *Lowell Obs. Bull.*, **5**, 61.
GICLAS, H. L.,
SLAUGHTER, C. D., and
BURNHAM, R.   1959   *Lowell Obs. Bull.*, **4**, 136.
GREENSTEIN, J. L.   1956   *Proc. 3d Berkeley Symp. Math. Stat. Prob.* (Berkeley: University of California Press), **3**, 11.
                       1958   *Hdb. d. Phys.*, ed. S. Flügge (Berlin: Springer-Verlag), **50**, 161.
                       1960   *Stellar Atmospheres*, ed. J. L. Greenstein (Chicago: University of Chicago Press), chap. 19.
                       1965   Unpublished.
HARRIS, D. L.   1956   *Ap. J.*, **124**, 665.
HUMASON, M. L., and
ZWICKY, F.   1947   *Ap. J.*, **105**, 85.
IRIARTE, B., and
CHAVIRA, E.   1957   *Bull. Obs. Tonantzintla y Tacubaya*, No. 16, p. 3.
IWANOWSKA, W., and
OPASKA-BURNICKA, A.   1962   *Bull. Acad. Polonaise, Ser. Math. Astr. Phys.*, **10**, 547.
JOY, A. H.   1947   *Ap. J.*, **105**, 96.
KLEMOLA, A. R.   1962   *A.J.*, **67**, 740.
KRON, G. E.   1956   *Proc. 3d Berkeley Symp. Math. Stat. Prob.* (Berkeley: University of California Press), **3**, 39.

KUKARKIN, B. W.   1954   *Erforschung der Struktur und Entwicklung der Sternsysteme* (Berlin: Akademie-Verlag).

LUYTEN, W. J.   1949   *Ap. J.*, **109**, 528.

     1952   *Proc. Amer. Acad. Arts Sci.*, **81**, 255.

     1953–   *A Search for Faint Blue Stars*, I–XXXV (pub-
     1963   lished as separate pamphlets by the University of Minnesota).

     1958   *On the Frequency of White Dwarfs in Space* (following *A Search for Faint Blue Stars*, XVI).

     1961   *Pub. Obs. Univ. Minnesota*, **3**, No. 9.

     1963   *Ibid.*, **2**, No. 17.

MUMFORD, G. S.   1956a   *A.J.*, **61**, 213.

     1956b   *Ibid.*, p. 224.

O'DELL, C. R.   1962   *Ap. J.*, **135**, 371.

OGORODNIKOV, K. F.   1948   *Advances in Astronomical Science*, **4**, 3.

PARENAGO, P. P.   1946   *A.J. U.S.S.R.*, **23**, 31.

     1948a   *Ibid.*, **25**, 123.

     1948b   *Advances in Astronomical Science*, **4**, 69.

POPPER, D. M.   1942   *Ap. J.*, **95**, 307.

     1943   *Ibid.*, **98**, 209.

ROMAN, N. G.   1954   *A.J.*, **59**, 307.

SANDAGE, A. R., and
EGGEN, O. J.   1959   *M.N.*, **119**, 278.

SLETTEBAK, A., BAHNER,
K., and STOCK, J.   1961   *Ap. J.*, **134**, 195.

VORONTSOV-VELYAMINOV,
B. A.   1953   *Gasnebel und Neue Sterne* (Berlin: Verlag Kultur u. Fortschritt), p. 604, and elsewhere.

VYSSOTSKY, A. N.   1956   *A. J.*, **61**, 201.

     1957   *Pub. A.S.P.*, **69**, 109.

WALLERSTEIN, G.   1962   *Ap. J. Suppl.*, **6**, 407.

WEIDEMANN, V.   1963   *Zs. f. Ap.*, **57**, 87.

WILDEY, R. L.,
BURBIDGE, E. M.,
SANDAGE, A. R., and
BURBIDGE, G. R.   1962   *Ap. J.*, **135**, 94.

WILSON, R. E.   1953   *General Catalogue of Stellar Radial Velocities* (Washington: Carnegie Institution of Washington), Pub. 601.

WOOLLEY, R. V. D. R.   1958   *M.N.*, **118**, 45.

CHAPTER 18

Blue Stars at High Galactic Latitudes

W. J. LUYTEN
University of Minnesota

§ 1. HISTORICAL

THE pioneer work in the search for faint blue stars at high galactic latitudes was done by Humason and Zwicky (1947). Their original aim was to find more white dwarfs by looking for faint blue stars in (*a*) obscured regions, such as the Hyades, or (*b*) in high galactic latitude where distant blue stars were presumed to be absent. Their first publication contained data for forty-eight stars: a large proportion of the fifteen stars listed in the Hyades region did, indeed, prove to be white dwarfs but of the thirty-three stars found near the north galactic pole only one is a classical white dwarf and most of the others are the first representatives of the class of coronal blue stars.

§ 2. METHODS OF SEARCH

Since that time similar searches have been made, mainly by the present author at Minnesota and by Haro and his staff at Tonantzintla. Two different techniques have been used for the detection of these stars. Zwicky, Humason, and the present author blinked pairs of plates taken in different colors—generally blue and red—and the stars in question are found by the same technique as that used for variable stars. If exposures are adjusted such that stars of spectral class G have images of equal intensity on both plates, most stars will, in blinking, show little change in brightness or strength of image. The very red stars brighten considerably on the red plates but the blue stars which, in general, are much less numerous than the red stars, and generally amount to less than one per cent of the total number, will appear fainter on the red plates and thus are fairly easily detected.

The advantages of this method are (*a*) that the plates can be exposed until the limiting magnitude of the telescope is reached, and (*b*) that because the colors are judged differentially, the adjustment of the exposures is not too critical. Some of the disadvantages are that, especially with the small images of

393

Schmidt plates, high magnification is needed before the contraction-expansion of the blue-star images stands out sufficiently, and high magnification means small fields, and hence more time to be spent in blinking. To blink a pair of 48-inch Schmidt Palomar plates carefully takes the author at least fifteen hours, and even then a large number of blue stars are usually overlooked. Blinking in this manner appears to be a very subjective operation and the observer's alertness varies between wide limits: one blinking will usually net less than half or even one-third of the total number of blue stars present.

Haro (1956) at Tonantzintla has developed an entirely different technique and uses three exposures on the same plate through an ultraviolet, a yellow, and a blue filter, respectively. The exposures are made on 103aD plates and adjusted in length such that all three images are equal for a normal, unreddened A0 star. The great advantage of this method is that the blue stars—which show a faint central image flanked by two brighter ones, whereas the vast majority of stars show a bright central image flanked by two fainter ones—stand out and are easily recognized. This greatly reduces the time needed for careful examination of the plate as against the blinking method, and at the same time greatly increases the completeness in the number of stars found. However, small differences in effective exposure, in plate sensitivity to different colors, differential reciprocity failure, especially near the plate limit, render this method very sensitive to all sorts of observational imperfections. There is something to be said for both methods, Haro's method being mainly faster and more complete, and better for the brighter stars, but the blink method must be resorted to in order to get down to the faintest stars observable.

Rapid variables, especially red flare stars, may be mistaken for blue stars in blinking, but they are generally immediately recognized in the three-image method because of the abnormal relationship in the strength of the three exposures. However, there would seem to be no real objection to detecting these stars as they are interesting enough in themselves. Unrecognized blue galaxies may also be included but this is merely a calculated risk. In theory, searches for faint blue stars could also be made spectroscopically, with objective prisms, but it is evident that these are somewhat less efficient as they cannot reach the same limiting magnitude and there is more danger of overlapping.

§ 3. SURVEYS

Humason and Zwicky (1947) made their original survey in the region of the Hyades and the north galactic pole, and listed 48 blue stars. The present author's surveys (Luyten 1953, 1954, 1955, 1956, and separate pamphlets published by the University of Minnesota under the title *A Search for Faint Blue Stars*, see references) in which a total of 6300 faint blue stars have been published, were made in the region of the Hyades, Pleiades, Praesepe, M67, and other galactic clusters; the north and south galactic poles, the Ursa Major region (with Miller), in some of the Kapteyn Selected Areas (with Carpenter), and in some regions spaced out in different galactic latitudes (with Seyfert); in a large region in the far southern hemisphere, near the Magellanic Clouds (with Anderson), and in several heavily obscured regions such as rho Ophiuchi, Taurus, the North America region, etc.

At Tonantzintla, Iriarte and Chavira (1957) and Chavira (1958, 1959) have made extensive searches in the north and south galactic polar caps, and have published a total of about 2200 stars. Haro and Luyten (1962) have examined about 2000 square degrees near the south galactic pole on Palomar Schmidt plates taken with Haro's three-image method, and have found 8700 faint blue stars. Feige (1958) has searched some Palomar Schmidt survey plates and has published a list of 112 blue stars found on them.

In regions blinked by the author (unpublished) on Palomar Schmidt plates near the galactic poles and in the Praesepe and delta Lyrae regions about 125 blue stars brighter than $m = 21$ were found per square degree—and this number is certainly incomplete. Zwicky's (unpublished) recent work with the 200-inch telescope indicates that these same blue stars continue to be present in large numbers down to $m = 23$. From preliminary discussions the author (1958a) found indications that the numbers of faint blue stars increased nearly fourfold per magnitude, at least until $m = 17$, thus suggesting constant space density. In the Haro-Luyten (1962) south galactic pole survey which goes to at least $m = 18.5$ and in Luyten's (1962a) galactic pole searches down to $m = 21$ this is probably no longer true. There is, however, no doubt but that the increase in numbers with apparent magnitude is much nearer the constant-density factor of four for these faint blue stars than for stars in general. Judging from these high-latitude regions the total number of faint blue stars brighter than $m = 21$ in the entire sky should be well over a million.

There are some indications that even in regions where obscuration is believed to be very small or absent there are considerable variations in the frequencies of these blue stars. Around the region of 15^h and $+30°$ there appears to be an excess of them. Whether this can be due to observational selection or errors of some kind, it is too early to say. The author has searched for a possible filamentary connection containing these stars, stretching between our Galaxy and the Magellanic Clouds, a sort of umbilical cord, but has found no definite evidence either for or against it. Similarly, Haro and Luyten have not found any certain evidence for the same feature possibly connecting the Galaxy with M31 or M33.

§ 4. COLORS

The author, when blinking for blue stars, attempted to estimate the $B - V$ of the stars found by the differential method which, while subject to fairly large errors, at least has a quantitative basis. Generally the bluest stars found received a color estimate of -0.6, corresponding approximately to a $B - V$ of -0.3 while it was attempted to include no stars redder than $B - V = +0.1$. When using Tonantzintla three-image plates the author estimated the difference between the blue and yellow, and between the ultraviolet and blue images and found that his former value corresponded fairly well to the usual $B - V$ whereas the latter amounted to about fifty to sixty per cent of the usual $U - B$. Iriarte and Chavira (1957), in using Haro's three-image method classified their stars into three groups, violet, decidedly violet, and extremely violet, again ranging from about $+0.1$ to -0.3 in $B - V$. Accurate photoelectric colors have thus far been published for only a small number of these stars, mainly by Iriarte (1959) who found evidence of some four or five different physical groups among these stars, each with a different relationship between $B - V$ and $U - B$. The stars with negative values of $B - V$ show a large range of $U - B$; relative to the main-sequence relation they show an ultraviolet excess up to 1^m or an ultraviolet deficiency as large as $\frac{1}{2}^m$ or more. Stars with positive values of $B - V$ show ultraviolet excesses ranging up to about 1^m, a combination often occurring among white dwarfs. The converse is not necessarily true and in general it appears that it is not yet possible to predict luminosities or other physical characteristics of these stars from their photoelectric colors alone.

§ 5. SPECTRA AND RADIAL VELOCITIES

Humason and Zwicky (1947) obtained spectra for all their original forty-eight stars. Among the stars at high galactic latitude one definitely appeared similar to a normal white dwarf, some showed characteristics of low luminosity while others might be main-sequence stars. Greenstein (this series, Vol. VI) has continued this work and found that most of the stars observed revealed subluminous characteristics. The present author would not go as far as Greenstein has gone in calling many of these stars white dwarfs, and would, for the time being, restrict the term white dwarf to stars lying at least eight magnitudes below the main sequence, and with luminosities smaller than that corresponding to $M = +9$. We may hope that after sufficient observations of all kinds have been obtained for these stars the picture will clarify and we shall be able to define our terms more rigorously. Meanwhile, it does not yet appear possible to determine the luminosities and other physical characteristics of these blue stars from their spectra alone.

The radial velocities of these blue stars are dealt with in detail by Greenstein in chapter 17. All that need be said here is that while most of them are of the order of 20 or 30 km/sec, very large velocities are not too uncommon.

§ 6. PROPER MOTIONS

The author (1953) has determined proper motions for all but two of the Zwicky-Humason stars in the Hyades and, with Miller (1951), for all 33 Z-H stars near the north galactic pole. Pels and Perek (1951) have determined motions for a few of the brighter specimens of the latter group, and Pels and Blaauw (1953) similarly for many more. Plates of varying scale were used by Pels and Blaauw, and these were reduced by optical means to the same scale. Since it is well known that strange errors may be introduced by this method these last-mentioned motions may well be subject to systematic errors. The present author has further measured motions for 34 stars in Selected Areas (Luyten 1955), for 100 of the stars found by Feige (Luyten 1959), for 300 such stars near the Hyades and the two galactic poles, and some 100 faint blue stars in the far southern hemisphere (Luyten 1960a, 1962b). Altogether, therefore, fairly accurate motions are now known for more than 600 faint blue stars, mainly brighter than $m = 17$. Among the stars found in the Hyades and other obscured regions a substantial proportion appear to be white dwarfs. Among the remaining stars —the bulk of those for which motions are now known—no more than twenty have motions large enough to suggest they are genuine white dwarfs. Because of their unequal distribution over the sky—searches having been made principally near the galactic poles—it is not yet possible to determine accurately the solar motion for these stars. All that can safely be said now is that their motions seem to be consistent with a solar apex near 19 hours and $+38°$ (Luyten and Anderson 1962). Further, assuming a solar velocity of around 35 km/sec, one is led to the estimate that the luminosities of these stars probably lie between $+4$ and -2, although at present it is not yet possible to say whether the luminosities are distributed continuously or come in discrete and separate groups. Nor does it seem possible to determine now what the relative frequencies are of the several values for the luminosity. It does seem clearly indicated that among the brighter specimens we find main-sequence supergiants while among the fainter ones—down to $m = 17$ or 18—SS Cygni variables with M down to $+9$ may be quite prevalent.

§ 7. FREQUENCY IN SPACE

Except for white dwarfs, blue stars similar in appearance to these coronal blue stars appear to be rare in the neighborhood of the sun. The present author (1957) has given a list of 12 such objects which includes CoD $-42°16457$, possibly the first object of this kind to be discovered (Luyten 1923). The star was rediscovered by Jackson (1938). Blue stars of intermediate luminosities appear to constitute no more than 0.1 per cent of all stars in the solar neighborhood. In high galactic latitude—e.g., on the two Palomar survey pairs of plates covering the north, and south galactic polar regions—these same stars appear to constitute at least one per cent of all stars down to $m = 21$. Making due allowance for a substantial fraction of these being white dwarfs of lower luminosity than other stars of the same apparent magnitude, it seems that most of these blue stars are more luminous, and hence more distant than the bulk of stars of the same apparent magnitude. Yet it is virtually certain that these blue stars are not the only objects occupying the outer galactic corona—even though they seem to be almost the only objects we can identify there with certainty. Hence it seems difficult to escape the conclusion that the star density at great distances from the galactic plane may well be substantially greater than has been assumed heretofore. This conclusion is further strengthened by the results from recent star counts made by the author (1960b) near the south galactic pole which indicate that for stars fainter than $m = 15$ the percentages of stars of color classes f and g are actually increasing rapidly down to $m = 19$.

It is beginning to be evident that, while existing over-all star counts may not be changed very much, their interpretation may well undergo radical changes which will also involve our ideas on the star density at great distances from the galactic plane. Even more than this is involved: if indeed faint coronal blue stars continue to exist in large numbers down to $m = 23$, which in turn implies, as suggested by Haro and the author (1960), that the galactic corona extends as far as the Magellanic Clouds and perhaps even far enough to meet a similar extension of the Andromeda galaxy, then the problem of how these blue stars got there poses itself. There does not now appear to be sufficient gas or other matter in intergalactic space which could have served as a matrix for the formation of these stars. On the other hand, a star of $m = 23$, $M = +3$ would, if formed in and ejected from the disk with a near-parabolic velocity, have needed of the order of a billion years to get out that far. Obviously, theories on stellar ages and evolution will soon become involved in this problem.

§ 8. POSSIBLE USES

The faint blue stars may yet serve another purpose. A coronal object with $m = 20$, $M = +3$ and $r = 2.5 \times 10^4$ parsecs could be expected to have an annual proper motion relative to the sun of the order of $0\overset{''}{.}001$ with a dispersion of the same order. Blue stars of $m = 20$ occur in high galactic latitude with a frequency of some 30 to 50 per square degree. Hence, they rather than faint galaxies, may well become useful as anchors for the determination of proper motions, especially since their images are stellar and hence no systematic errors are introduced into the measures. Moreover, their great frequency will make it possible to restrict measures to small areas of the sky whereas with faint galaxies of the right type (ellipticals with color index of around $+1.0$) one can expect to have to measure large areas at once in order to obtain enough galaxies as comparison objects to eliminate the systematic errors of measurement.

Whether or not this suggestion will prove workable will depend on our ability to recognize the different groups of luminosities from, say, their colors or spectra.

§ 9. SUGGESTIONS FOR FUTURE WORK

It does not yet appear possible that the various luminosity types existing among these faint blue stars can be recognized from either accurate three-color photometry or spectroscopic classification, or both. The author would urge a concerted attack on this problem with all means available: colors, spectra, radial velocities, and especially proper motions are needed for as many and as faint stars as possible. Concomitant with this, all large obscured areas in low galactic latitude should be carefully searched for faint blue stars in the hope of settling the vexing question of the frequency of white dwarfs in space and even of the relative frequencies of degenerate stars of different luminosities and colors. Theoreticians are often affirming that white dwarfs amount to five or even ten per cent of the stars in space but there is at present no observational evidence to place this fraction higher than two per cent (Luyten 1958b). Here again, this discrepancy may well be due to a difference in the definition of what is a white dwarf. Degenerate stars less luminous than $M = +15$ are extremely difficult to find, and while they are now presumed to be the oldest, their presumed frequent occurrence can be derived from theory alone, as yet.

Finally, large numbers of small sample areas all over the sky and down to the lowest galactic latitudes workable, should be searched for these blue stars, down to the faintest magnitudes, in order to obtain reliable data on the uniformity, or non-uniformity, of their distribution and on the possible existence of umbilical cords stretching to neighboring galaxies.

REFERENCES

CHAVIRA, E.	1958	*Bull. Obs. Tonantzintla y Tacubaya*, No. 17.
	1959	*Ibid.*, No. 18.
FEIGE, J.	1958	*Ap. J.*, **128**, 267.
HARO, G.	1956	*Mitt. A. G. 1955*, 60.
HARO, G., and		
LUYTEN, W. J.	1960	*A.J.*, **65**, 490.
	1962	*Bull. Obs. Tonantzintla y Tacubaya*, No. 22.
HUMASON, M. L., and		
ZWICKY, F.	1947	*Ap. J.*, **105**, 85.
IRIARTE, B.	1959	*Lowell Obs. Bull.*, **4**, 136.
IRIARTE, B., and		
CHAVIRA, E.	1957	*Bull. Obs. Tonantzintla y Tacubaya*, No. 16.
JACKSON, J.	1938	*M.N.*, **98**, 491 (cf. p. 506).
LUYTEN, W. J.	1923	*Pub. A.S.P.*, **35**, 68.
	1953	*A Search for Faint Blue Stars*, I; *A.J.*, **58**, 75.
	1954	*Ibid.*, II; *A.J.*, **59**, 224.
	1955	*Ibid.*, III; *A.J.*, **60**, 429.
	1956	*Ibid.*, IV; *A.J.*, **61**, 261. (From No. VII on, *A Search for Faint Blue Stars* was published as separate pamphlets by the University of Minnesota.)
	1957	*Ibid.*, IX.
	1958a	*Ibid.*, XV.
	1958b	*On the Frequency of White Dwarfs in Space* (following *A Search for Faint Blue Stars*, XVI).
	1959	*A Search for Faint Blue Stars*, XVII.
	1960a	*Ibid.*, XXI.
	1960b	*Ibid.*, XXII.
	1962a	*Ibid.*, XXVI and XXVII.
	1962b	*Ibid.*, XXIX.

LUYTEN, W. J., and
    ANDERSON, J. H.   1962   *A Search for Faint Blue Stars*, XXX.
LUYTEN, W. J., and
    MILLER, F. D.   1956   *A Search for Faint Blue Stars*, V; *A.J.*, **61**, 262.
LUYTEN, W. J., and
    MILLER, W. C.   1951   *Ap. J.*, **114**, 488.
LUYTEN, W. J., and
    SEYFERT, C. K.   1956   *A Search for Faint Blue Stars*, VI; *A.J.*, **61**, 264.
PELS, G., and BLAAUW, A.   1953   *B.A.N.*, **12**, 7.
PELS, G., and PEREK, L.   1951   *B.A.N.*, **11**, 281.

CHAPTER 19

Globular Clusters in the Galaxy

HALTON C. ARP

Mount Wilson and Palomar Observatories
Carnegie Institution of Washington, California Institute of Technology

§ 1. INTRODUCTION

In this chapter globular clusters will be treated primarily as indicators of galactic structure. We will derive and summarize the best available description of the system of globular clusters as it pertains to the over-all picture of our Galaxy. Before discussing extensively the structure of this system, however, it is helpful to consider briefly the nature of globular clusters and their importance historically.

There is no rigorous definition of a globular cluster. Astronomers have conventionally used this term to refer to the very rich, roughly spherical aggregates of up to millions of stars, found in the central and halo regions of a galaxy. Globular clusters were originally designated solely by their geometrical appearance. When the nearby ones were investigated, however, it turned out that they contained very distinctive kinds of stars (Shapley 1917; Greenstein 1939; Hachenberg 1939; Arp, Baum, and Sandage 1953). The brightest stars were red, two or three magnitudes fainter than this the RR Lyrae cepheids were usually encountered, and finally there were overwhelming numbers of fainter, redder stars. In 1944, Baade designated globular cluster stars as the prototype of population II. Population II became very important in the problem of distance scales, stellar evolution, and galactic structure. As a consequence, globular clusters became very well known for the kind of stars they contained rather than their geometrical appearance.

Color-magnitude diagrams of seven of the nearest globular clusters proved remarkably similar (Arp 1955). It was felt, therefore, that the most significant aspects of these clusters were the physical properties of their stars and the fact that they contained essentially the same kinds of stars. The term "globular cluster" came to imply more about the color-magnitude diagram of particular kinds of stars than about the geometrical structure of the cluster.

Difficulty with this connotation was first encountered in the Small Magellanic Cloud. There it was recognized that some of the rich spherical clusters could not contain the expected kinds of stars because their integrated color index was too blue (Gascoigne 1954). Other less severe problems had been previously encountered in our own Galaxy. Galactic clusters were classically distinguished from globular clusters by the small number of stars they contained and by their occurrence in low galactic latitude. But it was difficult to assign certain radially symmetric clusters of low concentration like M67 to a specific category. Another star cluster, NGC 2158, in the plane of the Galaxy but far out toward the rim, was found to be not only a transition in geometrical form and richness but also in age and metal content between the kind of stars usually found in galactic and those in globular clusters. It has also been shown (Morgan 1959) that the still fairly rich and spherical star clusters at low latitude toward the center of the Galaxy contain stars richer in metals than the nearby globular clusters. These examples demonstrated the danger in attempting to cover too many cluster characteristics with one term. Star clusters should be classified by all the following parameters:

Geometrical

1) Shape (spherical, elongated, etc.)
2) Density gradient of stars
3) Numerical richness of stars

Physical

4) Chemical composition of stars
5) Age of stars
6) Luminosity function.

It would be difficult, however, to return—against usage—the term globular cluster to its original, even though loose, geometrical definition. In this chapter the term will be used as astronomers have conventionally done, to describe slightly more than one hundred roughly spherical star clusters that have integrated color indices between $B - V = 0.6$ and 0.8 mag, and intrinsic magnitudes between $M_B = -4$ and -10 mag. They are distributed about the center of the Galaxy. Prototypes of globular clusters are objects such as M3, M5, M13, ω Cen, M92, M15, and M2. Such clusters contain stars which are very old, perhaps about 10 billion years (Woolf 1962; Arp 1962b), and metal poor by factors of from 200 to 17 relative to the sun (Arp 1961).

The importance of the globular clusters lies in the fact that they are very bright and can be seen at great distances. Historically, globular clusters furnished the first clue to the scale of the Galaxy (Shapley 1930). Today, because we have nearly complete discovery of all globular clusters, we are able to investigate the structure of the Galaxy completely from the standpoint of this one class of objects. Recently it has also become possible to study the change of stellar content of these clusters as a function of the position of the cluster in the

Galaxy. Therefore, it is now not only possible to investigate the distribution and dimensions of mass aggregates in the Galaxy, but it becomes possible to also study the change in the kind or quality of the material throughout the Galaxy.

In the course of this chapter we will first study the completeness of the sample of globular clusters known in the Galaxy. Then we will discuss what is known about the integrated properties of individual clusters, luminosity, mass, etc. Next we will review what these properties lead to in the way of distribution within the Galaxy and our distance from the center of the Galaxy. Finally, we consider briefly the kinematics and dynamics of the globular cluster system.

§ 2. THE COMPLETENESS OF THE KNOWN SAMPLE

2.1. COMPLETENESS AT HIGH LATITUDES

The total number of globular clusters presently known in or near the Galaxy is 119 (Hogg 1959).[1] Of these, 102 have NGC designations. Since there are 7840 non-stellar objects listed in the NGC catalogue, it is apparent that only a small percentage of nebulous objects in the sky are globular clusters. Of 5386 predominantly fainter objects listed in the Index catalogues, only two have been identified as globular clusters. This suggests that most of the globular clusters that belong to our Galaxy have been discovered. (Most of them were, in fact, known in John Herschel's time, 1864, so that Bailey was led to suggest, in 1915, that the limits of our system of globular clusters had been reached.)

This point can only be discussed more rigorously if the completeness of the NGC catalogue (Dreyer 1888) is known. Holmberg (1958) shows that the Shapley-Ames (1932) catalogue is complete to $m_{pg} = 11.9$ mag. Hubble (1936) points out that the Shapley-Ames catalogue contains 1188 NGC objects, 48 IC objects, and 13 new nebulae, an indication, therefore, that the NGC catalogue is more than 95 per cent complete down to $m_{pg} = 11.9$ mag. The NGC and IC catalogues together are more than 99 per cent complete to this magnitude limit.

Figure 1 shows the distribution of globular clusters that have measured integrated magnitudes and for which the galactic latitude $|b^{II}| \geq 8°$. (Seventy-six of the 119 listed globular clusters are in this category.) By $m_{pg} = 12$ mag, the numbers of known globular clusters are falling sharply, which means that most globular clusters occur in the magnitude range where catalogues are complete,

---

[1] I have dropped NGC 2158 from Mrs. Hogg's list, because although Arp and Cuffey (1962) have shown this to be a transitional cluster in many aspects, it is nevertheless similar in stellar content to NGC 7789 and NGC 752, which have been traditionally classified as galactic clusters. I have also dropped the so-called "Russian cluster" because under high resolution it proves to be a cluster of galaxies. I have added a faint, sparse globular cluster at $19^h 30^m$ and $-30°$, a plate of which was found in Baade's files, and a globular cluster at low latitude, NGC 6749, pictured in Setteducati and Weaver (1962), as well as a faint, distant cluster discovered by Arp and van den Bergh (1960). The last is very similar to the Palomar globular clusters and was, in fact, first noticed on the Sky Survey plates.

and that we therefore have nearly complete knowledge of all globular clusters in this latitude range. An extrapolation below $m_{pg} = 12$ mag in Figure 1 would predict very roughly six additional faint globular clusters.

This point can be checked to some extent because much fainter globular clusters were searched for on the 48-inch Schmidt, *National Geographic Society—Palomar Sky Atlas* (Abell 1955), with the result that eleven new ones were discovered. A twelfth was added by Arp and van den Bergh (1960). Ten of these twelve new, faint globular clusters were higher than galactic latitude 8°. These clusters had integrated apparent magnitudes about $m_{pg} = 15$ mag. (For the only two measured, Burbidge and Sandage [1958] give $V = 14.4$ mag for

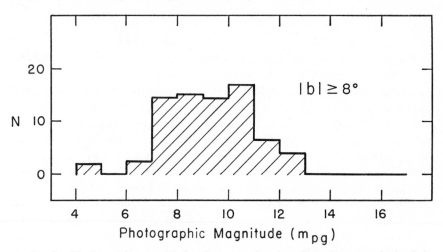

Fig. 1.—Number of known globular clusters as function of apparent magnitude. Only globular clusters at galactic latitude $b^{II} = 8°$ or higher are plotted. Magnitudes from Hogg (1959).

Palomar No. 4 and $V = 14.7$ mag for Palomar No. 3, which yields $m_{pg} = 15.0$ and 15.3 mag, respectively.) More important, however, is the fact that only two, Palomar Nos. 2 and 8, had concentration classes more condensed than XI or XII. Therefore, this newly discovered group escaped detection in the NGC and IC catalogues more because of their lack of concentrated differentiation from the field stars than from the faintness of the integrated light of the cluster. For the definition of the concentration classes I (most compact clusters) to XII (loosest clusters) see Shapley (1930; chap. 2).

It is clear that to $m_{pg} = 12$ mag and excluding very low latitudes, we have catalogued 99 per cent of the detectable clusters in the sky. To the fainter limiting magnitude of $m_{pg} = 15$ mag we have catalogued more than 98 per cent of the globular clusters of concentration class X or tighter. (It is estimated that less than two globular clusters remain to be discovered in the 13 to 15 mag range of concentration class tighter than X.) To estimate how large a fraction of the total number of globular clusters this represents, we must estimate how many globular clusters have escaped detection by heavy obscuration in the plane of the Galaxy.

2.2. Completeness at Low Latitudes

The globular clusters are distributed roughly spherically around the center of our Galaxy, increasing in space density toward the center. Therefore, as we

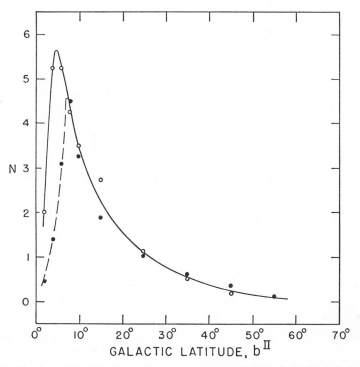

Fig. 2.—Number of globular clusters known at each galactic latitude b. Filled circles represent clusters with bright integrated magnitudes (7 mag $\leq m_{\mathrm{pg}} \leq$ 10 mag). Open circles represent faint clusters (10 mag $\leq m_{\mathrm{pg}} \leq$ 13 mag). A factor of 1.6, which is the ratio of the numbers above 8° latitude in each group, has been applied to the faint group.

look toward the center where the overwhelming predominance of the clusters are projected, and look to lower and lower galactic latitudes, we expect the counted numbers of globular clusters to increase because we are looking through a greater volume of the sphere, and are also looking through a richer volume of space.

Figure 2 shows that the counted numbers do increase to lower galactic latitudes. The filled circles represent bright globular clusters (integrated m_{pg} between 7 and 10 mag). The open circles represent the fainter globular clusters (integrated m_{pg} between 10 and 13 mag). There are 44 clusters in the bright group and $27\frac{1}{2}$ in the faint group in Figure 1 (at latitudes above 8°). This gives a ratio of 1.6, which is exactly the scale factor which must be applied to the numbers in the faint group in Figure 2 to obtain the same increase with latitude for both groups. Figure 2 thus shows that for relatively unobscured latitudes bright and faint globular clusters have the same distribution.

The bright clusters suddenly fall off at about $b^{\mathrm{II}} = 8°$. It would be expected generally that this fall-off was due to increasing absorption with decreasing latitude. At $b^{\mathrm{II}} = 8°$ the cosecant absorption reaches $A_B = 1.7$ mag and begins

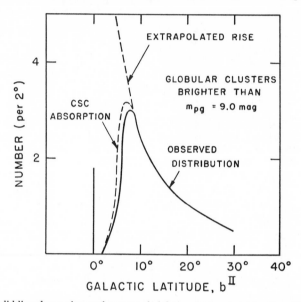

Fig. 3.—Solid line shows observed counts of globular clusters brighter than 9th magnitude as a function of galactic latitude. Upper dashed line shows extrapolated rise to lower latitudes; lower dashed line shows how csc absorption $A_B = 0.24 \csc b$ produces observed fall-off of corrected numbers.

to appreciably shift the bright clusters shown in Figure 1 into the faint range. At $b^{\mathrm{II}} = 5°$ the absorption has increased to $A_B = 2.76$ mag, almost all the bright clusters are gone and the counts drop rapidly to zero. This is shown in Figure 3 where the behavior of the clusters brighter than $m_{\mathrm{pg}} = 9.0$ mag is pictured.

If we use an absorption law of $A_B = 0.24 \csc b$ (see sec. 3.2) and assume the list of known globular clusters as complete to $m_{\mathrm{pg}} = 15$ mag, then we can correct the distribution of faint globular clusters in Figure 2 for the effects of low latitude absorption. This process is an inversion of that used in Figure 3. We find, however, that the abrupt fall-off of the *faint* globular clusters at about $b^{\mathrm{II}} = 4°$ remains essentially unchanged when corrected for csc law absorption. In order to obtain continually increasing numbers to the very lowest latitudes, we would either have to (1) assume our globular cluster list was only complete to $m_{pg} = 13$ instead of 15 mag, or (2) use a cosecant absorption law with twice as strong a coefficient. The first suggestion seems unlikely because we estimated, in the previous section, that more than 98 per cent of the globular clusters were known to $m_{pg} = 15$ mag. Some faint clusters were discovered at low latitudes in the Palomar Sky Survey, $b^{II} = +1°$ and $+3°$, so they can obviously be detected at very low latitudes. However, more of them were found at high latitudes, indicating that there was not a great number waiting to be discovered at very low latitudes. The second suggestion also seems unlikely because at latitudes below $b^{II} = 20°$ the absorption appears to vary *less*, not more steeply than the csc law (Hubble 1936; Holmberg 1958). It is clearly very difficult to know accurately what the law of absorption below $b^{II} = 4°$ actually is, but it should be pointed out that the number of globular clusters in the very center of the Galaxy might, in fact, actually level off or decline. Conditions may not have favored formation in the innermost 700 parsecs (700 parsecs at the center subtends 4°; of course, it is not clear how long such a hole would last in the presence of the globular cluster velocity field). A precedent is available in the distribution of novae in M31 (Arp 1956), where there were indications that after building up toward the center their numbers suddenly dropped off within 800 parsecs from the center. In addition, visual inspection of these inner M31 regions does not reveal many globular clusters.

Conditions at the very center of the Galaxy are both interesting and puzzling, but our task in this section is to estimate how many globular clusters are blocked from view by absorption at low latitudes. Fortunately it does not matter very sensitively how the density of globular clusters increases to the very center because the total volume involved is small. Correcting the Figure 2 counts by the $A_B = 0.24 \csc b$ law used in the present chapter, we find that a total of 5 clusters have been undetected at very low latitudes. If the counts did not drop toward the center but held at the value which they have at $b^{II} = 4°$, then 22 clusters would have been undiscovered. If the counts continued to increase at a roughly extrapolated rate, then about 34 clusters would have been missed. The doubled absorption law coefficient below 4° would have hidden about 70. Because the absorption cannot be infinite in the actual plane, and because it would take total absorption of the order of 10 mag to hide all effects of interior globular clusters, the standard absorption law $A = 0.24 \csc b$ is considered here as an upper limit, indicating that our catalogue of 119 globular clusters in Table 1 is 98 per cent complete above $b^{II} = 8°$ and, assuming 5 clusters hidden in low latitudes, that the over-all count in the catalogue is about 94 per cent complete for concentration classes less than XI.

We compute then that the total number of globular clusters in our Galaxy is about 126 (± 7 estimated error). As a check, we note in Table 1 that we have 34 globular clusters with known distances in the north galactic hemisphere ($+z$). If we plot their number as a function of R, their distance to the galactic nucleus, and allow for a 4° unobserved wedge toward the center, we can integrate the curve and find a predicted total of 127 for the whole Galaxy. This is better than expected agreement for a less accurate but reasonably independent computation from space densities. It is interesting to compare this number of 126 from our own system with the estimated number of globular clusters in M31, about 300–400 (Baade, private communication). The diameter of M31 is about 10 per cent larger than that of our Galaxy (Arp, unpublished), and the mass of M31 appears to be about two times larger. In comparing the total number of globular clusters in the two systems, the density gradient in the exact center is again, of course, a difficult point because M31 cannot be searched for globular clusters closer than about 400 parsecs from the center. Comparison of the cluster systems must thus be made outside this central "core."

Schmidt (1956) computed, as a by-product of a density investigation, the total number of concentration class I–VIII clusters in the Galaxy to be 160. That would correspond to about 270 clusters of all concentration classes and be about twice as large as our estimated total. Schmidt, however, used distances given by Lohmann (1952). Examination of the 54 clusters used reveals that the distances were about one-half, on the average, of our estimates of the distances (see Table 1). These distances were systematically too small because Lohmann (1952) used too large a coefficient in the csc law of absorption (0.34 mag × csc b). His already large absorptions were further increased by taking, where available, Stebbins and Whitford short base-line photoelectric colors of the globular clusters and integrated spectra, in most cases obtaining very much larger absorptions. Extreme examples, NGC 6366 and NGC 6171, which here, with cosecant law absorption, are found to be about 17 kpc distant, were thought by Lohmann to be about 2.5 kpc away. This caused the densities which Schmidt computed to be too high, particularly toward the plane and extrapolated into the center (see sec. 3.6.2).

As a general procedure, it seems better to determine the total number of clusters in the Galaxy as we have done here, by using the total catalogue of known globular clusters. Working only with clusters of known distances drastically cuts the number in the sample, introduces selection effects and possible systematic distance errors. The resulting densities still have to be extrapolated inward, whereas, in the procedure used in the present chapter, only the short extrapolation from $b^{II} = 4°$ to $b^{II} = 0°$ is necessary.

§ 3. INTRINSIC PROPERTIES AND DISTANCES

With such complete knowledge of the positions of nearly all the globular clusters, it would be possible to study the dimensions and structure of the globular cluster system if individual cluster distances were known. Unfortunately, distances to globular clusters on one, accurate, internally consistent system are difficult to obtain. There are four main sources of uncertainties: (1) photometry, (2) reddening, (3) variation of intrinsic properties, and (4) the absolute magnitude of any given class of stars in a globular cluster (usually the RR Lyrae stars). These sources of errors will be discussed in the following sections and the best present correction estimated. It is to be anticipated, however, that all these measures will be obtained more accurately in the future and that the derived structure of the globular cluster system will, therefore, become more accurately known.

3.1. PHOTOMETRY

The only measures which have any possibility of being homogeneous, and which at the same time cover any large number of the known globular clusters, are those of the mean apparent photographic magnitude of the 25 brightest stars. The sources of these measures vary from very recent ones to those as early as Shapley and Sawyer (1929). The early measures, before the advent of photoelectric photometry, depended on photographic transfers of magnitude scales from some standard regions such as the Selected Areas, the Harvard C-Regions, or the North Polar Sequence. Ordinarily such photographic transfers are subject to accidental errors of up to 0.5 mag in zero point and in scale. Usually the transferred magnitudes are in error by from 0.2 to 0.4 mag at any given magnitude.

The scales photographically transferred into the globular clusters will probably depend on the brightness of the stellar background. This will lead to a systematic error depending on latitude.

There is a systematic error in the original magnitude scales in the standard regions themselves, which we can correct for at this point. All the early measures until the photoelectric recalibration of the Selected Areas (Stebbins, Whitford, and Johnson 1950), and therefore all the photographic transfers, suffer from this scale error. To transform the pre-1950 measures to the P system requires the following correction:

$$P = m_{pg} \qquad \text{(for } m_{pg} < 14 \text{ mag),}$$
$$P = m_{pg} + 0.1 \, (m_{pg} - 14.0) \qquad \text{(for } m_{pg} > 14 \text{ mag).}$$

Assuming a mean color index of the stars involved of about $B - V = 1.0$ mag yields a correction to the B system of another 0.1 mag (Arp 1957). The final correction is

$$B = m_{pg} + 0.1 \qquad (m_{pg} < 14 \text{ mag),}$$
$$B = m_{pg} + 0.1 \, (m_{pg} - 14.0) + 0.1 \qquad (m_{pg} > 14 \text{ mag).}$$

This correction has been applied to obtain any B magnitudes quoted here which have been derived from older sources. In particular, the correction has been used to obtain the mean B magnitude of the 25 brightest stars as gathered from various sources by Hogg (1959). In most cases these corrections do not exceed 0.3 mag.

The apparent B magnitudes of the mean of the 25 brightest stars (which have been adopted in the present chapter) are listed in the 11th column of Table 1.

TABLE 1

Catalogue of Known Globular Clusters

NGC	Name	Con-Cen. Class	α (1950)	δ (1950)	l^II	b^II	Absorption 0.24 csc b	A_B Kron-Mayall Case II	Diameter $D_{0.9}$	25 Br.St. B	Mod $(m-M)_{app}$	r† kpc	x kpc	y kpc	z kpc	Integrated B	Apparent B−V	Integrated M_B	Intrinsic $(B-V)_0$	Sp. Type	Rad. Vel. (km/sec)
104	47 Tuc	III	00ʰ21ᵐ.9	−72°21′	306°	−45°	0.34			13.54	13.75*	5.0	+2.1	−2.9	−3.5	4.35		−9.5		G3‡	−24
288	Δ 62	X	50.2	−26 52	(147)	−89	0.24			14.98	15.78	14.8	−0.2	−0.0	−14.8	8.56		−7.5		F8‡	−47
362		III	01 07	−71 07	302	−47	0.33			14.23	15.03	9.7	+3.5	−5.7	−7.0	7.6		−7.6		F8‡	+221
1261		II	03 10.9	−55 25	270	−51	0.31														+46
Pal 1		XII	25.7	+79 20	130	+20	0.70														
Pal 2		IX	04 43.1	+31 23	171	9	1.53			19.6	20.4	87.1	−52.6	+62.8	+29.8	8.00					
1841			52.5	−84 05	297	−30	0.48														+309
1851	Δ 508	II	05 12.4	−40 05	244	−35	0.42			15.52	16.32	16.5	9.7	−10.7	−8.0			−8.6		F7‡	+196
1904	M79	V	22.2	−24 34	228	−29	0.50	0.54												F6‡	+64
2298		VI	06 47.2	−36 57	246	−16	0.87													F7‡	
2419		II	07 34.8	+39 00	181	+26	0.55			18.32	20.0*	83.2	−74.8	−1.3	+36.5	11.07		−9.1		F6	+14
2808		L	09 10.9	−64 39	283	−11	1.26			15.09	15.89	9.1	+2.0	−8.7	+1.8	7.4		−8.7		F8‡	+101
Pal 3			10 03	+00 18	241	+42	0.36				20.3*	100.0	−36.0	−65.0	+66.9						
3201	Δ 445	X	15.5	−46 09	277	+09	1.53		3.4								0.71		0.57		+493
Pal 4		X	11 26.6	+29 15	202	+77	0.25		6.4	20.59	20.3*	100.0	−29.0	−11.6	+95.1						
4147		VI:	12 07.6	+07 24	251	+77	0.25	0.00	8.3	16.94	16.55*	18.7	−1.4	−9.8	+18.2	10.59	0.56	−6.0	0.50	A6§	+191
4372		XII	23.0	−72 24	301	−10	1.38			14.98	15.78		+5.4				0.67		0.57	A7§	+66
4590	M68	X	36.8	−26 29	299	+37	0.40	0.38		15.28	16.7*	14.0		−1.5	+8.4	8.71		−7.4		F4	−116
4833		VIII	56.0	−70 36	304	+13	1.72														+204
5024	M53	V	13 10.5	+18 26	333	+80	0.24	0.00				20.0	+3.1		+19.7	8.28	0.58	−8.5	0.52		−112
5053		XI	13.9	+17 57	335	+79	0.24	0.12		15.86	16.25*	16.4	+1.3	−2.1	+16.1	10.5	0.63	−5.8	0.57	(F5)	
5139	ω Cen	VIII	23.8	−47 03	309	+15	0.93		9.3	14.35	14.28*	5.2	+3.2	−3.9	+1.3	4.8		−9.4		F7‡	+230
5272	M3	VI	39.9	+28 38	42	+78	0.25	0.27			15.32*	10.6	+1.6	−1.3	+10.4	6.86	0.64	−8.5	0.58	F7	−153
5286	Δ 388	V	14 03.2	−51 07	312	+11	1.26								+20.4					F8‡	+45
5466		XII	27.0	+28 46	42	+73	0.25			15.99		21.3				9.95				(F5)	
5634		IV	36.7	−05 45	342	+49	0.32	0.54		16.65	16.79		+4.6	+4.7	+20.2		0.71	−6.9	0.65	F5	−63
5694		VII	52.7	−26 19	331	+30	0.48	0.27	2.3	17.17	17.45	26.8	+16.7	+5.7	+15.9	10.4	0.64	−7.5	0.56	F0	−187
I 4499		XI	15 00.9	−82 02	308	−21	0.67	0.54	3.3	17.27	17.97	31.6	+23.9	+13.2		10.44	0.69		0.57	(F5)	
5824		I	13.5	−32 53	332	+22	0.64								+24.9					F5	−58
Pal 5		XII		+00 05	1	+45	0.34	0.65			18.07	35.2	+24.9	+0.4			0.71		0.55		
5897		XI	14.5	−20 50	343	+30	0.48	0.54	(15.7)	15.49	16.2*	14.5	+12.0	−3.6	+7.3	9.19	0.70	−7.1	0.58	(F5)	
5904	M5	V	16.0	+02 16	4	+47	0.33	0.27	10.7	14.07	14.80*	8.1	+5.5	+0.7	+5.9	6.69	0.70	−8.2	0.62	F6	+49
5927		VIII	24.5	−50 29	326	+4	2.75													G2‡	−96
5946		IX	31.8	−50 30	327	+4	3.44														
5986	Δ 552	VII	42.8	−37 37	337	+14	0.99	0.92	8.6	15.07		83.2	+54.0	+30.0	+55.6		0.82		0.57	G1	+2
A-vdB‖			16 08.8	+15 02	29	+42	0.36				20										
6093	M80	II	14.1	−22 52	353	+19	0.74	0.81	8.6		15.87	12.6	+11.9	−1.1	+4.1	8.00	0.83	−8.2	0.64	F9	+18
6101		X	20.0	−72 06	318	+16	0.87														
6121	M4	IX	20.6	−26 24	351	+16	0.87	0.57	22.6	13.21	14.01	4.3	+4.1	−0.6	+1.2	7.05	0.98	−7.0	0.76	(G0)	+65
6139		II	16ʰ24ᵐ.3	−38°44′	342°	+7°	1.97	1.57												F8‡	+20

* From $\bar{V}_{hor.\ br.}$, Table 6.

† Adjusted to RR Lyrae distance scale via Figure 7.

‡ Spectral type from Kinman (1959b).

§ Kinman (1959b) gives F2.

‖ Arp-Van den Bergh.

Unmarked entries are from Kron and Mayall (1960).

TABLE 1—Continued

NGC	Name	Con-cen. Class	α (1950)	δ	l^{II}	b^{II}	Absorption 0.24 csc b	A_B Kron-Mayall Case II	Diameter $D_{0.9}$	25 Br. St. B	Mod $(m-M)_{app}$	r† kpc	x kpc	y kpc	z kpc	Integrated B	Apparent B−V	Integrated M_B	Intrinsic $(B−V)_0$	Sp. Type	Rad. Vel. (km/sec)
6144		XI	16h24m2	−25°56′	352°	+15°	0.93	0.81	11′.1	16.04	16.84	16.9	+16.2	−2.2	+4.4	10.41	0.89	−6.7	0.66	G0	
6171		V	29.7	−12 57	3	+23	0.61	1.57	12.8	15.75	16.55	17.1	+15.7	+0.7	+6.6	9.67	1.03	−7.1	0.88	G3	−147
6205	M13	X	39.9	+36 33	59	+41	0.37	0.12	12.9	13.85	14.3*	7.6	+2.4	+4.1	+4.1	6.43	0.65	−7.9	0.56	F6	−241
6218	M12	IX	44.6	−01 52	15	+26	0.55	0.92	21.5	14.07	14.87	7.4	+6.4	+1.6	+3.3	7.58	0.84	−7.3	0.70	F8	−16
6229		IV	45.6	+47 37	73	+40	0.37	0.38	3.6	16.50	17.30	24.7	+5.6	+18.0	+15.9	9.81	0.71	−7.5	0.62	F8	−150
6235		XII	50.4	−22 06	359	+13	1.07	1.08	16.2	16.56	17.36	19.4	+18.9	+0.8	+4.4	10.4	0.86	−7.3	0.71	G1	+71
6254	M10	IV	54.5	−04 02	15	+23	0.61	2.00	8.8	14.17	14.42*	6.2	+5.5	+1.6	+2.4	7.26	1.01	−9.5	0.52	G2	+75
6266	M62	VIII	58.1	−30 03	353	+7	1.97	1.57	9.3	14.16	14.96	11.7	+11.4	+1.7	+1.2	7.77	0.96	−7.9	0.58	F3	+102
6273	M19	IX:	59.5	−26 11	357	+9	1.53	1.31	5.7	14.98	15.78	7.1	+7.0	+0.4	+1.2	7.90	0.97	−7.9	0.62	G2	+22
6284			17 01.5	−24 41	358	+10	1.38			16.37	17.17	16.3	+16.0	−0.5	+2.8	10.17		−7.3			
6287		VII	02.1	−22 38	0	+11	1.26	2.38	5.8	16.39	17.19	17.0	+16.7	0.0	+3.3	10.80	1.20	−6.6	0.88	(G5)	−73
6293		IV	07.1	−26 30	357	+8	1.72	1.46	6.2	15.63	16.43	9.8	+9.7	−0.5	+1.4	8.96	0.93	−7.7	0.50	F0	−98
6304		VI	13.4	−29 24	356	+6	2.75	2.65	7.2								1.29		0.60	G4	
6316		III	15.0	−28 05	357	+5	2.75	3.69	7.9								1.24		0.55	(G5)	
6325		IV:	16.2	−23 42	1	+8	1.72	1.57	7.9	15.75	16.55*	12.8	+12.6	+1.1	+4.5	8.52	1.61	−8.4	1.18	(G5)	+224
6333	M9	VIII	18.6	−18 28	5	+10	1.38	0.12	12.3	13.96	14.80*	7.9	+2.4	+6.0	+2.2	6.94	0.94	−8.0	0.59	P2	−118
6341	M92	IV	16.2	+43 12	68	+35	0.42	2.11	4.7								0.61		0.50	F1	
6342		XI:	18.2	−19 32	5	+9	1.53										1.27		0.89	(G5)	
6352			21.6	−48 26	342	−32															
6355			20.9	−26 19	359	+7	2.75	2.92	6.1								1.49		0.80	(G5)	
6356		II	20.7	−17 46	7	+10	1.38	1.84	6.3	16.72	17.4*	19.1	+18.7	+2.0	+3.3	9.26	1.12	−8.5	0.77	G4	+31
H P		IX	24.9	−29 57	357	+3	4.59														
6362	Δ 225	XI	26.6	−67 01	326	−17	0.82		10.8	16.06	16.86	17.4	+16.0	+5.0	+4.8	11.6		−5.5		G4	−18
6366			25.1	−05 02	18	+16	0.87	2.38													
6380		III:	31.9	−39 02	350	−7	3.44										1.24			0.24	G3‡	
6388	Δ 366	IX	32.6	−44 43	345	−12	1.97	2.69	5.8								1.19			F5‡	+81
6397			35.8	−53 39	339	−18	1.15	2.38		12.71	13.51	2.9	+2.7	−1.1	−0.6	6.9		−6.5		(G5)	+11
6401		VIII	35.0	−23 53	21	+4	3.44		7.7											G1	
6402	M14	XI	40.6	−03 15	21	+14	0.99		4.0	15.68	16.48	14.5	+13.1	+5.0	+3.5	9.01		−7.8	0.94	(G5)	−129
Pal 6			17 40.6	−26 12	2	+1	13.75		3.0	20.7	21.5						1.19				G1	
6426		IX	17 42.4	+03 12	28	+16	0.87	1.31	13.8								0.92		0.70	(G0)	
6440		V	45.9	−20 21	7	+3	4.59	4.76									1.92		0.77	G5	−133
6441		III	46.8	−37 02	353	−5	2.75										1.10			G2‡	−70
6453		IV	48.0	−34 37	355	−10	3.44	2.38											0.24	(G5)	
6496		XII	55.5	−44 13	348	+4	1.38	4.49									1.77					
6517		IV	59.1	−08 57	19	+6	2.30	4.84									1.08		1.19	(G0)	
6522		VI	18 00.4	−30 02	1	−4	3.44	2.33									1.35		0.22	F8	
6528		V	01.6	−30 04	0	−5	2.75												0.66	(G5)	
6535		XI:	01.3	−00 18	27	+10	1.38	4.49	13.8	16.27	17.07	15.6	+13.8	+6.9	+2.7	11.5	1.77	−5.9			
6539		X	18 02.1	−07 35	21°	+6°	2.30												1.19	(G0)	

411

TABLE 1—Continued

CLUSTER NGC	Name	CONCEN. CLASS	1950 α	1950 δ	GAL. COORD. l^{II}	GAL. COORD. b^{II}	ABSORPTION 0.24 csc b	A_B KRON-MAYALL CASE II	DIAMETER D_{0-9}	25 BR. ST. B	MOD $(m-M)_{app}$	r† kpc	x kpc	y kpc	z kpc	INTEGRATED B	AP. PARENT B-V	INTEGRATED M_B	INTRINSIC $(B-V)_0$	SP. TYPE	RAD. VEL. (km/sec)
6541	Δ 473	III	18ʰ04ᵐ4	−43°44′	349°	−11°	1.26			13.45	14.25	4.0	+3.9	−0.7	−0.7	7.5		−6.8		F6‡	−148
6514		XI	04.3	−25 01	6	−3	6.88	2.92	(8(4))								1.35		0.32	G2	−12
6553			06.3	−25 56	5	−3	4.59	3.57	8.2	18.5	19.3	25.1	+23.1	+9.3	+2.6		1.47			(G5)	
6558		XII	07.0	−31 47	6	−6	2.30		6.6												
I 1276		VIII	08.0	−07 14	22	+7	1.97	2.11									1.18		.69	(G5)	+160
6569		VIII	10.4	−31 50	0	−17	0.82		4.2										.63	F7‡	
6584	Δ 376	VI	14.6	−52 14	343	−17	1.72	1.57	9.1	14.90	15.70	4.8	+4.7	−0.6	+0.5	8.10	1.06	−7.6	.45	G5	+69
6624		IV	20.5	−30 23	2	−7	2.30	1.57	6.8								1.03		.62	G1	+1
6626	M28	V	21.5	−24 54	7	−6	1.26	1.08									0.94			G5	+95
6637	M69		28.1	−32 23	1	−11															
6638		VI	27.9	−25 32	8	−8	1.72	1.57	4.3	16.54	17.34	15.2	+14.9	+2.2	−2.1	9.80	1.02	−7.8	.59	G4	−14
6642		VI:	28.4	−23 30	10	−6	2.30														
6652		VII	32.5	−33 02	1	−12	1.15	0.65	4.2	13.03	13.7*	3.0	+2.9	+0.6	−0.4	6.15	0.85	−8.0	.56	G4	−124
6656	M22	V	33.3	−23 58	9	−8	1.72	1.73	26.2	19.6	20.4	47.9	+11.5	+46.1	−5.8		0.93		.50	F7	−144
Pal 8		X	38.5	−19 52	14	−7	1.97		5.1												
6681	M70	V	40.0	−32 21	2	−13	1.07	0.12	5.1	15.59	15.85*	5.7	+5.1	+2.5	−0.5	9.55	0.67	−7.0	.40	G3	+198
6712		IX:	50.3	−08 47	27	−5	2.75	2.00	12.3		17.1		+14.1				1.10		.41	G5	−131
6715	M54	III	52.0	−30 32	5	−15	0.93	0.81	4.8	16.3	17.1	14.7	+14.1	+3.3	−2.8		1.10	−7.0	.87	F8	+122
6717		VIII	52.1	−22 47	13	−11	1.26			14.32	15.12	7.4	+7.0	0.0	−2.3						
6723	Δ 573	VII	56.2	−36 42	0	−18	0.78	0.27	11.7	14.32	15.12	7.4	+7.0	+3.3	−2.3	7.37	0.69	−7.7	.49	G4	−3
6749			19 02.6	+01 48	36	−2	6.88	3.96		13.36	14.16	5.3	+4.3	−1.9	−2.3						
6752	Δ 295	VI	06.4	−60 04	337	−26	0.55	1.08	8.9	17.15	17.95	8.4	+6.8	+4.8	+1.6	6.8	1.64	−7.4	.78	F6‡	−39
6760		IX:	08.6	+00 57	36	−4	3.44		10.1	15.54	16.34	10.5	+4.8	+9.1	+1.7	10.81	0.81	−7.3	.43	(G0)	
6779	M56	X	14.6	+30 05	62	+9	1.53			20.7	21.5	8.3	+5.0	+6.6	+0.4	9.14		−7.5		F6	−145
Pal 10		XII	16.0	+18 28	53	+3	6.88	0.27	21.1												
Anon			25.6	−30 27	9	−20	0.59			13.68	14.48	6.0	+5.4	+1.2	−2.4	6.72	0.63	−7.8	.48	(F5)	+170
6809	M55	XI	36.9	−31 03	9	−24	0.70	1.31	10.2	17.4	18.2	28.8	+23.3	+14.7	−7.9	7.9	1.01	−7.0	.32	G6	−80
6838	M71		42.6	−08 09	32	−16	0.87	0.81	4.9	15.00	14.15*	2.6	+1.4		−0.2	9.03	0.78	−9.2	.64	G2	−198
6864	M75	I	20 03.2	−22 04	56	−26	2.75			17.47	18.27	35.1	+29.6	+10.8	−15.3						
6934		VIII	31.7	+07 14	52	−19	0.74	0.27	3.3	16.06	16.86	18.3	+10.6	+13.6	−6.0	9.58	0.70	−7.5	.51	G0	−360
6981	M72	IX	50.7	−12 44	35	−33	0.44	0.00	6.4	16.95	16.95	21.1	+10.2	+10.2	−11.4	9.80	0.65	−7.3	.54	G3	−255
7006		I	59.1	+16 00	64	−19	0.74	0.54	3.0	17.51	18.6*	39.8	+16.5	+33.8	−13.0	11.01	0.69	−8.7	.50	F2	−348
7078	M15	IV	21 27.6	+11 57	65	−27	0.53	0.27	9.4	14.44	15.50*	10.5	+8.4	+8.1	−4.8	6.96	0.67	−8.9	.54	F2	−107
7089	M2	II	30.9	−01 03	54	−36	0.41	0.27	6.8	14.77	15.75*	12.3	+5.8	+8.1	−7.2	6.94	0.67	−7.8	.55	F4	−5
7099	M30	V	37.7	−23 25	27	−47	0.33	0.00	6.8	14.79	15.59	13.3	+8.1	+4.1	−9.8	8.19	0.56		0.48	A#	−174
Pal 12		XII	21 04.2	−21 28	31	−48	0.32			17.4	18.2	38.0	+21.8	+13.1	−28.2						
Pal 13		XII	23 04.2	−21 28	87	−43	0.36			19.6	20.4	100.0	+3.8	+73.0	−68.2						
7492		XII	23 05ᵐ7	−15 54	53°	−63°	0.27			17.20	18.00	34.7	+9.5	+12.6	−30.9						

* From $\bar{V}_{hel. br.}$, Table 6.
† Adjusted to RR Lyrae distance scale via Figure 7.
‡ Spectral type from Kinman (1956b). Unmarked entries are from Kron and Mayall (1960).
# Kinman (1959b) gives F3.

412

3.2. Reddening and Normal Colors

It has long been recognized that the low-latitude globular clusters were reddened by the interstellar material in the plane of the Galaxy. Usually the csc law has been used to obtain the best available average approximation, but because of the patchy nature of the low-latitude absorption, the reddening of any individual object derived was not usually trusted. When high-latitude globular clusters were carefully analyzed in order to obtain the absolute magnitudes of their RR Lyrae cepheids, an attempt was made to derive individual reddenings for each cluster by independent photometric methods. The colors of RR Lyrae cepheids in the clusters or those of foreground field stars were used, resulting in zero reddening for a large number of high-latitude globular clusters, an untenable contradiction with the csc law derived from the galaxies and from the globular clusters (see below) themselves (Arp 1962b).

It is possible to continue to use the csc reddening law throughout, but greater accuracy would be achieved if we could estimate reddenings of individual globular clusters. Integrated color indices of 65 globular clusters in the Galaxy have been measured by Kron and Mayall (1960). They used two assumed alternative relationships (cases I and II) between intrinsic color and spectral type to estimate color excesses. Reddenings so derived showed satisfactory agreement with the cosecant law as obtained from counts of galaxies.

Since differences in age and chemical composition change the position and population of sequences in the color-magnitude diagram, there may not exist a unique relation between intrinsic color and spectral type. The integrated spectral type is, however, a first-order reflection of the integrated color and the procedure followed by Kron and Mayall appears to give the best present estimate of individual reddenings.

The color indices given by Kron and Mayall (1960) have been transformed into $B - V$ by the relation given in their paper. The integrated $B - V$ of each cluster measured is given in Table 1, column 18. The intrinsic colors $(B - V)_0$ given in column 20 have been obtained by correcting for cosecant law reddening, $E(B - V) = 0.06 \csc b$. The frequency distribution of the intrinsic color indices of the 44 clusters which have galactic latitude $b^{\mathrm{II}} > 8°$ is shown in Figure 4. The distribution of intrinsic colors obtained using the csc reddening correction gives a narrow, centrally peaked distribution like that found by Kron and Mayall in case II. If the central clusters are intrinsically redder than the outer ones, and the csc law overcorrects at low latitudes, we then obtain a spuriously narrow distribution of colors. If the color distribution actually is narrow, neither law of absorption has much accidental error in it because the distributions which they yield are also quite narrow.

Both case II of Kron and Mayall (1960) and the csc law reddening will be used for computations in this chapter. In the latter case, some accuracy may be sacrificed in deriving reddenings of individual clusters, but a more serious, possibly systematic, error may be avoided by not allowing any intrinsic aspect of the clusters to influence the applied reddening. The csc law reddening is, of course, available for all clusters, whereas individual reddening values are available for only part of the group. Column 8 of Table 1 lists the csc law absorption with $A_B = 0.24$ csc b, and column 9 lists the Kron-Mayall case II absorption (with their conversion to the $B - V$ system $E_{B-V} = 0.96 \, E_{P-V}$). In computations of distances in section 3.6, both methods of computing reddening are used and the data on distances are compared.

3.3. Variation of Intrinsic Properties

If we know accurately the absorption in front of a cluster and the apparent magnitude as well as the intrinsic brightness of a certain type of star in it, we

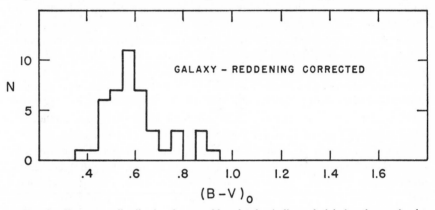

Fig. 4.—Frequency distribution for unreddened color indices of globular clusters in the Galaxy.

can easily compute its distance. Usually the RR Lyrae cepheids or the associated horizontal branch are calibrated as an absolute-magnitude zero point in a globular cluster. The next section will include the question of the actual absolute magnitude of the RR Lyrae cepheids. Not all clusters contain the same numbers and kinds of stars; this fact affects the distances, which we will discuss briefly here.

Morgan (1959) demonstrated that the intrinsic properties of the globular clusters change with galactic latitude. Figure 5 shows the integrated spectral types of globular clusters as a function of galactic latitude. The spectral types are taken from Kron and Mayall (1960). The diagram demonstrates that there is a discrete group of globular clusters near the galactic plane, which stand out from the general, widespread distribution of halo globular clusters. These clusters are also concentrated to the galactic center. The fact that these interior clusters are of a later spectral type does not necessarily imply that their stars have a lower average temperature. The classification of a later spectral type may be made because of richer metal content.

Table 2 lists the globular clusters whose integrated spectra have been classified on the Morgan system, from I for very weak metallic lines to VIII for the strongest metal abundance. It is apparent from the column of galactic latitudes that the metal-rich clusters are concentrated toward the center. This central concentration is even more marked in Figure 6, where the mean distance from the center of the Galaxy, $\bar{R}$, is plotted against each Morgan classification from I through VIII. It may be that star formation and metal enrichment took place more quickly in the denser central regions of our Galaxy. Therefore, star clusters that belong to and were formed in the central regions are richer in metals. In Figure 6 it can be seen that Morgan's low-metal-content globular clusters, classes I through III, average about 12 to 16 kpc distance from the nucleus. The globular clusters of higher metal content, classes IV through VI, are found, on the average, from 4 to 8 kpc from the galactic nucleus. Kinman (1959b) also derives the same result, namely, that clusters of early spectral type and low metal abundance form an extended spherical distribution with little concentration to the plane, while clusters of late type and relatively high metal abundance show a stronger concentration to the plane.

It should be noted that the spectra of individual giant stars in globular clusters offer a more exact measure of metallic abundance. The ultraviolet excess of the giants at $B - V = 1.0$ is also a quantitatively more precise measure of metal abundance. Table 3 shows the latter two quantities as exactly cor-

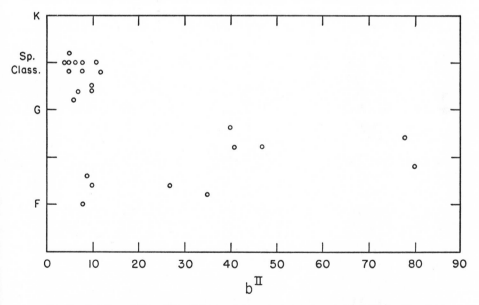

Fig. 5.—Relation of Kron-Mayall integrated spectral class to galactic latitude. The distribution demonstrates that the later spectral types occur primarily near the plane of the Galaxy. They are also concentrated to the galactic center.

related with each other, whereas the integrated spectral type classifications are only generally correlated. Presumably, variations in age distribute the stars in different sequences in globular clusters of the same chemical composition and impair, to some extent, our ability to discriminate metal abundances in the composite spectrum. Nevertheless, the Morgan types are the only measures we have for the interior globular clusters and hence the only way in which we can demonstrate the change in metal abundance toward the interior. It is worth mentioning that if the ultraviolet excesses can be measured for the nuclear globular clusters, we can derive actual percentage metal abundances relative to the sun by using the Wallerstein-Carlson calibration for nearby subdwarfs (Arp 1959).

From the observed color-magnitude diagrams of metal-rich clusters (San-

TABLE 2

DISTRIBUTION OF GLOBULAR CLUSTERS OF DIFFERENT
CHEMICAL COMPOSITION

Morgan Type	NGC	M	Galactic Latitude b^{II}	Distance from Nucleus R ($R_0 =$ 10.0 kpc)
I........	6341	92	$+35°$	10.7
	7078	15	-27	11.4
II......	5024	53	$+80$	20.9
	5139	ω Cen	$+16$	....
	5272	3	$+78$	13.4
	5904	5	$+47$	7.5
	6656	22	-8	7.1
	6981	72	-33	15.9
	7006	....	-19	36.8
	7089	2	-36	11.6
III......	6205	13	$+41$	9.6
	6229	....	$+40$	24.4
	6642	....	-6	....
	6715	54	-15	....
	6809	55	-24	5.3
IV.......	6254	10	$+23$	6.2
	6273	19	$+9$	3.3
	6402	14	$+14$	6.8
	6522	....	-4	....
V........	6712	....	-5	5.5
VI.......	6356	....	$+10$	9.5
	6760	....	-4	5.8
	6838	71	-5	8.9
VII......	6440	....	$+4$	....
	6637	69	-11	....
VIII.....	6528	....	-5	....
	6553	....	-3	....

dage and Wallerstein 1960; Wildey 1961; Smith *et al.* 1963), it is apparent that the usual features do not occur at the same relative magnitudes as in the better known, metal-poor clusters. Table 4 shows that the magnitude difference between the giant branch and the horizontal branch (often a very truncated horizontal branch in metal-rich globular clusters) is a more or less systematic function of metal abundance. These differences need not be entirely a function of chemical composition because some of them may be due to differences in age.

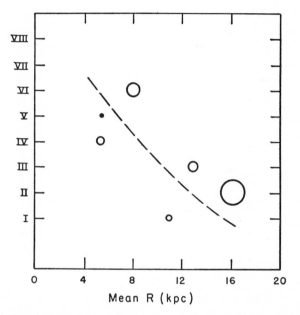

Fig. 6.—Relation of Morgan's spectral groups to galactocentric distance R (cf. Table 2). Size of circles is proportional to number of clusters in average. The diagram indicates that metal richness increases toward center of Galaxy.

TABLE 3

Some Globular Clusters in Order of
Increasing Metal Abundance

Cluster		$\delta(U-B)$ of Giants at $B-V = 1.0$*	Spectra of Giants (Deutsch)	Integrated Spectra (Morgan)
NGC	M			
6341	92	−0.27	C	I
4147	....	−0.23	B	....
7089	2	−0.21	B	II
5272	3	−0.12	A to B	II
6205	13	−0.11	A	III
5904	5	−0.09	A	II

* Csc law reddening applied to all clusters.

It is difficult to distinguish age effects from those due to chemical composition because the metal abundance probably depends on the time of formation.

It is apparent that if the giant branch is fainter relative to the horizontal branch in the metal-rich clusters, the criterion of the brightest stars will give distances which are systematically too large for the metal-rich cluster. The metal-rich clusters tend to have few or no RR Lyrae cepheids. In 47 Tuc the two suspected RR Lyrae cepheids lie appreciably above the short horizontal branch

TABLE 4

CLUSTER CHARACTERISTICS CORRELATED WITH METAL ABUNDANCE

CLUSTER		ΔV^* MAG	DEUTSCH TYPE	MORGAN TYPE	RR LYRAES	
NGC	M				No.	Mean Period
5024	53	3.10	....	II	45	0.642
5053	....	....	....	....	10	.673
5466	....	3.0	....	....	18	.636
5897	....	3.10	....	....	4	....
6254	10	2.85	....	IV	0	....
6341	92	2.92	C	I	15	.626
7078	15	3.10	C	I	93	.645
7089	2	2.98	B	II	13	.629
		3.01±0.08	C+	II	....	....
4147	....	2.45:	....	....	16	.531
5272	3	2.64	A to B	II	201	.550
5904	5	2.58	A	II	99	.546
6205	13	2.55	A	III	3	....
6656	22	2.50	....	II	19	.651
		2.54±0.06	A	II+	....	....
6712	....	2.0	....	V	6	0.54
104	47 Tuc	2.15	....	....	2	....
6356	....	2.15	....	VI	0	....
6838	71	2.1	....	VI	0	....
		2.10±0.03	....	VI−	....	....

* Difference between horizontal branch and giant branch read at $(B-V)_0 = 1.4$ mag.

(Wildey 1961). There is no way of making certain, without further investigation, whether the horizontal branches, the RR Lyrae cepheids, or both of them, are at different absolute magnitudes in the metal-rich clusters than in the more normal globular clusters.

Of the 45 clusters in Table 1 which have Kron-Mayall integrated spectral types, those between F and G average to $M_B = -8$ mag and those of later than G to about $M_B = -7.5$ mag. Therefore, the nuclear globular clusters tend to be less luminous. One reason for this could be that the clusters inhabiting the dense central regions of the Galaxy are probably limited by tidal effects to smaller dimensions than elsewhere. This subject is treated by Burbidge and

Sandage (1958), Hodge (1961), and King (1962). This number effect works in the direction of making the mean of their 25 brightest stars too faint with respect to high-latitude globular clusters.

In summary, there are two effects which cause us to overestimate systematically distances to the nuclear globular clusters: (a) The giant branch is fainter relative to the horizontal branch. (b) The nuclear globular clusters contain fewer bright stars. There is one effect which can lead us to underestimate distances: photographic transfers to the central regions where globular clusters occur should tend to give too bright a magnitude scale (because of brighter background fields).

There are two effects for which we cannot at present guess the direction of possible correction: (a) The magnitudes of the RR Lyrae cepheids and of the horizontal branch may be unequal, and it may be that neither are the same as in normal globular clusters. (b) The nuclear globular clusters are predominantly in the galactic plane and it is, thus, difficult to say whether the reddening has been over- or underestimated.

In studying the structure of the globular cluster system and in measuring the distance to the center of the Galaxy, it will be necessary, then, to restrict ourselves to clusters that are fairly normal. Clusters which we suspect as having similar properties will, on the average, yield a distance which we can regard as fairly unbiased. As will be shown in section 3.6.1, it is possible to work with reasonably high-latitude globular clusters and still derive a meaningful centroid which will give the distance to the center of the Galaxy.

3.4. Distance Criteria and Distances

3.4.1. *Absolute magnitudes of RR Lyrae cepheids.*—If we exclude clusters at very low latitudes, $|b| \leq 8°$, there remains a fairly homogeneous group of globular clusters composed essentially of Morgan types I through IV. In these clusters we will assume that all the features occur at the same absolute magnitude and also that the horizontal branch and the RR Lyrae cepheids have the same luminosity. The problem now is to obtain the best present absolute magnitude for the RR Lyrae cepheids.[2]

Table 5 lists the four globular clusters that have so far been photometrically analyzed down to their main sequence. After careful corrections for line blanketing, they have been fitted to a Hyades-like main sequence with Haselgrove-Hoyle low-metal evolution (Arp 1962a; Sandage 1962). This is the only fundamental way of calibrating the globular clusters, but until 1962, zero reddening

---

[2] Lewis Smith has pointed out to me that for globular clusters in Table 6 with integrated spectra earlier than F4 the distances derived from horizontal-branch brightness are about 15% greater than from brightest star criteria. This result is expected generally, since we believe that giants are progressively brighter, relative to the horizontal-branch stars, in the earlier spectral-type clusters (see Table 4). The correction is somewhat uncertain, however, and we have not applied it here, assuming, as just stated, that features in all clusters occur at the same absolute magnitude. (About 14% of the clusters in Table 1 are of spectral type F4 or earlier.)

had been adopted for them. It is now clear (Arp 1962*b*) that something like csc law reddening must be used. Table 5 shows that with these new values of reddening, brighter absolute magnitudes are obtained for the RR Lyrae cepheids. Values in use in 1962 for RR Lyrae cepheids were

$$M_V = +0.7, \quad B - V = +0.3, \quad M_B = +1.0.$$

TABLE 5

GLOBULAR CLUSTERS FITTED TO MAIN SEQUENCES

CLUSTERS		PREVIOUS ASSUMED REDDENING		csc LAW REDDENING		REDDENING FROM INTEGRATED COLORS (KRON AND MAYALL CASE II)		REFERENCES
NGC	M	E_{B-V}	M_V RR Lyr	E_{B-V}	M_V RR Lyr	E_{B-V}	M_V RR Lyr	
5272	3	0.0	+0.7	0.06	+0.4	0.07	+0.3	(1),(2)
5904	5	.0	+0.7	.08	+ .2	.07	+ .3	(2)
6205	13	.0	+0.2	.09	− .3	.03	+ .1	(3),(4),(5)
7089	2	0.0	+1.0	0.10	+0.4	0.07	+0.6	(4)

Ave. +0.2   Ave. +0.3

RR LYRAE CEPHEIDS WITH PRESUMED MOVING GROUP PARALLAXES

RR Lyr........		0.05	+0.65	0.11*	+0.5	....		(6),(3)
TU UMa.......		.0	+.4	.06	+ .2	....		(6)
SU Dra........		.0	+.8	.08	+ .6	....		(6),(8)
X Ari..........		.0	+.8	.10	+ .5	....		(6),(7)
W CVn........		0.0	+0.2	0.06	+0.0	....		(6)

Ave. +0.3

* Original reddening used (6), which is also the color of M3 RR Lyraes +0.06 mag.

(1) Johnson and Sandage (1956)
(2) Arp (1962*a*)
(3) Baum, Hiltner, Johnson, and Sandage (1959)
(4) Arp (1959)
(5) Sandage (1962)
(6) Eggen and Sandage (1959)
(7) Preston (1961)
(8) Spinrad (1961)

Our new, adopted values, using the csc law reddening, are:

$$M_V = +0.3, \quad B - V = +0.24, \quad M_B = +0.5.$$

Table 5 also shows that the RR Lyrae cepheids that have tentative moving group parallaxes (Eggen and Sandage 1959) confirm the above value of absolute magnitude for the RR Lyrae cepheids in globular clusters.

Accurate modern photometry down to the horizontal branch is available for 21 clusters. Their distances are computed in Table 6, on the assumption that the mean visual magnitude of the horizontal branch is equivalent to that of the RR Lyraes.

3.4.2. *Bright-star criteria.*—On the old value of $M_{pg} = 0.0$ mag for the RR Lyrae cepheids, Arp (1955) gives the absolute brightness of the mean of the 25 brightest stars in 6 clusters. With the new value of $M_B = 0.5$ mag for the RR Lyraes we have, by transformation,

Cluster	M_B (Mean 25 b.s.)
M3	−0.7
M5	−0.7
M13	−0.7
M10	−0.7
M15	−1.1
M12	−0.9
	Mean −0.8 mag

Distances computed from this value of the mean absolute magnitude of the 25 brightest stars may be compared with those based on the magnitude of the horizontal branch. Figure 7 shows the relation for the clusters listed in Table 6. It can be seen that the more accurate photometry gives slightly greater distances, on the average, for clusters more distant than 7 kpc. It is uncertain how a larger number of observations might affect this picture; but as it now appears, there is no choice but to apply this small systematic correction to all the bright star distances. If real, it is not clear whether the small systematic underestimate of the clusters more distant than 7 kpc by the 25 b.s. method is due to measurements giving progressively greater systematic errors for the more distant clusters, or to intrinsic properties changing for the more distant clusters. Whatever the cause, Figure 7 gives the best independent confirmation of the accuracy (exclusive of the RR Lyrae zero point) of the globular cluster distances which appear to be internally accurate to better than 10 per cent.

Table 1 lists all 119 known globular clusters. Column 11 gives the mean magnitude of the 25 brightest stars corrected to the B system, as described in section 3.1. Their mean magnitude, $M_B = -0.8$ mag, leads to the apparent distance modulus given in column 12. The distances listed in column 13 follow after allowing for the absorption $A_B = 0.24$ csc$b$ listed in column 8, and after correction to the horizontal-branch distance scale as shown in Figure 7.

3.4.3. *Other distance criteria.*—The basic list of globular cluster distances was given by Shapley and Sawyer (1929); they used the two criteria discussed above, magnitudes of variable stars and of brightest stars, and, in addition, the apparent diameters and integrated magnitudes. We know now that different kinds of clusters have different diameters (cf. sec. 3.5.2) and this criterion can introduce systematic errors owing to their systematic location in the Galaxy. Van de Kamp (1930) criticized the use of diameters as distance criteria, but some authors, as for example Lohmann (1952), still used Shapley-Sawyer and Mowbray diameters to study absorption.

TABLE 6

GLOBULAR CLUSTERS WITH ACCURATE PHOTOMETRY
DOWN TO THE HORIZONTAL BRANCH

NGC	Name	$\overline{V}$ (RR Lyr)	$\overline{V}$ (Horiz. Br.)	E_{B-V} (csc Law)	$(m-M)_{true}$	r (kpc)	References
104	47 Tuc	13.90	14.05	0.09	13.49	4.99	(1)
2419	....	....	20.3	.14	19.6	83.2	(2)
Pal 3	....	....	20.6	.09	20.0	100.0	(3)
Pal 4	....	....	20.5	.06	20.0	100.0	(3)
4147	....	....	16.85	.06	16.36	18.71	(4)
5024	M53	....	17.0	.06	16.5	20.0	(5)
5053	....	....	16.55	.06	16.07	16.37	(6)
5139	ω Cen	14.58	....	.23	13.58	5.20	(7)
5272	M3	....	15.62	.06	15.13	10.62	(8)
5897	....	....	16.5	.12	15.8	14.45	(6)
5904	M5	....	15.10	.08	14.55	8.13	(9)
6205	M13	14.6	....	.09	14.0	6.3	(8)
6254	M10	....	14.72	.15	13.96	6.19	(8)
6341	M92	....	15.10	.11	14.48	7.87	(6)
6356	....	....	17.7	.35	16.4	19.1	(10)
6656	M22	....	14.0	.43	12.4	3.0	(11)
6712	....	....	16.15	.69	13.79	5.73	(12)
6838	M71	....	14.45	.69	12.09	2.62	(13)
7006	....	18.9	....	.19	18.0	39.8	(14)
7078	M15	....	15.80	.13	15.10	10.47	(6)
7089	M2	....	16.05	0.10	15.44	12.25	(8)

(1) Wildey (1961)
(2) Kinman, private communication
(3) Burbidge and Sandage (1958)
(4) Sandage and Walker (1955)
(5) Cuffey (1958)
(6) Sandage, unpublished
(7) Belserene (1959)
(8) Arp (1955)
(9) Arp (1962a)
(10) Sandage and Wallerstein (1960)
(11) Arp and Melbourne (1959)
(12) Smith and Sandage (1961)
(13) Arp, unpublished
(14) Sandage (1954b)

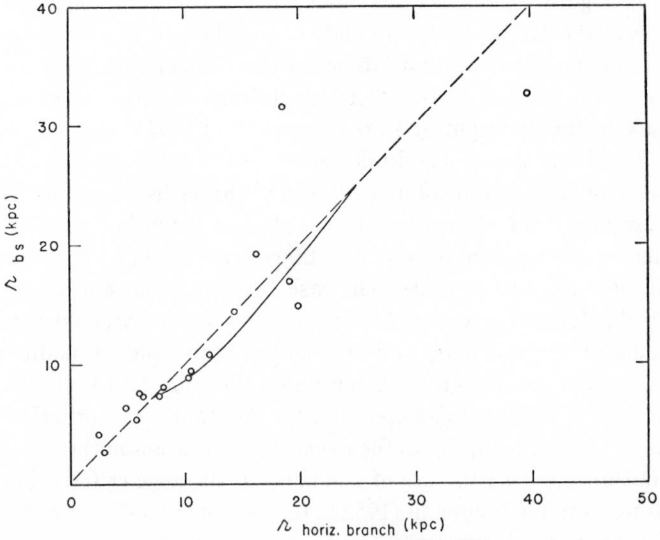

FIG. 7.—Comparison of distances derived from the 25 brightest stars criterion to distances derived from apparent magnitude of horizontal branch. Dashed line represents identity.

Similarly one can use the mean absolute magnitude of a globular cluster as a distance criterion, and, indeed, for distant galaxies the mean of a few globular clusters is sometimes valuable. The average difference of a cluster from the mean, however, is about one magnitude. This introduces individual errors of the order of a factor of 1.6 in distance. In addition, we find the same sort of systematic difficulties as with the use of diameters.

Modern lists of distances to globular clusters within our Galaxy have therefore come to rely more and more on the two criteria of apparent brightness of variables and of brightest stars. Lists of distances to globular clusters (Shapley 1930; de Kort 1941; Lohmann 1952; Kinman 1959a; Hogg 1959) have included more clusters and revised distances as new data became available. The list of distances in this chapter (see Table 1) uses the best observational material now available. The scale of distances in Table 1 can be changed if a different value of the RR Lyrae zero point is used, or if different reddening is used. But, significant improvement in the basic observational data could only be obtained by modern photometry of individual stars in a larger number of globular clusters. Since much of the basic photometry dates back far in time, more observations with modern techniques would obviously improve the list of globular cluster distances.

3.5. Physical Properties of Globular Clusters

3.5.1. *Absolute magnitudes.*—Kron and Mayall (1960) measured the apparent magnitudes of a large number of globular clusters in our Galaxy through a series of different diaphragm sizes. This procedure enabled them to accurately derive the total light of the cluster. In Table 1, the Kron-Mayall measures have been transformed onto the Johnson V system, transformed color indices have been applied, and their B magnitudes listed in column 17. Absolute magnitudes can be computed for 44 of the clusters that have distances. Column 19 lists these M_B's on the basis of the csc reddening law.

Earlier measures of integrated globular cluster magnitudes by Christie (Hogg 1959) can be compared to the Kron-Mayall measures. Transforming both sets of measures onto the Johnson B system, it can be shown that the 43 common measures show a very good correlation, with an average scatter of less than ± 0.2 mag, except for NGC 6838, which Kron and Mayall measure nearly 1 mag fainter. We then obtain

$$B_{\text{integ}}(\text{Kron-Mayall}) = B_{\text{integ}}(\text{Christie}) - 0.5 \text{ mag}.$$

Putting 12 Christie measures of clusters not measured by Kron and Mayall onto their system gives us 56 clusters with known, absolute integrated magnitudes (Table 1). Figure 8 shows the luminosity function for these globular clusters in the Galaxy. Their mean magnitude is $M_B = -7.5$ mag. Note that one globular cluster, ω Cen, in Table 1 has not been included because the data were obtained from a different source (Gascoigne and Burr 1956). The median magnitude is $M_B = -7.3$ mag for the distribution shown in Figure 8. The total light of the globular cluster system is between $M_B = -13$ and $M_B = -14$ mag. This can be compared to the light of an average Sb galaxy, which is about $M_B = -20$ mag, or to the light of a dwarf elliptical like NGC 147, which is $M_B = -14$ mag.

3.5.2. *Absolute diameters.*—Any of the diameters given by Kron and Mayall (1960) and column 10 of Table 1 can be turned into absolute diameters by applying the distances listed in Table 1. The diameter of a globular cluster is an indefinite quantity, however, in the sense that there is no sharp boundary to measure. Kron and Mayall measure through successive diaphragm sizes and are

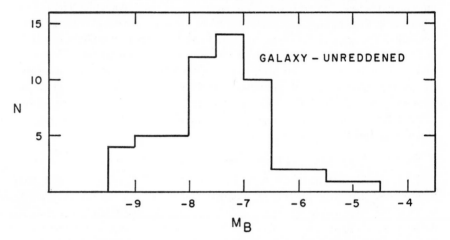

Fig. 8.—Distribution of absolute magnitudes, M_B, of 56 globular clusters

able to define a diameter within which 0.9 of the light is contained. This diameter for M3 comes out a little less than 30 parsecs. The diameter of M3 judged by the most outlying RR Lyrae members, however, is of the order of 100 parsecs.

It can be readily seen that diameters are very poor criteria for measuring distances to globular clusters. King (1962) has shown that the outer limits of a globular cluster are determined by tidal forces at perigalactic passage. The diameters of the core can be demonstrated as equally unsuitable by plotting distances derived from Mowbray's (1946) diameters which include half the light of the cluster (closely corresponding to King's "core" diameters). It is seen that the average core diameter is about 2 parsecs, but, if this diameter were used as a measure of distance, more than a third of the distances would be wrong by a factor of two or more.

3.5.3. *Masses.*—The masses of the globular clusters are very imperfectly known. Only two have been measured directly, by velocity dispersion of individual stars in the cluster, viz., M92 (Wilson and Coffeen 1954; Schwarzschild and Bernstein 1955) and 47 Tuc (Feast and Thackeray 1960). When the distance in Table 1 is adopted for M92, we obtain the mass $\mathfrak{M} = 1.1$ $(\pm 0.5) \times 10^5$ $\mathfrak{M}\odot$. Feast and Thackeray (1960) obtain an upper limit for the mass of 47 Tuc, using the same kind of measures, of $\mathfrak{M} \leq 2.5$ to 6×10^6 $\mathfrak{M}\odot$.

Since we know of no globular clusters in dynamical orbits about each other, we cannot compute masses as we do for double galaxies. The only other method of checking the above mass is by counting the number of stars in a globular cluster, assigning a probable mass to each one, and adding up the total mass. Unfortunately, most of the mass, unlike most of the light, in a globular cluster is contributed by stars too faint to observe. Sandage (1954a) estimates that if the van Rhijn (solar neighborhood) luminosity function holds fainter than $M_V = +7$ mag for the globular cluster M3, its total mass is roughly 1.4×10^5 $\mathfrak{M}\odot$. (Oort and van Herk [1959] give a model for M3 which gives $\mathfrak{M} = 1.5 \times 10^5$ $\mathfrak{M}\odot$.) This is a very uncertain estimate, but it shows that a mass of the order of 10^5 $\mathfrak{M}\odot$ is approximately correct for a fairly large globular cluster. (The M_B for M92 is -8.0 mag, whereas the average M_B for 56 clusters is -7.5 mag.) The total mass, therefore, of the 119 globular clusters which make up our system is about 10^7 $\mathfrak{M}\odot$. This is only about 10^{-4} of the mass of the Galaxy.

3.6. The Globular Cluster System

3.6.1. *Distance to the center of the Galaxy.*—Columns 14, 15, and 16 in Table 1 give the coordinates x, y, z in a coordinate system centered on the sun with x directed toward the galactic center, y in the direction of rotation, and z perpendicular to the plane. In order to get a coordinate system centered on the Galaxy instead of the sun, it is only necessary to subtract R_0, the distance between the sun and the center of the Galaxy, from x.

Figure 9 is a plot of the globular clusters in Table 1 with computable distances. The clusters are projected onto the x, z plane and the centroid of the system is clearly seen to be about 10 kpc from the sun along the x axis.

In deriving the exact distance from the sun to the center, however, a straight mean of the x coordinates cannot be taken because below $|b| = 8°$ there is some blocking of clusters by obscuration and distances are more uncertain due to uncertain absorption corrections (see sec. 2.2). Above $b = 8°$ we do not wish to bias x toward the sun because the expanding wedge of avoidance causes us to miss some clusters on the far side. But we see from Figure 9 that above $z = 2.5$ kpc, there is a complete sample extending to about 10 kpc on either side of the galactic center. We can take the mean x of the globular clusters above this z and obtain an unbiased centroid of the globular clusters that are symmetrically distributed around this region of the center.

Before doing this, however, it will be wise to discard the small clusters because: (1) intrinsically faint globular clusters do not contribute much to the mass definition of the globular cluster centroid; (2) these clusters are most likely to contain different kinds of stars which will give false distance criteria; (3)

they will contain fewer stars, which will bias the 25 brightest stars criterion; and
(4) they will be the most difficult kinds of globular clusters to discover and,
therefore, will run the greatest risk of providing an incomplete sample. Among
the clusters plotted in Figure 9, the 7 that are fainter than $M_B = -7.0$ mag
have been omitted from the determination of the mean $\bar{x}$. These faint clusters,
it should be noted, are also, in general, members of the very loose concentration
classes; among the 7 clusters omitted, 5 are in concentration classes XI or XII.

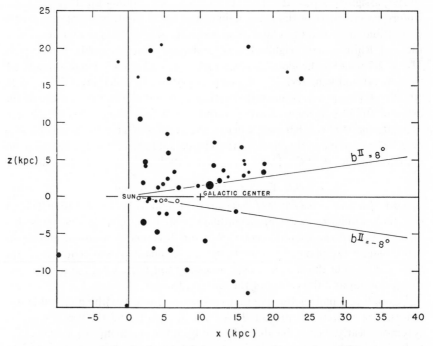

F IG. 9.—Projected distribution of globular clusters in the x, z plane. Distances are from
Table 1. Smallest circles represent globular clusters which are fainter than $M_B = -7$; next
larger circles from $M_B = -8$ to -7; then $M_B = -9$ to -8; and finally $M_B = -10$ to -9 mag.
Open circles represent a few clusters lower than $|b^{II}| = 8°$.

In order to discover whether there is any systematic difference between the
centroid given by high-latitude and that given by low-latitude globular clusters,
owing either to the use of an incorrect reddening law or to intrinsic differences
between high- and low-latitude galactic clusters, we derive $\bar{x}$ from the 5 clusters
above $z = 10$ kpc and obtain $\bar{x} = 10.2$ kpc. The 12 clusters between $z = 2.5$ kpc
and $z = 10$ kpc give an $\bar{x} = 10.7$ kpc. This is very satisfactory agreement in
view of the small numbers. (The mean errors of these two determinations are
3.3 kpc and 1.5 kpc, respectively, but, because of the peculiar distribution of x
coordinates of the high-z clusters, I do not consider this to be a meaningful
indication of the error of the mean. Table 7, a comparison of several different

determinations, gives a more reliable estimate for the adopted distance to the center.)

It will be noted that the globular clusters with negative z have not been used in these computations. The reason, apparent from inspection of Figure 9, is that the sample is much less complete for these essentially southern-declination globular clusters and is biased toward the nearby ones. This does not mean that there is any large number of southern-hemisphere clusters missing from Table 1. There are 58 clusters with negative b^{II} in Table 1, and 60 with positive b^{II}. The bias in Figure 9 merely indicates that the 25 brightest stars in many of the southern clusters have not been measured (39 clusters in the north and 29 in the south have been measured). This is to be expected because so much of the 25 brightest stars work was done by Shapley from the northern hemisphere.

When we have assured ourselves that there is no appreciable systematic difference between the distance to the center, $\bar{x}$, derived from clusters above $z = 10$ kpc and those between $z = 2.5$ kpc and 10 kpc, we can treat the whole body of data together. Solving by this method for all 17 clusters with $z \geq 2.5$ kpc, we get $R_0 = 10.5$ kpc. Kron-Mayall individual color excesses are available for 15 of these 17 clusters. Using these, we get from the same 17 clusters $\bar{x} = 9.6$ kpc. It is possible that the csc law reddening gives too much reddening below $b = 20°$ and hence causes the derived distances to be too great in the first solution.

There are two other independent derivations of the distance to the center with which we can compare our figures. Kron and Mayall (1960) used the apparent magnitudes of 23 central clusters, an absolute total visual magnitude of $M_V = -8.2$ mag and their two cases of assumed reddening to get an average true modulus to the center of $m - M = 15.5$ mag. (We will correct this modulus to our system presently.) The other method uses Baade's measures of the field RR Lyrae cepheids in the galactic center region near NGC 6522. Both Kron-Mayall reddening cases give a true modulus for these cepheids of $m - M = 15.4$ mag. These moduli are both based on the assumption $M_P = 0.0$ mag for the RR Lyraes. For the approximate observed colors of the RR Lyrae cepheids in globular clusters, Kron's $P \approx B$. Therefore, on our adopted scale for the RR Lyrae cepheids, $M_B = +0.5$ mag, the two moduli above become $m - M = 15.0$ and 14.9, respectively.

It is difficult to estimate the accuracy of the derived distance to the center, $R_0 = 9.9$ kpc, because the different determinations in Table 7 are not completely independent. Some use the same objects with different reddening, and others use different objects with the same reddening. All the determinations fall so close to $R_0 = 10$ kpc, however, that the adopted brightness for the RR Lyrae cepheids themselves clearly is the most uncertain quantity. The present RR Lyrae cepheids zero point could not be more accurate than ± 0.1 mag; therefore, the estimated error of R_0 is given as the error in distance corresponding to an error of 0.1 mag in the RR Lyraes, that is, $\pm \frac{1}{2}$ kpc. The true error of R_0 may be somewhat larger.

It is encouraging to compare this distance to the center derived from globular clusters to the value recently available from galactic rotation measures, in which $AR_0 = 152$ km/sec (Schmidt 1961) and $A = 15$ km/sec kpc (Kraft and Schmidt 1963). This also gives an R_0 of about 10 kpc to the center. (See chap. 22 by Schmidt, in this volume, for fuller discussion.) Another recent value derived from galactic rotation and from an estimated galactic mass (Brandt 1962) gives $R_0 = 10.5$ kpc $\pm$ 1.5 kpc. Fernie (1962) has recently derived a value of 9.7 kpc for the distance to the center.

TABLE 7

DISTANCE TO GALACTIC CENTER*

$\bar{x}$	Source
10.5 kpc.......	Distances to 17 globular clusters, csc law reddening.
9.6..........	Distances to 17 globular clusters, Kron-Mayall case II reddening.
10.0..........	Absolute magnitude distances to 23 central clusters, Kron-Mayall reddening cases I and II averaged.
9.5..........	R R Lyrae cepheids in center, Kron-Mayall reddening I and II.

* Adopted $R_0 = 9.9$ kpc $\pm$ 0.5 (based on $M_B = +0.5$ mag $\pm$ 0.1 for RR Lyrae cepheids).

3.6.2. *Density of globular clusters in the Galaxy.*—As noted earlier (sec. 2.2), the density of numbers of globular clusters in different parts of the Galaxy is difficult to compute accurately. There are only 34 clusters in Table 1 with known distances which are in the relatively complete northern galactic hemisphere. The density of these clusters at different radii, R, from the galactic center can be computed. The same scale factor, 1.73, which brings the 34 with known distances to the 49 expected total in a hemisphere (sec. 2.2) can be applied to the computed densities. The final computed densities are:

R Distance from Center of Galaxy	ρ Density of Globular Clusters	Based on Number of Clusters
5–10 kpc	1×10^{-2} kpc^{-3}	16
10–15	2×10^{-3}	5
15–20	2×10^{-4}	1
20–25	7×10^{-4}	6

These densities are, of course, very approximate because of the small number of clusters in each shell and because the slight flattening to the disk of the inner clusters, as shown in Figure 9, is ignored.

§ 4. KINEMATICS AND ROTATION

Mayall (1946) gives radial velocities for 50 globular clusters. Kinman (1959a) measured 20 additional radial velocities of southern clusters, and analyzed the motions of the whole group of 70. The major result confirmed Mayall's original work, namely, that the globular cluster system is in rotation about the galactic center, but not in as rapid rotation as the galactic disk in the solar neighborhood.

Figure 10 shows this situation very simply. There the positions of 34 globular clusters are projected onto the x, y plane and represent all those clusters in Table 1 that have both known x, y positions and measured radial velocities. The x and y components of the radial velocities have been averaged in each of the regions pictured, A through F, and the mean velocity vector plotted at the centroid of the positions in each region. No significance is to be attached to the

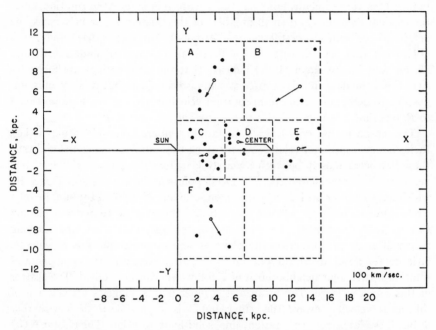

FIG. 10.—Projection on the x, y plane of all globular clusters in Table 1 that have measured radial velocities. The net vector velocities, with respect to the sun, are shown for all the clusters in the six marked-off areas.

fact that the mean vectors shown in Figure 10 do not pass exactly through the sun. The centers of region A and F are at 9.2 and 9.5 kpc distance from the galactic center, respectively. Therefore, at about the sun's radius, we see the clusters in the direction of rotation approaching us with a velocity of about 100 km/sec, and those in the opposite direction receding at about 96 km/sec. This implies a counter rotation of the globular clusters (relative to the sun) of about 114 km/sec (in the direction of counter rotation, not merely along the line of sight to centroids A and F). Allowing a projection factor of 1.2 for the average galactic latitude, yields a rotation velocity of about 140 km/sec for the globular cluster system relative to the sun. Kinman (1959c) found a relative rotation of 167 km/sec with respect to the sun; Schmidt (1956) found 136 km/

sec. If we take the rotational velocity of the sun as 250 km/sec (see chap. 22, this volume), and give the greatest weight to the present determination, we derive an absolute rotation of the globular cluster system of 110 km/sec ± 10 (estimated error).

This, of course, describes the absolute rotation at roughly the sun's distance from the galactic center. We would expect that the globular cluster system would not be in rotation like a solid body and that the linear velocity of rotation would, therefore, not increase as fast outward as directly proportional to the radius. It is very difficult, however, to measure this differential rotation, since the random velocities and small numbers of the clusters apparently mask the details of the rotation of the system. Although Parenago (1947) and Perek (1948) felt they had detected this differential rotation, Schmidt (1956) and Sharov and Pavlovskaya (1961) indicate that the observations are inconclusive. From the data in this chapter we can also conclude that it is not only impossible to detect deviation from rotation velocities that increase proportional to R, but that it is very difficult to see any dependence on R.

The reason is that only a few globular clusters are favorably situated (i.e., their circular rotational velocity nearly along the radial line of sight) and that these few occur mostly between 8 and 10 kpc from the center, with very few nearer to the center than 8 kpc. The loci of points in the x, y plane of Figure 10, which have circular orbital velocities along the line of sight to the sun, lie on a circle centered halfway between the sun and the galactic center and passing through both those points. By choosing points close to this circle and allowing for small angle projection on the plane as well as projection due to galactic latitude, the absolute orbital rotation values, after extracting the component of rotation of the solar neighborhood of 250 km/sec, can be studied. The scatter of the points is large. The mean of the inner points suggests a reduction of rotational velocity toward the center, but it is impossible to decide whether or not it deviates from the straight-line, solid-body rotation. The cluster NGC 3201 with the large negative orbital velocity is certainly retrograde. Some of the others are probably also retrograde, but the scatter makes it difficult to be certain in individual cases.

Kinman (1959c) shows that the globular clusters have the same apparent rotational velocity as the system of field RR Lyrae cepheids as seen from the sun. Newkirk (1952) shows that the RR Lyrae stars have very eccentric orbits. Von Hoerner (1955) and Perek (1954) show that the globular cluster orbits are also highly eccentric. Preston (1959) proved that the metal-poor RR Lyrae stars have the same velocities as the globular cluster system. We conclude, then, that the RR Lyrae cepheids in the general field have motions similar to those of the globular clusters. This condition is to be expected if the halo field and the globular clusters were formed together. The evidence indicates, therefore, that it can be assumed that the globular cluster system and the field are equivalent.

Globular clusters toward the center of the Galaxy are, on the whole, of later

spectral types, are more metal-rich, and would be expected to exhibit more of
the later formed, disk-star motions. Kinman (1959c) found some evidence
indicating that the interior clusters have a smaller solar motion, that is, a
higher absolute rotation, than the outer ones. He obtains this effect by dividing
clusters according to spectral type and also distance from center:

Solar Motion (U)

149 ± 41 km/sec	$R < 9$ kpc
80 ± 82 km/sec	G0 − G5
183 ± 51 km/sec	$R > 9$ kpc
162 ± 36 km/sec	F2 − F9

Unfortunately, the probable errors are too large for quantitative accuracy, but
they do suggest the mean direction of the effect.

It can be seen from the x, z plane in Figure 9, that the inner globular clusters,
$R < 9$ kpc, show a flattening to the plane, an oblateness which we would expect
of a system formed when rotating. The ratio of semi-major axes by eye estimate
is about 8:5, which gives an ellipticity, $\epsilon = (a - c)/a = \frac{3}{8}$, where a and c are
the major and minor semi-axes. Using an approximate formula from King
(1961), this flattening enables us to estimate the rotational portion, T_{rot}, of the
total internal kinetic energy, T,

$$\frac{T_{\text{rot}}}{T} = \frac{8\epsilon}{5} = \tfrac{3}{5};$$

the ratio of rotational to random kinetic energy is

$$\frac{T_{\text{rot}}}{T_{\text{rand}}} = \left(\frac{5}{8\epsilon} - 1\right)^{-1} = \tfrac{3}{2}.$$

From data given by Kinman (1959c), we estimate that the average, random
line-of-sight velocity for a globular cluster is about ± 120 (± 15) km/sec. Thus,
the above equation would predict that the velocity of rotation, $v_{\text{rot}} \approx 1.22$
$v_{\text{rand}} \approx 147$ (± 18) km/sec. This is in fair agreement with the velocity of rotation of 110 (± 10) km/sec derived at the beginning of this section and demonstrates that the oblateness of the globular cluster system is real and is, dynamically, about as we would expect it to be as a consequence of its rotation. The
outer clusters are much more difficult to judge, but they appear to show no
oblateness in their cross sectional distribution.

REFERENCES

Abell, G. O.	1955	*Pub. A.S.P.*, **67**, 258.
Arp, H. C.	1955	*A.J.*, **60**, 1.
	1956	*Ibid.*, **61**, 15.
	1957	*Ibid.*, **62**, 129.
	1959	*Ibid.*, **64**, 441.

	1961	*Science*, **134**, 810.
	1962*a*	*Ap. J.*, **135**, 311.
	1962*b*	*Ibid.*, p. 971.
ARP, H. C., BAUM, W. A., and SANDAGE, A. R.	1953	*A.J.*, **58**, 4.
ARP, H. C., and BERGH, S. VAN DEN	1960	*Pub. A.S.P.*, **72**, 48.
ARP, H. C., and CUFFEY, J.	1962	*Ap. J.*, **136**, 51.
ARP, H. C., and MELBOURNE, W. G.	1959	*A.J.*, **64**, 28.
BAADE, W.	1944	*Ap. J.*, **100**, 137.
BAUM, W. A., HILTNER, W. A., JOHNSON, H. L., and SANDAGE, A. R.	1959	*Ap. J.*, **130**, 749.
BELSERENE, E. P.	1959	*A.J.*, **64**, 58.
BRANDT, J. C.	1962	*Pub. A.S.P.*, **73**, 324.
BURBIDGE, E. M., and SANDAGE, A. R.	1958	*Ap. J.*, **127**, 527.
CUFFEY, J.	1958	*Ap. J.*, **128**, 219.
DREYER, J. L. E.	1888	*Mem. R.A.S.*, **49**, 1.
EGGEN, O. J., and SANDAGE, A. R.	1959	*M.N.*, **119**, 255.
FEAST, M. W., and THACKERAY, A. D.	1960	*M.N.*, **120**, 463.
FERNIE, J. D.	1962	*A.J.*, **67**, 769.
GASCOIGNE, S. C. B.	1954	*Australian J. Sci.*, **17**; Suppl. **3**, 23.
GASCOIGNE, S. C. B., and BURR, E. J.	1956	*M.N.*, **116**, 570.
GREENSTEIN, J. L.	1939	*Ap. J.* **90**, 387.
HACHENBERG, O.	1939	*Zs. f. Ap.*, **18**, 49.
HODGE, P.	1961	*A.J.*, **66**, 249.
HOERNER, S. VON	1955	*Zs. f. Ap.*, **35**, 255.
HOGG, HELEN SAWYER	1959	*Hdb. d. Phys.*, ed. S. FLÜGGE (Berlin: Springer-Verlag), **53**, 129.
HOLMBERG, E.	1958	*Medd. Lunds Obs.*, Ser. II, No. 136.
HUBBLE, E. P.	1936	*Realm of the Nebulae* (New Haven: Yale University Press).
HUMASON, M. L., MAYALL, N. U., and SANDAGE, A. R.	1956	*A.J.*, **61**, 97.
JOHNSON, H. L., and SANDAGE, A. R.	1956	*Ap. J.*, **124**, 379.
KAMP, P. VAN DE	1930	*A.J.*, **40**, 145.
KING, I.	1961	*A.J.*, **66**, 68.
	1962	*Ibid.*, **67**, 471.

KINMAN, T. D.   1959a *M.N.*, **119**, 157.
                                 1959b *Ibid.*, p. 538.
                                 1959c *Ibid.*, p. 559.
KORT, J. DE   1941   *B.A.N.*, **9**, 189.
KRAFT, R. P., and
  SCHMIDT, M.   1963   *Ap. J.*, **137**, 249.
KRON, G. E., and
  MAYALL, N. U.   1960   *A.J.*, **65**, 581.
LOHMANN, W.   1952   *Zs. f. Ap.*, **30**, 234.
MAYALL, N. U.   1946   *Ap. J.*, **104**, 290.
MORGAN, W. W.   1959   *A.J.*, **64**, 432.
MOWBRAY, A. G.   1946   *Ap. J.*, **104**, 47.
NEWKIRK, J. M.   1952   *Harvard Bull.*, No. 921, 15.
OORT, J. H.   1941   *B.A.N.*, **9**, 193.
OORT, J. H., and
  HERK, G. VAN   1959   *B.A.N.*, **14**, 299.
PARENAGO, P. P.   1947   *A.J. U.S.S.R.*, **24**, 167.
PEREK, L.   1948   *Ann. d'ap.*, **11**, 185.
                                 1954   *Contr. Astr. Inst. Masaryk Univ.*, **1**, No. 12.
PRESTON, G. W.   1959   *Ap. J.*, **130**, 507.
                                 1961   *Ibid.*, **134**, 633.
SANDAGE, A. R.   1954a *A.J.*, **59**, 162.
                                 1954b *Pub. A.S.P.*, **66**, 324.
                                 1956   *Ap. J.*, **123**, 278.
                                 1962   *Ibid.*, **135**, 349.
SANDAGE, A. R., and
  WALKER, M. F.   1955   *A.J.*, **60**, 230.
SANDAGE, A. R., and
  WALLERSTEIN, G.   1960   *Ap. J.*, **131**, 598.
SCHMIDT, M.   1956   *B.A.N.*, **13**, 15.
                                 1961   *Pub. A.S.P.*, **73**, 103.
SCHWARZSCHILD, M., and
  BERNSTEIN, S.   1955   *Ap. J.*, **122**, 200.
SETTEDUCATI, A. F., and
  WEAVER, H. F.   1962   *Newly Found Star Clusters*, Vol. 1 (Berkeley: University of California, Radio Astronomy Laboratory).
SHAPLEY, H.   1917   *Ap. J.*, **45**, 118.
                                 1930   *Star Clusters* (New York: McGraw-Hill Book Co.)
SHAPLEY, H., and
  AMES, A.   1932   *Harvard Ann.*, **88**, No. 2.
SHAPLEY, H., and
  SAWYER, H. B.   1929   *Harvard Bull.*, No. 869, 1.
SHAROV, A. S., and
  PAVLOVSKAYA, E. D.   1961   *A.J. U.S.S.R.*, **38**, 939.

SMITH, L. L., and
  SANDAGE, A. R.   1961   *A.J.*, **67**, 121.
SMITH, L. L., SANDAGE,
  A. R., LYNDEN-BELL, D.,
  and NORTON, R. H.   1963   *A.J.*, **68**, 293.
SPINRAD, H.   1961   *Ap. J.*, **133**, 479.
STEBBINS, J.,
  WHITFORD, A. E., and
  JOHNSON, H. L.   1950   *Ap. J.*, **112**, 469.
WILDEY, R. L.   1961   *Ap. J.*, **133**, 430.
WILSON, O. C., and
  COFFEEN, M.   1954   *Ap. J.*, **119**, 197.
WOOLF, N.   1962   *Ap. J.*, **135**, 644.

CHAPTER **20**

The Concept of Stellar Populations

A. BLAAUW

Kapteyn Laboratory, Groningen

§ 1. INTRODUCTION; HISTORY

THE concept of stellar population types was introduced by Baade (1944*a*, *b*). Baade had succeeded in resolving into individual stars, first, the amorphous central parts of the Andromeda nebula and its elliptical companions M32 and NGC 205, and subsequently, two more members of the Local Group, the dwarf elliptical galaxies NGC 147 and NGC 185. Baade recognized that these resolved stars were identical with the brightest stars in the globular clusters of the Galaxy, and he surmised that the HR diagram of the stars in the elliptical systems was similar to that of the globular clusters. The fact that the globular clusters thus appeared to be typical representatives of a wide category of systems, extending to at least the Local Group of galaxies, led Baade to advance the hypothesis of the existence of two types of stellar populations. The name type II was assigned to the contents of the globular clusters, type I to the population represented by the HR diagram of the stars in the solar neighborhood, more specifically, to the slow moving stars with respect to the local standard of rest. The two types were supposed to coexist in the intermediate and late-type stellar systems as they were found to do in the Galaxy. Plate I is a reproduction of Figure 1 in Baade's original paper; it gives a schematic representation of the HR diagrams of type I (shaded) and type II (hatched).

The concept of the coexistence of different stellar population types was readily accepted at the time of Baade's postulate, although some difference of opinion was expressed, particularly by the Soviet astronomers, as to whether only the two types of Baade should be assumed rather than a series of types with continuously changing characteristics. The general feeling was, however, that the concept of the two populations provided a very suitable working hypothesis for galactic and extragalactic research. It not only formulated in a most concise, although perhaps somewhat oversimplified, manner the existence

435

of different physical subsystems in the Galaxy; it also stressed the evidence for the uniformity, on the extragalactic scale, of the constitution of the universe.

In Baade's original work, the distinction between the two types was primarily one based on the *physical properties*, spectral class, and luminosity, in combination with the *location* of the objects in the systems. Reference to the *kinematic* properties was made only in connection with the high-velocity stars in the Galaxy, which were classified as population II. Soon afterward, kinematic properties became more and more used as an additional—and sometimes even as the most important—parameter. This was possible because the dynamical theory of stellar systems, through the work of Jeans, Lindblad, Oort, and others, had established certain relations between the density distribution and kinematic properties in a system in dynamical equilibrium. These relations are described in chapter 21 of this volume. (Lindblad [1925, 1926, and subsequent papers], in particular, had, on the basis of these theories, arrived at a description of the Galaxy as a superposition of subsystems with varying degrees of flattening and with correspondingly different velocity dispersions and different mean rotational velocities.) The dynamical relations had been successfully checked in a number of cases, and thus a satisfactory basis existed at the time of Baade's postulate for also including the kinematical parameters in the discussion of population types.

At that time, the investigation of the differences between the *chemical compositions* of different stars was still in its initial stage. Uniformity of chemical composition, rather than variations in it, had been the most impressive result of abundance investigations. It is true that Lindblad, in 1922, and others later, had noted the CN bands of the brightest stars in M13 to be weaker than those of giants of similar spectral class in open clusters. Moreover, this CN anomaly had also been observed in high-velocity K giants (Morgan, Keenan, and Kellman 1943), and high-velocity carbon stars with very strong CH bands had been observed by Keenan (1942). However, these findings formed an insufficient basis for correlating observed chemical composition with general distributional or kinematical properties, and no basis at all for relating it to the population types. Yet the obvious explanation for the differences between the HR diagrams of the two populations seemed to lie in differences of chemical composition and of age.

The concept of the stellar populations has provided a research domain of common interest to astronomers working in such different fields as stellar motions, stellar space distribution, stellar spectroscopy, and galactic dynamics. As more and more data became available, and hence the nature and content of the different populations became better known, questions regarding the origin of the populations gained more and more prominence. In this way, the concept of stellar populations has greatly contributed to the intense research into stellar evolution which characterizes astronomy today.

§ 2. BASIC DATA BEARING ON SPACE
DISTRIBUTION AND MOTIONS

Before discussing the classification into population types, we shall briefly review some basic data on space distribution and motions. These are collected in Table 1.

It gives, for the most abundant components of the galactic population and for a number of objects of particular interest, the values of some parameters which characterize the distributional and kinematic properties. Table 1 is a revision of a version given earlier by the author (Blaauw 1951), other revisions of which have been given, among others, by Payne-Gaposchkin (1954) and by Oort (1958).

Column (1) gives the contribution to the local mass density, expressed in solar masses per 1000 pc³. Columns (2) and (3) describe the concentration of the objects to the galactic plane. The quantity $z(0.1)$ in column (2) is the distance from the plane at which the density is one-tenth of that in the plane, and $\langle |z| \rangle$, in column (3), is the mean distance from the plane. Both these quantities hold for a cylinder perpendicular to the plane at the position of the sun. Since ir most cases the density distribution perpendicular to the plane may be de scribed as lying between a Gaussian and an exponential one, the ratio between the quantities $z(0.1)$ and $\langle |z| \rangle$ as a rule lies between 2.7 and 2.3. As both quantities have been used in the literature, we present both in Table 1. The quantity $\partial \log \nu / \partial R$ in column (4) is the logarithmic density gradient parallel to the plane in the solar region of the Galaxy, as it has been derived from the space distribution. Column (5) gives the values of this quantity, as inferred from kinematical properties on the basis of equation (1), to be discussed below. Column (6) gives a qualitative estimate of the degree of concentration based, in most cases, on the apparent distribution of the objects in the sky. Column (7) gives the root-mean-square velocity perpendicular to the galactic plane, σ_Z, and column (8) the asymmetric drift, $S \equiv \Theta_c - \Theta_m$, discussed later. References to the sources of the tabulated quantities are given in the right-hand part of the table.

The numbers in column (1) show the well-known fact that the principal contributors to the local mass density are the interstellar matter (about 17%) and the main-sequence stars of types K and M (about 25%). In computing these percentages, we have adopted the total local mass density of 0.15 solar masses per pc³ given at the bottom of Table 1, column (1), derived from dynamical considerations (Oort 1960). This implies that as much as 43 per cent of the local mass density has not been accounted for in terms of the listed objects. These unknown objects probably have z-distributions like that of the common giants ($\langle |z| \rangle = 550$ pc) or larger mean distances from the plane (see chap. 21). Appreciable contributions are also due to the white dwarfs, and to the main-sequence G, F, and A stars. Integration of the mass densities over a column perpendicular to the galactic plane gives somewhat different relative contribu-

TABLE 1

DATA ON SPACE DISTRIBUTIONS AND MOTIONS

OBJECTS	DENSITY IN SOLAR MASSES (per 1000 pc³) (1)	z(0.1) (pc) (2)	⟨|z|⟩ (pc) (3)	−(∂ LOG ν)/∂R (per kpc near sun) — Directly Observed (4)	−(∂ LOG ν)/∂R — Inferred from Kinematics (5)	CONCENTRATION TO GALACTIC CENTER (6)	KINEMATICS σ_z (km/sec) (7)	KINEMATICS $S \equiv \Theta_c - \Theta_m$ (km/sec) (8)	REFERENCES (1)	(2)	(3)	(4)	(5)	(6)	(7)	(8)
Interstellar Matter	25	280	125			None			1	2,3	2,3					
O–B5	0.11	100	50			None	4		4	5					5	
Cepheids	3×10⁻⁴	140	70			None	5		Derived from 6	Derived from 6	6				5	
Open clusters O–B6	0.03	120	50			} None	} 6		7	Derived from 7	7				} 5	
Open clusters B7–F	0.05	170	80						7	Derived from 7	7					
B8–A5	1.7	200	70			None	9		4	8	8				5	
F	2.5	400	130				14		9	8	8				4	} 10
dG	3.5	550	180	} 0.23	} <0.29		20	< +10	9	8,5	8,1	} 5	} 12		11	
dK	9	800	270				19		9	5	1				11	
dM	29	800	270				19		9	5	1				11	
gG 5–8	0.2	} 550	180				16		8,13	} 8,13	} 8,13				11	
gK 0–5	0.5						17		8,13						11	
gM	0.01						17		8,13						11	
Dark companions	5:								5						1	
White dwarfs	8:						19	+ 23	9						1	10

* The numbers refer to the following sources and remarks which concern the items in the corresponding columns in the left-hand part of this table:

1. Oort (1958); see also chapter 21 in this volume.
2. Van Rhijn (1946, 1949).
3. Schmidt (1957).
4. Derived from data given by McCuskey in chapter 1 of this volume.
5. Blaauw (1951); for the density gradient of main-sequence dwarfs in column (4) we take Oort's (1938) result after reduction by Schmidt to the galactic plane, see section 2.
6. Kraft and Schmidt (1963).
7. Becker (1963); mass densities were computed in the present chapter with an average of 500 solar masses per cluster.
8. Derived from data given by Elvius in chapter 3 of this volume. Elvius' densities for low distances z have in some cases been corrected to bring them into agreement with those presented by McCuskey in chapter 1. This has mainly affected the quantities z(0.1) and ⟨|z|⟩.

9. Gliese (1956).
10. Based on data compiled by Delhaye in chapter 4, Table 2 of this volume.
11. Based on data compiled by Delhaye in chapter 4, Table 1 of this volume.
12. Estimated from Table 2.
13. Oort (1960).
14. Eggen et al. (1962).
15. Oort and van Tulder (1942).
16. Kukarkin (1954).
17. Feast (1963).
18. Plaut (1963); see also chapter 13 in this volume.
19. Perek (1951); see also chapter 13 in this volume.
20. Oort, chapter 21 of this volume.
21. Kinman (1959a).
22. Kinman (1959b).

TABLE 1—*Continued*

OBJECTS	DENSITY IN SOLAR MASSES (per 1000 pc³) (1)	z(0.1) (pc) (2)	⟨|z|⟩ (pc) (3)	−(∂ LOG ν)/∂R (per kpc near sun) Directly Observed (4)	Inferred from Kinematics (5)	CONCENTRATION TO GALACTIC CENTER (6)	KINEMATICS σz (km/sec) (7)	ṡ ≡ Θc−Θm (km/sec) (8)	REFERENCES AND REMARKS* (1)	(2)	(3)	(4)	(5)	(6)	(7)	(8)
Subdwarfs:																
δ(U−B)<0.1	1.5						25		1						14	10
0.1<δ(U−B)<0.2							40	+130							14	
0.2<δ(U−B)<0.3							70								14	
Planetary nebulae			300			Strong										
Novae						Strong										
Long-period variables:																
P<150 d. and >250 d.	10⁻³	1300		0.28			29	+20	5	5		15, 16	17		17	17
200–250 days					0.20		50	+53							17	17
150–200 days							61	+109							17	17
RR Lyrae variables:																
ΔS<5	3×10⁻⁵	1100		0.12	0.32	Strong	34	+51	18	18		19	20		20	20
ΔS≥5		5000			0.12		91	+220		18			20		20	20
RV Tauri variables:																
"low velocity"	<10⁻⁵				0.01:			0:					18			18
"high velocity"					0.14:	Strong		+250:					18			18
Globular clusters:																
G0–G5	10⁻³	6000	2300			Strong	120:	+150	5	21	21				5	22
F6–F9		13000	5400							21	21					
F2–F6		20000	10000							21	21					
Unidentified matter	64															
Total mass	150								1							

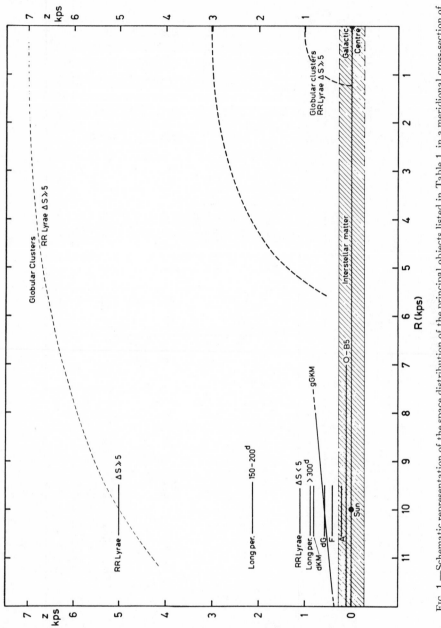

Fig. 1.—Schematic representation of the space distribution of the principal objects listed in Table 1, in a meridional cross-section of the Galaxy through the sun. The horizontal lines in the left-hand part indicate the levels $z(0.1)$ given in column (2). The spheroidal distributions exhibited by the globular clusters and RR Lyrae variables are indicated by the elliptical contours.

tions; the percentage due to the late-type main-sequence stars becomes larger, and the objects with still larger $z(0.1)$ gain even more in importance.

The quantities $\langle|z|\rangle$ and σ_Z are related to each other through the force field, $K(z)$, perpendicular to the plane in the solar neighborhood, at least for stars for which $\langle|z|\rangle$ is small compared to the distance from the galactic center, so that the period of oscillation is short compared to that of the galactic revolution. Thus, we expect for $\sigma_Z = 12.5$ km/sec, $\langle|z|\rangle = 120$ pc, and for $\sigma_Z = 25.0$ km/sec, $\langle|z|\rangle = 300$ pc (values inferred from Oort, chap. 21, Table 1). This condition is satisfactorily met by the relevant objects in Table 1.

Density gradients in the direction toward the galactic center, parallel to the plane, may be derived from studies of the space distribution of a few types of objects only, namely those for which these studies are relatively little hampered by the interstellar absorption (see col. [4]). For the main-sequence dwarf stars we take the value adopted by Schmidt (chap. 22) after reducing Oort's (1938) result for intermediate- and high-latitude dwarfs to the galactic plane. For some objects, like the planetary nebulae and novae, which can be detected up to large distances, the presence of a strong concentration toward the galactic center is revealed by the apparent distribution on the sky. Since the degree of concentration toward the center is an important quantity in population-type considerations, it is important that an estimate of the gradient $\partial \log \nu/\partial R$ may be derived indirectly from some kinematical quantities under the assumption of dynamic equilibrium. These quantities are: the asymmetric drift S given in column (7); the velocity dispersions in the galactic plane, σ_{Π} and σ_{Θ} in the radial and tangential directions, respectively; and the gradient $\partial \sigma_{\Pi}^2/\partial R$. The relation is

$$-\frac{\partial \log \nu}{\partial R} = \frac{\text{Mod}}{R_0}\left[\left(1 - \frac{\sigma_{\Theta}^2}{\sigma_{\Pi}^2}\right) + \left(1 - \frac{\sigma_Z^2}{\sigma_{\Pi}^2}\right) + \frac{1}{\sigma_{\Pi}^2}S(2\Theta_c - S) + \frac{\partial \log \sigma_{\Pi}^2}{\partial \log R}\right], \quad (1)$$

where R is the distance of the galactic center, and Θ_c the circular velocity at R_0 (see also, in chap. 21, eq. [10] of sec. 2.5 and eq. [38] of sec. 4.5).

For practical applications the last term in (1), representing the change of the velocity dispersion σ_{Π} with the distance from the galactic center, may be entirely neglected. Table 2 shows the predicted values of $\partial \log \nu/\partial R$ for different σ_{Π} and S, if we assume: $R_0 = 10$ kpc, $\Theta_c = 250$ km/sec, $\sigma_{\Pi}^2/\sigma_Z^2 = \sigma_{\Pi}^2/\sigma_{\Theta}^2 = 2.5$, the latter ratio corresponding to the rotational constants $A = 15$ km/sec per kpc and $B = -10$ km/sec per kpc, through the relation $\sigma_{\Pi}^2/\sigma_{\Theta}^2 = 1 - (A/B)$. The validity of the value adopted for $\sigma_{\Pi}^2/\sigma_Z^2$ may be argued, but the numerical contribution of the relevant term in equation (1) is virtually insignificant for our present purpose.

The logarithmic density gradients given in column (5) of Table 1 are based on the relevant data in chapters 4, 13, and 21 of this volume. Insofar as both directly and indirectly observed values of the gradient are available, the agreement is satisfactory. Values derived by means of Table 2 may therefore help in estimating the nature of the density distribution of objects for which only kinematical data exist.

The general character of the space distribution of the various kinds of objects of Table 1 is also illustrated in Figure 1 which represents a meridian cross-section of the Galaxy through the sun. The thickness of the layers is indicated by the value of $z(0.1)$. Dashed lines represent, *very schematically*, the spheroidal shape of the equidensity surfaces of the systems of the globular clusters and of the RR Lyrae variables.

Figure 1 demonstrates the enormous differences between the distributions of different objects. They range from the extreme flatness of the layers of the interstellar matter, and of the earliest types of stars, to the nearly spherical and strongly centrally concentrated distribution of the globular clusters.

TABLE 2

THE DENSITY GRADIENT $-\partial \log \nu/\partial R$ PER KPC ACCORDING TO
EQ. (1) FOR VARIOUS VALUES OF σ_{II} AND S

σ_{II} km/sec	S (km/sec)						
	5	10	30	50	100	150	200
10......	1.13	2.19	....	....	....	....	....
20......	0.32	0.59	1.59	2.50	....	....	....
30......	0.18	0.29	0.74	1.14	1.99	2.59	2.96
40......	0.12	0.19	0.44	0.67	1.14	1.48	1.69
60......	0.09	0.12	0.23	0.33	0.54	0.69	0.78
80......	0.07	0.09	0.15	0.26	0.33	0.41	0.46
120......	0.06	0.07	0.10	0.12	0.18	0.21	0.24

The kinematical and distributional properties of the components of the galactic population, shown in Figure 2 and Table 1, were mostly known at the time of Baade's postulate of the two population types. This knowledge, together with increasing evidence on the differences between the physical properties of the objects of the "flat" and the "spherical" systems, and the recognition of the same state of affairs in M31, provided the fertile ground for the further development of the concept of populations I and II.

§ 3. THE SCHEME OF POPULATION TYPES OF
THE VATICAN CONFERENCE (1957)

The profound influence of the concept of stellar-population types on galactic research in the first decade following Baade's postulate is reflected by the report on the "Semaine d'étude on the problem of the stellar populations," a conference organized by the Vatican Academy of Sciences in 1957 (O'Connell 1958). By the time of this conference, the available data on distributional, kinematical, and chemical abundance properties called for a more detailed subdivision into populations than Baade's. Accordingly, the intermediary type "disk population" was added to the types I and II, and these three were then subdivided into five categories representing a more or less continuous series of properties, ranging from "halo population II" to "extreme population I" (see Table 3). In some, mostly minor, respects, the arrangement represented a compromise between different points of view.

The assignments in Table 3 must be seen against the background of a picture of the evolution of the Galaxy which, although admittedly conjectural, was generally considered to be a fruitful working hypothesis at the Vatican Conference and has remained so since.

The velocity dispersions were supposed to be correlated with the ages of the stars. The oldest objects, halo population II, were thought to be born at a time when the mass of gas from which the Galaxy was formed must have had an irregular shape, without a sensible concentration to a disk or a center. Apparently, in the course of time, the stars formed during this stage became thoroughly mixed, and formed a system which was symmetrical around an axis and had a plane of symmetry perpendicular to this axis. The original mass of gas must have had an appreciable resultant angular momentum; this determined the direction of the axis of symmetry of the Galaxy. In the process of rearrangement the halo population must have become concentrated to the center, the measure of concentration being determined by the irregular motions in the primeval body of gas and the gravitational potential of the system as it finally evolved. But there is no way in which the mixing process could lead to a considerable flattening: in respect to flattening, the system of the primeval stars must have conserved roughly the same shape as the original mass of gas from which it emerged.

That part of the gas which was not condensed into stars in these early phases evolved in a different manner. It contracted under its own gravitation, gradually transforming its original potential and kinetic energy into heat and radiation through collisions of clouds, or through mixing of large-scale internal streams. The contraction may finally have resulted in a thin disk, with strong concentration toward the center.

Stars must have formed during the contracting stage as well as after its completion. The former will have formed "systems" of intermediate flattening. These are the stars referred to as intermediate population II. The stars born after the gas had completely contracted should all lie close to the galactic plane. The process of star formation must have been fastest where the gas was densest. It is therefore likely that the star formation in the disk in its earliest stage was strongly concentrated to the center. After this early stage it must have gradually slowed down, though it is continuing up to the present time. The stars formed in the last half-billion years or so of the last stage are called population I stars. They are the ones that in their distribution and motions have conserved evidence of the irregular, probably spiral, structure in which they were born.

The lifetimes of the evolutionary stages corresponding to the various popula-

TABLE 3

The Classification of Stellar Populations at the Vatican Conference of 1957

	POPULATION II		DISK POPULATION	POPULATION I	
	Halo Pop. II	Intermediate Pop. II		Older Pop. I	Extreme Pop. I
	Subdwarfs	High-velocity stars with z-velocities > 30 km/sec	Stars of galactic nucleus	A-type stars	Gas
	Globular clusters		Planetary nebulae	Strong-line stars	Young stars associated with the present spiral structure
	RR Lyrae stars with periods longer than 0.4 days	Long-period variables with periods <250 days and spectral types earlier than M5e	Novae	Me dwarfs	Supergiants
			RR Lyrae stars with periods <0.4 days		Cepheids
			Weak-line stars		T Tauri stars
					Galactic clusters of Trumpler's class I
$\langle|z|\rangle$ (parsecs)	2000	700	400	160	120
$\langle|Z|\rangle$ (km/sec)	75	25	17	10	8
Axial ratio of spheroidal distribution	2	5	25?	?	100
Concentration toward center	Strong	Strong	Strong?	Little	Little
Distribution	Smooth	Smooth	Smooth?	Patchy, spiral arms	Extremely patchy, spiral arms
$z_{h.e.}$	0.003	0.01	0.02	0.03	0.04
Age (10⁹ years)	6	6.0 to 5.0	1.5 to 5.0	0.1 to 1.5	<0.1
Total mass (10⁹ ⊙)	16	47		5	2

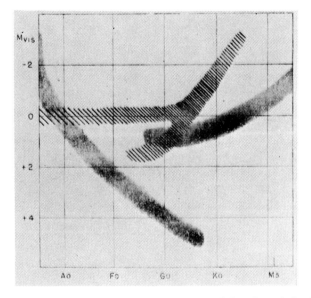

PLATE I.—The different HR diagrams of population I (shaded) and population II (hatched), reproduced from Baade's first paper on the stellar populations (Baade 1944a).

tion subgroups, as they were estimated at the time of the Vatican Conference, are indicated in the second line from the bottom of Table 3. The assignment of the values $Z_{h.e.}$ (the interstellar abundance of elements heavier than helium expressed in the ratio between their total mass and that of hydrogen) in the line next to the ages, implies that the chemical abundances were supposed to be a monotonic function of the age of the Galaxy. Since the distributional and the kinematical parameters, i.e., $\langle |z| \rangle$, σ_Z, the axial ratio of the spheroidal space distribution, and the degree of concentration to the galactic center, were also supposed to change monotonically with age, the scheme of Table 3 is essentially a one-dimensional one. The desirability of introducing a second dimension, by allowing stars to be simultaneously formed with different chemical abundances, possibly in different regions of the Galaxy, was contemplated at the Vatican Conference, but the assumption of a unique relation between chemical constitution and age appeared to be satisfactory at that time. With respect to the modern view on these matters, we draw attention to the remarks at the end of this chapter.

The assignment, in Table 3, of various kinds of stars to these population types was based on either the distributional or on such kinematical properties as are represented in Table 1, sometimes in combination with the spectroscopic properties. Since for most kinds of objects only one or two of these properties were well known, the picture of the evolution of the Galaxy described before served to tie them together in one comprehensive system. Examples of objects classified on the basis of such partial information are: the subdwarfs (classified primarily on the basis of the kinematic and spectroscopic properties, with no direct information on space distribution); novae (primarily based on space distribution, with no data on motions); weak-line and strong-line stars (based on kinematic and spectroscopic properties, with no direct information on the differences between their large-scale distributions in the Galaxy); Me dwarfs (based on kinematic properties, with no data on space distribution); etc. On the whole, the kinematic properties played an important role in the proposed classifications; this is easily understood because for many objects little or nothing was known about their large-scale space distribution, whereas the kinematics were well known for many of the nearest objects. Table 3 also gives an estimate of the total masses contained in the various subdivisions. These estimates were based on models of the mass distribution in the Galaxy, chosen so as to fit the known kinematical properties and the local mass density and density gradients. If such models are composed of different subsystems whose properties roughly correspond to those of the three main categories of the population of Table 3, it is found that the disk population contains about 70 per cent of the total mass (see, for instance, Perek [1959]).

This most massive component is, unfortunately, the one for which the distributional properties are the least well known, and it is therefore the one most in need of further investigation. An important problem is its subdivision into components with different degrees of central concentration. Among these are such conspicuous objects as the novae and the planetary nebulae (see chaps. 14 and 15), which show pronounced central concentration without considerable extension perpendicular to the galactic plane, but these represent a negligible fraction of the mass. For the majority of the kinds of stars in the disk, research on these properties is hampered by the prohibitively large interstellar absorption and by the fact that this population contains no objects of high luminosity like population I. The most promising objects for determining the large-scale density distribution are the red giants, through the spectral classification in the near infrared (see chap. 12).

These difficulties are also the reasons why the question of subdividing the disk population into categories with different degrees of central concentration formed a controversial subject at the Vatican Conference. We do not know how much larger the concentration toward the galactic center of the bright red giants is as compared to that of the weak-line stars. Some light may be thrown on this problem by studies of the spectral properties of the central and outer parts of other stellar systems, like M31, but this cannot, obviously, replace the direct information pertaining to the Galaxy itself.

§ 4. MODERN WORK ON THE RELATION BETWEEN THE KINEMATICAL AND DISTRIBUTIONAL PROPERTIES AND CHEMICAL PARAMETERS

Since the scheme of the Vatican Symposium was drawn up, emphasis in research of the stellar populations has been on finding ways to distinguish components of the galactic population by means of parameters indicating the chemical composition.

With regard to the globular clusters, which played such an important role in Baade's early work, we mention the results obtained by Kinman (1959a, b). This author gave, among other items, data on spectral classifications and on the galactic positions of 63 globular clusters. For the objects with strong metal lines, a mean distance $\langle |z| \rangle$ was found of about 2 kpc, whereas for those with weak metal lines $\langle |z| \rangle$ was found to be between 5 and 6 kpc. These results are in qualitative agreement with the picture described before of the galactic collapse accompanied by enrichment with metals. Kinman's work was preceded by investigations of the spectra of globular clusters by Mayall and by Morgan, for an account of which we refer to Morgan (1956, 1959).

4.1. ROMAN'S CLASSIFICATION INTO STRONG-LINE AND WEAK-LINE STARS

Of particular significance are those investigations which deal with the components of the population representing the bulk of the galactic mass, i.e., the main-sequence and the giant types of Table 1, also referred to as the "common stars." These belong to the difficult to disentangle disk population. The modern work on this problem was preceded and induced by the recognition by Roman (1950) of the existence among the late F and early G stars of the "strong-line"

and "weak-line" stars with different kinematical properties. In the solar neighborhood these two categories together form about 85 per cent of the types mentioned. A similar subdivision was subsequently introduced by Roman among
the G8 to K1 giants. The strong-line stars have generally low velocities, the
weak-line stars higher velocities, and they occur in about equal numbers in the
solar neighborhood. The publication of a list of spectral classifications, including
these characteristics for the stars brighter than 5.5 visual magnitude and north
of declination $-20°$, by the same author (Roman 1952), as well as a list of high-
velocity stars (Roman 1955), have provided a basis for detailed researches into
these properties. In addition to the strong-line and weak-line stars, Roman introduced two more groups: the "4150" stars which, although spectroscopically
distinct from the weak-line stars, seem to have the same kinematical properties,
and the "weak CN" stars which have very high velocities. The strong-line and

TABLE 4

PROPORTIONS OF THE VARIOUS SUBGROUPS
AMONG THE K-GIANTS

SUBGROUP	$\langle |Z| \rangle$ (km/sec)	FRACTION OF ALL K GIANTS	
		at $z = 0$	at $z = 1000$ pc
(1)	(2)	(3)	(4)
Strong-line.............	8.9	0.42	0.015
Weak-line.............	14.9	.42	.250
"High-velocity"........	24.0	.15	.577
"Halo-type"..........	56.2	0.01	0.158

weak-line stars were subsequently recognized also among the faint stars by
Vyssotsky and Skumanich (1953).

For the K giants, the proportions of stars belonging to these subgroups have
been the subject of analyses by Hill (1960) and Oort (1960), in connection with
the derivation of the force $K(z)$. Of the population of these types in the galactic
plane, the strong-line stars form about 42 per cent, the weak-line stars also 42
per cent, the high-velocity component 15 per cent, and in addition, according to
Oort, there is probably a very high velocity component belonging to the halo
population II, contributing about one per cent. The mean velocities in the z-
direction of these four groups are in the second column of Table 4. At larger distances from the plane, these proportions change for obvious reasons: column
(4) of Table 4 gives the percentages at $z = 1000$ pc as they were estimated by
Oort (see also Perek [1959] for similar estimates). At that level, the strong-line
stars contribute only 1.5 per cent of the total population, the majority being
high-velocity stars. At still larger distances, the relative proportion of the
"halo" type must increase more and more.

One of the important conclusions which follows from these computations is that the types of stars which form the majority of the population at distances beyond 1000 pc from the plane, form only an almost negligible fraction of the bright nearby population. The question of the difference between the concentration toward the galactic center, which probably accompanies the difference in the concentration toward the plane, is therefore difficult to solve by means of investigations of the density distribution of the bright stars.

The spectral classifications used by Roman for her division into subclasses were the result of visual inspection of spectrograms of low dispersion (about 100 A/mm). They therefore were not a suitable basis for studies of the population differences in terms of quantitative measures of the metal abundance, nor did they lend themselves to extensions of this work to the more distant, fainter stars by other observers in such a way that homogeneity of the classification system would be preserved. For this purpose the visual estimates had to be replaced by quantitative photometric or spectrophotometric measures. It was suspected, though, that the differences between the weak-line and the strong-line stars were due to differences in the relative metal contents, and accordingly criteria were sought which are a measure of the metal content. In the following section, we shall briefly describe some of these criteria which deserve particular attention: the ultraviolet excess, Strömgren's metal index m, van den Bergh's criteria, and Preston's ΔS, and refer to their relation with quantitative abundance measures.

4.2. Some Currently Used Metal-Abundance Parameters

4.2.1. *Ultraviolet excesses.*—A relation between the ultraviolet excess and high velocity was shown to exist by Roman (1954) for seventeen F-type stars. Since it was demonstrated that the UV excess is a measure of the metal abundance (see, for instance, Schwarzschild, Searle, and Howard [1955] and Wildey, Burbidge, Sandage, and Burbidge [1962]), it has become a powerful tool in studying population characteristics. We refer in particular to recent discussions by Eggen, Lynden-Bell, and Sandage (1962), and to two notes by Dixon (1963*a*, *b*). For the definition of the UV excess, denoted by $\delta(U - B)$, see, for instance, Sandage and Eggen (1959).

Eggen, Lynden-Bell, and Sandage, analyzing motions and photometry of a sample of dwarf stars, discuss among other items the relation between $\delta(U - B)$ and the velocity component Z perpendicular to the galactic plane (denoted by W by these authors); it is reproduced in our Figure 2. Dots are bright, nearby stars, circles are a sample of high-velocity stars. It is evident that, with increasing UV excess, high velocities are increasingly frequent. The fact that we are dealing with a selection of high-velocity stars prevents the derivation, from these data, of the relation between the UV excess and the mean-velocity component $\langle |Z| \rangle$. However, the diagram confirms quite convincingly the collapse theory referred to earlier in this chapter, according to which the earliest star formation, out of matter with low metal abundance, occurred at much larger mean distances from the galactic plane than the present star formation.

Dixon, using Cape photometry of nearby stars, considers the distribution of the main-sequence stars in the $U - B$, $B - V$ plane. He shows that it allows separation of an older population, with various metal contents, from the younger population, among which low metal content is very rare. The boundary between the two groups corresponds approximately with the blanketing

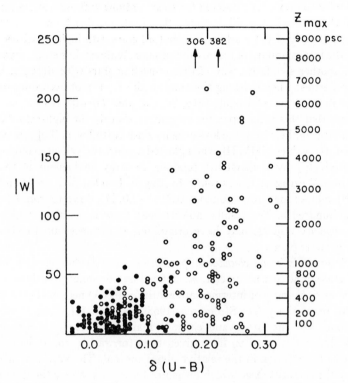

Fig. 2.—The correlation between the velocity perpendicular to the galactic plane, here indicated by $|W|$, and the UV excess $\delta(U - B)$ of G dwarfs according to Eggen *et al.* (1962). Dots are bright, nearby stars; circles are a selection of high-velocity stars.

line for stars of a given bolometric absolute magnitude. Dixon's diagram, therefore, may be interpreted as showing that for ages below the maximum age corresponding to a given bolometric absolute magnitude, star formation took place almost exclusively with high metal content, in marked contrast with the preceding stages.

Studies like these have shown the usefulness of the UV excess as a population parameter. The relation between the UV excess and measures of metal abundances for main-sequence spectral types around G0 has been comprehensively discussed by Wallerstein (1962), who incorporated earlier abundance and UV-excess determinations by other authors. A narrow correlation appeared to exist between $\delta(U - B)$ and the iron abundance, the latter represented by the quantity [Fe/H] = log (abundance Fe/abundance H)$_{star}$ minus log (abundance Fe/abundance H)$_{sun}$. The relation would seem to allow, for the types of stars considered, translation of UV-excess measures into the quantity [Fe/H], and thus to provide metal-abundance values for larger numbers of stars. Of great significance for the study of stellar populations is Wallerstein's U, V velocity diagram (velocity components corrected for solar motion) with discrimination according to the values of [Fe/H]. It shows that both metal-rich and metal-poor stars occur in nearly circular orbits, but that all stars with high velocities with respect to the local standard of rest are metal-poor. Wallerstein's study revealed, moreover, another significant way of discriminating stars with different kinematical properties: when marking the stars in the U, V plot according to the abundance ratio of the a-elements (Mg, Sc, Ca, and Ti) with respect to iron, it was found that this ratio separates even more sharply the high-velocity objects (with large [a/Fe]) from the low-velocity ones (with low [a/Fe]). As would be expected, the values of [Fe/H], when plotted against the velocity component $|Z|$ (denoted $|W|$ by Wallerstein), produce an array analoguous to that of $|W|$ against UV excess as it was found by Eggen, Lynden-Bell, and Sandage. The [Fe/H] values range from around +0.5 to −2.0, i.e., down to iron deficiencies of one-hundredth. The results indicate that these latter stars, which are very high-velocity objects, may have originated at distances up to 6000 pc above the galactic plane.

4.2.2. *Strömgren's metal-abundance parameter, m_1.*—Strömgren has introduced a metal-abundance parameter, m_1, defined by photometry in three wavelength regions u, b, and y of intermediate width (∼400 A) near λ 4110, λ 4670, and λ 5470, respectively (see Strömgren [1963] and Vol. III, chap. 9, of this Compendium]. For the late F and early G main-sequence stars, Strömgren shows that the variation of m_1 for a given type (or, rather, for a given color $b − y$) is due to variation in the relative metal content. The variation of m_1 is denoted by the quantity Δm_1, which measures for a given $b − y$ the difference in m_1 with respect to the m_1, $b − y$ relation of the Hyades main sequence, with positive Δm_1 indicating metal deficiency. A plot of Δm_1 against Wallerstein's values of [Fe/H] referred to in the preceding section shows a linear relation with negligible cosmical scatter. It has the form [Fe/H] = 0.3 − 1.2 Δm_1. Hence, measures of m_1 for the spectral types concerned may be used as an equivalent of the direct abundance determinations. As is to be expected, a narrow correlation of m_1 with UV excess exists also. The measures of the metal-content parameter were extended, with Strömgren's filters, to late G stars by Borgman (1959).

4.2.3. *Van den Bergh's criteria.*—Van den Bergh (1963) and van den Bergh and Henry (1962) have drawn attention to two photometric parameters which may be profitably used for classification according to metal abundance in G stars. One, denoted by Δ, measures the discontinuity near λ 4000, the other, r, the ratio of the continuum intensities on either side of Hζ. Plots of Δ against $B − V$ clearly show separate arrays depending on the metal content of these stars, and the same holds for plots of r against $B - V$. Thus observations of $B - V$ and Δ in late F and G stars allow evaluation of $\delta(U - B)$, and the same holds for observations of $B - V$ and r in late G stars. The feasibility of measuring the parameter Δ also in globular clusters, and its correlation with Morgan's (1959) metallic line-strength classification, promises extension of the quantitative metal-contents observations to these objects.

4.2.4. *Preston's quantity ΔS in cluster variables.*—We finally refer to the quantity ΔS introduced by Preston (1959) to measure the metal deficiency in cluster-type variables. It is defined as $\Delta S = 10 \left[\text{Sp (H)} - \text{Sp (Ca II)} \right]$, measuring the difference between the spectral types deduced from the hydrogen and from the Ca II lines. The relation between ΔS and the kinematic properties of these stars has been demonstrated by Preston (see Table 1 and chaps. 13 and 21 of this volume).

In a coarse analysis of three RR Lyrae stars, Preston (1961) has made a first step toward establishing the relation between ΔS and chemical abundance. For these three stars, whose values of ΔS are 2, 6, and 10, the values of [Fe/H] are found to be 0.0, -1.2, and -2.8, respectively, thus clearly confirming the low metal content for the types with largest ΔS. More stars and more refined analysis will be required to establish the exact relation and its scatter. It is clear that the parameter ΔS, via the relation with [Fe/H], may allow this important class of variable stars to be studied in terms of a common parameter with the main-sequence objects discussed in the preceding paragraphs.

4.3. Conclusions

As the measures of metal abundances accumulate, either directly or indirectly by means of the parameters described in the preceding section, and as the data on stellar distribution and kinematics increase, more and more refined subdivision of the galactic population into chemically defined subgroups will be possible as a basis for the study of galactic evolution.

Important progress along these lines has been made already. A detailed account of current work on the evolution of the Galaxy is beyond the scope of this chapter, but we shall refer briefly to some results which seem to be of great significance. Investigations along various lines indicate that the collapse from the halo to the disk has proceeded in a short lapse of time as compared to the age of the Galaxy, 10^9 years or less, and that already during these first evolutionary stages considerable metal enrichment of the interstellar medium took place and, consequently, considerable increase of the metal contents of the stars formed out of it. We refer to the compilation of the ages and chemical compositions of galactic and globular clusters by Arp (1962), indicating increase of [Fe/H] up to almost its present average value during the first quarter of the age of the Galaxy; to statistical considerations with regard to the rates of star formation and of metal creation by Schmidt (1963) and by van den Bergh (1962); to the studies of samples of stars by Wallerstein (1962) and by Eggen, Lynden-Bell, and Sandage (1962); and to the discussions held at the Herstmonceux colloquium on Star Clusters and Stellar Evolution (Eggen and Herbig 1964).

In the scheme of stellar populations of Table 3, narrow correlation between age and chemical composition was assumed. The degree to which *variations* of the metal abundances, either as a function of R or locally, have occurred at given epochs is the subject of present investigation. Evidence for the occur-rence of galactic clusters of fairly recent formation and of equal age but of different chemical composition has been presented by Arp (1962).

It must be anticipated that, in the course of these new developments, the subdivision of the galactic population into types, such as those represented by Table 3, will be gradually replaced by one using more exact chemical-abundance parameters such as those described before, in combination with the data on stellar kinematics and space distribution.

REFERENCES

ARP, H. C.	1962	"Problems of Extragalactic Research," *I.A.U. Symp.*, No. 15, p. 42.
BAADE, W.	1944a	*Ap. J.*, **100**, 137; *Mt. W. Contr.*, No. 696.
	1944b	*Ap. J.*, **100**, 147; *Mt. W. Contr.*, No. 697.
BECKER, W.	1963	*Zs. f. Ap.*, **57**, 117.
BERGH, S. VAN DEN	1962	*A.J.*, **67**, 486.
	1963	*Ibid.*, **68**, 413.
BERGH, S. VAN DEN, and		
HENRY, R. C.	1962	*Pub. David Dunlap Obs., Toronto*, **2**, 281.
BLAAUW, A.	1951	*Nederlands Tijdschrift voor Natuurkunde*, **27**, 31.
BORGMAN, J.	1959	*Ap. J.*, **129**, 362.
DIXON, M. E.	1963a	*Observatory*, **83**, 30.
	1963b	*Ibid.*, p. 170.
EGGEN, O. J., and		
HERBIG, G. H.	1964	*Royal Obs. Bull.*, No. 82.
EGGEN, O. J., LYNDEN-BELL, D., and		
SANDAGE, A. R.	1962	*Ap. J.*, **136**, 748.
FEAST, M. W.	1963	*M.N.*, **125**, 367.
GLIESE, W.	1956	*Zs. f. Ap.*, **39**, 1.
HILL, E. R.	1960	*B.A.N.*, **15**, 1.
KEENAN, P. C.	1942	*Ap. J.*, **96**, 101; *Contr. McDonald Obs.*, No. 51.
KINMAN, T. D.	1959a	*M.N.*, **119**, 538.
	1959b	*Ibid.*, p. 559.
KRAFT, R. P., and		
SCHMIDT, M.	1963	*Ap. J.*, **137**, 249.
KUKARKIN, B. V.	1954	*Erforschung der Struktur und Entwicklung der Sterne auf der Grundlage des Studiums veränderlicher Sterne* (Berlin: Akademie-Verlag).
LINDBLAD, B.	1925	*Ark. f. Mat., Astr., och Fysik*, **19A**, No. 21.
	1926	*Ibid.*, **19B**, No. 7.

MORGAN, W. W.   1956   *Pub. A.S.P.*, **68**, 509.

     1959   *A.J.*, **64**, 432.

MORGAN, W. W.,
   KEENAN, P. C., and
   KELLMAN, E.   1943   *An Atlas of Stellar Spectra* (Chicago: University of Chicago Press).

O'CONNELL, D. J. K.   1958   *Ric. Astr. Specola Vaticana*, **5** ("Stellar Populations").

OORT, J. H.   1938   *B.A.N.*, **8**, 233.

     1958   *Ric. Astr. Specola Vaticana*, **5**, 415 ("Stellar Populations").

     1960   *B.A.N.*, **15**, 45.

OORT, J. H., and
   TULDER, J. J. M. VAN   1942   *B.A.N.*, **9**, 327.

PAYNE-GAPOSCHKIN, C.   1954   *Variable Stars and Galactic Structure* (London: Athlone Press).

PEREK, L.   1951   *Contr. Astr. Inst. Masaryk Univ., Brno*, **1**, No. 8.

     1959   *Bull. Astr. Inst. Czechoslovakia*, **10**, 15.

PLAUT, L.   1963   *B.A.N.*, **17**, 81.

PRESTON, G.   1959   *Ap. J.*, **130**, 507; *Contr. Lick Obs.*, Ser. II, No. 96.

     1961   *Ap. J.*, **134**, 633.

RHIJN, P. J. VAN   1946   *Pub. Kapteyn Astr. Lab.*, No. 50.

     1949   *Ibid.*, No. 53.

ROMAN, N. G.   1950   *Ap. J.*, **112**, 554.

     1952   *Ibid.*, **116**, 122.

     1954   *A.J.*, **59**, 307.

     1955   *Ap. J. Suppl.*, **2**, 195.

SANDAGE, A. R., and
   EGGEN, O. J.   1959   *M.N.*, **119**, 278.

SCHMIDT, M.   1957   *B.A.N.*, **13**, 247.

     1963   *Ap. J.*, **137**, 758.

SCHWARZSCHILD, M.,
   SEARLE, L., and
   HOWARD, R.   1955   *Ap. J.*, **122**, 353.

STRÖMGREN, B.   1963   *Quart. J. R.A.S.*, **4**, 8.

VYSSOTSKY, A. N., and
   SKUMANICH, A.   1953   *A.J.*, **58**, 96.

WALLERSTEIN, G.   1962   *Ap. J. Suppl.*, **6**, 407.

WILDEY, R. L.,
   BURBIDGE, E. M.,
   SANDAGE, A. R., and
   BURBIDGE, G. R.   1962   *Ap. J.*, **135**, 94.

CHAPTER 21

Stellar Dynamics

J. H. OORT
Leiden Observatory
with a Section on Three-dimensional Orbits by
A. OLLONGREN
University of Leiden

THIS chapter deals with the part of stellar dynamics that is directly related to the structure of the Galactic System and the motions of its members. No attempt has been made to present a complete report on the many investigations that have been carried out in this domain. Such a report would have surpassed the scope of the present work. Moreover, excellent general accounts have appeared in various textbooks on stellar dynamics. In particular, the reader may be referred to the recent, rather complete, survey of galactic dynamics given by Lindblad (1959) in Volume 53 of the *Encyclopedia of Physics*. To repeat this in the present Compendium would have been neither useful nor efficient. For the same reasons no derivations are given for the formulae. These can be found in the references given at the end of the chapter.

In selecting the themes to be treated more specifically, emphasis has been laid, first, on the problems permitting direct confrontation with observations and, second, on subjects in which special advances have been made in recent years.

§ 1. AIMS OF DYNAMICS OF THE GALACTIC SYSTEM

The aim of stellar dynamics may be described as follows. Starting from an observed density and velocity distribution of stars, we wish to derive the relations between these two distributions. These relations will depend on the gravitational field and on whether the system considered is in dynamical equilibrium. If there is evidence, either from the observations themselves or from theoretical considerations, that an approximately steady state has been attained, the theory of stellar dynamics may serve to derive the gravitational field and, therefore, to determine the mass distribution in the system. If the system is *not* in a steady state, stellar dynamics can contribute to finding the way in which velocity and density distribution will change with time, and, in particular, to obtaining information on how they must have been in the past.

The problem of how a dynamically steady state should be defined and how one can ascertain whether dynamical equilibrium has been attained will be considered in the following section.

Ultimately, we aim at a still further goal. We want to know why stellar systems are built such as they are. In some few cases, for instance in star clusters, the answer can largely be found from stellar-dynamical considerations. Usually, however, conditions are too complicated, and one must introduce gas-dynamical considerations. In the Galaxy, for instance, we observe that different types of stars show widely diverse distributions in space as well as in velocity. These differences cannot simply be explained as due to differences in age and in dynamical evolution of the stars concerned. They must principally be connected with the evolution of the mass of *gas* from which the stars have condensed. Therefore, in order to understand the complicated structure of our Galaxy, we would have to understand how the primordial lump of gas contracted to a disk and in what stages of this contraction various types of stars were formed. The problem is thus primarily one of the evolution of a mass of gas with presumably large-scale internal currents, and of the star-formation processes in such an evolving mass.

The main part of this evolution lies far in the past, but the distribution and motions of stars are also influenced by gas-dynamical processes that are taking place at the present time. Stars are formed in spiral arms, and the structure and motions of these arms are determined by the dynamics of the interstellar gas and possibly by the magnetic fields embedded in this gas. While we can still apply stellar dynamics to investigate what happens to the stars after they have been formed, the causes which shape and maintain spiral arms may include, besides gravitation, purely gas-dynamical phenomena, such as collisions between gas clouds. These lie outside the domain treated in the present chapter.

§ 2. DYNAMICAL EQUILIBRIUM

2.1. INTRODUCTION

It is evident from the presence of spiral structure that the Galaxy has no axial symmetry, and that it has not reached a steady state. But the interstellar gas, and the bright young stars which are the most prominent constituents of the spiral arms, may represent only a small fraction of the total mass of the system, the bulk of which probably consists of much older stars. These older stars may well have made an approach to an axially symmetrical distribution and to a dynamically steady state. It is, therefore, useful to study the conditions which the density and velocity distributions should fulfil if there were a steady state.

Before doing so we shall try to estimate which fraction of the mass still consists of gas and very young stars. From measures of the 21-cm line the average density of H I in the region surrounding the sun may be estimated as 1.3 × 10^{-24} g/cm³. Adding 10 per cent H II, 15 per cent He, and 0.4 × 10^{-24} g/cm³ for extreme population I stars (Me dwarfs), we arrive at a total of 2.0 × 10^{-24} g/cm³ or 0.030 solar masses per pc³. The density of all stars younger than 10^9 years, including all stars earlier than F0, is roughly 0.004 solar masses per pc³. To the density just mentioned an unknown amount of molecular hydrogen must still be added. There are, as yet, no observations from which the density of H_2 can be determined. Nor can the processes by which H_2 molecules are formed and dissociated be evaluated with sufficient approximation to make a significant estimate of the average relative density of these molecules. All that can be said at the moment is that the ratio of the average mass density of molecular hydrogen to that of atomic hydrogen will probably lie between 0.1 and 10 (cf. Gould, Gold, and Salpeter 1963).

As we shall see in Section 3.1.3, the total mass density near the sun is approximately 0.150 solar masses per pc³. Of this density about 0.060 can be attributed to known stars, and, as estimated above, about 0.030 to known interstellar gas and extreme population I stars. We do not know how the rest is divided between invisible stars and invisible gas. If it were all stellar, we would conclude that about 80 per cent of the mass density near the sun would be made up of older stars. This is for a *volume* element near the sun. If we consider the mass contained in a *cylinder* perpendicular to the galactic plane we find that the contribution by older stars is about 92 per cent. For the entire Galaxy the combined mass of the interstellar gas and the stars in the galactic disk, excluding the stars concentrated to the center, which were presumably formed soon after the initial contraction of the Galaxy, is estimated to be about 3/100 of the total mass of the Galaxy.

In this case the gravitational field in the system must be almost entirely due to stars formed in an early stage of the evolution of the Galaxy, stars which have made about 100 revolutions, and which therefore may have assumed a smooth distribution. To some extent this can be verified from direct observations: a study of the counts of faint stars in Kapteyn's Selected Areas indicates a rather smooth distribution in galactic latitude as well as in longitude for the areas above 10° latitude, where absorption effects are sufficiently small to be adequately corrected for. The region covered does not extend to more than about 1.5 kpc from the sun, but this is enough to show the smooth increase of the density of these stars toward the galactic plane as well as toward the galactic center.

Alternatively, if all the unknown mass is assumed to consist of molecular hydrogen, the local density of gas and extreme population I must be 0.15 (cf. Sec. 3.1.3) as against 0.06 for the older stars. Of the total mass in a cylinder perpendicular to the galactic plane 51 per cent then consists of interstellar gas, while of the total mass of the Galaxy as much as 15 per cent is gaseous. However, so high a density of the interstellar medium appears to conflict with the steep gradient in the total mass density in the general vicinity of the sun, which follows from the way in which the circular velocity varies with the distance from the center. For a discussion of this important problem the reader is referred to Section 3.1.3. It appears from that discussion that the mass of gas contained in a cylinder perpendicular to the galactic plane must be less than 20 per cent of the total. The total amount of gas in the Galaxy must be less than 5 per cent of the mass of the system.

It thus appears that the bulk of the system must in any case consist of old stars, and that, therefore, we may have a gravitational field which, at least for the higher velocity stars, can in first approximation be considered to be axially symmetrical.

That older systems can actually reach smooth conditions throughout is shown by the elliptical galaxies. The appearance of these galaxies suggests strongly that they have attained some kind of equilibrium, and that the application of the equations of dynamical equilibrium is meaningful. We shall have to investigate how far these are also meaningful in the case of the Galaxy.

2.2. The Distribution Function; Liouville's Theorem; Equation of Poisson

We can describe a stellar system by the distribution of density and velocities throughout the system. This will have to be given for each type of stars and also for the interstellar gas. The quantities referring to the gas will be indicated by a subscript g. In the following we shall deal almost exclusively with the stars.

Let x, y, z be rectangular coordinates, U, V, W the corresponding velocities, and $f(M, x, y, z, U, V, W, t)$ the distribution function for stars of a given type, characterized by the letter M. This function is not entirely arbitrary. Besides the obvious condition that it must be always positive or zero, it must satisfy a condition of continuity. The stars which at a time t_1 lie in a volume $dx_1\, dy_1\, dz_1$ at x_1, y_1, z_1, with velocities between U_1 and $U_1 + dU_1$, V_1 and $V_1 + dV_1$, W_1 and $W_1 + dW_1$, will, at a time t_2, lie in a volume $dx_2\, dy_2\, dz_2$ at x_2, y_2, z_2 and have velocities between U_2 and $U_2 + dU_2$, V_2 and $V_2 + dV_2$, W_2 and $W_2 + dW_2$, the relation between $U_1, V_1, W_1, dU_1, dV_1, dW_1$ and $U_2, V_2, W_2, dU_2, dV_2, dW_2$ being determined by $t_2 - t_1$ and by the field of force. Let this field of force be given by a smoothly varying potential $-\Phi$, which is determined by the system as a whole. In this chapter Φ always denotes the potential energy per unit mass. The above condition may then be expressed by the equation

$$\frac{\partial f}{\partial t} + U \frac{\partial f}{\partial x} + V \frac{\partial f}{\partial y} + W \frac{\partial f}{\partial z} - \frac{\partial \Phi}{\partial x} \frac{\partial f}{\partial U} - \frac{\partial \Phi}{\partial y} \frac{\partial f}{\partial V} - \frac{\partial \Phi}{\partial z} \frac{\partial f}{\partial W} = 0, \quad (1)$$

which simply expresses the fact that the difference between the stars moving into the six-dimensional element of phase space $dx\,dy\,dz\,dU\,dV\,dW$ in a time dt and those moving out of it in the same time must be equal to the increase in f in this element. It states, in other words, that no new stars are created and no stars are destroyed, and it also implies that in the present context the motions of the stars are not influenced by individual encounters with other stars.

Equation (1) is often called the equation of continuity, or Liouville's theorem. In an abbreviated form it may be written as $Df/Dt = 0$.

In addition to the equation of continuity, we must satisfy the condition that the gravitational force under which the stars move is due to the stars and gas in the system. This condition can be conveniently expressed by Poisson's equation

$$\frac{\partial^2\Phi}{\partial x^2} + \frac{\partial^2\Phi}{\partial y^2} + \frac{\partial^2\Phi}{\partial z^2} \equiv \nabla^2\Phi = 4\pi G\rho,\tag{2}$$

where ρ is the total mass density, given by

$$\rho = \sum_{\mathfrak{M}} \mathfrak{M} \iiint f(\mathfrak{M}, x, y, z, U, V, W, t)\, dU\, dV\, dW + \rho_g.\tag{3}$$

The letter $\mathfrak{M}$ is now taken to be the mass of a star of a given type; the summation must evidently be done over all types, the integration over all values of the velocities; ρ_g is the gas density.

2.3. Steady State

If the system is in a steady state, f must be independent of t, or,

$$\frac{\partial f}{\partial t} = 0.\tag{4}$$

Combining this with the equation of continuity, we get

$$U\frac{\partial f}{\partial x} + V\frac{\partial f}{\partial y} + W\frac{\partial f}{\partial z} - \frac{\partial\Phi}{\partial x}\frac{\partial f}{\partial U} - \frac{\partial\Phi}{\partial y}\frac{\partial f}{\partial V} - \frac{\partial\Phi}{\partial z}\frac{\partial f}{\partial W} = 0.\tag{5}$$

As has been stated above, the influence of stellar encounters has not been considered in this equation. It can be shown that the effect of such encounters is quite negligible during times of the order of the time of revolution in the Galaxy, so that we were justified in considering the motions of the stars to be governed entirely by the regular potential Φ of the whole system. In the long run, however, the motions of the slower moving stars may be influenced by irregularities in the gravitational field arising from large agglomerations of interstellar matter, such as those in Orion, in Taurus, and in Ophiuchus-Scorpius. This effect, by which the random motions of the stars are gradually increased, has been worked out by Spitzer and Schwarszchild (1953).

Effects of encounters with individual stars are important only in clusters. In general, they are still unimportant during one revolution within the cluster, but in the course of time they tend to establish a velocity distribution of the same type as the Maxwellian distribution produced in a gas as a consequence of the collisions between molecules. These encounters will again establish some sort of semi-steady state, which we might describe as "statistical" equilibrium, in distinction to the "dynamical" equilibrium considered above. A true statistical equilibrium, such as in a gas, cannot, however, be reached in a system of stars, because the "free path" is always long compared to the dimensions of the system. In a globular cluster the encounters will produce a progressive depletion of the central regions in favor of the outer parts. Moreover, the encounters will cause some stars to escape entirely from the cluster, which, as a consequence, will gradually evaporate.

Before proceeding to apply the equation of dynamical equilibrium to the Galaxy, it is desirable to inquire a little more deeply into the meaning of such an equilibrium. We may ask in particular how this kind of steady state can establish itself, and how far the deviations from a steady state which were present in the beginning (i.e., when the stars condensed from the interstellar medium) will have been smoothed out. To discuss this, we shall consider two simple cases.

We first consider a system consisting of a flat disk. The variations of the density in the plane of the disk are assumed to be negligible over the region traversed by a star in the course of its motion around the center of the system. Similarly, the component of the gravitational force perpendicular to the plane of the disk (to be denoted as K_z) will be taken to be independent of the coordinates in the plane; it will depend only on the distance z from the central plane of the disk. We wish to discuss the density and velocity distribution in the direction of z. The velocity components in this direction will be denoted by Z.

If K_z is given, this one-dimensional distribution may be fully described by giving the distribution Ψ of the velocities Z_0 with which the stars pass through the central layer and the time t_0 of a given passage. If we describe the system in this way, by giving the distribution of what we may call the orbital elements of the stars, the problem of the condition of continuity does not arise. A steady state might be defined by requiring that Ψ be independent of t, but this would not be a very practical definition, because it cannot be verified by observation. A practical definition is to say that in a steady state at any z the density of stars of given Z must be proportional to the time spent by such stars in a layer of unit thickness at z as a fraction of the period of oscillation in z. *This* could, in principle, be checked by observation. The check presupposes that K_z be known, but even if K_z is not known, observations can still provide a powerful verification of the steady state. If the observations show that for stars at various distances on both sides of the central plane the algebraic average motion $\langle Z \rangle$ is everywhere zero, and that the distribution of Z is symmetrical, we can practically consider this as a proof that the condition of a steady or well-mixed state is fulfilled. As we shall see in Section 3.1, such appears to be the case for the z-motions in the Galaxy.

We should still inquire how such a well-mixed condition can have arisen. It may be that there was already a sufficient amount of regularity in the z-direction at the time the stars were formed, but it is likely that the mixing has also been furthered by the randomizing action of the attraction by large conglomerations of interstellar gas.

As our second example we choose a case in which the gravitational potential is due to a point mass in the center of the system, which mass is so much larger than the combined mass of all the ordinary members of the system that the attraction by these latter can be neglected. The system is therefore analogous to that of the minor planets in the solar system.

The system can again be described either by a distribution of the coordinates and the velocities, which must satisfy equation (1), or, alternatively, by a distribution function Ψ of the orbital elements. As there are six elements, Ψ is a function of six variables. It can be any arbitrary positive function of these six variables. If we want a steady-state system, we must leave out the element equivalent to the time of pericenter passage. Any arbitrary positive function of the five remaining elements represents a system in dynamical equilibrium. We can thus produce steady-state systems of very queer shapes. This freedom is due to the special form of the potential, which produces simple, closed orbits. For the actual minor planets the freedom has apparently been limited by the way in which they have originated and by the subsequent perturbations by the major planets. These effects have caused their distribution function to be almost strictly axially symmetrical as well as symmetrical with respect to the invariable plane of the planetary system. The distribution has thus become independent of the longitude of the ascending node and the longitude of perihelion, and it has become symmetrical in the inclination, i, so that the system can be completely described by a function $\Psi\,(a,\,e,\,i^2)$.

The case of the stars in the Galaxy is considerably more complex than that of the minor planets. In the first place the motion of a star cannot be described by such simple orbital elements as a, e, i, Ω, and ω. The star follows a complicated three-dimensional orbit, which in general is not closed. In the second place there is good evidence that the stars which were formed since the gas had contracted to the galactic disk have generally been formed in spiral arms, and that the initial conditions, therefore, deviate systematically from an axially symmetrical distribution. It is quite uncertain whether the deviations from axial symmetry in the gravitational field, which must accompany the spiral structure, have tended to even out these asymmetries in the distribution of the older stars.

2.4. General Solution of the Equation of Dynamical Equilibrium for an Axially Symmetrical Case

It may, nevertheless, be useful to consider the solution of the equation of dynamical equilibrium for an axially symmetrical system. For, as we have already remarked, there undoubtedly exist stellar systems having such symmetry, and to a certain extent this condition may have been approached by the Galaxy.

As in the two examples considered above, the solution of equation (5) is an arbitrary positive function of the "orbital elements" of the stars in the system. As orbital elements we can use any independent quantities by which the orbit of a star can be completely defined. One such quantity can be immediately and simply specified, viz., the total energy of a star. In the case of axial symmetry one can also simply specify a second orbital parameter: the angular momentum around the axis of symmetry. These parameters are usually called integrals of the equation of motion, and their values per unit mass are usually denoted by I_1 and I_2, respectively. It has long been an unsolved and much debated problem whether the equation of motion in an axially symmetrical system admits of a third integral, or, in other words, whether we need more than two independent parameters to specify an orbit. The work of Contopoulos (1960), and in particular the recent studies of three-dimensional stellar orbits by Ollongren and Miss Torgård (cf. Ollongren 1962, and this chap., Sec. 5), have shown that at least in the Galaxy, but presumably in all axisymmetrical systems in which the density decreases monotonically with increasing distance from the center, *in practice* a third parameter is needed to define a stellar orbit. The latter authors showed that a three-dimensional orbit has always a minimum distance to the center, and that at this point (which lies in the plane of symmetry) the Z-velocity is not infinitesimally small. Let us denote this distance to the center by q—in analogy to the notation for the perihelion distance of a planetary orbit—and the velocity component perpendicular to the galactic plane at this point by Z_q. The galactic system can then be completely described by giving the distribution function $\Psi (I_1, I_2, Z_q^2)$ for each type of stars. The third parameter Z_q^2 (which we might also call an "integral") is of a somewhat different kind: it does not, like I_1 and I_2, provide an explicit relation between coordinates, velocity components, and potential at each point. From I_2 we can at each point of the orbit find at once the velocity component Θ perpendicular to the axis. With known Φ, I_1 then permits us to find the total velocity in the plane perpendicular to Θ, but not its direction in that plane. This direction is fixed by the third parameter Z_q^2, but not in an explicit form: in order to find it we must carry out a numerical integration of the three-dimensional orbit all the way from the starting point $(q, 0)$ until we hit the point considered. The parameter Z_q^2 is therefore not a very practical one; but no more satisfactory quantity has yet been suggested, except in special cases.

It is still debatable whether Z_q^2 is an independent parameter in a strict sense, or whether it would not change if we considered very many more revolutions than the Galactic System has made. We should also consider what would happen if there were irregularities in the gravitational field, such as might be caused by spiral or ring structures. These would have a randomizing effect on the velocity distribution, and might ultimately lead to an equality between the distributions of Π (the linear velocity component in radial direction) and Z. It appears improbable that the irregularities in the field of our Galaxy could have been sufficient to bring about such equality for high-velocity stars. The observed *in*equality between the two distributions for all known objects in the Galaxy need not, therefore, cause any worry about the applicability of the concept of dynamical equilibrium.

A particularly simple case is that in which, for the orbits considered, K_z is independent of the distance from the rotation axis, ϖ. The variables ϖ and z can then be separated; for the third integral we can then take the energy of the z-motion per unit of mass:

$$I_3 = \tfrac{1}{2}Z_0^2 = \tfrac{1}{2}Z^2 - \int_0^z K_z\,dz\,, \tag{6}$$

where Z_0 is again the Z-velocity with which the star passes the galactic plane. Provided K_z is given, this now permits a direct computation of Z at each point. For small velocities in the Galaxy this case may be closely approached.

2.5. HYDRODYNAMICAL EQUATIONS

We shall now use the equation of steady state to derive some relations between observable quantities, such as the vectorial mean motion of the stars in an element of volume, and the mean random velocities. We start, again, with the case of axial symmetry. In this case it is practical to use cylindrical coordinates ϖ, ϑ, z, instead of the rectangular coordinates x, y, z. The distance from the axis of rotation is denoted by ϖ, the position angle around this axis by ϑ, while z is the distance from the galactic plane, which is assumed to be a plane of symmetry. The rectangular coordinate system is oriented in such a way that its z-axis coincides with the axis of rotation, and therefore with the z-axis of cylindrical coordinates. The linear velocities corresponding to the cylindrical coordinates will be denoted by the capitals Π, Θ, Z. In the new coordinates, equation (5) becomes

$$\Pi\frac{\partial f}{\partial \varpi} + \frac{\Theta}{\varpi}\left(\Theta\frac{\partial f}{\partial \Pi} - \Pi\frac{\partial f}{\partial \Theta}\right) + Z\frac{\partial f}{\partial z} + K_\varpi\frac{\partial f}{\partial \Pi} + K_z\frac{\partial f}{\partial Z} = 0\,. \tag{7}$$

For convenience we have written K_ϖ for $-\partial\Phi/\partial\varpi$ and K_z for $-\partial\Phi/\partial z$.

The relations in which we are interested are obtained by multiplying equation (7) by Π and integrating over all values of Π, Θ, and Z. Denoting average values by $\langle\ \rangle$ and denoting the number of stars per unit by volume by ν, we find

$$\frac{\partial\,(\nu\langle\Pi^2\rangle)}{\partial\varpi} + \frac{\nu}{\varpi}(\langle\Pi^2\rangle - \langle\Theta^2\rangle) + \frac{\partial\,(\nu\langle\Pi Z\rangle)}{\partial z} = \nu K_\varpi. \tag{8}$$

If we multiply (7) by Z and again integrate over all velocities, we obtain

$$\frac{\partial\,(\nu\langle Z^2\rangle)}{\partial z} + \frac{\nu\langle\Pi Z\rangle}{\varpi} + \frac{\partial\,(\nu\langle\Pi Z\rangle)}{\partial\varpi} = \nu K_z. \tag{9}$$

Equations of this type were first derived by Jeans (1922). He supposed (1915) that the distribution function would be a function of only two orbital parameters, $I_1 = \Pi^2 + \Theta^2 + Z^2 + 2\Phi$ and $I_2 = \varpi\Theta$. In this case the velocity components Π and Z appear in exactly the same way in the distribution function. At each point in the system the velocity distributions in the ϖ- and z-directions should then be identical. With a circularly symmetrical distribution in the Π, Z plane the average value of the product ΠZ must evidently be zero, so that the terms with $\langle \Pi Z \rangle$ in the left-hand members of equations (8) and (9) vanish. The equations become then identical with the well-known and widely used equations of Jeans (1922).

It has long been known that conditions in the Galaxy do not conform with these equations, because for practically all types of stars the velocity dispersion in the z-direction is between 1.5 and 2 times smaller than that in the ϖ-direction. Although there is no such direct observational evidence to show that $\langle \Pi Z \rangle$ differs from zero, it is likely that it will differ from zero outside the galactic plane, and that for $z = 0$ the derivative $\partial \langle \Pi Z \rangle / \partial z$ will have a fairly small, positive value. We shall give an estimate of the numerical value in Section 4.5.

For practical applications we introduce the mean Θ of the stars in an element of volume; we denote this by Θ_m, and the square of the dispersion around this mean by $\langle (\Theta - \Theta_m)^2 \rangle$. We have, then, $\langle \Theta^2 \rangle = \Theta_m^2 + \langle (\Theta - \Theta_m)^2 \rangle$. Inserting this in equation (8), and dividing by ν, we get

$$- K_\varpi = \frac{\Theta_m^2}{\varpi} - \langle \Pi^2 \rangle \left[\frac{\partial \ln (\nu \langle \Pi^2 \rangle)}{\partial \varpi} \right.$$
$$\left. + \frac{1}{\varpi} \left\{ 1 - \frac{\langle (\Theta - \Theta_m)^2 \rangle}{\langle \Pi^2 \rangle} \right\} + \frac{\langle \Pi Z \rangle}{\langle \Pi^2 \rangle} \frac{\partial \ln (\nu \langle \Pi Z \rangle)}{\partial z} \right], \tag{10}$$

where ln denotes the natural logarithm. The first term on the right-hand side represents the centrifugal force corresponding to the rotational velocity Θ_m, the second term is equivalent to the pressure gradient in the case of a gas. The last two terms do not occur in a gas, because the collisions enforce equality of the velocity dispersions in the three coordinates. For points in the galactic plane the last term between the brackets reduces to

$$\frac{1}{\langle \Pi^2 \rangle} \frac{\partial \langle \Pi Z \rangle}{\partial z}.$$

2.6. Particular Solutions of the Equation of Dynamical Equilibrium; Ellipsoidal Velocity Distributions

In order to obtain a complete solution we have to make specific assumptions concerning the velocity distribution. For the stars that are common in the vicinity of the sun, the distribution of the random motions below 60 km/sec in any one coordinate can be closely approximated by a Gaussian function. An example of this is given in Figures 3 and 4 of Chandrasekhar's *Principles of Stellar Dynamics* (1942). It is, therefore, practical to introduce the following form for the distribution function

$$f(\varpi, z, \Pi, \Theta, Z)$$
$$= \frac{h k l}{\pi^{3/2}} \nu \exp [- h^2 \Pi^2 - k^2 (\Theta - \Theta_m)^2 - l^2 Z^2 \tag{11}$$
$$- m \Pi (\Theta - \Theta_m) - n \Pi Z - p (\Theta - \Theta_m) Z].$$

The star density ν, the rotation Θ_m, and the coefficients h, k, l, m, n, and p are functions of ϖ and z. An "ellipsoidal" velocity distribution of this type was first proposed by K. Schwarzschild (1907, 1908) as an interpretation of the "star streams" discovered by Kapteyn (1905).

If we insert the form (11) for f in equation (7), and add the condition that the plane $z = 0$ must be a plane of symmetry, we obtain the following explicit solutions for the coefficients of the velocity distribution and for Θ_m (see Oort 1928)

$$h^2 = c_1 + \tfrac{1}{2} c_5 z^2 ,$$

$$k^2 = c_1 + c_2 \varpi^2 + \tfrac{1}{2} c_5 z^2 ,$$

$$l^2 = c_4 + \tfrac{1}{2} c_5 \varpi^2 , \tag{12}$$

$$n = - c_5 \varpi z ,$$

$$m = p = 0 ,$$

$$\Theta_m = \frac{c_3 \varpi}{c_1 + c_2 \varpi^2 + \tfrac{1}{2} c_5 z^2} . \tag{13}$$

In a former investigation (Oort 1928) the constant c_5 has been assumed to be zero. However, in the case applying to the Galaxy, where disp II differs from disp Z, c_5 will differ from zero. The constant is related to the inclination of the major axis of the velocity ellipsoid to the galactic plane for points outside this plane.

The parameters $c_1 \ldots c_5$ are positive constants. The density depends on the gravitational potential. If the potential is known, the density can be obtained in the galactic plane by integration of the following expression:

$$\frac{\partial \ln \nu}{\partial \varpi} = 2 c_1 K_\varpi + \frac{- c_2^2 \varpi^3 + (2 c_1 c_3^2 - c_1 c_2) \varpi}{(c_2 \varpi^2 + c_1)^2} - \frac{c_5 \varpi}{c_5 \varpi^2 + 2 c_4} . \tag{14}$$

Away from the plane it can be found from

$$\frac{\partial \ln \nu}{\partial z} = (c_5 \varpi^2 + 2 c_4) K_z - c_5 z \left[\varpi K_\varpi + \frac{2(c_2 + 2 c_3^2) \varpi^2 + c_5 z^2 + 2 c_1}{(2 c_2 \varpi^2 + c_5 z^2 + 2 c_1)^2} \right.$$
$$\left. + \frac{1}{c_5 z^2 + 2 c_1} \right] . \tag{15}$$

It should be emphasized that in the actual cases with which we shall be dealing, equations (12) to (15) are at best only applicable to a region within 2 or 3 kpc from the sun, or possibly to a torus of about 2-kpc radius centered on the circle with radius ϖ_0 in the galactic plane. (In the following, quantities referring to the position of the sun and the mean velocity of stars or gas at that point will be indicated by the subscript 0.) From regions for which ϖ differs more than 3 kpc from ϖ_0, only a few rather exceptional objects of high velocity can penetrate to the region of the sun. In general, these will not fit in the exponential, ellipsoidal velocity distribution (11). Moreover, even if we would choose a more complicated velocity distribution, they would not be representative of the conditions at the distance ϖ, and would not provide sufficient information to enable us to infer the general velocity distribution and the density at that distance from the center.

Because of the conservation of angular momentum, stars coming from a region of smaller ϖ, which had Θ-components equal to $\Theta_m(\varpi)$ in that region, will in the neighborhood of the sun have Θ-components smaller than $\Theta_m(\varpi_0)$. The opposite will hold for stars coming from regions farther from the center than the sun, but because the stellar density increases strongly with decreasing ϖ, the former will be in the majority. As a consequence, at any given point, the stars with large negative $\Theta - \Theta_m$ will predominate over those with large positive values of $\Theta - \Theta_m$. This asymmetry in the distribution of $\Theta - \Theta_m$ for high velocities is clearly shown in the observations. It will be discussed further in Section 4.5.

We can, of course, very simply introduce an asymmetry by representing the distribution function by a sum of expressions of the type (11) with different values of h, k, l, n, and Θ_m. This might be practical for some types of analysis, but it does not produce a satisfactory reproduction of the velocity distributions as actually observed.

In any analysis of this kind, we still have to impose the condition that the combination of the distribution functions for all types of stars plus the interstellar gas must satisfy Poisson's equation. This imposes a very stringent limitation.

Chandrasekhar (1942) has worked out a different generalization of the distribution function. He investigated functions of the generalized Schwarzschild type:

$$\Psi(Q + \sigma), \tag{16}$$

where, in rectangular coordinates,

$$Q = a(U - U_m)^2 + b(V - V_m)^2 + c(W - W_m)^2$$
$$+ 2f(V - V_m)(W - W_m) + 2g(U - U_m)(W - W_m) \tag{17}$$
$$+ 2h(U - U_m)(V - V_m),$$

and σ is a quantity connected with the star density. The coefficients of the velocity ellipsoid (17) and σ are continuous functions of position. He has investigated "under what circumstances will the equation of continuity, regarded as a partial differential equation for Ψ, admit of a solution of the form (16)?"

It will be noted that (11) is a special case of (16) and (17), fitted to the observed velocity distribution near the sun. Chandrasekhar's analysis covers a much richer variety of functions of the symmetrical type. Moreover, his analysis provides the possibility of considering systems that have no rotational symmetry, and systems that are not in dynamical equilibrium.

§ 3. SMALL DEVIATIONS FROM CIRCULAR MOTION

3.1. Motions Perpendicular to the Galactic Plane

3.1.1. *Dynamical equilibrium; velocity distribution.*—We use the same notation as in Section 2, namely, z for the distance from the galactic plane, Z for the corresponding velocity component after correction for solar motion, and K_z for the acceleration in the z-direction. All three are counted positive in the direction of the north galactic pole. The subscript 0 will be used to denote values at $z = 0$, while in the present section the letter ν will indicate, for an arbitrary z, the density in a thin cylinder, whose axis passes through the sun and is directed toward the galactic pole. Let us assume that at any point of the orbit of a star which is at present in this cylinder, K_z is equal to the acceleration at a point at the same z "vertically above" the sun. There is reason to believe that this assumption will lead to a good approximation if we consider stars whose motions parallel to the galactic plane do not differ by more than about 40 km/sec from circular motion, because if, for all stars in the cylinder having a given value of z and Z, we compute the average value of K_z over many oscillations in the coordinates ϖ and ϑ, this average will, for any z, correspond approximately to K_z in the cylinder.

If we are dealing with a "well-mixed" system, the density at a distance z from the plane should, for stars of a given energy in the z-direction (i.e., of a given Z_0), be proportional to the fraction of the time spent in a unit interval at z during their oscillating motion. If, for the type of stars considered, the Z-velocity distribution is denoted by $\varphi(Z)$, this proportionality can be expressed by the equation

$$\frac{\nu\varphi(Z)\,dZ}{\nu_0\varphi_0(Z_0)\,dZ_0} = \frac{Z_0}{Z}. \tag{18}$$

With the working hypothesis used, the energy in the z-direction must be constant, so that Z and Z_0 are related by

$$\tfrac{1}{2}Z^2 = \tfrac{1}{2}Z_0^2 + \int_0^z K_z\,dz. \tag{19}$$

Using (19), we can reduce equation (18) to

$$\nu\varphi(Z) = \nu_0\varphi_0(Z_0). \tag{20}$$

The hypothesis of a well-mixed, or steady, state cannot in this case be supported by theoretical arguments, such as can be used in discussing the dynamics of globular clusters. We can, however, check its truth by observations. If these would indicate that the Z-velocity distribution at $z = 0$, as well as at different distances on either side of the galactic plane, is symmetrical, and if the velocity around which it is symmetrical is everywhere the same, this would indicate with a high degree of probability that the mixing in the z-direction is sufficiently complete for our purpose. Unfortunately no recent verifications of this type have been made. The tests that *have* been made show no significant deviations (Oort 1932).

In all cases investigated the distribution of the velocities Z can be well represented by sums of a small number of Gaussian distributions:

$$\varphi_0(Z_0) = \sum_i \theta_i \frac{l_i}{\sqrt{\pi}} \exp(-l_i^2 Z_0^2), \qquad (21)$$

where, in case of a normalized distribution, $\Sigma \theta_i = 1$.

If a Z_0 distribution of the form $(l/\sqrt{\pi}) \exp(-l^2 Z_0^2)$ is substituted in equations (19) and (20), we obtain

$$\nu\varphi(Z) = \nu_0 \exp\left(2l^2 \int_0^z K_z dz\right) \frac{l}{\sqrt{\pi}} \exp(-l^2 Z^2). \qquad (22)$$

It follows that

$$\nu = \nu_0 \exp\left(2l^2 \int_0^z K_z dz\right). \qquad (23)$$

The velocity distribution is then identical at all z, and the density distribution is the same as in an isothermal layer of gas. Equation (23) is equivalent to equation (15) of Section 2.6, if the second term in the right-hand member is omitted. For small values of z, such as considered in the present section, this term is negligibly small. The essential factors in this term are $\langle \Pi Z \rangle$ and $\partial \nu / \partial \varpi$ (cf. eq. [9]). If we use the estimates for these quantities as given in Section 4.5, we find that the inclusion of the term would have caused a decrease of about 3 per cent in the absolute values of K_z and of the density as derived from the distribution of K giants in Sections 3.2 and 3.3.

If $\varphi_0(Z_0)$ can be represented by a sum of Gaussian distributions with different moduli, as in (21), the density is given by a sum of terms like (23):

$$\nu = \nu_0 \sum_i \theta_i \exp\left(2l_i^2 \int_0^z K_z dz\right). \qquad (24)$$

In this case, the velocity dispersion increases with increasing z. In fact, the best method of determining the Gaussian components with largest dispersions is to measure radial velocities of stars at large z near the galactic poles.

If, for a given type of stars, the velocity distribution at $z = 0$ is known with sufficient accuracy, and if also the distribution of the density of these stars in the z-direction is known, we can use (24) to derive K_z. It is evident that a determination of K_z over a considerable range of z would give extremely important data for our knowledge of the gravitational potential in the Galactic System, and eventually of the mass density at various z. Actually, the observational material to be used for such a determination is still extremely unsatisfactory; the density distribution in particular is very uncertain. With present data one cannot reasonably hope to determine more than the average slope of K_z over the first few hundred parsecs. An early determination of K_z was made by Oort

(1932) for stars of various spectral types. An extensive study based on K-type stars was published by Hill in 1960. Other determinations of the value of $\partial K_z/\partial z$, or of the total mass density near $z = 0$, were made by Kuzmin (1955), Nahon (1957), Woolley (1957), Eelsalu (1958), and Jones (1962).

3.1.2. *Conditions imposed by the equation of Poisson; the total density of matter near $z = 0$.*—Though we have no a priori knowledge of the total mass density near the sun—in fact, this is just what we wish to determine from the observed motions—we *do* know *something* about this density from direct observations of the nearest stars and interstellar matter. As we shall see below, about two-thirds of the total density can be accounted for by known stars and interstellar gas. For these two-thirds we can, for any given K_z, predict approximately how the density should vary with z; for the remaining third we may make a more or less plausible assumption about this variation. It is clear that this information concerning the distribution of mass density, incomplete though it is, imposes severe restrictions on the shape of the K_z function to be determined from the motions and density distributions of test objects like K giants or A-type stars; besides having to fulfil the equation of dynamical equilibrium for these special objects, K_z must also fulfil the condition that it corresponds to the attraction exerted by all the stars and other matter present.

The mathematical problem of finding what general velocity distributions are possible in plane-parallel systems that are in equilibrium under their own gravitation has been investigated by Camm (1950) and by Prendergast (1954). The velocity distribution (21), which represents the observed velocities, belongs to the general class of solutions found by these authors. Prendergast shows how, if we have a system in which all stars have the same mass, the potential $\Phi(z)$ can be computed for any distribution function of the form $f(z, Z) \equiv F[\frac{1}{2}Z^2 + \Phi(z)]$, where F is an arbitrary positive function.

The Galaxy deviates somewhat from the idealized plane-parallel case. If the acceleration in the direction of ϖ is written as K_ϖ, Poisson's law for an axially symmetrical system may be written

$$\frac{\partial K_\varpi}{\partial \varpi} + \frac{K_\varpi}{\varpi} + \frac{\partial K_z}{\partial z} = -4\pi G\rho, \qquad (25)$$

where ρ is the total mass density and G the constant of gravitation. In the galactic plane the sum of the first two terms is equal to $2(A - B)(A + B)$, where A and B are the constants of differential galactic rotation, as defined in chapter 22. With assumed values of $+15.0\,\mathrm{km/sec}$ per kpc for A and $-10\,\mathrm{km/sec}$ per kpc for B, or $+4.86 \times 10^{-16}$ and -3.24×10^{-16} in units of sec^{-1}, the sum of the first two terms for $z = 0$ is $0.26 \times 10^{-30}\,\mathrm{sec}^{-2}$. This is 34 times smaller than $\partial K_z/\partial z$. Therefore, the uncertainty of A and B is of no serious consequence for the use of equation (25) at $z = 0$. For points outside the galactic plane we have to rely on a model of the mass distribution in the galactic system for determining $\partial K_\varpi/\partial \varpi + K_\varpi/\varpi$; but no very serious uncertainty is introduced until we get to distances of the order of 1 kpc. Such large distances are of no importance in the present connection.

The use of equation (25) in combination with (24) permits the determination of K_z as well as of ρ.

Attempts to satisfy simultaneously the equation of dynamical equilibrium and that of Poisson, using available observational data, have recently been made by Oort (1960) and by Jones (1962). Oort used the density and velocity distribution of K-type giants derived by Hill (1960). Under the assumption that the unknown mass was distributed in z like the K giants themselves, he found

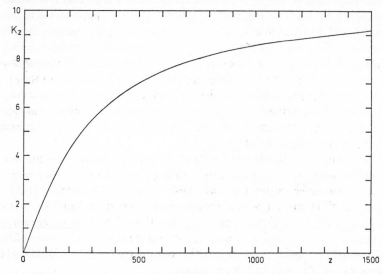

Fig. 1.—The force per unit mass in the direction perpendicular to the galactic plane. Units: abscissa, parsecs; ordinate, 10^{-9} cm/sec².

K_z as shown approximately by the curve in Figure 1. Strictly, the curve has been adjusted to correspond with the density of 10.0×10^{-24} near $z = 0$, which was adopted as the most probable value for this density (see Sec. 3.1.3).

3.1.3. *Mass density in the galactic plane.*—These computations yield at the same time the total mass density ρ_0 near the galactic plane. The result depends to a certain extent on the z-distribution adopted for the unknown stars. From the 21-cm measures the average gas density in the surroundings of the sun, including H II, He, and extreme population I objects, may be estimated as 2.0×10^{-24} g/cm³. From surveys of nearby stars the density of "ordinary" low-velocity stars can be roughly estimated to be 4.0×10^{-24} g/cm³ (Gliese 1956). These latter are assumed to have a z-distribution like K giants. For the unknown mass density which must be added in order to produce the total attraction, K_z, required to represent the motions and densities of K giants, we shall consider three alternatives for the distribution in z: (*a*) It is distributed like the gas (possibly in the form of hydrogen molecules); (b) it is distributed like the common low-velocity stars ("disk population," for which the distribution of K giants will be supposed to be representative); (c) it is distributed like objects of the halo population II, for which the average Z velocity is taken to be 67 km/sec.

We obtain the following results for the densities at $z = 0$. Hypothesis (a). The gas density would have to be 5.0 times higher than the value of 2.0×10^{-24} quoted above, i.e., 10.1×10^{-24} g/cm^3. The total mass density near the sun would become 14.1×10^{-24} g/cm^3. Hypothesis (b). The total density of disk population stars would be 2.1 times that assumed above for the known stars. The total mass density near the sun would become 10.4×10^{-24} g/cm^3. Hypothesis (c). The unknown halo population II should have a density of 2.8×10^{-24}, i.e., about 0.7 times that of the known stars. The total mass density at $z = 0$ becomes 8.7×10^{-24} g/cm^3.

The first case seems unlikely. It would imply that the interstellar mass density of molecular hydrogen would be six times higher than that of the hydrogen atoms. Though such a ratio might just be permissible on the basis of our very incomplete knowledge of the rates of formation and dissociation of molecules in the interstellar medium (see Sec. 2.1), it seems incompatible with what we know about the gradient of the total mass density near the sun. The run of the circular velocity with distance from the center indicates that between $\varpi = 8$ and $\varpi = 12$ kpc the mass density decreases by a factor of 1.44 per kpc (see Schmidt in chap. 22, Sec. 5, of this volume). In order to compare this with what we would get if all the unknown mass were gaseous, we consider the total mass contained in a cylinder through the sun and perpendicular to the galactic plane. Of the mass in such a cylinder, 51 per cent would then be gas, according to Section 2.1. In the range of ϖ considered, the amount of gas in a cylinder of unit cross-section *increases* by an average factor of about 1.05 per kpc. In order to get a rate of decrease of the total mass in the cylinder by a factor of 1.44 per kpc the density due to *stars* would then have to decrease by a factor of 3.1 per kpc. Such a gradient is far outside the range of possibilities. The known stars in an element of volume are in the majority slow-moving objects, which have at most a small density gradient.

It would seem that the steep gradient in the mass density can only be produced by the unknown *stars*, the density of which must then decrease by a factor of between 2 and $2\frac{1}{2}$ per kpc. These would have to belong to an old disk population, or an intermediate population II; for the latter, density gradients of this order have been found (cf. Sec. 4.5).

These considerations indicate that the density of interstellar hydrogen cannot be much larger than what is observed in the form of H I and H II. Even an increase of the interstellar density by a factor of two would already lead to implausibly high density gradients for the stars.

Independent, but much less convincing, evidence tending to the same conclusion may be found in the motions and density distribution of the A0 stars. If the gas density near the galactic plane were as high as in case (a), the investigations of A0 stars should have given a density of 14.1×10^{-24}. In reality, they yield much the same value for the local mass density as the K giants (Woolley 1957, Jones 1962). Jones finds 0.14 solar masses per pc^3, corresponding with 9.5×10^{-24} g/cm^3. The agreement with the value derived from the K giants is remarkable, but it should be kept in mind that both results are rather uncertain. The determinations from K giants and A stars are quite independent. The dispersions in Z_0 are 17.5 and 8.8 km/sec, respectively, and, as a consequence, the regions contributing effectively to the determination of K_z and ρ_0 are quite different.

As regards case (c), this is certainly too extreme. With any plausible increase of the halo density toward the center it would give much too large a mass within the sun's distance from the center, and too large a value for the circular velocity near the sun. As indicated in Section 4.7, these arguments show that at most 15 per cent of the unknown mass can have a distribution like a halo population. It may be noted that if 15 per cent of the density near the sun consisted of stars of such a population, $\frac{2}{3}$ of the mass contained in a cylinder perpendicular to the galactic plane would consist of halo population II.

The most probable present value for the total mass density near the sun may be estimated at 10.0×10^{-24} g/cm^3, or 0.148 solar masses per pc^3. Of this density roughly 40 per cent must be due to stars or gas of unidentified type, and of which, therefore, we do not know the distribution in space. It is this unknown population that is the principal obstacle for deriving a model of the mass distribution in the Galaxy.

The size of the region for which the mass density derived above is representative may be estimated as follows. For the K giants the range of z contributing effectively to the determination of the local mass density near the plane extends from about 300 to 1500 pc. If we have a plane-parallel distribution of density, about half of K_z is then contributed by the mass within a cylinder of radius 1.0 kpc around the sun, and three-quarters by the matter within a cylinder of radius 2.5 kpc. For the A0 stars the dimensions of the equivalent regions are approximately four times smaller.

3.1.4. *Relation between velocity and density distribution in the z-direction; period of oscillation.*—If K_z is known, we can compute the density distribution in the z-coordinate corresponding to any arbitrary distribution of the velocities Z_0. Table 1 indicates the average distance from the galactic plane for stars with a Gaussian distribution of Z_0 and average velocity $\langle |Z_0| \rangle$ as indicated in the first column. For K_z the function indicated by the curve in Figure 1 was used.

The periods of oscillation in z, shown in the last column, refer to stars with Z_0 equal to the average velocity indicated in the first column. It should be stressed that for the higher velocities the numbers are uncertain for two reasons.

First, because K_z is poorly determined for large z and, second, because the one-dimensional motion considered is no longer a fair approximation.

For small and moderate Z_0 the oscillation periods are about one-fourth of the period of revolution in the galactic plane.

3.1.5. *Mass-to-light ratio.*—A quantity which is of particular interest for comparison with other galaxies is the ratio of mass density to light density. It is common practice to express both in solar units, i.e., in the mass and the photographic luminosity of the sun. We give this ratio for a unit of volume at $z = 0$, as well as for the total of a cylinder of unit cross-section perpendicular to the galactic plane; this latter is the quantity we can observe most directly in other galaxies.

TABLE 1

MEAN DISTANCES $\langle |z| \rangle$ OF STARS
WITH GAUSSIAN DISTRIBUTION
OF Z_0 CHARACTERIZED BY THE
MEAN VALUES $\langle |Z_0| \rangle$, AND
PERIODS OF OSCILLATION, T,
CORRESPONDING WITH THESE
VALUES OF Z_0

$\langle |Z_0| \rangle$ (km/sec)	$\langle |z| \rangle$ (pc)	T (10^6 years)
5........	58	....
10........	121	68
15........	200	....
20........	300	79
30........	520	....
40........	780	92
50........	1100	....
75........	1900	....

From van Rhijn's luminosity function (van Rhijn 1936; see also chap. 2) the total light per pc^3 near the sun is found to be 0.068 times the photographic luminosity of the sun (for which an absolute magnitude $+5.37$ as determined by Stebbins and Kron [1957] was adopted). With a mass density of 0.148 solar masses per pc^3, the mass-to-light ratio, M/L, is found to be 2.2.

The ratios M/L for a cylinder depend strongly, of course, on the assumption concerning the distribution of the unknown stars. From star counts near the galactic poles one can derive the total light in a cylinder of 1 pc^2 cross-section as 21 solar units. The total mass in the cylinder is found to be 70, 79, and 281 times the mass of the sun for the three cases (a), (b), and (c) of Section 3.1.3, respectively. The corresponding M/L ratios are 3.4, 3.8, and 13.4. It is interesting to note that the latter value agrees closely with the M/L value found in the corresponding regions of the Andromeda nebula (de Vaucouleurs 1958). It should, however, be kept in mind that hypothesis (c) corresponds to a very extreme case. As pointed out in Section 3.1.3, the truth is likely to be close to (b).

3.2. Motions in the Galactic Plane

3.2.1. *Epicyclic motion; ellipsoidal velocity distribution.*—We shall suppose, again, that the motions in the plane are independent of those in the z-coordinate. We assume, also, that the deviations, v, from circular motion are small compared to the circular velocity, Θ_c, itself; v will be called the peculiar velocity of the star. In what follows terms of second and higher power in v/Θ_c have been neglected.

We use the same notation as in Section 2, except that in the consideration of the orbits in the galactic plane the notation ϖ will be replaced by R; the *velocity* in the radial direction will still be denoted by Π. The angular velocity Θ/R will be denoted by ω. Θ_c and ω_c are the velocities corresponding to circular motion. Values near the sun are indicated by a subscript 0. For the sake of convenience the subscript c is omitted when we want to indicate circular velocities near the sun, which will therefore be written Θ_0 and ω_0, while the derivatives of the circular velocity near the sun will be written as $\partial\Theta_0/\partial R$ and $\partial\omega_0/\partial R$. The position angle, ϑ, is measured in radians from a radius vector which at $t = 0$ passes through the sun and rotates with an angular velocity ω_0.

We consider, first, the orbit of a star which at $t = 0$ was near the sun, and had, then, a velocity Π_0 in the radial direction, while its transverse velocity Θ was equal to the circular velocity Θ_0. The orbit can be represented by the following formulae

$$R - R_0 = \frac{\Pi_0}{\kappa} \sin \kappa t$$

$$\vartheta = \frac{\Pi_0}{-2BR_0}(\cos \kappa t - 1) \qquad (26)$$

$$\kappa = 2\sqrt{[-B(A-B)]},$$

A and B being the constants of differential galactic rotation. With $A = 15.0$, $B = -10$, we have $\kappa = 31.6$ km/sec per kpc $= 32.4$ $(10^9$ years$)^{-1}$.

In the coordinate system in which ϑ is measured, i.e., a system rotating with an angular velocity equal to the circular angular velocity, ω_0, near the sun, the orbit is an ellipse with a semi-minor axis of Π_0/κ in radial direction, and a linear semi-major axis of $\Pi_0/-2B$ in the transverse direction. The axial ratio of this ellipse, which has its center on the circle with radius R_0, is $-2B/\kappa$, or $\sqrt{[-B/(A-B)]}$; with the above values for A and B this is 0.63. In analogy with the description used by Ptolemy for the motions of planets, the orbit of a low-velocity star may be described as a motion along an "epicycle," the center of which revolves with uniform velocity around the galactic center (Fig. 2). As in the Ptolemaic system the epicyclic motion is retrograde, but, while the classical epicycles were circular, the stellar ones are elliptical.

The period of the epicyclic motion is, in the rotating coordinate system, $2\pi/\kappa = 194$ million years. The period of revolution of the coordinate system itself, or the time of revolution of the Galaxy in the neighborhood of the sun, is $2\pi/(A - B) = 245$ million years.

The average peculiar velocity in the R-direction for ordinary late-type stars is about 25 km/sec. According to equation (26) the corresponding semi-amplitude in R is $25/\kappa$, or 0.79 kpc. During their revolution around the galactic center, the stars near the sun therefore populate a ring which, on the average, extends from $R_0 - 1$ to $R_0 + 1$ kpc. They might be considered to be representative for this volume of space.

All low-velocity stars in the general region of the sun describe similar epicycles, with, to the first order, identical axial ratios. The shapes of the epicycles cannot be observed, but we can observe their effect on the distribution of stellar motions. For this purpose we determine the average peculiar motion in the R and ϑ direction for a complete revolution in an epicycle. For the Π component

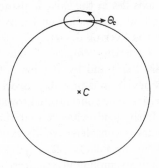

Fɪɢ. 2.—Epicyclic motion

this is $2\Pi_0/\pi$. When the peculiar velocity is defined as the difference from the instantaneous circular velocity, the average of the Θ-component is obtained by averaging $|\Theta - \Theta_c(R)|$ over the epicycle. We find $(2\Pi_0/\pi) \sqrt{[-B/(A - B)]}$. The ratio of the average peculiar velocity in the ϑ-direction to that in the R-direction is, therefore, $\sqrt{[-B/(A - B)]}$. This is just the inverse of the axial ratio of the epicycle itself. With $A = 15$, $B = -10$, the ratio is 0.63.

Indeed, observations show the existence of pronounced differences between the dispersion of the random velocities in different directions, with ratios of roughly this size. These differences were interpreted by their discoverer, Kapteyn, as "streams" of stars. Later, K. Schwarzschild introduced the notion of ellipsoidal distribution of velocities. The explanation of the phenomenon as a necessary consequence of the rotation of the Galaxy and of the manner in which its gravitational attraction varies with R is due to Lindblad (1927a, b). Lindblad also introduced the representation by epicyclic motions.

It may be noted that the difference between the two galactic axes can also be directly derived from the analysis in Section 2.6. If the velocity distribution is of the type given in formula (11), then, by formula (12), the ratio of the transverse to the radial axis in the galactic plane is, for $z = 0$, equal to $\sqrt{[c_1/(c_1 + c_2 R^2)]}$. According to (13), we can write this as

$$\frac{h}{k} = \sqrt{\left[\frac{R}{2\Theta_m}\left(\frac{\Theta_m}{R} + \frac{\partial\Theta_m}{\partial R}\right)\right]} = \sqrt{\left(\frac{-B'}{A' - B'}\right)}, \qquad (27)$$

in which A' and B' are defined in the same way as A and B, except that the *circular* velocity Θ_c is replaced by the *average* rotational velocity Θ_m.

3.2.2. *Deviation of the vertex.*—Though the observations agree with the general theory in showing an elongated velocity distribution, they do *not* agree concerning the *direction* of the elongation. In a well-mixed system this should coincide with the direction of the galactic center. Actually, for most types of stars, the major axis of the "velocity ellipsoid" deviates considerably from the direction of the center. The observational evidence has been discussed by Delhaye in chapter 4. The major axis lies in the galactic plane, but its longitude, l^{II}, is generally between 10° and 30°, depending on the type of stars. This angle is commonly referred to as the "vertex deviation." Attempts to investigate the nature of this deviation from the "empirical" side have been made, among others, by Delhaye (1952, 1953) and by Blaauw (1958). These authors have indicated that the vertex deviation is probably associated with a general tendency for the smaller velocities to be concentrated toward discrete regions of the velocity plane. There is fairly good evidence that the vertex deviation disappears if a sampling of stars is considered which extends over a space with a radius greater than 1 kpc in the galactic plane (Hins and Blaauw 1948).

If we confine ourselves to a sampling like that used by Hins and Blaauw, or to those types of brighter stars where the vertex deviation is less than 15°, we can use the ratio of the galactic axes to determine the constant B, the direct determination of which has a large uncertainty. Unfortunately, the agreement between the axial ratio of 0.49 ± 0.04 (m.e.) determined by Hins and Blaauw, and the value of about 0.60 found from the brighter stars, is not very good. We might provisionally adopt 0.55 as the best estimate. This deviates somewhat from the value 0.63 deduced above from the adopted values for the constants A and B. A discussion of this difference is given by Schmidt in chapter 22.

It is plausible to suppose that the deviation from a dynamically steady state —or from axial symmetry—which is observed in the vertex deviation, is connected with the striking departure from axial symmetry which we find in the spiral structure of the Galaxy. Suppose the stars are born in spiral arms, and suppose they acquire at the time of their formation sizable random velocities, then they will generally, in the course of time, move away from the arms. In a suitable rotating frame of reference they will describe epicyclic orbits. Their position angle in the epicycle will be related to their age. In a given point we shall at a given moment find stars "coming" from different parts of the spiral pattern even among stars of the same age group. These will be at different epicyclic position angles, and we shall, accordingly, find a certain randomness in the motions. But the randomness may differ systematically from that which we would find in a well-mixed system with rotational symmetry. The nature of the difference will depend on various factors, such as the position of the observer with respect to the spiral, the manner in which the gas in the arms deviates systematically from the "gravitational" circular velocity, and the age of the stars considered. A first primitive attempt to explain the vertex deviation in such a manner was made by Oort (1940). Nothing being known at that time about the actual spiral structure, the idea was not pursued. Recently, the subject has been taken up by Young (1961), who showed how, under certain assumptions of the motion of spiral arms, the vertex deviation could be roughly reproduced.

3.2.3. *Dispersion orbits.*—It is important to note in this connection that, even if we confine ourselves to motions of *stars*, and to a system in which the gravitational field has axial symmetry, certain types of large-scale departure from rotational symmetry may be conserved during many revolutions. Suppose that, after the "proto" Galaxy had contracted to a flat disk, there existed large-scale departures from axial symmetry, for instance a bar-type structure; it is then probable that the motions would also deviate systematically from circular motions. We may ask how the stars formed in these features would disperse in the course of time. In a non-rotating coordinate system, the orbit of a star will not generally be closed. But we can always choose a rotating coordinate system, such that specific orbits in this system are closed. Lindblad (1956; see also General References) has shown that in the Galaxy we can choose a rotating system of coordinates which satisfies this condition simultaneously for different values of R. He considers a system rotating with an angular velocity equal to $\omega_c - \frac{1}{2}\kappa$ and points out that the quantity $\omega_c - \frac{1}{2}\kappa$ varies very little over the range from $R = 4$ to $R = 10$ kpc. κ is the average angular velocity in an epicycle in a coordinate system rotating with angular velocity ω_c. For the vicinity of the sun, κ has been defined in equation (26); for an arbitrary R, it is defined by

$$\kappa = \sqrt{\{2\omega_c[\omega_c + (\partial\Theta_c/\partial R)]\}}. \qquad (28)$$

In a coordinate system rotating with angular velocity $\omega_c - \frac{1}{2}\kappa$, the center of the epicycle rotates with an angular velocity $\omega_c - (\omega_c - \frac{1}{2}\kappa) = \frac{1}{2}\kappa$. In one revolution in the chosen coordinate system a star will thus go twice round its epicycle, and reach a maximum R twice. The orbit is an ellipse whose center coincides with the center of the Galaxy. If in this coordinate system we consider the orbits of stars originating from the same "feature," but with random motions superposed on the systematic motion of this feature, these orbits will be grouped around the central ellipse corresponding to the mean motion of the said feature. There will be differences in the periods of revolution, and as a consequence, the stars will in the long run spread over the entire elliptical ring. The orbits in a rotating frame of reference of this kind have therefore been named "dispersion orbits." The phenomenon is the same as the well-known gradual spreading of meteor debris along the elliptical orbit of a comet.

The elliptical dispersion rings may be quite long-lived features. If the original deviations from axial symmetry extended over a large part of the Galaxy, the dispersion rings might provide an explanation for at least some of the striking deviations from axial symmetry that are so common in galaxies. This line of thought has been worked out extensively by astronomers at the Stockholm Observatory.

If the stars in the region around the sun were moving in dispersion orbits having a pronounced elliptical shape, the distribution of the *random* motions would also differ from the distribution corresponding to a truly steady state. The possibility of explaining the vertex deviation on the basis of this theory has been discussed by Lindblad (General References).

3.2.4. *General orbit of a low-velocity star in the galactic plane.*—For any more detailed discussion of the problems mentioned, we need to know, in the first place, the orbit of a star which starts from a given point in the galactic plane with given velocity components Π and Θ. We consider orbits which cross the circle with radius R_0. Let Π_0 and $\Delta\Theta_0$ be the radial and transverse components of the peculiar motion of the star at the time it passes this circle, $\Delta\Theta_0$ being the difference between the Θ component of the star's motion and the circular velocity Θ_0. As before, we count the time from the moment when the star crosses the circle R_0, and we count ϑ relative to a coordinate system rotating with the circular velocity ω_0; ϑ is taken zero at $t = 0$. The following formulae, expressing R, ϑ, Π, and Θ in t, A, B, κ, and the orbital parameters Π_0 and $\Delta\Theta_0$, are found by straightforward computation:

$$R - R_0 = \frac{\Delta\Theta_0}{-2B} + \frac{\Pi_0}{\kappa} \sin \kappa t - \frac{\Delta\Theta_0}{-2B} \cos \kappa t,$$

$$\vartheta = \frac{1}{-2BR_0}\left[-2A\,t\Delta\Theta_0 - \Pi_0(1 - \cos \kappa t) + \Delta\Theta_0\sqrt{\left(\frac{A-B}{-B}\right)} \sin \kappa t\right]; \qquad (29)$$

$$\Pi = \Pi_0 \cos \kappa t + \Delta\Theta_0 \sqrt{\left(\frac{A-B}{-B}\right)} \sin \kappa t,$$

$$\Theta = \Theta_0 - \Delta\Theta_0 \frac{A+B}{-2B} - \tfrac{1}{2}\Pi_0 \sqrt{\left(\frac{A-B}{-B}\right)} \sin \kappa t + \Delta\Theta_0 \frac{A-B}{-2B} \cos \kappa t. \qquad (30)$$

As before, $\kappa = 2\sqrt{[-B(A - B)]}$. Besides the periodic "epicyclic" terms, the formula for $R - R_0$ gives a constant shift, which depends solely on the value of $\Delta\Theta_0$. In ϑ there is a constant shift determined entirely by Π_0, and a progressive term proportional to t. The coefficient of this latter term is proportional to $\Delta\Theta_0$. With $A = 15$, $B = -10$, and $R_0 = 10$ kpc, the center of the epicycle shifts by $-0.153\Delta\Theta_0$ radians per 10^9 years relative to the chosen frame of reference, if $\Delta\Theta_0$ is expressed in km/sec.

Formulae of this type were used by Blaauw (1946, 1952) to investigate the evolution of expanding associations. They were also used extensively by Lindblad (General References) in connection with his work on dispersion orbits. Blaauw showed among other things how the age of an expanding association can be determined from its shape and from the orientation of its long axis.

Formulae (29) and (30) can, of course, also be used for orbits which do not cross the circle of radius R_0. In such cases we replace the constants A, B, and κ by the corresponding quantities pertaining to the region studied. If we would have a suitable model of the structure of the spiral arms and of the systematic motion of the gas through the arms, the above formulae would enable us to study exhaustively how stars of various ages, formed in the spiral arms and endowed with certain initial random motions with respect to the gas in the arms, will be distributed in space as well as in velocity.

§ 4. LARGE DEVIATIONS FROM CIRCULAR MOTION

We must now consider stars of which the motions deviate considerably from circular orbits. In the general case the orbits are complicated, and the problem of the relation between velocity distribution and density distribution—in which we are especially interested—has not yet been satisfactorily investigated. Some features of the three-dimensional orbits will be discussed in Section 5.

4.1. Motions Approximately in the Galactic Plane

We begin by considering those motions for which the z-component is small compared with the components in the galactic plane; in this case we can, in a first approximation, confine ourselves to a study of the motions in the plane.

As in Section 3.1, we represent the density of the class of stars to be studied by ν, and the normalized velocity distribution by φ. The subscript 0 is again used to indicate quantities near the sun. We suppose that the type of stars considered has reached a steady, or well-mixed, state, and that the distribution is symmetrical around the galactic center. Expressing this state by the condition that for stars of given orbital parameters the number in a ring of radius R and unit thickness must be proportional to the time which they spend in this ring, and, therefore, inversely proportional to the velocity Π, we have the following relation:

$$R\nu(R)\,\varphi_R(\Pi, \Theta)\,d\Pi d\Theta = (\Pi_0/\Pi)R_0\nu(R_0)\,\varphi_0(\Pi_0, \Theta_0)\,d\Pi_0 d\Theta_0 . \quad (31)$$

The velocities Π and Θ are connected with Π_0 and Θ_0 through the equations of motion, which we shall express by the conditions of constancy of energy and angular momentum:

$$\Pi^2 + \Theta^2 + 2\Phi(R) = \Pi_0^2 + \Theta_0^2 + 2\Phi(R_0), \quad (32)$$

$$R\Theta = R_0\Theta_0 , \quad (33)$$

where Φ is again the potential. From these equations we see that

$$\Pi d\Pi = \Pi_0 d\Pi_0 \quad \text{and} \quad R d\Theta = R_0 d\Theta_0 . \quad (34)$$

Inserting these relations in (31), we get

$$\nu(R)\,\varphi_R(\Pi, \Theta) = \nu(R_0)\,\varphi_0(\Pi_0, \Theta_0). \tag{35}$$

If for a given type of star the density near the sun and the velocity distribution is known, equations (35), (32), and (33) enable us to compute the numbers of these stars per unit of volume at a distance R having velocities Π, Θ. The equations do *not* enable us to predict the *complete* velocity distribution at R, for part of the stars at R will have orbits which do not cross the circle with radius R_0. Another part will cross the circle R_0 with such high radial motions that they are quite rare per unit of volume at R_0, though they may be frequent at R.

The extent to which these circumstances restrict the possibility of predicting the velocity distribution and density at distance R from the observed velocity

TABLE 2

VELOCITIES Π AND $\Theta - \Theta_c$ WITH WHICH STARS NEAR
THE SUN REACH $R = 5$ KPC

Π_0	$\Delta\Theta_0 = -20$	-40	-80	-120	-160
0.......	....	....	....	180	242
40.......	....	....	....	184	246
80.......	....	....	52	197	255
120.......	....	....	103	216	270
160.......	....	....	148	241	290
240.......	....	91	232	300	341
320.......	163	230	314	367	401
$\Theta - \Theta_c$.....	$+233$	$+193$	$+113$	$+33$	-47

distribution at R_0 can best be seen by considering some examples. Table 2 shows the values of Π at $R = 5$ which correspond to the velocities Π_0 and $\Delta\Theta_0$ given at the left and the top of the table; $\Delta\Theta_0$ is the difference between the transverse velocity at R_0 and the circular velocity. The values of $\Theta - \Theta_c$ at $R = 5$ are shown in the bottom line; these depend only on $\Delta\Theta_0$, not on Π_0. Table 3 gives similar data for $R = 15$.

We see from Table 2 that only stars which have quite high peculiar velocities near the sun can penetrate into the central region, and that their motions in this central region cover only a very limited domain of the velocity plane. At $R = 5$, stars must either have a Π-velocity of the order of 200 km/sec, or a Θ-velocity at least 100 km/sec higher than Θ_c in order to penetrate to the distance of the sun. A similar conclusion can be drawn from Table 3 with regard to the outer regions. Only rather exceptional stars penetrate to $R = 15$ kpc. It is estimated that, for instance, only about 8 per cent of the K giants in the neighborhood of the sun can reach distances of more than 15 kpc from the center. Even a superficial inspection of the table shows that these are not at all representative of the general stars at $R = 15$, as they fill only a special part of the velocity field.

A further illustration of the extent to which stars in our vicinity can penetrate into other parts of the Galaxy is given in Table 4. This lists under R_p and R_a the pericenter and apocenter distance for stars with velocities Π_0 and Θ_0 as given in the first two columns.

It is clear that for common stars we cannot, from the observed velocity distribution near the sun, derive any important information on their density or

TABLE 3

VELOCITIES Π AND $\Theta - \Theta_c$ WITH WHICH STARS NEAR
THE SUN REACH $R = 15$ KPC

Π_0	$\Delta\Theta_0 = 0$	$+10$	$+20$	$+40$	$+60$
0......	....	....	....	40	91
40......	....	....	....	57	99
80......	....	....	42	90	121
120......	63	83	99	127	150
160......	123	134	145	165	184
$\Theta - \Theta_c$......	-51	-45	-38	-25	-11

TABLE 4

PERICENTER AND APOCENTER DISTANCES, R_p AND R_a (IN KPC), FOR
VARIOUS VALUES OF THE VELOCITY COMPONENTS
Θ_0 AND Π_0 (IN KM/SEC)

Θ_0	Π_0	R_p	R_a	Θ_0	Π_0	R_p	R_a
250......	50	8.7	11.9	150.....	0	4.5	10.0
250......	100	7.7	14.8	150.....	100	4.1	11.3
250......	200	6.4	30.7	150.....	200	3.6	16.6
200......	0	6.6	10.0	300......	0	10.0	18.6
200......	100	5.9	12.1	300......	100	8.7	25.8
200......	200	4.9	20.2	300......	200	7.2	(100)

their velocity distribution at widely different values of R, not even if the gravitational potential is supposed to be known. In this connection the simple relations between the density and the velocity distribution and the coordinates given in formulae (12)–(15) of Section 2 may be misleading. They are valid only for the case where the velocity distribution is *everywhere* strictly of the exponential ellipsoidal type; it is not known whether this condition is fulfilled for any type of star.

For types of stars which have high random velocities, conditions are somewhat more favorable, but even here knowledge of the velocity distribution near the sun does not generally suffice to determine the relation between density and potential throughout the entire system. One quantity we *can* determine from it is the density gradient near R_0. This will be discussed in Section 4.5.

4.2. Velocity Distribution of Types of Stars with Large Random
Motions; Remarks on the Evolution of the Galaxy

Table 5 gives some characteristics of the velocity distribution for types of
objects which are known to have high random velocities. It is arranged approximately in order of increasing velocity dispersion. It gives in the third column
the difference between the circular velocity near the sun and the average
velocity of rotation, Θ_m, of the stars considered. This difference is often called
the asymmetrical drift. The table further lists the velocity dispersions along the
three principal galactic axes, and the density gradient near the sun which will be
discussed in Section 4.5.

Table 5 illustrates how complicated the structure of the Galaxy is. It consists
of a mixture of types of stars having widely different velocity distributions, and
therefore also widely different distributions in space. Actually, these differences
are even greater than shown in the table. The bulk of the stars near the sun have
a velocity dispersion in Z which is from $1\frac{1}{2}$ to 2 times smaller than the objects
with lowest velocity dispersion in the table. They were not listed because their
asymmetrical drift is too small to be determined with certainty. For B stars
and interstellar clouds this dispersion is even a factor 5 smaller.

For a rough understanding of the phenomena with which we shall be dealing
it is useful to consider them against the background of the currently adopted
picture of the evolution of the Galaxy which has been sketched in Section 3 of
the preceding chapter, and in the light of the concept of the stellar populations
which is based on this picture. The stars with highest Z velocities (the so-called
halo population II) must have formed soon after the mass of gas from which the
Galaxy was formed had separated itself from the rest of the universe. The remaining interstellar gas presumably contracted into a flat disk with strong concentration of density toward the center. All the stars with small velocity dispersion must have been formed after this collapse. Stars must have been born
also during the contraction stage. These types of stars have been called intermediate population II. We shall mention some examples below.

The contraction must have proceeded rather fast, for there is no observable
difference in age between the oldest halo clusters and the oldest clusters in the
disk, both having ages of about 12×10^9 years according to a recent estimate
by Sandage (1963).

Formation of stars in the disk has continued up to the present time, though
with decreasing speed as the gas was gradually used up. The stars born in the
last half-billion years are referred to as population I.

The duality of the Galaxy is illustrated schematically in Figure 3, which indicates the distribution of globular clusters belonging to the halo population II,
the general mass distribution, and the distribution of the interstellar gas as
representative of the extreme population I.

Objects formed during the different stages of the evolution of the Galaxy can be distinguished by specific intrinsic properties, not only because the intrinsic properties of a star change with its age, but also—and, in fact, principally—because the composition of the interstellar matter has changed systematically with time. Observations show that part of the objects formed during the halo phase of the system have metal abundances which are up to several hundred times lower than those of stars formed today. But there is also a considerable fraction of the halo clusters which shows only moderate metal deficiency. Among the disk clusters there seem to be none that are really metal-poor, not even among the

TABLE 5

ASYMMETRICAL DRIFT, VELOCITY DISPERSIONS, AND DENSITY GRADIENT

Type*	n	$\Theta_c - \Theta_m$	Θ_m	disp Π	disp Θ	disp Z	$\dfrac{\partial \log \nu}{\partial \log R}$	Rel. m.e.
Planetary nebulae.....	110	$+ 18\pm 5$	$+232$	40 ± 4	....	27	-4.2 ± 1.8	±0.33
Long-per. var. $>300^{\mathrm{d}}$...	167	$+ 10\pm 4$	$+240$	39 ± 4	40 ± 4	32 ± 7	-3.3 ± 1.5	$\pm .47$
Long-per. var. 200–300^{d}	143	$+ 31\pm 7$	$+219$	55 ± 8	45 ± 9	45 ± 11	-6.3 ± 1.2	$\pm .24$
RR Lyrae var. $\Delta S < 5$..	16	$+ 51\pm14$	$+199$	60 ± 9	50 ± 7	34 ± 5	-7.4 ± 2.4	$\pm .36$
Long-per. var. 150–200^{d}	41	$+103\pm25$	$+147$	94 ± 24	91 ± 28	61 ± 51	-4.7 ± 1.2	$\pm .31$
Globular clusters......	70	$+167\pm30$	$+ 83$	145 ± 10	....	......	(-4.0 ± 0.5)	$\pm .16$
Extreme subdwarfs....	22	$+183\pm19$	$+ 67$	172 ± 27	91 ± 14	66 ± 10	-3.5 ± 0.6	$\pm .22$
RR Lyrae var. $\Delta S \geq 5$..	33	$+220\pm23$	$+ 30$	210 ± 27	119 ± 17	91 ± 12	-2.9 ± 0.4	±0.19

* Notes to Table 5.

All errors in the table are mean errors (r.m.s. errors). The results for the planetary nebulae, long-period variables, and globular clusters were derived from radial velocities; those for the RR Lyrae variables and subdwarfs are based on space velocities. The columns disp Π, disp Θ, and disp Z give the mean square residuals as found directly from the observations. In reality, simple averages without regard to sign were computed, and these were multiplied by 1.25 to obtain the dispersions. In cases where no space velocities were available, the determination of the three axes of the velocity ellipsoid is very much less precise than that of the dispersion of the residual radial velocities. For the long-period variables and the globular clusters the value of disp Π used in the derivation of the density gradient has therefore been calculated from the dispersion in radial velocity multiplied by an appropriate factor. The factor was based on average results for the ratios of the axes as found from the other classes of objects in the table.

Planetary nebulae. Data were taken from an early discussion of the radial velocities by Oort (1928). The velocities determined after 1928 are almost all of nebulae in the central part of the Galaxy, and do not contribute, therefore, to the evaluation of the rotation velocity near the sun. The velocity dispersion given is that of the velocities in the line of sight; for lack of sufficient information it was assumed that the ratio of the galactic axes of the velocity ellipsoid was 1. Disp Z was computed with the aid of Table 1 from an estimated value of 340 pc for the mean distance from the galactic plane.

Long-period variables. The data were taken from a recent exhaustive study by Feast (1963). The dispersions are from his paper. I recomputed the density gradients, using values of disp Π derived in the way described above, and using $R_0 = 10$ kpc and $\Theta_0 = 250$ km/sec, as well as a standard solar motion of 20 km/sec toward $18^{\mathrm{h}}0^{\mathrm{m}}$, $+30°$, instead of the values used by Feast. The mean errors of the gradients were also computed in a slightly different manner.

RR Lyrae variables. The results were derived with the aid of proper motions determined by van Herk (1965). The numbers in the table have been computed from space motions, based on these new proper motions and partly on new photometric data. The median visual magnitude was assumed to be $+0.5$ for both groups. The mean errors of $\Theta_c - \Theta_m$ do not include the uncertainty in the adopted absolute magnitude. An error of 0.3 in the absolute magnitude corresponds to errors of approximately 10% in $\Theta_c - \Theta_m$ and disp Π. If the real absolute magnitude were $+0.8$ instead of $+0.5$, the absolute values of $\partial \log \nu / \partial \log R$ would increase by about 10 %. They would similarly increase by approximately 10% if Θ_c were increased by 10%.

The variables were divided into two categories according to their metal abundance indicated by ΔS, large ΔS corresponding with low metal content. This quantity has been introduced by Preston (1959), who showed that there is a strong correlation between ΔS and the velocity distribution as determined from radial velocities.

A similar, but slightly less pronounced, correlation between *period* and velocity distribution had previously been noted by Struve (1950). From all stars for which radial velocities are known at present (which are about three times as numerous as those for which ΔS determinations are available), van Herk (private comm.) finds from the radial velocities $\Theta_c - \Theta_m = +53$ km/sec ± 9 (m.e.) for the variables with periods shorter than 0.42 day (41 stars), and $\Theta_c - \Theta_m = +168$ km/sec ± 9 (m.e.) for those with periods between 0.42 and 1.0 day (123 stars).

Subdwarfs. The results were computed from the space velocities of 22 subdwarfs with ultraviolet excesses comparable to that of the globular cluster M 13, given by Eggen and Sandage (1959, Table VI).

Globular clusters. The data for the globular clusters are not entirely comparable to those for the other objects figuring in the table, because the clusters are not confined, like the others, to a relatively small region around the sun, but are spread over a large part of the Galaxy. Notwithstanding this wide distribution the velocities indicated may be considered as more or less representative of conditions near $R = 10$ kpc. The numbers in the table were taken from Kinman (1959). The number of objects is so small that a treatment in which various regions are discussed separately cannot be very significant. Attempts have been made by Kinman, as well as by Sharov and Pavlovskaya (1961), to which we shall return in Section 4.3.

oldest. In the latter the metals are about five times less abundant than in the
present interstellar medium. These facts indicate that the formation of elements
heavier than hydrogen and helium must have started soon after the birth of the
Galaxy, well before the halo gas had appreciably contracted. There is even some
evidence that the process of the formation of heavier elements has been more intense in this earliest period than during the later stages. The building of the
heavier elements has presumably taken place in the cores of heavy stars, the
material being returned to the interstellar medium by explosions of these stars.

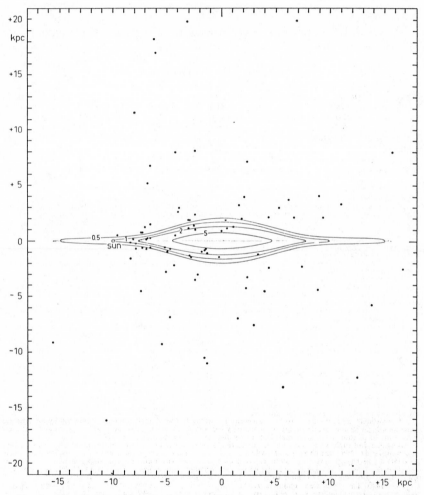

FIG. 3.—Distribution of globular clusters projected on a plane perpendicular to the galactic
plane and passing through the sun and the center, and lines of equal mass density (unit: density
near the sun). The steep increase in density in the inner parts has not been indicated. Shaded
parts give a schematic representation of the distribution of interstellar gas and extreme
population I.

It is mainly by these differences in relative abundance of elements that individual stars of different age groups can be recognized (see chaps. 16 and 17).

Sometimes a specific composition leads to a specific type of light variation; stars of such type, if sufficiently luminous, are then easily discoverable throughout most of the Galaxy. This is the case for the RR Lyrae and long-period variables. In both cases the velocity distribution—and, therefore, also the distribution in space—is strongly correlated with period. This may be seen for the long-period variables in Table 5. For the RR Lyrae variables some data are given in the notes following Table 5.

Examples of each of the three population groups described may be found in Table 5. The extreme subdwarfs and the RR Lyrae variables with $\Delta S \geq 5$ are almost pure samples of the *halo population II*. We return to these in Section 4.3.

The RR Lyrae variables with $\Delta S < 5$ are representatives of an *intermediate population II*. As indicated in Table 5 the dispersion of their Z-velocities is about half that of the halo population; on the other hand it is nearly twice the dispersion in Z of intermediate-age disk populations. The mean velocity of rotation is 199 km/sec, very much higher than the rotation of about 50 km/sec found for the objects of the halo population II, but sensibly smaller than the circular velocity of 250 km/sec. It should be pointed out that these objects belong to a truly intermediate population, and cannot be considered as a mixture of a halo population with a disk population. For if this were the case, part of the velocities should be distributed practically symmetrically around $\Theta = +30$ km/sec ($\Theta - 250 = -220$ km/sec) while another part should have an almost negligible asymmetrical drift, like the planetary nebulae or the variables with periods longer than 300 days. It is clear from Figure 4, and from a comparison of this figure with Figure 6, that neither of these conditions is fulfilled. Figure 4 shows the velocity distribution of the RR Lyrae variables with $\Delta S < 5$ for which space velocities are known with mean errors of less than 50 km/sec. In computing the value of Θ_m given in Table 5 we excluded from the group $\Delta S < 5$ two stars which probably belong to the halo population. A similar exclusion was made for the calculation of the dispersions. The dispersions have, moreover, been corrected for the effect of the accidental errors in the velocities.

Figure 6 shows the velocity distribution for the variables with $\Delta S \geq 5$. In both figures, the curves marked R_p 4 kpc indicate the velocities Π, Θ with which a star with zero Z-velocity would reach a minimum distance of 4 kpc from the center. Parts of the corresponding curves for a minimum distance of 2 kpc have likewise been indicated.

In Figure 5 the distributions of the Θ-components for both classes of RR Lyrae variables are compared. It clearly illustrates the very large difference between the kinematics of the two groups. It shows also the pronounced asymmetry in the curve for the group with $\Delta S < 5$.

Finally, we may note that there is a pronounced, and undoubtedly real, difference between the dispersions in the Π- and Z-velocities. According to the data

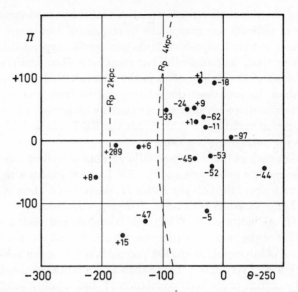

Fig. 4.—Velocity distribution of RR Lyrae variables belonging to an intermediate population II, with relatively high metal abundance ($\Delta S < 5$). The origin of the coordinates is the local standard of rest. The averare mean error of the components is ± 27 km/sec. The Z components in km/sec are indicated by numbers. The dashed curves show the values of Π and Θ, for which a star with $z = Z = 0$ has a perigalacticum, R_p, at 4 or 2 kpc from the center.

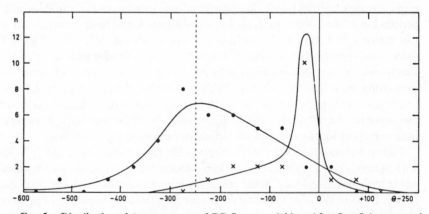

Fig. 5.—Distribution of Θ components of RR Lyrae variables with $\Delta S < 5$ (crosses and curve with steep maximum) and $\Delta S \geq 5$ (filled circles and curve with broad maximum). The crosses and dots are the numbers counted per interval of 50 km/sec. The solid vertical line shows the velocity of a point moving with circular velocity, assumed to be 250 km/sec, and coincides with the local standard of rest. The dashed vertical line indicates zero velocity with respect to the galactic center.

in Table 5, the dispersion in Z for variables with $\Delta S < 5$ is only 0.57 times that in II.

The two groups of long-period variables with periods from 200 to 300 days, and from 150 to 200 days, respectively, also belong to the intermediate population II. The variables with periods between 150 and 200 days represent apparently a somewhat earlier stage in the contraction process. But they are definitely not halo stars; only five per cent have radial velocities exceeding 200 km/sec, while in a pure halo population about half of the stars have radial velocities above this limit.

Although the *oldest disk population* (or disk population II, as we have called

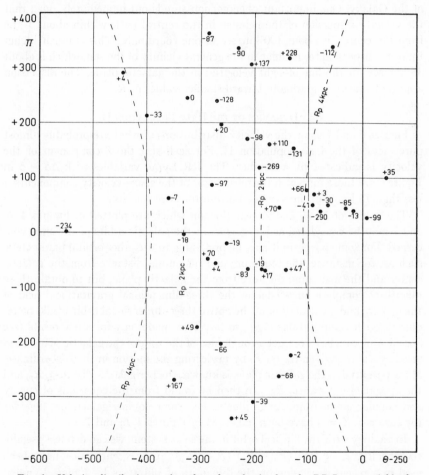

FIG. 6.—Velocity distribution projected on the galactic plane for RR Lyrae variables belonging to the halo population II (low metal abundance: $\Delta S \geq 5$). The average mean error for each component is ± 34 km/sec. Z components are indicated by numbers. The origin of the coordinates is the local standard of rest.

it above) is probably an important constituent of the Galaxy, we know very little about this group from direct observation. The only objects observable through large parts of the system, and identified with certainty as belonging to it, are planetary nebulae, novae, and variables with periods in excess of 300 days (cf. Table 5).

The most important information can be obtained from the planetary nebulae. Not only can these be rather easily discovered, even at the largest distances occurring in the Galaxy, but their emission spectra also make it possible to determine radial velocities (see chap. 15). In conjunction with the density distribution these may give important information on the gravitational field near the nucleus of the Galaxy. One important phenomenon stands out immediately, viz., that the velocity dispersion of the nebulae in the central part, within about 1 kpc from the center, is about 100 km/sec in one coordinate. This is much higher than the dispersion for nebulae in the general vicinity of the sun, which is about 35 km/sec for the line-of-sight velocities in the galactic plane. The dispersion appears to increase gradually toward smaller values of R.

4.3. Dynamics of the Halo Population II

Figures 6 and 7 show the velocity distributions of what are probably almost pure races of the halo population II. For each star the Z-component of the velocity is indicated by a number. The RR Lyrae variables with $\Delta S \geq 5$ in Figure 6 are those for which the mean error of the space-velocity components is less than 75 km/sec; the average mean error is 34 km/sec.

The values of Π, Θ, and Z near the sun which are plotted in Figures 4, 6, and 7 may be considered as parameters of the galactic orbits of the stars concerned. For some purposes it may be preferable to use other orbital parameters, such as, for instance, the minimum and maximum distance from the galactic center and the maximum distance from the galactic plane, but to obtain these quantities complete knowledge of the three-dimensional gravitational field of the Galaxy and a calculation of the entire three-dimensional orbit would be required. Such computations have, so far, been made only for a few orbits (see Sec. 5). One can, however, get a rough idea of the zone of the galactic plane traversed by a star of given Π_0, Θ_0, Z_0 by neglecting the motion in the Z-coordinate. If the potential in the galactic plane is known, the perigalactic distance, R_p, and the apogalactic distance, R_a, can then be found from the equations of energy and angular momentum. As an illustration, some equiperigalacticum lines for the case $z = Z = 0$ have been indicated in Figures 4, 6, and 7.

In analogy with an elliptical orbit in the solar system, we can define a pseudo-eccentricity, e, by $e = (R_a - R_p)/(R_a + R_p)$. Such eccentricities have been used in a recent discussion on the dynamics of old stars by Eggen, Lynden-Bell, and Sandage (1963). It should, however, be kept in mind that for halo stars the Z-components are almost as large, on the average, as the Θ-components, so that the quantities e, which apply to the special case $Z = 0$, do not give an adequate impression of the actual orbital characteristics. For halo objects the distinction between the Z- and Θ-components is, in fact, rather irrelevant, because they were presumably formed before a plane of symmetry or a rotation around an axis existed. Their motions must have been determined originally by large-scale currents existing in the mass of gas at the time when it detached itself from the expanding universe, and subsequently modified by the probably quite unsymmetrical distribution of the initial gravitational field. The pronounced elongation of the velocity distribution in the radial direction may be considered as the indirect consequence of the expansion of the universe.

It seems probable that the 42 RR Lyrae variables in Figure 6 are an almost pure halo specimen. There is still a slight contamination by another population, as is indicated by the 9 points to the right of the right-hand section of the curve

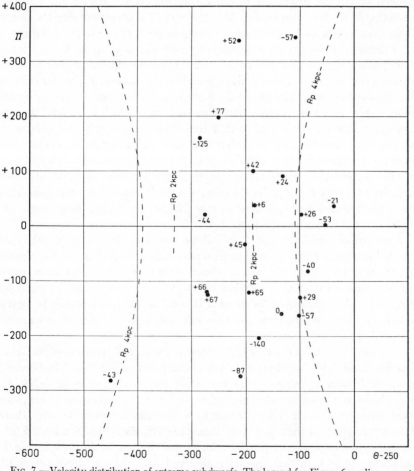

Fig. 7.—Velocity distribution of extreme subdwarfs. The legend for Figure 6 applies, except for the mean errors.

R_p 4 kpc. The majority of these must belong to an intermediate population II. In deriving the numbers for the RR Lyrae variables with $\Delta S \geq 5$ in Table 5 an attempt has been made to separate out these intermediate stars, and to obtain data representative of a pure halo population. The mean velocity of rotation for these halo RR Lyrae variables is only 30 km/sec ± 23 (m.e.). The true uncertainty is larger than indicated by the mean error because of the uncertainty in the adopted value of 250 km/sec for Θ_c, which is of the order of ± 20 km/sec. It may be concluded that the rotational velocity of the halo population II near the sun is likely to be less than 50 or 60 km/sec.

If we leave the tail of intermediate-population stars on the right-hand side out of consideration, the most striking feature of Figure 6 is its elongation in the II-direction. As shown in Table 5 the dispersion in Θ is only 0.57 times the dispersion in II. The dispersion in the Z-components is likewise much smaller than that in II, the factor being 0.43 in this case. The conditions deviate greatly from those predicted by Jeans for a system in strict dynamical equilibrium.

Although the velocity distribution is strongly elongated in the II-direction, it is definitely not so that the halo objects move in almost rectilinear orbits through the center. This had been suggested for the motions of globular clusters, but the evidence was quite uncertain. Such a conclusion is not supported by the more direct space-velocity data just discussed, from which it is found that the average transverse component is 0.71 times the average radial component. It would, moreover, be hard to understand how nearly rectilinear orbits could exist for stars reaching large distances from the galactic plane. Dr. Ollongren has kindly agreed to compute some sample orbits for stars released with zero velocity at a large ϖ and z. On the basis of a rough estimate he concludes that, for a star released in this manner at $\varpi = 12$ kpc, $z = 5$ kpc, the average ratio $\langle |II| \rangle / \langle |Z| \rangle$ would become about 1.4.

Comparing Figures 6 and 7 it will be seen that the extreme subdwarfs plotted in Figure 7 may be slightly less pure halo objects than the variables in Figure 6, there being only one subdwarf with $\Theta - 250$ smaller than -300, while there are 8 RR Lyrae variables below this same limit. A similar slight difference is indicated in the dispersions of II and Z in Table 5. It should be kept in mind, however, that differences of this order might well be due to errors in the adopted absolute magnitudes.

The distributions of the II- and Z-velocities can be well represented by Gaussian functions. The distribution of the Θ-components, illustrated in Figure 5, shows a distinct asymmetry with respect to the average value of -220, the right-hand part being considerably higher. In a first approximation we can, however, represent also the Θ distribution by a Gaussian function. We may, therefore, try to apply to these stars equations (12)–(15) derived in Section 2.6 for a stellar system having an ellipsoidal velocity distribution. In the present case the velocities are so high that the stars observed near the sun move practically through the entire system. As may be seen from Figure 6, almost all halo population II stars observed near the sun describe orbits in which the shortest distance to the galactic center is less than 4 kpc, while about 60 per cent must come to within 2 kpc from the center. For the halo stars we can, therefore, reasonably attempt to predict from the velocity distribution observed near the sun the velocity distribution and the density in other parts of the Galaxy, if the gravitational field is assumed to be known.

As an example we consider the system of halo globular clusters. If the distribution of the II-components would be accurately Gaussian, the mean II velocity should be the same at all distances from the center. This condition appears indeed to be approximately fulfilled. Sharov and Pavlovskaya (1961) find only a small variation with R. Assuming that near the sun $h/k = 0.8$ for this mixture of halo and intermediate populations, that disp II $= 125$ km/sec, and $\Theta_m = 80$ km/sec for $R = 10$ kpc, we compute from equation (13) the values listed in Table 6 for Θ_m and for the angular velocity, ω_m, in km/sec per kpc. We see that the angular velocity changes very little. The radial velocities of clusters

TABLE 6

ROTATIONAL VELOCITIES EXPECT-
ED IN THE SYSTEM OF
GLOBULAR CLUSTERS

R (kpc)	Θ_m (km/sec)	ω_m (km/sec per kpc)
1.......	12	12.4
3.......	36	12.0
5.......	55	11.0
10.......	80	8.0
20.......	77	3.8

are in accordance with this result. Kinman (1959) finds that for clusters with $R < 9$ kpc the angular velocity is 18.2 km/sec·kpc $\pm$ 5.0 (m.e.) smaller than the circular angular velocity near the sun, while for clusters with $R > 9$ kpc it is 22.4 $\pm$ 6.2 smaller. Taking $\omega_0 = 25.0$, we have, therefore, $\omega_m = 6.8$ and 2.6 for the two groups, respectively. The differences from the values in Table 6 are well within the mean errors. Sharov and Pavlovskaya (1961) find a variation of ω_m ranging from about 22 at $R = 4$ to 11 at $R = R_0$, and about 5 for R between 10 and 20 kpc. These values must have about the same uncertainty as those of Kinman.

We compute, further, relative densities by integrating equation (14). This gives, if we omit the small term with c_5,

$$\ln \nu - \ln \nu_0 = -2 c_1 \int_R^{R_0} K_R dR + \tfrac{1}{2}\left[\frac{a - R^2}{b + R^2} + \ln (b + R^2)\right]\Big|_R^{R_0}, \quad (36)$$

where

$$a = 2 \frac{c_1 c_3^2}{c_2^2} - \frac{c_1}{c_2},$$

$$b = \frac{c_1}{c_2}.$$

Using the expression for K_R given by Schmidt (chap. 22 this volume), we find that at $R = 3$ kpc the density of the common-type globular clusters should be about 60 times higher than near the sun, while for the halo-population RR Lyrae variables it should be 10 times higher than in our vicinity. Direct density estimates give factors of roughly 50 for globular clusters, and 25 for the RR Lyrae variables. Considering the uncertainty in these densities, the agreement with the dynamical estimate should be considered satisfactory. Elaborate calculations concerning the distribution of RR Lyrae variables have been made by Perek (1951) and Plaut and Soudan (1963).

Ultimately, the computations may be reversed, and the observed densities used to determine the gravitational field in our Galaxy, but this will only be possible when reliable densities are available from general surveys of RR Lyrae variables, such as are now being made by Plaut at the Kapteyn Astronomical Laboratory in Groningen, in collaboration with the Mount Wilson and Palomar Observatories, and by Kinman and Wirtanen (1963) at the Lick Observatory. A necessary condition is also that radial velocities of such variables be measured in various regions of the Galaxy.

4.4 Moving Groups in the Halo

An interesting phenomenon has been suggested by Eggen, who has investigated the possibility that some stars of high velocity form "moving groups" (see chap. 4). Several of the suggested groups belong to the halo population II (Eggen 1960). One of these, called the Groombridge 1830 group, has been extensively discussed by Eggen and Sandage (1959). Of the five stars which the authors provisionally identified as members, four are F- and G-type subdwarfs; the fifth is RR Lyrae. If the equality of the motions of these five stars is confirmed by improved data, Eggen's suggestion would lead to interesting inferences. A plausible interpretation of such high-velocity groups would be that they are disintegration products of former globular clusters. From the existence of several such groups in the neighborhood of the sun, we must then conclude that the original number of globular clusters in the halo must have been at least an order of magnitude larger than the present number. With an original limiting radius of a globular cluster of 100 pc the debris would in 10^{10} years spread over a total length of about 60 kpc along the three-dimensional orbit of the cluster, forming a tube-like swarm with a cross-section of the order of 0.1 kpc². Taking account of the total volume of the Galaxy, the probability that the sun would be inside a given swarm would be of the order of 10^{-3}. In order to obtain a sufficient probability we would have to conclude that the number of disintegrated globular clusters would be of the order of 10^3. Once a swarm crosses the region of the sun the expected number of observable members within 100 pc of the sun would be of the order of 10^{-3} times the total original membership of the cluster. In the Groombridge 1830 group four subdwarfs were found within 100 pc from the sun. This leads to a plausible total membership of the parent cluster.

4.5. Density Gradient and Asymmetrical Drift

The relation between density gradient, velocity distribution, and K_R may be studied with the aid of equation (10). The value of the second term between the brackets can be determined from the observed velocities. For all stars of high and moderately high velocities it is an order smaller than the first term within the brackets, so that an approximate knowledge of the former term is sufficient. Splitting the first term in the brackets into $(\partial \ln \nu/\partial \varpi) + (\partial \ln \langle \Pi^2 \rangle/\partial \varpi)$, we note that the second part is so small that it is not measurable from existing velocity observations. Neglecting this part as well as the second and third terms between the brackets for a first approximation, writing Θ_c^2/R for $-K_\varpi$, and replacing ϖ by R, we can write equation (10) in the following way

$$\Theta_c - \Theta_m = - (\Theta_c + \Theta_m)^{-1} \langle \Pi^2 \rangle \frac{\partial \log \nu}{\partial \log R}. \tag{37}$$

As the density generally decreases with increasing R, the right-hand member is positive. The average Θ motion of the stars in an element of volume is therefore smaller than the circular velocity, as we have seen already in Section 4.2. For types of stars with the same density gradient the difference $\Theta_c - \Theta_m$, the "asymmetrical drift," increases with increasing average random motion. As long as $\Theta_c - \Theta_m$ is small compared with Θ_c, it is approximately proportional to $\langle \Pi^2 \rangle$. Such a relation has indeed been found roughly to represent the observations (Strömberg 1924, 1925).

In computing the density gradient from equation (10), we have neglected the term depending on the gradient of the velocity dispersion, but the second and third terms between the brackets have been taken into account. The last term was computed on the hypothesis that for points outside the galactic plane the major axis of the velocity ellipsoid is inclined with respect to this plane in such a way that it remains pointed to the galactic center. This is likely to be a good approximation, at least for the halo objects. We can then derive the following relation: $\langle \Pi Z \rangle = (z/\varpi)(\langle \Pi^2 \rangle - \langle Z^2 \rangle)$, and the equation to be used for the determination of the density gradient becomes

$$\frac{\partial \log \nu}{\partial \log R} = - \frac{\Theta_c^2 - \Theta_m^2}{\text{disp}^2 \, \Pi} - \left(1 - \frac{\text{disp}^2 \, \Theta}{\text{disp}^2 \, \Pi}\right) - \left(1 - \frac{\text{disp}^2 \, Z}{\text{disp}^2 \, \Pi}\right). \tag{38}$$

The term $(1 - \text{disp}^2 \, \Theta/\text{disp}^2 \, \Pi)$ can alternatively be written as $A'/(A' - B')$ (see eq. [27]).

Density gradients have in this way been computed for the various categories of stars listed in Table 5. They are given in the last column. We see from this column that the average logarithmic density gradient for the high-velocity objects considered is about 4. The density therefore decreases as the inverse fourth power of R. There is some indication that the gradient is steeper for the classes of moderately high velocity than for those with highest velocity, but it is doubtful whether this is real. The gradient of the halo population comes close to a decrease with the inverse third power of R, which is typical of the variation of the light-density in elliptical galaxies and halos of spirals. However, considerably more data on objects of both populations are required before these facts can be established with confidence.

It is of interest to note that there is some evidence that the density of halo objects continues to increase with about the same inverse power of R down to the central region of the system. According to Baade's investigations (1951, 1958; see also Alexander 1960, who has shown that a majority of the variables in Baade's field have periods in excess of 0.41 day) the density of halo population II RR Lyrae variables at 1 kpc from the center is roughly 1000 times that near the sun, while the variation between $R = 1$ and $R = 3$ is also approximately as R^{-3}. A rather similar concentration to the central part of the system has been found for the halo globular clusters (Schmidt 1956).

Values of $\partial \log_{10} v / \partial R$ corresponding to the above results for $\partial \log v / \partial \log R$ may be obtained by dividing the latter by 23; they are -0.23 ± 0.04(m.e.) for the objects with moderate velocity dispersion, and -0.14 ± 0.02 (m.e.) for the halo population II.

There are, as yet, no sufficiently reliable *direct* data on density gradients near the sun to be compared with these dynamical determinations. It was shown by Oort and van Tulder (1942) that the long-period variables give clear evidence of a density gradient. But the numerical value, estimated at -0.25 ± 0.03 (m.e.) is uncertain because of possible systematic error. Similarly the RR Lyrae variables, globular clusters, and planetary nebulae all show a pronounced increase in density with decreasing R. But again all we can say from available data is that the gradient near the sun is probably of the same order as the value found from the motions. The only somewhat reliable determination of the density gradient is that obtained from general stars (mostly K giants) at distances between about 800 and 1600 pc from the galactic plane. These yield $\partial \log_{10} v / \partial R = -0.14$ (Oort 1938).

All these density variations are for objects of population II. Population I probably increases very little, if at all, toward the center. This can be concluded from the distribution of neutral hydrogen (see chap. 9).

For the common, apparently bright, stars the asymmetrical drift is so small that it cannot be reliably measured. Moreover, these stars have systematic motions indicating rather important deviations from a steady state (see Sec. 3.2.2). These may perfectly mask the effects of a density gradient; the more so, because the gradient is probably small, as a large fraction of these bright stars belongs to population I. It is, however, of importance to investigate the motions of older disk populations, because they may ultimately enable us to derive the circular velocity corresponding to the gravitational field, and to determine how far the motion of the interstellar gas deviates from this circular velocity. As an example, we may consider the K-type giants. These have a II-velocity dispersion of about 30 km/sec. If we assume their gradient to be half that found for population II, or −0.10, the asymmetrical drift would be 1.8 km/sec. The circular velocity would then be about 2 km/sec higher than the average velocity of the K giants. As the K giants have very nearly the same velocity as the interstellar gas, it would follow that the local rotational motion of the gas would be about the same amount lower than the circular velocity corresponding to the gravitational force. However, all the data involved are so uncertain that, as yet, no real significance can be attached to this result.

4.6. DISTRIBUTION OF THE MOTIONS OF NEARBY STARS; SOME GENERAL CHARACTERISTICS OF HIGH VELOCITIES

The stars in Table 5 have been chosen on the basis of certain intrinsic characteristics which had been found to be typical of population II objects. It is evident that this does not give us a picture of the average conditions in the Galaxy. In fact, all objects in the table are quite rare. In total they contribute only a fraction of the order 1/10000 to the mass of the system.

If we wish to aim at obtaining an adequate model of the Galactic System, we must proceed in a different way. We should seek to determine for each of various "populations," defined by intrinsic properties of the stars, the velocity and space distribution throughout the system, as well as the contribution of each of these populations to the total mass. It is evident that we are still very far from this ideal.

A reverse approach has been made by Woolley and Eggen (1958), who classified the stars according to the measure in which their motions deviate from a circular orbit. They have discussed the color-magnitude arrays for stars with different classes of orbits.

In trying to get a quantitative picture of the mixture of the stars of different velocity and space distributions from which the Galaxy is composed, it is natural to start with the nearest stars. For our knowledge of these is, of course, the most complete. As we have seen in Section 3.1.3, they can inform us concerning approximately half of the total mass density of stars in a volume element near the sun.

Figure 8, copied from an old study (Oort 1928), illustrates the general nature of the velocity distribution in the galactic plane for stars nearer than 20 pc. Though it contains only a very limited number of stars, it suffices to give an idea of the transition between the more or less symmetrical distribution of the low velocities and the asymmetrical distribution of the higher velocities. For more detailed information on the velocity distributions the reader is referred to investigations by Gliese (1956) and Woolley (1958), which rest on a much larger body of material, but which do not give plots of individual velocities.

We note in the first place that the great majority of stars have velocities lower than 65 km/sec. The diagram clearly displays the ellipsoidal distribution for these stars, with major axis in the direction of Π; the distribution is roughly symmetrical with respect to the "local standard of rest," indicated by a black square. For velocities higher than about 65 km/sec with respect to this local standard of rest an asymmetry sets in for the distribution of Θ. There are no stars with a Θ-component larger than $\Theta_c + 65$, but there is an appreciable number with Θ smaller than $\Theta_c - 65$. The latter have a dispersion in Π which is much larger than that for the bulk of the stars; the same increase in disp Π is already apparent for stars with $\Theta - \Theta_c$ between -40 and -65 km/sec.

The number of high-velocity objects among the nearest stars is rather small. In order to get a better insight into the phenomena described it is desirable to extend the material of high velocities by including more distant stars as well. This has been done in Figure 8. In studying the distribution of these high velocities it should be kept in mind that these do not form a representative sample of the stars in a volume of space.

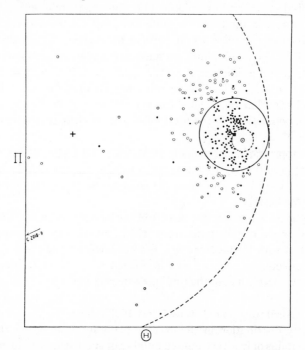

Fig. 8.—Distribution of velocity components Π and Θ for a representative sample of stars within 20 pc (filled circles) and for a sample of "ordinary" high-velocity stars (open circles). The cross marks the velocity of the center of mass of the Galaxy, the square the local standard of rest, and the encircled dot the velocity of the sun. Stars with velocities differing less than 20 km/sec from the solar velocity (within the small broken circle) have been omitted because they were very incomplete. For the other nearby stars the incompleteness was compensated by giving slightly larger radii to the dots where the sample was incomplete. The full-drawn circle has a radius of 65 km/sec. No velocities were known to lie outside the large dashed circle (Oort 1928).

A much larger sampling of high velocities has been studied by Fricke (1949). Figure 9, taken from his article, shows the distribution of Π and Θ for about 600 stars whose space velocities relative to the local standard of rest are larger than 63 km/sec. This limit, as we have mentioned above, appears to mark the transition between stars for which the Θ-components are roughly symmetrical around Θ_c and those which show a pronounced asymmetry in this distribution. It was indicated by Oort (1922, 1926) that the transition between the two distributions occurs rather suddenly.

In Figure 9 a circle of radius $\Theta_c + 63$ km/sec has been drawn around the velocity of the galactic center. There are no well-determined velocities outside this circle. The statement, made above, that there are no stars with Θ larger than $\Theta_c + 65$ may therefore be more adequately formulated by saying that there are no stars for which the space velocity relative to the galactic center exceeds $\Theta_c + 65$ km/sec. It has previously been suggested that the limit of

TABLE 7

RATIO OF DISP Z TO DISP Π

Space Velocity (km/sec)	No.	$\sqrt{(\langle Z^2 \rangle / \langle \Pi^2 \rangle)}$
63–100............	385	0.49
101–150............	128	.52
>150............	85	0.44

$\Theta_c + 65$ might represent the velocity of escape from a point near the sun. However, there is now fairly convincing evidence that the velocity of escape from the Galaxy is considerably higher (see chap. 22), and that the velocity $\Theta_c + 65$ must rather correspond to some sort of boundary of the Galaxy at about 25 kpc from the center.

A striking feature of the distribution of high velocities is the elongation in the Π-direction. This is similar to the ellipsoidal velocity distribution among ordinary stars, only still more pronounced (see Fig. 9). It is illustrated also in Figure 10, taken from Miczaika (1940), which gives the distribution of the high-velocity vectors (relative to the local standard of rest) in galactic longitude. There are maxima at roughly $l^{\Pi} = 210°$ and $340°$. The two maxima seem unequal. It would be desirable to investigate how far this difference can have been caused by selection effects.

The Z-components of the high-velocity stars are, in general, much smaller than the components in the galactic plane. The ratio of the dispersion in Z to that in Π is shown in Table 7 (from data by Fricke, 1949).

For the most frequent high-velocity stars, with velocities between 63 and 100 km/sec, the average velocity in the z-direction is only 23 km/sec (which may still be somewhat too high as a consequence of selection effects). It seems prob-

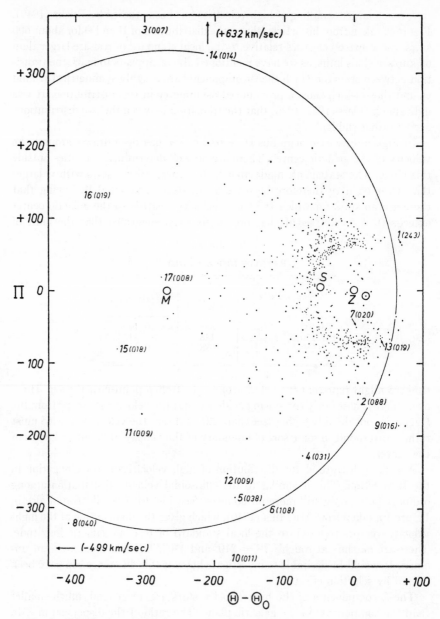

FIG. 9.—Distribution of Π and $\Theta - \Theta_0$ for a larger material of high-velocity stars (Fricke 1949). The figure is analogous to Figure 8.

able that these stars belong to an old disk population. It is not yet understood how they can have acquired their relatively high random velocities in the galactic plane without getting high velocities in the z-coordinate.

The most striking characteristic of Figures 8 and 9 is that even among the high-velocity stars there is a very strong concentration to the right-hand side of the velocity space, such as would be expected for a disk population. In the region of space and the domain of absolute magnitude considered, *disk* populations with considerable velocity dispersion in II apparently preponderate greatly over the halo population as well as over the intermediate population II. But the really *low*-velocity population is evidently by far the most abundant.

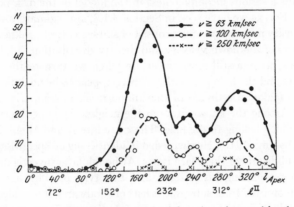

Fig. 10.—Distribution in old galactic longitude of the apices of stars with velocities relative to the local standard of rest above various limits (Miczaika 1940). New longitudes l^{II} are also indicated.

4.7. Considerations concerning a Model of the Galactic System

The ratio of high- to low-velocity population may become totally different at smaller distances from the center. If, for instance, the disk population II would increase in the way indicated in Section 4.5, while the density of the younger, low-velocity, populations would stay approximately constant, then, in a sample such as that shown in Figure 8, the high-velocity stars would begin to outweigh the low-velocities already near $R = 6$ kpc.

We have, as yet, no sufficient data to enable us to distinguish different age and velocity groups in the sample of nearby stars. Strömgren (1963) has recently obtained a quantitative determination of ages of bright stars, to an upper limit of 900 million years, but this gives only information on relatively young stars and is, therefore, restricted to a small fraction of the total mass in an element of volume. Roman's (1952) classes of strong-line and weak-line stars, which are also largely a classification according to age, extend over a larger domain, but are still inadequate for our purpose. At the Mount Wilson and Palomar Observatories, Eggen (1962) has determined ultraviolet excesses for a large number of nearby stars; these have been shown by various authors to be strongly correlated with velocity dispersion. In combination with infrared colors of M dwarfs, such as have been determined by Kron (1956; see also chap. 17), these may ultimately yield adequate data for dissecting the nearby stars into groups which are homogeneous with respect to age and velocity dispersion.

It might then be possible to determine density gradients for various older groups and even to make a tentative extrapolation to the inner regions of the system, since a rough idea of the density increase of old disk populations toward the center may be obtained from surveys of easily recognizable objects such as planetary nebulae and novae. Even when all these data are available, there remains a serious incompleteness in the model of the disk populations of the Galaxy. For, as we have seen in Section 3.1.3, approximately 40 per cent of the mass density near the sun must consist of stars of entirely unknown type and, therefore, also of unknown velocity and density distribution.

Conditions become still more uncertain when we turn to the intermediate population II and the halo population. There appear to be no data which would enable us to make an estimate of their importance in comparison to the disk population. Among the known stars in the neighborhood of the sun, there are only a few which belong to the halo. These are late K and M subdwarfs classified as such by Joy (1947). He succeeded in identifying on spectroscopic grounds a group of subdwarfs of these late types. Although later investigators have had difficulty in recognizing his criteria, and this type of stars has, as a consequence, been omitted from subsequent lists of subdwarfs, it is evident from their velocity distribution that practically all of Joy's stars belong to the subdwarf class. The distribution of the space velocities of the ten K5 to M4 subdwarfs in Joy's list which are not fainter companions of stars classified as normal M dwarfs can be shown to be practically the same as that of the recognized F and G subdwarfs as given in Table 5. (For further information on subdwarfs the reader is referred to chap. 17 of this volume.) There are four late-type subdwarfs known within 10 pc of the sun. Taking account of the incompleteness of Joy's survey, we find that their density must at least amount to 0.4 solar masses per 1000 pc³, that is about 0.3 per cent of the total mass density near the sun. Because of their wide distribution in z, we may estimate that they would represent 2 or 3 per cent of the total mass of the Galaxy. These subdwarfs are among the intrinsically faintest stars known. There is no way of estimating what fraction of the still fainter stars, which must make up the unidentified 40 per cent of the total mass density near the sun, belongs to the subdwarfs, but evidently this may be an important fraction. It is quite possible that there might be enough halo stars to make the halo an important contributor, or even *the* most important contributor to the mass of the Galaxy. If we assume that, for $R > 1$, the density of the halo population varies as R^{-3}, as indicated by the known stars of this population as well as by the light variation in the spheroidal components of other galaxies, and if we further assume an axial ratio of 0.5 for the equidensity surfaces, then, if the density is supposed to be constant within $R =$

1, the total mass of the halo within R_0 is 1.66×10^{13} $\rho_{0,h}$ solar masses, where $\rho_{0,h}$ is the halo density near the sun in solar masses per pc³. An upper limit to the halo mass within R_0 is given by the observed circular velocity, taking into account the minimum attraction exerted by the known stars in the disk. On the extreme assumption that the density of the latter does not increase toward the center, they would yield about a third of the total attraction. The maximum mass of the part of the halo within the sun's distance from the center is then 0.9×10^{11} solar masses. The corresponding upper limit for the density of the halo population near the sun is 0.005 solar masses per pc³. I am indebted to M. Schmidt for drawing my attention to this possibility of estimating an upper limit to the halo density. The density of the known M-type subdwarfs is about one-twelfth of this value, which indicates that the mass of the halo must be at least 5 per cent of the total mass of the Galaxy. The actual mass is likely to be considerably larger. The density of unknown faint stars in the neighborhood of the sun is about 0.06 solar masses per pc³. If 10 per cent of this were halo stars, the halo would be the preponderant constituent of the Galactic System. The above reasoning shows that certainly not more than 10 per cent of the unknown stars can belong to the halo population.

The requirements which should ultimately be satisfied by a model of the Galaxy are not only that there must be consistency between the velocity and density distribution for each of the various populations, but also that the sum of all populations must give a field of force fitting the rotation curve.

For an account of various attempts that have been made in the past to construct models of the Galaxy, see Schmidt, chapter 22 of this volume, and Fricke (1951).

§ 5. THREE-DIMENSIONAL ORBITS OF HIGH-VELOCITY STARS

A. OLLONGREN
Central Computing Institute of the University of Leiden

5.1. STATEMENT OF THE PROBLEM

The motion of a star of unit mass moving in the gravitational field of force of the Galaxy can be described by the Newtonian law

$$\ddot{r} = -\text{grad } \Phi,\tag{39}$$

in which r is the vector displacement of the star with respect to the galactic center and Φ is the potential function determined by the system as a whole (see Sec. 1). The equivalent equations in the cylindrical coordinates ϖ, ϑ, and z are

$$\ddot{\varpi} = \varpi\dot{\vartheta}^2 - \frac{\partial \Phi}{\partial \varpi}$$

$$\frac{d\varpi^2\dot{\vartheta}}{dt} = -\frac{\partial \Phi}{\partial \vartheta}\tag{40}$$

$$\ddot{z} = -\frac{\partial \Phi}{\partial z}.$$

We shall now use the assumption that the mass distribution in the Galaxy has axial symmetry. The function Φ is then independent of ϑ and the second of the equations of motion can be integrated:

$$\varpi^2 \dot{\vartheta} = h , \qquad (41)$$

in which h is the area constant. This integral is the integral of angular momentum I_2 mentioned before. Introducing the function U defined as

$$U = \frac{h^2}{2\varpi^2} + \Phi , \qquad (42)$$

we transform the remaining two equations into

$$\ddot{\varpi} = -\frac{\partial U}{\partial \varpi} ,$$

$$\ddot{z} = -\frac{\partial U}{\partial z} , \qquad (43)$$

which set of equations describes the motion of a star in the two-dimensional (ϖ, z) plane. This (moving) plane, containing the z-axis and the position of the star, may be called the meridian plane. The motion around the z-axis is given by

$$\dot{\vartheta} = \frac{h}{\varpi^2} . \qquad (44)$$

In the (ϖ, z)-system of coordinates (which is not an inertial system), the motion of a star with a given value of h is governed by the function U, which can be considered as a potential function. The forces in the meridian plane are given by

$$-\frac{\partial U}{\partial \varpi} = \frac{h^2}{\varpi^3} + K_\varpi ,$$

$$-\frac{\partial U}{\partial z} = K_z . \qquad (45)$$

The term h^2/ϖ^3 is an extra centripetal force introduced by using a moving co-ordinate system. For a given value of h there is one value of ϖ for which centripetal and centrifugal forces in the galactic plane are equal. We designate this value of ϖ by ϖ_c. In the meridian plane the function U has a minimum in the point $(\varpi_c, 0)$, as the variation δU is equal to zero there. Along the ϖ axis the centrifugal force will preponderate over the centripetal force for $\varpi < \varpi_c$, while for $\varpi > \varpi_c$ it will be the other way around. Therefore, the equipotential lines in the meridian plane $U = $ constant will be "centered" on the point $(\varpi_c, 0)$. Figure 11 shows some equipotential lines for the case $\varpi_c = 5.2$ kpc. They are based on the model of the distribution of mass in the Galaxy proposed by Schmidt (1956).

The point $(\varpi_c, 0)$ is a solution of the equations of motion (43). It corresponds to circular motion in the galactic plane at a distance ϖ_c from the galactic center. Obviously this motion in the meridian plane is that of lowest total energy, since the velocity components Π and Z are both equal to zero and the potential energy is at a minimum. For all other meridian orbits the total energy

$$\tfrac{1}{2}(\Pi^2+Z^2)+U=E \tag{46}$$

is larger than $U\,(\varpi_c,\,0)$.

The total energy E is an integral of motion both for the two-dimensional case of meridian motion (eq. [43]) and the three-dimensional case of motion in space (eq. [40]). In the latter case we have two integrals of motion, the energy

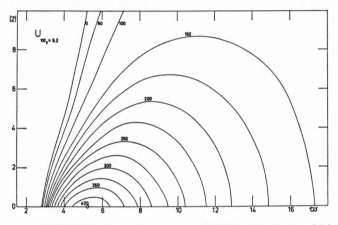

Fig. 11.—Equipotential curves in the moving meridian plane for $\varpi = 5.2$ kpc

and the area constant; in the case of meridian motion we have until now determined only one integral of motion. Besides these two integrals of motion there can only exist one additional independent integral of motion which contains the velocity components Π and Z. This integral, the existence of which we shall make plausible hereafter, will be called the third integral of motion I_3.

We can now formulate the problem of determining the space orbit of a high-velocity star as follows: given its initial position r_0 at $t = 0$, find its trajectory in the meridian plane by integrating the equations in (43), and obtain the third coordinate and velocity component from

$$\vartheta = \int_0^t \frac{h}{\varpi^2}\,dt$$

and   (47)

$$\Theta = \frac{h}{\varpi},$$

respectively. We shall in the following only be concerned with the problem of determining the meridian orbit.

5.2. Exact Solutions

Ollongren (1962) discussed the class of solutions which is obtained by introducing general curvilinear coordinates ξ and ζ in the meridian plane and by supposing that the equations of motion be separable in these coordinates. We shall not repeat his discussion, but confine ourselves to the simple case that the equations of motion are separable in the rectangular coordinates defined by the transformation

$$\xi = \varpi - \varpi_c , \qquad \zeta = z . \tag{48}$$

A discussion of this case is useful in two respects: (a) it reveals general characteristics of meridian orbits which are valid for the more complicated case of general curvilinear separation coordinates; (b) it provides a set of properties to which reference can be made when the results of numerical computations are reviewed.

Around the point ($\xi = 0, \zeta = 0$) we develop the function U in a Taylor series, which we terminate after three terms:

$$U = U_c + \tfrac{1}{2} m \, \xi^2 + \tfrac{1}{2} n \, \zeta^2 . \tag{49}$$

For this case the equations of motion are readily integrated, and the solution can be written

$$\begin{aligned}
\xi &= M \, \sin[\, \sqrt{(m)}\, t + \varphi_1], \\
\zeta &= N \, \sin[\, \sqrt{(n)}\, t + \varphi_2],
\end{aligned} \tag{50}$$

with M, N, φ_1, and φ_2 as the integration constants. We have here the case of a harmonic oscillator in two dimensions. The three independent integrals of motion are

$$\begin{aligned}
E_m &= \tfrac{1}{2} (\Pi^2 + m \, \xi^2), \\
E_n &= \tfrac{1}{2} (Z^2 + n \, \zeta^2), \\
F &= \frac{1}{\sqrt{m}} \arcsin \frac{\xi}{M} - \frac{1}{\sqrt{n}} \arcsin \frac{\zeta}{N} ,
\end{aligned} \tag{51}$$

while for the total energy we have

$$E = U_c + E_m + E_n . \tag{52}$$

Any linear function of the two integrals E_m and E_n can be used as a third integral of motion for space orbits, although its region of applicability in the Galaxy is limited to the immediate vicinity of the circular orbit in the galactic plane with radius $\varpi = \varpi_c$. This third integral of motion is quadratic in the velocity components, and it is a special case of the general quadratic integral of motion theoretically studied by van Albada (1952) and Kuzmin (1953) and recently, from a more practical point of view, by van de Hulst (1962). The latter gives a qualitative discussion of the applicability of this integral for low-velocity stars in the vicinity of the sun.

The last of the integrals in (51) is of a different nature than E_m and E_n. This is illustrated by the shape of the trajectory traced in the meridian plane for the ratio α of frequencies of the two independent oscillations, rational and irrational, respectively. If the field of force is such that $\alpha = (m/n)^{1/2}$ is rational, then the trajectory is a closed Lissajous figure for all initial conditions and all energies, but, if α is irrational, the Lissajous figure is open and a region with the shape of a rectangle is filled by the trajectory (see Fig. 12). In the former case the integral of motion F is called *isolating*. For a rigorous mathematical definition of this concept we refer to Wintner (1947); here we confine ourselves to the statement that isolating integrals can be recognized by their property of isolating points on the solution path from neighboring points in phase space.

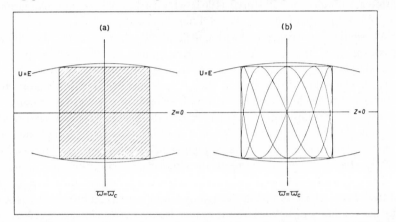

Fig. 12.—Meridian oscillations for small amplitudes for ratio of frequencies: (a) irrational (non-periodic orbit, F non-isolating), and (b) rational (periodic orbit, F isolating).

Thus, the integrals E_m and E_n are isolating since they isolate between themselves the mentioned rectangular region in the meridian plane.

Summarizing, we have seen that meridian orbits have the following properties if the equations of motion are separable in cartesian coordinates in the meridian plane: (a) There are three integrals of motion, two of which are isolating independent of the properties of the potential function U. (b) Each of these two integrals of motion containing the velocity components Π and Z can be used as the third integral of motion for the space orbit. (c) The remaining integral of motion is isolating only if the potential function U has the property that the frequency ratio of the meridian oscillations is a rational number. (d) If this integral is not isolating, a rectangular region in the meridian plane is filled by the orbit.

These properties also apply when the equations of motion are supposed to be separable in general curvilinear coordinates, as has been proved by Ollongren (1962). He has, however, also shown that, in general, the equations of motion cannot be separated in an arbitrary curvilinear coordinate system and that further insight into the general problem may be obtained by performing numerical integrations, in a field of force belonging to a model of the distribution of mass in the Galaxy.

5.3. NUMERICAL SOLUTIONS

All numerical integrations of the equations of motion to be discussed here are the result of a joint investigation by Torgård and Ollongren, and have been carried out at the Swedish Board for Computing Machinery, Stockholm. They concern orbits of high-velocity stars in the field of force belonging to the model of the distribution of mass in the Galaxy developed by Schmidt (1956). The force components K_ϖ and K_z were defined by means of an interpolation formula, obtained by Ollongren (1962) who used a rational approximation to Schmidt's potential function. We will not discuss this formula here.

We shall only be concerned with one family of orbits; namely, all orbits with fixed values of the area constant (corresponding to circular motion in the galactic plane at a distance of 5.2 kpc from the galactic center) and the total energy. The value of the latter is chosen such that $(\Pi^2 + Z^2)^{1/2}$ is equal to 50 km/sec at the neighborhood of the sun for an orbit belonging to the family. The corresponding equipotential curve $U = E$ in the meridional plane is marked by the number 250 in Figure 11. This family of orbits is an arbitrary one except that all its members are orbits of high-velocity stars with an area constant smaller than that corresponding to the circular motion of the sun.

In Figures 13 and 14 we illustrate the properties of the meridional trajectories of two classes of orbits within this family; the *box orbits* and the *tube orbits*. For further examples of box orbits the reader is referred to Ollongren (1962). The starting point, taken for all integrations on the ϖ-axis, is marked by a filled circle. Not the whole computed trajectory is shown; the curve is terminated when the general appearance of the trajectory has become clear. The numbers written in the trajectory count the number of oscillations in the z-direction from the start. The drawn egg-shaped curve is the equipotential curve in the meridian plane within which all trajectories of the family concerned are constrained to remain. The region within this curve may be called the admissible region. We can describe the properties of the box orbits as follows:

1) The trajectory fills a subregion of the admissible region in the meridian plane, which has the shape of a box; the four corners of the box (which can be proved to be rectangular) lie on the equipotential curve; the box is symmetrical with respect to the ϖ-axis.

2) The boundary of the box is an envelope to the trajectory, i.e., the orbit touches the envelope in a definite order as time proceeds.

3) Within the box the points of self-intersection of the trajectory define a vector field; in each point there are four velocity vectors of equal magnitude, and an orbit passing through this point with one of these velocity vectors will give a trajectory which fills the same box.

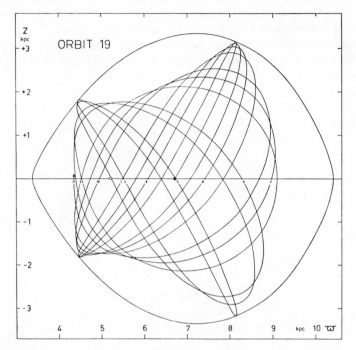

Fig. 13.—Example of a box orbit with intermediary ϖ and z amplitudes. The figures written in the trajectory count the number of completed z oscillations. The egg-shaped curve is the equipotential curve $E = U$ (curve of zero velocity).

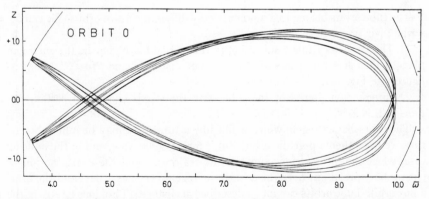

Fig. 14.—Example of a simple tube orbit: the tube-shaped subregion of the meridian plane, which is filled by the trajectory, is a Lissajous figure with certain "thickness."

4) There is a minimum distance q between the box orbit and the galactic center; it is the distance between the galactic center and the intersection of the box-shaped envelope and the ϖ-axis with smallest ϖ.

We can briefly describe a box orbit by stating that its trajectory is topologically equivalent to a Lissajous curve with a definite ratio of frequencies of oscillation. Thus, we can obtain by comparison to Lissajous curves the ratio of frequencies of oscillation in two orthogonal directions in the meridian plane (see Table 8). Note that this ratio is *not* constant, contrary to the case of small oscillations.

TABLE 8

BOX ORBITS

Orbit	q (kpc)	$\sqrt{(m/n)}$
13..........	3.43	0.487
36..........	3.52	.593
4..........	3.78	.754
19..........	4.35	.882
6..........	5.80	0.977

TABLE 9

TUBE ORBITS

Orbit	q (kpc)	$\sqrt{(m/n)}$
1A..........	3.45	1:2
0.............	....	2:3
15..........	3.70	5:7

The tube orbits belong to a fundamentally different class of orbits. We can describe their properties as follows:

1) The trajectory fills a subregion of the admissible region in the meridian plane, which has the shape of a closed but distorted and "fuzzy" Lissajous figure (see Fig. 14).

2) Intersection points of the orbit with the ϖ-axis cluster on certain sections of this axis.

The tube-shaped region which is filled by a tube orbit may be infinitely narrow; we have then a periodic orbit. But it may also be wide, and in the limiting case, when the intersection points of the trajectory and the ϖ-axis no longer cluster but spread out over the ϖ-axis, the region becomes a box, and the orbit a box orbit. Tube orbits cannot be described as distorted Lissajous figures in the sense that box orbits could be described. Therefore, it is not possible to define the ratio of oscillation frequencies in the same way as for those orbits. However, one can define a ratio of oscillation frequencies for the periodic orbit "around" which a given tube orbit oscillates. Using this definition the values given in Table 9 have been obtained. The minimum distance q from the galactic center in the galactic plane can be defined for orbits 1A and 15 in the same way as it was done for the box orbits. For orbit 0 one would have to use the maximum distance from the galactic center instead.

We have given a concise description of two classes of orbits of a selected family of meridian orbits. The family is an arbitrary one, and the properties of meridian trajectories revealed by the numerical computations may therefore be considered as general. Summarizing those, we have seen that both box orbits and tube orbits are either periodic, in which case the trajectory is a closed line, or they fill a subregion within the curve $U = E$. This situation is similar to the cases considered in which there exists a third isolating integral of motion for the space orbit. The numerical solutions, therefore, give empirical proof of the existence of a third integral of motion. Until now, however, no function of ϖ, z, Π, and Z has been suggested for this integral.

GENERAL REFERENCES

CHANDRASEKHAR, S.   1942   *Principles of Stellar Dynamics* (Chicago: University of Chicago Press).

LINDBLAD, B.   1959   "Galactic Dynamics," *Hdb. d. Phys.*, ed. S. Flügge (Berlin: Springer-Verlag), **53**, 21–99.

PAHLEN, E. VON DER   1947   *Einführung in die Dynamik von Sternsystemen* (Basel: Verlag-Birkhäuser).

SMART, W. M.   1938   *Stellar Dynamics* (Cambridge: University Press).

REFERENCES

ALBADA, G. B. VAN   1952   *Proc. R. Acad. Sci. Amsterdam, Ser. B*, **55**, 620.

ALEXANDER, J. B.   1960   *Observatory*, **80**, 110.

BAADE, W.   1951   *Michigan Obs. Pub.*, **10**, 7.

1958   *Ric. Astr. Specola Vaticana*, **5**, 303 ("Stellar Populations").

BLAAUW, A.   1946   *Pub. Kapteyn Astr. Lab. Groningen*, No. 52.

1952   *B.A.N.*, **11**, 414.

1958   *Ric. Astr. Specola Vaticana*, **5**, 333 ("Stellar Populations").

CAMM, G. L.   1950   *M.N.*, **110**, 305.

CHANDRASEKHAR, S.   1942   *Principles of Stellar Dynamics* (Chicago: University of Chicago Press).

CONTOPOULOS, G.   1960   *Zs. f. Ap.*, **49**, 273.

DELHAYE, J.   1952   *Bull. Astr.*, **16**, 221.

1953   *C.R. Acad. Sci. Paris*, **237**, 294.

EELSALU, H.   1958   *Tartu Pub.*, **33**, 153.

EGGEN, O. J.   1960   *A.J.*, **65**, 393.

EGGEN, O. J., and
SANDAGE, A. R.   1959   *M.N.*, **119**, 255.

EGGEN, O. J.,
LYNDEN-BELL, D., and
SANDAGE, A. R.   1963   *Ap. J.*, **136**, 748.

FEAST, M. W. 1963 *M.N.*, **125**, 367.
FRICKE, W. 1949 *A.N.*, **277**, 241.
1951 *Ibid.*, **280**, 193.
GLIESE, W. 1956 *Zs. f. Ap.*, **39**, 1.
GOULD, R. J., GOLD, T.,
and SALPETER, E. E. 1963 *Ap. J.*, **138**, 408.
HERK, G. VAN 1965 *B.A.N.* (in press).
HILL, E. R. 1960 *B.A.N.*, **15**, 1.
HINS, C. H., and
BLAAUW, A. 1948 *B.A.N.*, **10**, 365.
HULST, H. C. VAN DE 1962 *B.A.N.*, **16**, 235.
JEANS, J. H. 1915 *M.N.*, **76**, 70.
1922 *Ibid.*, **82**, 122.
JONES, D. H. P. 1962 *Roy. Obs. Bull.*, No. 52.
JOY, A. H. 1947 *Ap. J.*, **105**, 96; *Mt. Wilson Contr.*, No. 726.
KAPTEYN, J. C. 1905 *Rept. Brit. Assoc., 1905*, 257.
KINMAN, T. D. 1959 *M.N.*, **119**, 559.
KINMAN, T. D., and
WIRTANEN, C. A. 1963 *Ap. J.*, **137**, 698.
KRON, G. E. 1956 *Proc. 3d Berkeley Symp. Math. Stat. Prob.* (Berke-
ley: University of California Press), p. 39.
KUZMIN, G. G. 1953 *Pub. Acad. Sci. Esthonian SSR*, **2**, 368; *Tartu
Astr. Obs. Teated*, No. 1.
1955 *Tartu Pub.*, **33**, 3.
LINDBLAD, B. 1927a *M.N.*, **87**, 553.
1927b *Arkiv. f. Mat., Astr. o. Fys., Ser. A*, **20**, No. 17.
1956 *Stockholms Obs. Ann.*, **19**, No. 7.
MICZAIKA, G. 1940 *A.N.*, **270**, 249.
NAHON, F. 1957 *Bull. Astr.*, **21**, 55.
OLLONGREN, A. 1962 *B.A.N.*, **16**, 241.
OORT, J. H. 1922 *B.A.N.*, **1**, 133.
1926 *Pub. Kapteyn Astr. Lab. Groningen*, No. 40.
1928 *B.A.N.*, **4**, 269.
1932 *Ibid.*, **6**, 249.
1938 *Ibid.*, **8**, 233.
1940 *Ap. J.*, **91**, 273.
1960 *B.A.N.*, **15**, 45.
OORT, J. H., and
TULDER, J. J. M. VAN 1942 *B.A.N.*, **9**, 327.
PEREK, L. 1951 *Contr. Astr. Inst. Masaryk Un. Brno.*, **1**, No. 8.
PLAUT, L., and
SOUDAN, A. 1963 *B.A.N.*, **17**, 70.
PRENDERGAST, K. H. 1954 *A.J.*, **59**, 260.
PRESTON, G. W. 1959 *Ap. J.*, **130**, 507.
RHIJN, P. J. VAN 1936 *Pub. Kapteyn Astr. Lab. Groningen*, No. 47.
ROMAN, N. G. 1952 *Ap. J.*, **116**, 122.

SANDAGE, A. R.   1963   "Ann. Rept. Dir. Mt. Wilson and Palomar Obs."
                                     (Carnegie Inst. of Washington Yearbook **62**), p.
                                     16.

SCHMIDT, M.   1956   *B.A.N.*, **13**, 15.
SCHWARZSCHILD, K.   1907   *Göttingen Nachr., 1907*, 614.
                              1908   *Ibid., 1908*, 191.

SHAROV, A. S., and
   PAVLOVSKAYA, E. D.   1961   *A.J. U.S.S.R.*, **38**, 939 (= *Soviet Astr.–A.J.*, **5**,
                                     716).

SPITZER, L., and
   SCHWARZSCHILD, M.   1953   *Ap. J.*, **118**, 106.
STEBBINS, J., and
   KRON, G. E.   1957   *Ap. J.*, **126**, 266.
STRÖMBERG, G.   1924   *Ap. J.*, **59**, 228; *Mt. Wilson Contr.*, No. 275.
                              1925   *Ap. J.*, **61**, 363; *Mt. Wilson Contr.*, No. 293.
STRÖMGREN, B.   1963   *Quart. J. R.A.S.*, **4**, 8.
STRUVE, O.   1950   *Pub. A.S.P.*, **62**, 217.
VAUCOULEURS, G. DE   1958   *Ap. J.*, **128**, 465.
WINTNER, A.   1947   *The Analytical Foundation of Celestial Mechanics*
                                     (Princeton: Princeton University Press).

WOOLLEY, R. V. D. R.   1957   *M.N.*, **117**, 198.
                              1958   *Ibid.*, **118**, 45.

WOOLLEY, R. V. D. R.,
   and EGGEN, O. J.   1958   *M.N.*, **118**, 57.
YOUNG, A. T.   1961   Thesis, Harvard University (unpublished).

CHAPTER 22

Rotation Parameters and Distribution of Mass in the Galaxy

MAARTEN SCHMIDT

Mount Wilson and Palomar Observatories

Carnegie Institution of Washington, California Institute of Technology

§ 1. INTRODUCTION

THE discovery of the rotation of the Galaxy (Lindblad 1926, Oort 1927) opened the possibility to determine the total mass and the distribution of mass in the Galaxy. Information about the rotation over a considerable range of distances from the center of the Galaxy, required for a determination of the mass distribution, became available less than a decade ago through measurements of the radial velocity of interstellar atomic hydrogen at 21-cm wavelength (Kwee, Muller, and Westerhout 1954).

The distribution of mass in the Galaxy is of interest for several reasons. The circular velocities derived in 21-cm investigations are limited to those parts of the Galaxy interior to the sun. The best way to estimate circular velocities in the outer parts of the Galaxy is through construction of a mass model based on the known part of the circular-velocity curve and other data. Such a model is also a prerequisite for the determination of orbits in the Galaxy, which are of interest in the study of moving groups (Eggen, this volume, chap. 6), runaway stars (Blaauw 1961), the possible existence of a third integral of motion (cf. Ollongren 1962, and Sec. 5 of chap. 21, this volume), etc.

The next section will deal briefly with some models of the mass distribution and with the techniques used in the construction of these models. Since most of the rotation curve in the Galaxy depends on 21-cm data, it is of interest to inquire whether the state of motion of the interstellar gas deviates appreciably from circular motion (Sec. 3). The distribution of mass as derived from the 21-cm data depends strongly on the sun's distance R_0 to the center, and on the values of the constants A and B of differential galactic rotation. All relevant in-

513

formation is discussed in Section 4; the values $R_0 = 10$ kpc, $A = 15$ km/sec per kpc, $B = -10$ km/sec per kpc are finally adopted. These values are used in the construction of a simple model of the distribution of mass which is described in the final section.

§ 2. TECHNIQUES OF MODEL CONSTRUCTION

Perek (1962) has given an extensive description of published models of the distribution of mass and of the techniques used in the construction of these models. The reader is referred to this work for many details; we shall limit ourselves to some simple formulae and a discussion of some critical points.

The first model of the distribution of mass was given by Oort (1932) in connection with the determination of $K(z)$ and the local density. This model, as well as two subsequent ones (Oort and van Woerkom 1941; Oort 1952), consisted of a central, spherical or spheroidal, mass and a number of homogeneous oblate spheroids.

The rotation curve determined by Kwee, Muller, and Westerhout (1954) from 21-cm observations showed surprisingly little variation in the circular velocity over a considerable range of distance from the center. This implied a strong increase of the density toward the center of the Galaxy. The construction of models covering a large range of density is facilitated by the use of spheroids in which the density varies with distance from the center. These inhomogeneous spheroids, in which surfaces of constant density are concentric spheroidal surfaces with constant eccentricity, were first investigated by Perek (1948), later by Schmidt (1956), and Burbidge, Burbidge, and Prendergast (1959).

It may be shown (Schmidt 1956) that the force per unit mass exerted by an oblate spheroid of eccentricity, e, in which the density, ρ, is a function of a, where a is given by

$$a^2 = \varpi^2 + z^2(1 - e^2)^{-1},$$ (1)

where $e < 1$, is

$$K_\varpi = 4\pi G e^{-3} \sqrt{(1 - e^2)} \varpi \int_0^{\arcsin e} \rho(a) \sin^2 \beta \, d\beta,$$ (2)

$$K_z = 4\pi G e^{-3} \sqrt{(1 - e^2)} z \int_0^{\arcsin e} \rho(a) \tan^2 \beta \, d\beta,$$ (3)

where β is defined by

$$\varpi^2 \sin^2 \beta + z^2 \tan^2 \beta = a^2 e^2,$$ (4)

in which ϖ is the distance to the axis of rotation, z the distance to the galactic plane. The 21-cm observations yield rotational velocities, as a function of ϖ, in the galactic plane. We assume that these are circular velocities (Sec. 3), so that

$$K_\varpi \varpi = \Theta_c^2(\varpi).$$ (5)

In the galactic plane, equation (2) reduces to

$$\Theta_c^2(\varpi) = 4\pi G \sqrt{(1 - e^2)} \int_0^\varpi \frac{\rho a^2 da}{\sqrt{(\varpi^2 - a^2 e^2)}}. \tag{6}$$

Since

$$dM = 4\pi\sqrt{(1 - e^2)} a^2 \rho(a) da, \tag{7}$$

we may write equation (6) as

$$\Theta_c^2(\varpi) = G \int_0^\varpi \frac{dM}{\sqrt{(\varpi^2 - a^2 e^2)}}. \tag{8}$$

Kuzmin (1952), and later Brandt (1960), noted that, for $e = 1$, equation (8) after proper substitution transforms into Abel's integral equation. This leads to

$$M(a) = \frac{2}{G\pi} \int_0^a \frac{\Theta_c^2(\varpi)\varpi d\varpi}{\sqrt{(a^2 - \varpi^2)}}. \tag{9}$$

Equations (7) and (9) show how at any point, interior of which the circular velocity as a function of distance is known, the value of $\rho\sqrt{(1 - e^2)}$ in the limiting case $e \to 1$ may be computed. Specifically, the logarithmic density gradient may be computed, and it may be shown that its value depends little on e, for $e \approx 1$. This is the basis for the relation (23) between the density gradient and other parameters such as the constants of differential galactic rotation, given in Section 4.6.

Note that only the distribution of mass interior to the last known point on the rotation curve can be determined. Here "interior" refers to all points in the Galaxy with a value of a smaller than that of our reference point. On the other hand, surface densities on the plane involve an integration of $\rho(a)$ over values of a larger than that of our reference point. This shows that the curve of circular velocity interior to a given point and the surface density at that point are unrelated. Therefore, an attempt by Belton and Brandt (1962) to establish a relation between the local surface density and the value of R_0 from 21-cm observations must depend critically on the density law assumed.

Returning to the case $e \neq 1$, Burbidge, Burbidge, and Prendergast (1959) solve for $\rho(a)$ from equation (6) by using a Taylor expansion,

$$\rho(a) = \rho_0 + \rho_1 a + \rho_2 a^2 + \ldots. \tag{10}$$

They show that

$$\Theta_c^2/\varpi^2 = v_0 + v_1\varpi + v_2\varpi^2 + \ldots, \tag{11}$$

where

$$v_n = 4\pi G e^{-n-3} \sqrt{(1 - e^2)} \rho_n \int_0^{\arcsin e} \sin^{n+2}\theta d\theta. \tag{12}$$

This method is straightforward in that each of the coefficients ρ_n is determined by the single corresponding coefficient v_n. An objection to the use of equation (10) in practice is that its form is not very suitable to represent densities that, in general, are decreasing functions of a. This leads to the requirement of a large number of terms for a fairly simple smoothly decreasing $\rho(a)$, with large coefficients ρ_n of alternating sign. This situation can be cured to some extent if we extend the series for ρ with terms involving a^{-1} and a^{-2}, i.e.,

$$\rho(a) = \rho_{-2}a^{-2} + \rho_{-1}a^{-1} + \rho_0 + \rho_1 a + \rho_2 a^2 + \ldots, \tag{13}$$

which leads to

$$\Theta_c^2/\varpi^2 = v_{-2}\varpi^{-2} + v_{-1}\varpi^{-1} + v_0 + v_1\varpi + v_2\varpi^2 + \ldots, \tag{14}$$

through equation (12).

The addition of these terms leads to a non-zero circular velocity or a non-zero force at the center, as well as infinite density at the center. However, the total mass involved remains finite, and if equation (14) is used to obtain a mathematical description of the circular velocity over a considerable part of a galaxy, these singularities are not serious. If we were primarily interested in the mass distribution in the nuclear parts of a galaxy, then, of course, the first two terms should not be used. In the Galaxy, circular velocities at 100 parsecs from the center are still of the same order as the circular velocity in the solar neighborhood (Rougoor and Oort 1960). Actually, a model for the part of the Galaxy interior to the sun, based on the first term of equations (13) and (14) only, represents an excellent first-order approximation for the distribution of mass.

With the introduction of these additional terms, and possibly a mass point at the center, the mass distribution can probably be sufficiently well represented by some four or five terms. Explicit expressions for the integral in equation (12) are given by Burbidge, Burbidge, and Prendergast (1959) for $n \geq 0$. In addition to those we have

$$v_{-2} = 4\pi G\rho_{-2}\sqrt{(1 - e^2)}e^{-1} \arcsin e,$$
$$v_{-1} = 4\pi G\rho_{-1}\sqrt{(1 - e^2)}e^{-2}[1 - \sqrt{(1 - e^2)}]. \tag{15}$$

We still are left with a problem in the outer parts of the Galaxy, since an approximation such as (13) has to be cut off at, say, a_s in order to keep the mass finite. Since there is little, if any, indication as yet of the way the density falls off with distance in the very outer parts of galaxies, we shall assume that beyond a_s the density varies as a^{-m}, with $m > 3$, such that at a_s the density and density gradient vary smoothly. This shell is formally represented as the difference of a spheroid with infinite extent, and a spheroid with outer boundary at a_s.

The procedure in constructing a model is to represent the circular-velocity curve by equation (14), then to compute the density from equation (13) through equation (12). The eccentricity e is chosen such that the density near the sun is represented. It turns out that e is slightly smaller than unity, in which case the product of the density and the axial ratio $\sqrt{(1 - e^2)}$ is almost independent of the value assumed for the axial ratio. The choice of a density law in the outer shell is somewhat arbitrary and depends on various considerations to be discussed (Secs. 4.8 and 5).

If additional information, such as the distribution of various kinds of stars in our neighborhood, is to be represented in the model, then one may construct a model consisting of several inhomogeneous spheroids, each of which corresponds to a specific kind of object. The eccentricity of the different spheroids may be chosen differently. In this way one may try to represent the nuclear bulge as seen in external galaxies or a halo with small eccentricity.

A model consisting mainly of four inhomogeneous spheroids has been given by Schmidt (1956). The components represent the interstellar gas, the common stars, the high-velocity stars, and unspecified matter. In the interior part of the Galaxy a density law was used consisting of the second and third terms of equation (13). The model was based on values of $A = 19.5$ km/sec per kpc, $B = -6.9$ km/sec per kpc, and $R_0 = 8.2$ kpc.

The mean logarithmic density gradient near the sun was found at -0.37. As the known matter in the solar neighborhood has a density gradient about half as large, the density gradient of the unknown material became extremely high. As may be seen from relation (23), which was derived from the 21-cm observations through equation (9), the density gradient depends critically on the ratio B/A. Luminosity and mass density gradients seen in the Andromeda nebula are nowhere nearly as large as the gradient found in the model. It seems quite unlikely now that the gradient is really as high as indicated by the model. We shall, in fact, give this evidence some weight in the discussion of the value of B in Section 4.8.

Due to the strong decrease of density in the model, the escape velocity near the sun was found to be only 70 km/sec larger than the circular velocity. This was in striking agreement with the cutoff at 63 km/sec found for motions in the direction of rotation. With a lower density gradient, the mass in the outer parts will be larger and so will be the escape velocity. We shall return to this point in Section 5.

Perek (1962), in his extensive review of mass distributions in stellar systems, has given what he considers to be the best model of the Galaxy. He represents population I by a very flat spheroid in which the density decreases exponentially with distance, the disk population by a similar spheroid with axial ratio 1/16, and population II by a spheroid with confocal strata in which the density falls off as the inverse sixth power of distance in the galactic plane. Perek assumes $R_0 = 8$ kpc, $\Theta_c(R_0) = 216$ km/sec. He finds the best fit for a model in which population II accounts for 17 per cent of the total mass in the Galaxy. The latter is found at 0.82×10^{11} solar masses; the local density is 0.12 solar masses per pc^3. The use of spheroids with confocal strata, which was introduced by Perek, is of interest, since it avoids the usual limitation that the axial ratio must be constant within a given spheroid with similar strata. In the latter case, one may alleviate this limitation by using a number of spheroids with different axial ratios. The spheroids with confocal strata have a practically constant density in the interior parts. This fits in well with the distribution of RR Lyrae stars as found by Perek himself. On the other hand, Baade (Baade and Minkowski 1954) derived a distribution that shows a strong concentration to the center of the Galaxy.

§ 3. THE MOTION OF INTERSTELLAR GAS

The rotation curve, which is required in the derivation of the mass distribution, gives the circular velocity in the plane as a function of distance R from the center of the Galaxy.

Available information on the rotation at various positions in the plane of the Galaxy depends on the motion of interstellar clouds of neutral atomic hydrogen observed at 21-cm wavelength. The average motion of interstellar gas may well deviate from circular motion. An example is the "3-kpc arm" which moves away from the galactic center with a velocity of 53 km/sec (this volume, chap. 9).

Kerr (1962) noted that the rotation curve determined from 21-cm observations in the southern hemisphere deviates from that found in the northern hemisphere. In order to avoid this asymmetry, he proposed that interstellar gas in our vicinity moves away from the center of the Galaxy with a speed of 7 km/sec. Since the outward component of the solar motion of interstellar gas and stars of all spectral types agree with each other to within a few km/sec, this would imply that all known matter in our neighborhood moves out with 7 km/sec. It is inconceivable that stars of all ages in a fixed gravitational potential field would happen to be moving out, on the average, at the present epoch. If the gravitational potential field is not constant, it would have to vary with a characteristic time of about one billion years, which seems quite improbably short. We are thus led to believe that the explanation for the observed anomaly should not be sought in an over-all expansion. In that case we are left with an asymmetry, either in motion or in distribution of hydrogen, between the two hemispheres. It may be noted, however, that this anomaly involves less than 1 per cent of the mass of the Galaxy.

Biermann and Davis (1960) have considered the effect of a magnetic field on the rotational velocity of interstellar gas. They investigate a model in which the gas has a velocity that is 15 km/sec less than the circular velocity and state that this possibility is supported by observations by G. and L. Münch (1960). In this investigation a rotation curve was derived from radial velocities of B-type stars. This curve shows at $R = 6$ kpc a rotational velocity 10 km/sec larger than that found from 21-cm investigations, while at $R = 4$ kpc it appeared to be 25 km/sec smaller. It is hard to believe that magneto-hydrodynamical effects on the interstellar gas could lead to opposite deviations from circular motion over so small a distance range. If the interstellar gas did indeed move 15 km/sec slower than the B-type stars locally, the deviations mentioned above would change to $+21$ km/sec at $R = 6$ kpc, and -18 km/sec at $R = 4$ kpc. There is no reason to prefer this pattern of deviations over that given above.

A direct way to detect a difference between the rotational velocity of interstellar gas and the circular velocity is through the component V (in the direction $l^{II} = 90°$, $b^{II} = 0°$) of solar motion. The value of V for the gas is about 14 from interstellar calcium clouds (Blaauw 1952), about 15 from 21-cm line studies at intermediate galactic latitude (Takakubo 1963), and about 13 from cepheids (Kraft and Schmidt 1963). The cepheids are young enough to still primarily represent the motion of the gas clouds from which they were formed. We adopt $V = 14$ for the interstellar gas. The value of V corresponding to the circular velocity cannot be determined reliably from A-type stars, as these show a nonrandom velocity distribution (see Eggen, this volume, chap. 6). F-type stars yield $V = 12$ (see Delhaye, this volume, chap. 4); their density gradient must be quite small, and the asymmetrical drift (see chap. 21, Sec. 4.5, eq. [38]) is probably negligible.

Accordingly, we take $V = 12$ to correspond to the local circular velocity. Comparison with $V = 14$ derived for the interstellar gas shows that it has a speed of rotation that is 2 ± 2 km/sec lower than the circular velocity. The error indicated is a subjective estimate of the uncertainty.

Local interstellar gas thus seems to have an average motion that is very little, if any, different from circular motion. We shall assume in this chapter that outside the 3-kpc arm the deviations of the motion of gas from circular motion can be neglected. Specifically, we base further discussion on the assumption that the 21-cm rotation curve determined in the northern hemisphere represents circular velocities in a steady, axially symmetric gravitational potential field.

§ 4. FUNDAMENTAL DATA

Since the observer takes part in the rotation of the Galaxy, it is essential to have information on his position in the Galaxy and his velocity. In the following subsections we shall discuss all available information on the value of the rotation constants A and B, and the sun's distance to the center R_0.

4.1. ROTATION CONSTANT A

The rotation constant A is defined as

$$A = -\tfrac{1}{2}R_0 \left(\frac{d\omega}{dR}\right)_{R=R_0},\tag{16}$$

where ω is the angular velocity of circular rotation, R the distance to the center of the Galaxy, R_0 that of the sun. In order to avoid the effect of localized deviations from circular velocities, it is desirable to derive the value of ω' at R_0 from a smoothed $\omega(R)$-curve determined from objects with a considerable range of

R. In this way, one may hope that the value of A so determined is representative for the distance R_0, rather than a purely local property in the sun's immediate neighborhood.

In principle, the $\omega(R)$ relation is determined from individual objects with known distance and radial velocity, through the equation

$$V_r = R_0[\omega(R) - \omega(R_0)] \sin l^{\mathrm{II}} \cos b^{\mathrm{II}} , \qquad (17)$$

which strictly applies to objects in circular motion in the galactic plane. It may be used for objects such as B-type stars, cepheids, and galactic clusters which have small peculiar velocities and are within a few hundreds of parsecs from the plane. Each object will yield a value of $\omega(R) - \omega(R_0)$, and, in principle, A could be determined from the slope of the relation at R_0. Individual points will have very different weights because of the factor $\sin l^{\mathrm{II}}$ in equation (17). In order to apply a least-squares solution, in which these variations are taken into account properly, equation (17) has to be linearized. Neglecting second and higher derivatives of $\omega(R)$, one gets

$$V_r = -2A(R - R_0) \sin l^{\mathrm{II}} \cos b^{\mathrm{II}} . \qquad (18)$$

If the objects considered are close to the sun, $R - R_0$ can be expressed in terms of r, the distance to the sun, and

$$V_r = Ar \sin 2l^{\mathrm{II}} \cos^2 b^{\mathrm{II}} . \qquad (19)$$

Returning to formula (18), one might consider adding a second term corresponding to ω'', if the range of R of the objects considered is large. This was done by Kraft and Schmidt (1963) in a discussion of cepheids, but it turned out that no reasonable value of ω'' could be found from the observations, probably due to localized deviations from circular motion.

Although R_0 appears in equations (17) and (18), the value of A determined from either of these equations depends very little on that of R_0, as is suggested also by the double approximation (19) in which R_0 does not appear. Equation (19) also suggests that the value of A found for a group of objects with given radial velocities will be inversely proportional to the distance scale used for the objects (Weaver 1961).

Recent determinations of the value of A are available, from B-type stars by Petrie, Cuttle, and Andrews (1956), Feast and Thackeray (1958); from galactic clusters by Johnson and Svolopoulos (1961); from cepheids by Stibbs (1956), Gascoigne and Eggen (1957), Walraven, Muller, and Oosterhoff (1958), Kraft and Schmidt (1963).

Petrie et al. found $A = 17.7$ from radial velocities of 79 B-type stars in the northern hemisphere. The value $A = 17.5$ found by Feast and Thackeray carries more weight since it involved many more stars distributed over all longitudes. Feast (private communication) has indicated that the distance scale based on Johnson's (1958) absolute-luminosity calibration is 1.09 times the scale corresponding to the Morgan-Keenan calibration used in the determination of A. This would reduce the published value $A = 17.5$ to about $A = 16.0$.

The distance scale of the galactic clusters is probably better known than that for the other objects. It is based on the distance of the Hyades, and the usual main-sequence fitting procedure for other clusters. Johnson and Svolopoulos used only 36 clusters in their determination of A, which gave a value of 15. This value is also found from a more extensive material of cepheids (Kraft and Schmidt 1963), the distance scale of which was tied to that of the galactic clusters through 5 cepheids which are members of clusters. It may be shown that the other three A values for cepheids are reduced to around 15 by correcting the distance scale to that corresponding to the clusters.

It is rather unsatisfactory that secular parallaxes of cepheids lead to a distance scale that is about 80 per cent of that based on galactic clusters (Kraft and Schmidt 1963). This alternate distance scale would increase the value of A as determined from cepheids to about 19.

The value of A may also be determined from proper motions, through

$$4.74 \, \mu_l = B + A \cos 2l^{\mathrm{II}}. \qquad (20)$$

Morgan and Oort (1951) give a value for A of 20 ± 2. This determination covers only a small region of space, depends on a small number of stars (Oort 1962), and may have been affected by local irregularities of motion.

In summary, then, the present situation is that the galactic-cluster distance scale leads to a value of A of around 15, while determinations based on proper motions, and, for cepheids, on secular parallaxes yield values of 19 or 20. The latter determinations are rather weak, and we tentatively conclude at a value of A of 15 km/sec per kpc, or slightly higher. The matter is further discussed in Section 4.8.

4.2. ROTATION CONSTANT B

The only way to obtain direct information about the value of B is from proper motions through equation (20). The value found depends on the fundamental system used. On the GC system its value is about -13, on the FK3 system and the N30 system about -7 (Morgan and Oort 1951; Mohr, Mayer, and Stohl 1957). The latter systems are far superior to that of the GC. Oort (1962) gives $B = -7 \pm 1.5$ but noted that it depends on a small region of space and a small number of stars. Thus, it may have been affected by local irregularities in motion. Considerable improvement in the determination of B may be expected from the Lick program of proper motions relative to galaxies. Even then, it would be important to have material extending to considerable distances, so as to avoid local irregularities.

We shall discuss in Section 4.8 further evidence on the value of B, in connection with that of A and R_0.

4.3. Distance R_0 to the Center

There are two ways to determine the distance to the center: (a) the direct method, in which a density maximum of some type of object observed in a direction close to that of the center is noted, and its distance determined, and (b) the indirect method, in which the distance to objects with zero radial velocity is determined, from which R_0 is found geometrically since these objects are at $R = R_0$, if equation (17) may be applied. (The determination of the product $A R_0$, which also yields information on R_0, will be discussed in Sec. 4.5.)

The direct method was applied to RR Lyrae variables in a field of relatively low absorption near NGC 6522 by Baade (1953). His value $R_0 = 8.2$ kpc served for many years as an accepted standard for our distance from the center. It is now believed that RR Lyrae stars are fainter than zero absolute magnitude, and improved estimates of the absorption are available (Kron and Mayall 1960). Arp (this volume, chap. 19) discusses evidence from RR Lyrae variables and globular clusters. He finds $R_0 = 9.9$ kpc if $M_B = +0.5$ for the RR Lyrae variables.

The indirect method has been applied to southern B-type stars by Feast and Thackeray (1958), who found $R_0 = 8.9$ kpc. Inspection of the data shows, however, that R_0 depends on the distance r. All stars with $r < 3.7$ kpc give $R_0 < 9$ kpc (average 6.9 kpc), while all those with $r > 3.7$ kpc give $R_0 > 9$ kpc (average 11.7 kpc). As it stands, the material seems to carry no consistent information on R_0.

In the northern hemisphere, only two suitable stars are available. They are $+27°3513$ and $+28°3487$ from the B-type star list of G. and L. Münch (1960). The values of R_0 found are 10.7 and 8.8 kpc, respectively. If we use a solar motion of 16 km/sec instead of the value 20 km/sec used by the Münchs, these values are lowered by about 0.5 kpc.

Thus, the indirect method does not yet yield decisive results; the values of R_0 found do not seem to be in conflict with that of about 10 kpc following from the direct method. Potentially, the indirect method is the better one, since it uses only objects at the same distance from the center as that of the sun. Thus, if composition or other properties of objects in the Galaxy were stratified in R, as has been foreseen (Schmidt 1960) but not proven, then it is for just these objects that we may trust to know their intrinsic properties from studies of nearby counterparts. The direct method makes use of objects that are strongly concentrated to the center, and it is more difficult to determine their intrinsic properties without making use of the value of R_0, which we wish to determine.

4.4. The Ratio of A and B

The ratio of A and B is related to the axial ratio of the velocity ellipsoid through

$$-B/A = b^2/(a^2 - b^2), \tag{21}$$

where a and b are the axes in the direction of the center, and that of the rotation, respectively. The axial ratio usually quoted (Oort 1962) for bright stars corresponds to $b^2/a^2 = 0.40$, so $-B/A = \frac{2}{3}$. Parenago (1950) has listed results for b/a for different subsystems. There is little variation for different subsystems. If we leave out the extremely flat and the spherical subsystems, the mean value of b/a is 0.65, corresponding to $-B/A = 0.73$. Woolley (1960), in a discussion of stars within 20 parsecs from the sun (Gliese 1957), noted that F-, G-, and K-type stars show practically no vertex deviation. He finds $b^2/a^2 = \frac{1}{3}$, leading to $-B/A = 0.5$.

A comparatively low value of $b/a = 0.49 \pm 0.04$ (m.e.) was found by Hins and Blaauw (1948) from proper motions of faint stars. In this investigation considerable weight was given to a determination of $b/a = 0.37$ from Selected Areas within 20° from the galactic plane. Mean parallaxes were derived from Binnendijk's work, with a correction depending on star counts. Binnendijk's values were derived on the assumption of an assumed value of b/a. The correlation between mean parallaxes and star counts was originally proposed for high latitudes, and its applicability near the galactic plane does not seem to be established. If we assume that the mean parallaxes in all Selected Areas used are identical, we find a value of 0.52 for the axial ratio, in better agreement with a value of 0.74 ± 0.20 found by Hins and Blaauw from an analysis which is practically independent of distance scale. The authors found from McCormick material values of 0.68 ± 0.08 and 0.54 ± 0.06, respectively. Considering the uncertainty in the mean parallaxes, the material is not necessarily in conflict with a value for b/a around 0.60 as found for brighter stars.

It is of interest to consider the value of $-B/A$ in the Andromeda nebula, for which the rotation curve is available out to a large distance from the center (van de Hulst, Raimond, and van Woerden 1957). One finds at 7 kpc from the center $-B/A = 1.1$, and values of 0.6 to 0.7 at larger distances from the center up to 20 kpc. Analogy considerations suggest that the position of the sun in the Galaxy corresponds with a point in the Andromeda nebula at least 10 kpc from its center.

Combining all the evidence, we conclude that the ratio $-B/A$ falls most likely in the range 0.5–0.73.

4.5. The Product AR_0

Along a direction $|l^{II}| < 90°$ in the galactic plane, an object with minimum distance to the galactic center will have $R_{min} = R_0|\sin l^{II}|$. Its radial velocity will be the largest found in that direction, and is, from equation (18),

$$V_{max} = 2\,AR_0 \sin l^{II}(1 - |\sin l^{II}|) . \tag{22}$$

Schmidt (1956) has derived a second-order correction term to this expression, on the assumption of a given analytical form of the force field in the range R_{min}

to R_0. Although higher order terms were neglected, it appears from some trial models that the correction term is a good approximation.

From 21-cm observations one can be fairly sure that there is hydrogen present at R_{min} at $l^I = 20°9$ and $18°4$ (Kwee, Muller, and Westerhout 1954; Schmidt 1957a) and in the southern hemisphere at $l^I = 264°8$ (Kerr 1962). The values found for AR_0 are collected in Table 1. The second column lists ΔAR_0, the second-order correction mentioned above. The next three columns give values of AR_0 for different assumptions about the solar motion, specified by the component U in the direction of $l^{II} = 180°$, and V toward $l^{II} = 90°$. The first solar motion is the standard solar motion. Takakubo (1963) has found from 21-cm work at intermediate latitude that the solar motion of interstellar hydrogen agrees with the standard solar motion to within 0.2 km/sec in both U and V. The next column represents the solar motion of interstellar calcium clouds

TABLE 1

VALUES OF AR_0 DERIVED FOR DIFFERENT COMPONENTS U, V
OF SOLAR MOTION

l^I	$\Delta A\,R_0$	$U = -10.5$ $V = +15.4$	$U = -11.6$ $V = +14.5$	$U = -10$ $V = +12$
20°9...........	−12	151	151	142
18°4...........	−14	143	143	135
264°8..........	− 6	146	140	132

(Blaauw 1952). The last column applies to an estimate of the solar motion relative to circular motion around the center of the Galaxy (see Sec. 3).

We see that AR_0 falls in the range 135–150 km/sec. It should be noted that a variation of 1 km/sec in V_{max} corresponds to 3 km/sec in AR_0 for the northern points, 5 km/sec for the southern point.

Use of the method for stellar objects is rather difficult, since one has to be sure that the objects involved are at R_{min}. If an object is not at R_{min}, the derived value of AR_0 will be too small. This may be the case for the value $AR_0 = 135$ derived by Feast and Thackeray (1958) from southern B-type stars. Thus, the method gives a lower limit to the value of AR_0 if there is appreciable uncertainty in the distances. In this connection, the stars $+12°3987$ and $+11°3946$ from the list of G. and L. Münch (1960) are of interest. Using the solar motion relative to circular motion mentioned above, they yield $AR_0 = 190 \pm 6$, and 167 ± 12, respectively. The first value is significantly higher than that following from the gas. The possibility that this star has a peculiar velocity of at least 15 km/sec (which would be required if $AR_0 = 150$) cannot be ruled out. A reliable determination of AR_0 from stellar objects will have to depend on a large number of objects at suitable positions in the Galaxy.

For the moment, the information derived from the 21-cm investigation carries practically all weight in the determination of $A R_0$. We consider the most likely value of $A R_0$ to be in the range 135–150 km/sec.

4.6. The Density Gradient

As discussed in Section 2, the logarithmic density gradient may be computed for a given circular-velocity curve in the limiting case $e \rightarrow 1$. We may compute this for the different rotation curves that can be derived from the 21-cm maximum radial velocities listed by Kwee, Muller, and Westerhout (1954) for different values of A, B, and R_0. These computations have been carried out for a number of A, B, R_0 combinations. The results can be well represented by the empirical relation

$$\frac{d \log \rho}{d \varpi} \cdot \frac{B}{A} \cdot R_0 = c , \tag{23}$$

where the value of c ranges from about 1.1 for $\Theta_0 = 216$, to 1.3 for $\Theta_0 = 287$. These values include a small correction to account for the expected deviation of the eccentricity e from unity.

If we approximate the density run in the immediate neighborhood of the sun by a power law ϖ^{-n}, then relation (23) leads to the following values of the ratio $-B/A$: 1.0 for $n = 3$, 0.7 for $n = 4$, 0.5 for $n = 5$.

We postpone further discussion until Section 4.8.

4.7. The Circular Velocity

Information about the local circular velocity $\Theta_c(R_0) = (A - B)R_0$ would be most useful in furnishing another relation between the constants we are discussing. The most interesting determination of the circular velocity is due to Fricke (1949). His value of 276 km/sec is derived on the assumption that a local rotational velocity of $\Theta_c(R_0) + 63$ km/sec corresponds to the local velocity of escape from the Galaxy. It seems quite unlikely now that this is the case (see Sec. 5). The limit of 63 km/sec may then be due to the density decrease and to the distribution of peculiar velocities in the outer parts of the Galaxy. If so, Fricke's derivation depends critically on the distribution of peculiar velocities of objects in the outer regions.

The solar motion of globular clusters contains the sun's rotational velocity except for the average rotation of the clusters about the center of the Galaxy. Since the latter is unknown, we do not gain any significant information about the circular velocity. A similar situation exists in the interpretation of the solar motion of galaxies in the Local Group, where the peculiar motion of the Galaxy is unknown.

Apparently, then, no reliable direct determination of the circular velocity can be obtained. Its value can only be derived from those of the constants A, B, and R_0.

4.8. Discussion

We shall now discuss the values to be adopted for A, B, and R_0 from evidence presented in the preceding sections. The direct determination of A gives about 15 km/sec per kpc, or slightly higher (Sec. 4.1), while that of R_0 leads to a value around 10 kpc (Sec. 4.3). The product AR_0 was found to be in the range 135–150 km/sec (Sec. 4.5). These three independent determinations are in remarkable agreement, especially considering that the value of A depends mainly on the distance scale of galactic clusters, that of R_0 on the absolute magnitude of RR Lyrae variables, while AR_0 is independent of distance. We adopt the round values $R_0 = 10$ kpc, $A = 15$ km/sec per kpc.

The value of B from proper motions in found at -7 km/sec per kpc. From the ratio of $-B/A$ of 0.5–0.73 arrived at in Section 4.4, we get, with $A = 15$, $B = -7.5$ to -11. We may also try to find B from the logarithmic density gradient in the solar neighborhood, through equation (23). The density gradient of the interstellar gas is essentially zero. Density gradients for common stars at intermediate latitudes have been derived by Oort (1938). After correction of the

TABLE 2

Adopted Values of A, B, and R_0

A.....................	$+15$ km sec^{-1} kpc^{-1}
B.....................	-10 km sec^{-1} kpc^{-1}
R_0...................	10 kpc

gradients to the galactic plane, one finds a logarithmic gradient of -0.23. Assuming that the gas contributes 20 per cent of the local mass, we find a logarithmic gradient of -0.18, which through equation (23) gives $B = -10$ km/sec per kpc.

Actually, almost half of the local total mass is in unknown form, and this makes the density gradient estimated above rather uncertain. We may look at the Andromeda nebula for additional information (Schmidt 1957b). In the range 7–19 kpc from its center, one finds $\varpi(d \log \rho/d\varpi) = -1.0$ to -1.2. The local density gradient found above leads to $\varpi(d \log \rho/d\varpi) = -1.8$. This might indicate that we have overestimated the local density gradient, which leads to an underestimate of $-B$. On the other hand, evidence from the axial ratio of the velocity ellipsoid yields a value of $-B$ of less than 11, while proper motions gave 7. We have compromised by adopting a value of B of -10 km/sec per kpc, but obviously the uncertainty in this value is considerable.

Table 2 lists the adopted values for A, B, and R_0. The local circular velocity is 250 km/sec. It is a difficult matter to estimate the uncertainty in the values adopted. A lot depends on the error in our present distance scales. The errors in A and R_0 would tend to be opposite in sign in connection with information regarding AR_0. One might hope that they are correct to within 10 per cent, while the uncertainty in B is about 20 per cent.

§ 5. A SIMPLE MODEL OF THE DISTRIBUTION OF MASS

With the values of the constants A, B, and R_0 adopted in the previous section, we shall describe in this section a simple model. It is by no means as extensive as the model published earlier (1956), yet the present model is to be preferred for the rotation curve in the outer parts, and for the total mass.

Evidence based on 21-cm observations (Rougoor and Oort 1960) shows that the circular velocity in the nuclear parts of the Galaxy is about 265 km/sec at 670 parsecs from the center and about 220 km/sec at 320 parsecs. From the 21-cm observations of Kwee, Muller, and Westerhout (1954) and the derived distribution of neutral hydrogen in the interior parts of the Galaxy (Schmidt 1957a), it appears that hydrogen is only present on the line of sight in three directions, i.e., at l^I = 20°.9 and 18°.4, 5°.9, and 348°.4. From the values of radial

TABLE 3

CIRCULAR VELOCITY AND FORCE PER UNIT
MASS AT VARIOUS DISTANCES
FROM THE CENTER

R (kpc)	Θ_c (km sec^{-1})	K_ϖ (km^2 sec^{-2} kpc^{-1})
0.32...........	220	152000
0.67...........	265	105000
3.53...........	206.4	12050
6.18...........	239.6	9280
7.74...........	248.5	7980
8.01...........	252.2	7940
10.............	250	6250

velocity given at these longitudes, we compute, with R_0 = 10 kpc and $\Theta_c(R_0)$ = 250 km/sec, the circular velocities and forces K_ϖ per unit mass as shown in Table 3. In constructing a model which represents these circular velocities, we have not attempted to represent the detailed run of the velocity as given by Rougoor and Oort. The mass involved in the nuclear parts of the Galaxy concerned is fairly small. We have represented the inner part by a point mass, such that K_ϖ = 30000 ϖ^{-2} (in km^2 sec^{-2} kpc^{-1}), which fits the observations at R about 0.5 kpc.

The remaining part of the data on K_ϖ consists of only four independent points, at roughly 3.5, 6, 8, and 10 kpc. The information from the points around 8 kpc yielded the value of $A R_0$ in the previous section, so that for the adopted values of A and R_0 the information from 8 kpc is not independent. Thus, we have independent information for K_ϖ at 3.5, 6, and 10 kpc, and for $dK_\varpi/d\varpi$ at 10 kpc (from A). In a first attempt, it was found that the formula

$$K_\varpi = 30000 \; \varpi^{-2} + 10000 + 5 \; \varpi - 41 \; \varpi^2$$

represents all the points satisfactorily, while it fulfills strictly $A = 15$, $B = -10$. In computing the density $\rho(a)$ following the method discussed in Section 2, it is found that the gradient at $R_0 = 10$ kpc is slightly steeper than corresponding to a ϖ^{-4} density law. Since we would like to add a shell outside the spheroid in which the density follows this law, we make a slight adjustment and finally end up with:

$$\sqrt{(1 - e^2)} = 0.05\,,$$

$$a_s e = 9.72\,,$$

$$K_\varpi = 30000\ \varpi^{-2} + 10120.2 - 41.722\ \varpi^2 \quad \text{(for } \varpi < a_s)\,,$$

$$\rho = 3.930\ \varpi^{-1} - 0.02489\ \varpi \qquad \text{(for } \varpi < a_s)\,,$$

$$\rho = 1449.2\ \varpi^{-4} \qquad\qquad\qquad \text{(for } \varpi > a_s)\,,$$

TABLE 4

CIRCULAR VELOCITIES DERIVED FROM A MASS MODEL

R (kpc)	Θ_c (km sec^{-1})	R (kpc)	Θ_c (km sec^{-1})	R (kpc)	Θ_c (km sec^{-1})
1........	200	11........	244	22........	185
2........	187	12........	238	24........	177
3........	198	13........	231	26........	171
4........	213	14........	225	28........	165
5........	227	15........	218	30........	160
6........	238	16........	213	40........	139
7........	247	17........	207	50........	125
8........	252	18........	202	....	....
9........	253	19........	197	....	....
10........	250	20........	193	....	....

where the density ρ is in solar masses per pc^3. The density near the sun, at $\varpi = 10$, is 0.145 solar masses per pc^3. This value was made to agree closely with the value found by Oort (1960), by adjusting the eccentricity e.

The mass of the central mass point is 0.07×10^{11} solar masses, that of the spheroid 0.82×10^{11} solar masses, and of the shell 0.93×10^{11} solar masses. The total mass is 1.8×10^{11} solar masses, half of which is interior to a spheroidal surface with axial ratio 0.05 drawn through the sun.

The escape velocity at the sun's position is about 380 km/sec. A star moving with 63 km/sec, relative to the local standard of rest, in the direction of rotation moves out to a distance $R = 24$ kpc, where the model density is 32 times lower than it is near the sun. Whether it is reasonable that we see no stars near the sun that reach parts of the Galaxy beyond 24 kpc depends on the velocity distribution of stars in the outer parts. If one were to conclude that this seems unreasonable, then one could replace the shell by one in which the density goes as ϖ^{-5} or ϖ^{-6}. This will lead to larger apogalactic distances for stars moving at the 63 km/sec limit, while at the same time the density in the outer parts decreases considerably. Eventually, this sensitive method may lead to a fairly good estimate of the mass in the outer parts of the Galaxy.

The circular velocities following from our model are given in Table 4. The local surface density in the model is 114 solar masses per pc^2; it depends rather strongly on the assumed density variation in the outer parts of the Galaxy. The density distribution near the sun in the z-direction is in fair agreement with the integrated distribution of gas and stars, if the latter are distributed on the average like the K-type giants (Oort 1960).

The present simple model seems satisfactory as a first approximation to the distribution of mass in the Galaxy. It does not account in detail for the different distribution of different populations in the Galaxy. Models of this kind, and based on the adopted values of A, B, and R_0, are not available as yet.

REFERENCES

BAADE, W.	1953	*Symposium on Astrophysics* (Ann Arbor, Mich.: University of Michigan), p. 25.
BAADE, W., and MINKOWSKI, R.	1954	*Ap. J.*, **119**, 215.
BELTON, M. J. S., and BRANDT, J. C.	1962	*Pub. A.S.P.*, **74**, 515.
BIERMANN, L., and DAVIS, L., JR.	1960	*Zs. f. Ap.*, **51**, 19.
BLAAUW, A.	1952	*B.A.N.*, **11**, 459.
	1961	*Ibid.*, **15**, 265.
BRANDT, J. C.	1960	*Ap. J.*, **131**, 293.
BURBIDGE, E. M., BURBIDGE, G. R., and PRENDERGAST, K. H.	1959	*Ap. J.*, **130**, 739.
FEAST, M. W., and THACKERAY, A. D.	1958	*M.N.*, **118**, 125.
FRICKE, W.	1949	*A.N.*, **278**, 49.
GASCOIGNE, S. C. B., and EGGEN, O. J.	1957	*M.N.*, **117**, 430.
GLIESE, W.	1957	*Heidelberg Astr. Rechen-Inst., Mitt. Ser. A*, No. 8.
HINS, C. H., and BLAAUW, A.	1948	*B.A.N.*, **10**, 365.
HULST, H. C. VAN DE, RAIMOND, E., and WOERDEN, H. VAN	1957	*B.A.N.*, **14**, 1.
JOHNSON, H. L.	1958	*Lowell Obs. Bull.*, **4**, 47.
JOHNSON, H. L., and SVOLOPOULOS, S. N.	1961	*Ap. J.*, **134**, 868.
KERR, F. J.	1962	*M.N.*, **123**, 327.
KRAFT, R. P., and SCHMIDT, M.	1963	*Ap. J.*, **137**, 249.

KRON, G. E., and
  MAYALL, N. U.   1960   *A.J.*, **65**, 581.
KUZMIN, G. G.   1952   *Pub. Astr. Obs. Tartu*, **32**, 211.
KWEE, K. K.,
  MULLER, C. A., and
  WESTERHOUT, G.   1954   *B.A.N.*, **12**, 211.
LINDBLAD, B.   1926   *Uppsala Medd.*, No. 3.
MOHR, J. M., MAYER,
  P., and STOHL, J.   1957   *B.A.C.*, **8**, 5.
MORGAN, H. R., and
  OORT, J. H.   1951   *B.A.N.*, **11**, 379.
MÜNCH, G., and
  MÜNCH, L.   1960   *Ap. J.*, **131**, 253.
OLLONGREN, A.   1962   *B.A.N.*, **16**, 241.
OORT, J. H.   1927   *B.A.N.*, **3**, 275.
                     1932   *Ibid.*, **6**, 249.
                     1938   *Ibid.*, **8**, 233.
                     1952   *Ap. J.*, **116**, 233.
                     1960   *B.A.N.*, **15**, 45.
                     1962   *Trans. I.A.U.*, **11B**, 397.
OORT, J. H., and
  WOERKOM, A. J. J. VAN   1941   *B.A.N.*, **9**, 185.
PARENAGO, P. P.   1950   *A.J. U.S.S.R.*, **27**, 150.
PEREK, L.   1948   *Contr. Astr. Inst. Masaryk Univ. Brno.*, **1**, No. 6.
                     1962   *Advances in Astronomy and Astrophysics* (London and New York: Academic Press), **1**, 165.
PETRIE, R. M.,
  CUTTLE, P. M., and
  ANDREWS, D. H.   1956   *A.J.*, **61**, 289.
ROUGOOR, G. W., and
  OORT, J. H.   1960   *Proc. Nat. Acad. Sci.*, **46**, 1.
SCHMIDT, M.   1956   *B.A.N.*, **13**, 15.
                   1957*a*   *Ibid.*, p. 247.
                   1957*b*   *Ibid.*, **14**, 17.
                     1960   *Mém. Soc. R. Sci. Liège, Ser. 5*, **3**, 130.
STIBBS, D. W. N.   1956   *M.N.*, **116**, 453.
TAKAKUBO, K.   1963   *Sendai Astron. Rap.*, No. 85.
WALRAVEN, TH.,
  MULLER, A. B., and
  OOSTERHOFF, P. TH.   1958   *B.A.N.*, **14**, 81.
WEAVER, H. F.   1961   *Pub. A.S.P.*, **73**, 88.
WOOLLEY, R. V. D. R.   1960   *Vistas in Astronomy* (London and New York: Pergamon Press), **3**, 3.

CHAPTER 23

Dynamics of Gas and Magnetic Fields; Spiral Structure

L. WOLTJER*

University of Leiden

A GALAXY is made up of a number of different ingredients: stars, gas, magnetic fields, and cosmic rays. The stars usually contribute most of the mass, though this is not the case in the early evolutionary phases. The dynamics of the stars are normally governed by a collision-free Boltzmann equation since the mean free path is long. The dominant force that acts on the stars is gravitation. We shall not further discuss the dynamics of the stars, as they have been treated in chapter 21 of this volume. The gas with the dust contributes only a few per cent to the total mass of a galaxy, but because the most luminous stars in spiral galaxies continuously form out of the gas, it plays an important role in shaping the aspect of a galaxy. The dominant force acting on the gas is again gravitation. As the mean free path of the atoms or ions is usually small a hydrodynamic description is permissible, provided some precautions are taken. The magnetic fields can have an important influence on the gas, while the motion of the gas, in turn, partly determines the structure of the magnetic field. Cosmic rays—particles of very high energy—are also present, and their energy density is comparable to the energy density of the random motions in the gas and to the magnetic energy density. The behavior of the cosmic-ray particles is dominated by the magnetic fields. Thus the gas, the magnetic fields, and the cosmic rays are dynamically coupled and should be treated as one system.

The gaseous component and the stars interact not only through gravitational effects, but also through processes like star formation, the formation of H II regions, and supernova explosions, to name a few. Thus, it is clear that the

* Now at Columbia University, N.Y. Parts of this chapter were written while the author was a visiting professor in the Department of Mathematics at the Massachusetts Institute of Technology, where his research was supported in part by the National Science Foundation, and in the Department of Physics and Astronomy at the University of Maryland.

531

study of the large-scale aspects of the gaseous components of our Galaxy, with which we shall be concerned in this chapter, forms an integral part of the study of galactic structure and galactic dynamics. At the moment we are still far from a satisfactory understanding of even the most basic features of the dynamics of the gaseous component. It is not surprising that many inconsistent or highly speculative theories have been proposed. Rather than discuss these at length, we shall first develop the basic principles on which a sound theory should be based and discuss the methods by which important physical parameters can be extracted from the observational data.[1] Subsequently though, we shall also enter some of the more uncertain aspects of the dynamics of the galactic gas. We shall deal only with the large-scale aspects of the galactic gas. We thus exclude from the discussion phenomena on a small scale, like H II regions, supernova shells, star formation, and interstellar gas clouds, except when directly relevant to the large-scale aspects. The small-scale phenomena have been treated by Spitzer in Volume VII of this Compendium.

§ 1. THE DYNAMICS OF GASEOUS SYSTEMS WITH MAGNETIC FIELDS

1.1. Basic Equations

Let us consider a fully ionized gas in which a magnetic field is embedded. By what equations shall this system be described? We can proceed on various levels. If we aim at a very detailed description, we must start with the Boltzmann equation. This equation describes the change of the distribution function of the particle momenta as a function of time and position owing to the motion of the particles, to the forces which act on them, and to the collisions which they make with other particles. In the case of charged particles, which interact by Coulomb forces, the discussion of these collisions presents certain difficulties. If we consider a fully ionized gas consisting of one kind of ions and electrons, we need two equations, one for the distribution function of the electrons and one for the distribution function of the ions. From the distribution functions the various macroscopic quantities like density, mean velocity, pressure, and others can be obtained. The difference in the mean velocity of ions and electrons corresponds to an electric current, and from Maxwell's equations this current will produce a magnetic field. The Boltzmann equation (together with the Maxwell equations for the electromagnetic fields) thus gives a very complete description of the dynamics of the system. It is, however, not easy to deal with.

If the mean free path of the particles is small compared to the characteristic length scale in the medium, in which case many collisions occur during a time in which significant changes take place in the system, the distribution functions will become nearly isotropic and Maxwellian around the mean velocity at each point. Then we can apply a hydrodynamic description, which can be derived

---

[1] In quoting data from various sources we have scaled the numerical values in such a way that they correspond to a distance of the sun to the galactic center of 10 kpc.

from the Boltzmann equation by the moment method. If we write down the hydrodynamic equations for ions and electrons separately and combine them in a suitable manner we obtain the equations of the "two-fluid theory." If we simply consider the plasma as one fluid in which electric currents may flow, but do not take the detailed dynamics of ions and electrons with their large mass ratio into account, we obtain the single-fluid hydromagnetic equations.

As indicated below, these can be used in many astrophysical circumstances. In the laboratory, where collisions are comparatively rare, the hydrodynamic equations are usually a poor approximation to reality and the same is true in certain small-scale processes in the interstellar medium, as in shock fronts. For a further discussion of the basic equations we refer the reader to Spitzer's (1962) book.

If we then consider a hydromagnetic system of gas and magnetic fields and if we assume that the viscosity and electrical resistivity can be neglected and if we denote the magnetic field by B, the fluid velocity by u, the gas density by ρ, the hydrostatic pressure by P, the temperature by T, the gas constant divided by the molecular weight by R, the increase in the heat energy of the medium per cm³ per second due to heat conduction, radiative processes, and the like by ϵ, the ratio of specific heats by γ (assumed to be constant), the gravitational potential by Φ, and the gravitational constant by G, the dynamics of the system are subject to the equations

$$\rho \frac{\partial u}{\partial t} = \frac{1}{4\pi}(\nabla \times B) \times B - \rho(\nabla \times u) \times u - \nabla P - \rho\nabla(\tfrac{1}{2}u^2 + \Phi), \quad (1)$$

$$\frac{\partial B}{\partial t} = \nabla \times (u \times B), \quad (2)$$

$$\frac{\partial \rho}{\partial t} = -\nabla \cdot (\rho u), \quad (3)$$

$$\nabla \cdot B = 0, \quad (4)$$

$$\nabla^2 \Phi = 4\pi G \rho_t, \quad (5)$$

$$P = R\rho T, \quad (6)$$

$$\frac{\partial P}{\partial t} = \gamma \frac{P}{\rho}\left(\frac{\partial \rho}{\partial t} + u \cdot \nabla\rho\right) - u \cdot \nabla P + \epsilon(\gamma - 1). \quad (7)$$

To these equations an energy-transfer equation connecting ϵ with ρ and T and their gradients should be added. The partial derivatives with respect to time are to be taken in an inertial frame of reference which does not move with the fluid. All velocity terms in equation (1) can be grouped together into a term Du/Dt on the left-hand side, D/Dt being the time derivative in a frame of reference which moves with the fluid. This equation thus states that the fluid is accelerated by the Lorentz force (current density $j = [1/4\pi]\nabla \times B$), minus the pressure gradient and the gravitational force. Equation (2) is equivalent to the statement that an observer who moves with the fluid should not experience an electric field if the electrical conductivity is infinite. From this equation it follows that the flux through any contour which moves with the fluid is conserved. The lines of force thus are frozen in the fluid if the conductivity is infinite. Equation (3) is the equation of continuity (conservation of mass) and equation (4) states that the lines of force should have neither beginning nor end. Equation (5) is Poisson's equation, which connects the gravitational potential with the total mass density ρ_t. The stellar mass density thus is included in ρ_t. In fact, since the mass of the stars in the Galaxy is one or two orders of magnitude larger than the mass of the gas, it is usually assumed that Φ is determined by the stars alone, independent of the distribution of the gas. This introduces a considerable simplification, but the assumption should be used with some care. Equation (6) is the perfect gas law and equation (7) is the heat equation. It can be written as $DP/Dt = (\gamma P/\rho)(D\rho/Dt) + \epsilon(\gamma - 1)$. When divided by $(\gamma - 1)$ the equation states that the change in the internal energy of a fluid element is due partly to the work done by the pressure forces and partly to heat transported to the element by heat conduction and other mechanisms. The ratio of specific heats γ is equal to $\frac{5}{3}$ for a monatomic or fully ionized gas. When the gas is in the process of being ionized it may be nearer to unity. R, which contains the molecular weight, also changes if the degree of ionization changes. The magnetic fields and the currents are not affected by changes in the ionization (unless the number of charged particles becomes very small). If, for example, the number of electrons is reduced by a factor of two, one might think that the current would be reduced by the same factor. However, as soon as the current decreases, the magnetic field decreases and an electric field is produced, in accordance with Maxwell's equations, which accelerates the remaining electrons so that ultimately the current is unchanged, if the inertia of the electrons is negligible.

In the two-fluid theory, some terms should be added to equations (1) and (2), while equations (6) and (7) should be written separately for ions and electrons. First, in equations (1) and (2) there are some terms due to the inertia of the electrons that are negligible if $L^2 \gg 10^{12} n_e^{-1}$, L being a characteristic length in cm and n_e the electron density. More importantly, two terms appear on the right-hand side of equation (2), the Hall term $-\nabla \times [(e n_e)^{-1} j \times B]$ which can also be written as $\nabla \times [(\Delta v) \times B]$, with Δv the velocity difference between electrons and ions, and the electron pressure term $\nabla \times [(e n_e)^{-1} \nabla P_e]$. Dimensionally the conditions that these terms are small compared with $\nabla \times (u \times B)$ are $u n_e L \gg 10^{29} B$ and $10^4 T_e \ll u B L$ (T_e = electron temperature). For typical interstellar circumstances (Table 1) these conditions are amply satisfied. But as indicated by Biermann and Schlüter (1950) the electron-pressure term is important if the origin of the first magnetic fields is considered. If $B = 0$ this is the only non-vanishing term in $\partial B/\partial t$. Finally in equation (1), in writing $j = (1/4\pi)\nabla \times B$ we have neglected the displacement current. This is permissible if velocities are well below the velocity of light. The conditions under which resistivity and viscosity can be neglected are discussed in the next section, where also the important situation in which the larger part of the gas is neutral is treated.

From equation (1) it can be seen that the velocity $v_A = B/(4\pi\rho)^{1/2}$, the so-called Alfvén velocity, is a characteristic velocity in hydromagnetic systems. It is the velocity with which transverse waves propagate along the field lines. Compressional waves along the field lines are not affected by the magnetic field and thus propagate with the ordinary sound velocity. But compressional waves transverse to the field propagate with a velocity the square of which is the sum of the squares of the Alfvén and sound velocities. If the Alfvén velocity exceeds the sound velocity it determines how soon one part of the system will experience the effects of events in another part. Generally one can say that in such a system the time in which an Alfvén wave can traverse the system is a characteristic time for dynamical developments. If one squares the characteristic velocity and multiplies by $\frac{1}{2}\rho$, he obtains a characteristic kinetic energy $\frac{1}{2}\rho v_A^2$ which is equal to a magnetic energy $B^2/8\pi$. On the basis of this and somewhat more complicated arguments, it is frequently argued that in cosmic media equipartition of kinetic and magnetic energy can be expected. In a truly turbulent medium this may well be the case, at least in certain parts of the turbulence spectrum. It is not clear whether it is also true for the largest turbulent elements, which may contain most of the energy (Chandrasekhar 1957). In a purely transverse Alfvén wave the perturbation of the magnetic energy is equal to the kinetic energy of the wave motion. But there may be in that case a much larger unperturbed magnetic energy. While in these cases the equipartition is already doubtful, in the general case of fluid motions and magnetic fields equipartition is certainly not at all to be expected. Thus, while the equipartition assumption may sometimes give useful results, it should be applied with caution.

1.2. EQUILIBRIUM

A hydrodynamic or hydromagnetic system is said to be in equilibrium if a rigid reference frame can be found in which the aspect of the system is time independent. The only possible motion of the rigid reference frame with respect to an inertial frame which moves with the center of gravity of the system is a rotation with constant angular velocity. Thus we shall say that a system is in equilibrium if there exists a reference frame which rotates rigidly around the center of gravity of the system in which all parameters of the system are independent of time. The need for a definition of this kind is apparent. If we would have put $\partial/\partial t = 0$ in equations (1)–(7) we would have excluded from our definition all non-axisymmetric equilibria with angular momentum (like barred spirals). If we introduce a frame of reference which rotates with an angular velocity Ω and if we denote the velocities measured in this system by u' and the time derivatives by $\partial/\partial\tau$, equation (1) becomes

$$\rho\frac{\partial u'}{\partial\tau} = \frac{1}{4\pi}(\nabla\times B)\times B - \rho(\nabla\times u')\times u' - 2\rho\Omega\times u'$$
$$- \rho\Omega\times(\Omega\times r) - \nabla P - \rho\nabla(\Phi + \tfrac{1}{2}u'^2). \tag{8}$$

The third term on the right is the Coriolis force. Equations (2)–(7) are unchanged, except for the fact that t should be replaced by τ and u by u'. Thus if a vector Ω can be found, so that $\partial/\partial\tau = 0$ in all these equations, the system is in equilibrium. If the configuration is axisymmetric around Ω, $\partial/\partial t = 0$ in equation (1)–(7) implies $\partial/\partial\tau = 0$ in the modified equations, and vice versa.

If a solution of the equilibrium equations, which satisfies suitable boundary conditions, has been found it is by no means certain that it can actually occur in nature. The solution should also be stable. An equilibrium configuration is said to be stable if a small perturbation causes oscillations around the equilibrium state. If the perturbation grows in time the solution is unstable. In the usual stability analysis the perturbation equations are linearized, i.e., the square and higher powers of the perturbation amplitudes are neglected. Such a procedure can only show whether a small perturbation will grow initially, but not whether it will grow to a very large value. But the analysis of non-linear stability is extremely difficult. The linear stability problem can be tackled in different ways. For static equilibria ($u = 0$) a variational principle (Hain et al. 1957; Bernstein et al. 1958) proves frequently useful. The essential statement contained in this principle is that it is a necessary and sufficient condition for stability that the potential energy (i.e., the sum of the magnetic, thermal, and gravitational energies) shall be a minimum for the equilibrium system. If this condition is not satisfied, the potential energy can be decreased by the perturbation and the kinetic energy of the instability can be increased, while the total energy is conserved.

1.3. THE VIRIAL THEOREM

Since the available information about astrophysical systems is limited, it is desirable to have theorems of wide generality at our disposal. A much used theorem is the virial theorem. In tensorial form it can be obtained (Chandrasekhar 1960) by taking (in Cartesian coordinates x_1, x_2, x_3) the i component of the equation of motion (1), multiplying it by x_k, and integrating over the volume of the configuration. If the resulting equation is split in a symmetric and an antisymmetric part, we obtain

$$\tfrac{1}{2}\frac{d^2 I_{ik}}{dt^2} = 2T_{ik} - 2\mathfrak{M}_{ik} + W_{ik} + \delta_{ik}(U + \mathfrak{M})$$
$$- \frac{1}{16\pi}\int_S x_k(B^2 dS_i - 2B_i B\cdot dS)$$
$$- \frac{1}{16\pi}\int_S x_i(B^2 dS_k - 2B_k B\cdot dS) \tag{9}$$
$$- \tfrac{1}{2}\int_S P(x_k dS_i + x_i dS_k)$$

and

$$\frac{dL_{ik}}{dt} = \frac{1}{8\pi}\int_S x_i(B^2 dS_k - 2B_k\boldsymbol{B}\cdot d\boldsymbol{S})$$

$$-\frac{1}{8\pi}\int_S x_k(B^2 dS_i - 2B_i\boldsymbol{B}\cdot d\boldsymbol{S}) \tag{10}$$

$$+\int_S P(x_i dS_k - x_k dS_i).$$

In these equations the following tensors have been introduced:

$$I_{ik} = \int \rho x_i x_k d\tau; \qquad W_{ik} = \int \rho x_i \frac{\partial \Phi}{\partial x_k} d\tau = \int \rho x_k \frac{\partial \Phi}{\partial x_i} d\tau;$$

$$T_{ik} = \tfrac{1}{2}\int \rho u_i u_k d\tau; \qquad L_{ik} = \int \rho \left(x_i \frac{dx_k}{dt} - x_k \frac{dx_i}{dt}\right) d\tau;$$

$$\mathfrak{M}_{ik} = \frac{1}{8\pi}\int B_i B_k d\tau; \qquad U = \int P d\tau$$

(L_{ik} is the angular momentum in the $\boldsymbol{e}_i \times \boldsymbol{e}_k$ direction). For a gas of constant γ, U is equal to the thermal energy multiplied with $(\gamma - 1)$. All surface integrals in these equations (element of area $d\boldsymbol{S}$) are extended over the surface which surrounds the volume of integration (element of volume $d\tau$). Upon contraction (i.e., taking $i = k$ and summing over the three i's), I_{ik}, T_{ik}, $\mathfrak{M}_{ik}$, and W_{ik} become the moment of inertia I, the kinetic energy T, the magnetic energy $\mathfrak{M}$, and the gravitational energy W. Contracting equation (9), we obtain the scalar form of the virial theorem (Chandrasekhar and Fermi 1953):

$$\tfrac{1}{2}\frac{d^2 I}{dt^2} = 2T + 3U + \mathfrak{M} + W + \frac{1}{4\pi}\int_S (\boldsymbol{r}\cdot\boldsymbol{B})\boldsymbol{B}\cdot d\boldsymbol{S} - \int_S \left(P + \frac{B^2}{8\pi}\right)\boldsymbol{r}\cdot d\boldsymbol{S}. \tag{11}$$

It should be noted that T, U, and $\mathfrak{M}$ are all positive definite, while W is negative. Thus, equilibrium in a given region is only possible if gravitational effects are important or if forces act from the outside.

1.4. Cylindrical Equilibria

We now discuss some equilibrium configurations that may have useful applications. Consider first an infinitely long cylinder in static equilibrium. From equation (1) we have

$$\frac{1}{4\pi}(\nabla\times\boldsymbol{B})\times\boldsymbol{B} = \nabla P + \rho\nabla\Phi. \tag{12}$$

Suppose that all variables depend only on the distance to the axis. Thus, in cylindrical coordinates ϖ, φ, z we have $\partial/\partial\varphi = 0$ and $\partial/\partial z = 0$. From $\nabla\cdot\boldsymbol{B} = 0$ it follows that B_ϖ should vanish if a singularity on the axis is to be avoided. Then equation (12) becomes

$$\frac{1}{8\pi}\left[\frac{dB_z^2}{d\varpi} + \frac{1}{\varpi^2}\frac{d(\varpi^2 B^2)}{d\varpi}\right] = \frac{1}{8\pi}\left[\frac{dB^2}{d\varpi} + \frac{2B^2}{\varpi}\right] = -\frac{dP}{d\varpi} - \frac{d\Phi}{d\varpi}. \tag{13}$$

Thus, if the field is of constant direction ($B_\varphi = 0$), it acts as a pressure. If not, the tension along the lines of force is also important and enters through the B_φ^2/ϖ term. In suitable configurations the two effects may cancel each other and the Lorentz force vanishes. Then the field is said to be force free. Thus, hydrostatic equilibrium is not affected by the presence of a force-free field. It should be noted that in a finite geometry a field cannot be force free everywhere. For if we surround the field-containing region by a surface so far from the system that the surface integrals vanish, the virial theorem (11) shows that the magnetic field must have dynamic effects. A force-free field is only possible in a given region if non–force-free fields are present outside that region.

Returning to the infinite cylinder, we note that when B^2 varies as ϖ^{2n} the Lorentz force compresses the gas if $n > 0$, but has the opposite effect if $n < -1$. Force-free fields thus are only possible if $-1 < n < 0$ (Schlüter 1957). If the gas is compressed the configuration is referred to as a linear pinch.

Both theoretical studies and laboratory experiments show that pinches tend to be very unstable. The two most serious instabilities are easily understood. Consider a pinch ($B_z = 0$) to which a kink-type perturbation is applied. Then the field is strongest at the concave of the kink. This stronger field exerts a force on the pinch in the same direction as the original displacement which thus is amplified. If the pinch is self-gravitating the instability persists (Kruskal and Schwarzschild 1954), but if a fixed gravitational force directed toward the axis is present the situation may be improved (Setti 1965). The second instability of the pinch is known as the sausage instability. If the pinch contracts somewhere the tension along the lines of force is increased, while where it expands the magnetic tension decreases. Thus, again, accelerations are produced in the direction of the perturbation. However, if a B_z field is present in the pinch the situation is changed.

1.5. TOROIDAL EQUILIBRIA

If we bend the cylinder and join the ends we obtain a torus. The cross-section of the torus will not be circular in general, and this makes it difficult to obtain exact solutions. But the qualitative properties of the toroidal configurations can be seen rather easily. They have general applications because it can be shown that in all axisymmetric configurations (or those obtainable from an axisymmetric one by continuous deformation) the lines of force lie all wholly on toroidal surfaces, the magnetic surfaces. Each line of force is a helix that winds around one of these surfaces. If the equilibrium system were in a state of non-uniform rotation around the axis of symmetry each magnetic surface should rotate as a solid body; if not it would be deformed. This is the statement contained in Ferraro's isorotation theorem (1937) that can be derived more formally from equation (2). For a general discussion of axisymmetric hydromagnetic equilibria see Woltjer (1959b).

Consider an axisymmetric rotating toroid. If only azimuthal motions (angular velocity Ω) are present the equilibrium equation (1) becomes

$$\frac{1}{4\pi}(\nabla \times B) \times B + \rho\Omega^2 \varpi e_\varpi - \nabla P - \rho\nabla\Phi = 0 . \tag{14}$$

It can be shown that in this case the Lorentz force is orthogonal to the magnetic surfaces. We integrate equation (14) along some curve on a magnetic surface. Then

$$\int_1^2 \left(\Omega^2 \varpi e_\varpi - \frac{1}{\rho}\nabla P - \nabla\Phi \right) \cdot d s = 0 . \tag{15}$$

But Ω is constant on a magnetic surface. Hence,

$$\tfrac{1}{2}\Omega^2(\varpi_2^2 - \varpi_1^2) - (\Phi_2 - \Phi_1) = \int_1^2 \frac{1}{\rho}\nabla P \cdot d s . \tag{16}$$

If the medium is isothermal ($P = q^2\rho$, with q^2 the mean-square random velocity in one coordinate), the pressure integral is equal to $q^2 \ln (\rho_2/\rho_1)$. Of course, equation (16) is of limited usefulness, as it can only be applied when the magnetic surfaces are known, that is, after the complete solution has been obtained. Nevertheless we can obtain from this equation a qualitative insight in the distribution of matter in the toroidal configurations.

Consider a very thin torus and a gravitational potential symmetric around $z = 0$. Let us expand the left-hand side of equation (16) to the second order in $\Delta\varpi = \varpi_2 - \varpi_1$ and z. Thus, for the isothermal case,

$$q^2 \ln \frac{\rho_2}{\rho_1} = \Omega^2[\, 2\varpi_1\Delta\varpi_1 + (\Delta\varpi)^2\,] - \left(\frac{\partial\Phi}{\partial\varpi}\right)_{\varpi_1}\Delta\varpi$$
$$- \tfrac{1}{2}\left(\frac{\partial^2\Phi}{\partial\varpi}\right)_{\varpi_1}(\Delta\varpi)^2 - \left(\frac{\partial^2\Phi}{\partial z^2}\right)_0 \Delta z^2 , \tag{17}$$

with $\Delta z^2 = z_2^2 - z_1^2$. We eliminate the radial derivatives of the potential in terms of the circular velocity Θ. We have

$$\frac{\partial\Phi}{\partial\varpi} = \frac{\Theta^2}{\varpi} . \tag{18}$$

Let us further write $\Omega\varpi_1 = \Theta_1 - \Delta\Theta$ with $\Delta\Theta$ the lag velocity. If we consider $\Delta\Theta/\Theta_1$ of the same order of smallness as $\Delta\varpi/\varpi_1$, equation (17) becomes to second order in small quantities

$$q^2 \ln \frac{\rho_2}{\rho_1} = 2\Theta_1\Delta\Theta \frac{\Delta\varpi}{\varpi_1} - \left[\frac{\Theta_1^2}{\varpi_1^2} - \frac{\Theta_1}{\varpi_1}\left(\frac{\partial\Theta_1}{\partial\varpi}\right)\right](\Delta\varpi)^2 - \left(\frac{\partial^2\Phi}{\partial z^2}\right)_0 \Delta z^2 . \tag{19}$$

The first term on the right shows that the gas tends to assemble on the inside of the magnetic surfaces if the rotational velocity is smaller than the circular velocity. Then there is a net acceleration inward and on the magnetic surfaces hydrostatic equilibrium prevails. The second term is due to the fact that Ω is constant on a magnetic surface while Θ/ϖ is not. Take for example $\Delta\Theta = 0$ and $\partial\Theta_1/\partial\varpi = 0$. Then for $\Delta\varpi > 0$ the gas rotates faster than would correspond to the circular velocity and is pushed outward by the centrifugal acceleration, while for $\Delta\varpi < 0$ the opposite is true. Thus, in such a case the gas would be squeezed out of the middle region of the magnetic surfaces toward both sides. It should be noted that the width of the gas layer in the z-direction can to a large extent be determined by forces in the ϖ-direction.

Before the preceding analysis can be useful the lag velocity $\Delta\Theta$ must be determined. Strictly this can only be done from the complete solution of the equilibrium equations. But if we suppose that all magnetic surfaces have the same angular velocity—or make some other simple assumption—progress can be made on the basis of the virial theorem (11) (cf. Biermann and Davis 1960). Suppose we have an isolated toroid in which only azimuthal motions are present. Then

$$\int \rho u_\varphi^2 d\tau + 3U + M + W = 0 . \tag{20}$$

If the pressure and the magnetic field would vanish the gas should rotate everywhere with the local circular velocity (self-gravitation of the gas being neglected) and from equation (9) we would have

$$\int \rho\Theta^2 d\tau = -W_{xx} - W_{yy} = -(W - W_{zz}) . \tag{21}$$

Thus, if P and $\boldsymbol{B}$ do not vanish, we have

$$\int \rho(\Theta^2 - u_\varphi^2) d\tau = 3U + M + W_{zz} \tag{22}$$

or, with $\Delta\Theta = \Theta - u_\varphi \ll \Theta$, approximately

$$2\int \rho\Theta\Delta\Theta d\tau = 3U + M + W_{zz} . \tag{23}$$

If the gravitational acceleration in the z-direction can be neglected the lag velocity is always positive. If the assumption of equal Ω throughout the toroid is made and if some ϖ_1 is chosen, $\Delta\Theta_1$ in equation (19) can be calculated from equation (23). It should be noted that magnetic fields outside the toroid, but associated with currents in the toroid, are also included in M. In addition, if current systems and gravitating matter are present outside the toroid so that it is not an isolated system, the surface terms in the virial theorem should be included in the analysis.

1.6. Angular Momentum

To conclude this section we consider transport of angular momentum by a magnetic field. Let us surround some region by a cylindrical surface S. We construct a system of cylindrical coordinates (ϖ, φ, z) with the z-axis as the axis of symmetry. Then we find from equation (20), for the change with time of the z-component of the angular momentum J_z $(= L_{xy})$ within S,

$$\frac{dJ_z}{dt} = \frac{1}{4\pi} \int_s B_\varpi dB_\varphi S . \tag{24}$$

Thus, magnetic fields with both radial and azimuthal components can transport angular momentum from one part of a system to another.

§ 2. PHYSICAL PARAMETERS IN THE INTERSTELLAR GAS

Up until now we have neglected viscosity and electrical resistivity. We have made use of the single fluid equations in which the different behavior of electrons and ions is neglected. We have assumed that a hydrodynamic description can be applied in which the medium is considered as continuous. This can only be done if the mean free path for the particles which constitute the fluid is much smaller than the lengths involved in the problem. It is therefore of interest to investigate the actual conditions in the interstellar gas to see whether the equations we have used are suitable for our purpose.

Three typical situations may be considered. Most of the interstellar hydrogen is neutral. In a typical H I region the temperature is of the order of 100° and the particle density 10 cm^{-3}. Only ions with ionization potentials less than that for hydrogen are ionized. From this the electron density is about 5×10^{-4} times the neutral hydrogen density. The total mass per hydrogen atom is 2.4×10^{-24} gram, if a helium abundance of 0.106 (Mathis 1962) is assumed.

A few per cent of the interstellar hydrogen is heated and ionized by radiation from stars or other processes. In a typical H II region the temperature is around 10^4 degrees and the density near 10 cm^{-3}. In the halo there may be a hot tenuous gas with a temperature near 10^6 degrees and a particle density around 10^{-3} cm^{-3}, the very uncertain evidence for which we shall review later. In Table 1 we have assembled crude order of magnitude estimates for some physical quantities in the three media.

In a fully ionized gas the mean free path of charged particles may be defined as the distance over which a particle, moving with the mean thermal velocity, is likely to be deflected by 90° from its original trajectory. For particles of unit charge (independent of the mass) $\lambda \approx 7 \times 10^3 \, T^2/n$ cm. In an H I region the mean free path for hydrogen atoms is about 10^{14} cm. The Larmor radius for a particle with unit charge, atomic weight A, and the mean thermal energy per particle in the medium is $0.95 \, (AT)^{1/2}/B$. It is thus 43 times smaller for electrons than for protons. The cyclotron period for electrons is 1840 times shorter than for protons. The time interval between collisions is a measure for the time it takes a disturbed plasma to come into equilibrium locally, that is, for the particles which constitute the plasma to acquire a Maxwellian velocity distribution. Since this time is 43 times shorter for electrons than for protons, the electrons will first attain a Maxwellian velocity distribution among themselves and only much later will the protons. Then it takes a time which is still a factor of 20 longer than the times indicated in Table 1 for the protons and electrons to come into equilibrium with each other, that is, to reach Maxwellian velocity distributions characterized by the same kinetic temperature.

If viscosity effects are important some terms must be added to the right-hand side of equation (1). For an incompressible fluid of constant kinematic viscosity, ν, only $+\nu\rho\nabla^2 u$ need to be considered. In general, some more terms are present, which have the same structure dimensionally. If the electric resistivity cannot be neglected a term $-\nabla \times [(4\pi\sigma)^{-1}\nabla \times B]$ appears on the right of equation (2). If heat conduction is dominant, ϵ in equation (7) is equal to $+\nabla\cdot(\kappa\nabla T)$. In order of magnitude, it follows from these expressions that a magnetic field is appreciably affected by the dissipation in a time t_σ equal to $4\pi\sigma L^2$. Similar relations hold for t_ν and t_κ. If the length scales become large the dissipative phenomena become rapidly less important. For a fully ionized gas, without a

TABLE 1

PHYSICAL PARAMETERS IN THE GAS*

Medium	L	n	T	B	λ	r_L	t_{coll}	t_{cyc}	v_s	v_A	t_A	t_σ	t_κ	t_{rad}
H I.........	10^{19}	10	10^2	10^{-5}	10^{10}	10^6	10^5	10^2	10^5	10^6	10^{13}	(10^{16})†	(10^{18})‡	10^{15}
H II.........	10^{19}	10	10^4	10^{-5}	10^{11}	10^7	10^5	10^2	10^6	10^6	10^{13}	10^{31}	10^{19}	10^{11}
Halo.........	10^{22}	10^{-3}	10^6	10^{-5}	10^{19}	10^8	10^{12}	10^2	10^7	10^8	10^{14}	10^{40}	10^{16}	10^{17}

* Length scale L, hydrogen density n, temperature T, magnetic field strength B, mean free path for a thermal particle with unit charge λ, proton Larmor radius r_L, time interval between collisions for protons t_{coll}, proton cyclotron period t_{cyc}, sound velocity v_s, Alfvén velocity v_A, time t_A needed for an Alfvén wave to traverse distance L, and the time scales on which effects of finite electric conductivity, heat conduction and radiative losses become important, t_σ, t_κ, and t_{rad}; all in cgs units.

† Ambipolar diffusion.

‡ Neutral particle thermal conductivity.

magnetic field, the coefficients of electrical conductivity, kinematic viscosity, and heat conductivity are (in the parameter range of interest to within a factor of 1.4) given by

$$\sigma = 6 \times 10^{-15}\, T^{3/2},$$

$$\nu = 4 \times 10^7\, n^{-1}\, T^{5/2}, \qquad (25)$$

$$\kappa = 2 \times 10^{-6}\, T^{5/2},$$

where all values are in electromagnetic or cgs units. If a magnetic field is present the viscosity and heat-conductivity coefficients are very much reduced in directions perpendicular to the magnetic field. The reduction factor for κ is likely to be of the order $(r_L/\lambda)^2$ and thus very small. In the absence of magnetic fields we obtain $t_\sigma = 8 \times 10^{-14}\, L^2 T^{3/2}$ sec and $t_\kappa = 2 \times 10^{-10}\, L^2 n T^{-5/2}$ sec, while in some simple cases the time scale for the viscous effects is two orders of magnitude larger than t_κ.

In an ordinary ionized gas an electric current flows as a result of a very small velocity difference between electrons and ions. If the region is large and the field weak this velocity difference may be quite small, in the H II and halo media of the order of 10^{-5} cm/sec. When the ions and electrons collide some energy is randomized, but since the relative velocity is so small the rate at which magnetic energy is transformed into thermal energy is very low. Let us now consider the case where neutral particles are present with only a few electrons and ions. The Lorentz force will act only on the charged particles. Thus it tends to push the ions and electrons through the neutral gas. This process is called ambipolar diffusion (Biermann and Schlüter 1950). The Lorentz force accelerates the ionized component, but collisions between ions and neutral particles retard it. In the steady state the drift velocity between the two, V_D, is such that the net acceleration just vanishes. From Spitzer's discussion (1965, eqs. 4–35) we have

$$V_D = \frac{(\nabla \times B) \times B}{8\pi n_i n_H m_H \langle \sigma V_t \rangle} \approx \frac{B^2}{8\pi L n_i n_H m_H \langle \sigma V_t \rangle} e , \qquad (26)$$

with n_i the ion density, n_H and m_H the neutral hydrogen density and atomic mass, $\langle \sigma V_t \rangle$ the average product of the cross-section for momentum transfer and the thermal velocity of the hydrogen atoms, L the characteristic length scale in the magnetic field and e a unit in the direction of the Lorentz force. Osterbrock (1961) has calculated the cross-section σ.

For $T = 100°$, $\sigma = 1.5 \times 10^{-14}$ cm^2, and for $T < 500°$, $\langle \sigma V_t \rangle = 2.3 \times 10^{-9}$ cm^3/sec independent of T. Equation (26) is only valid if V_D is smaller than the speed of sound in the neutral hydrogen. If V_D were much larger $\langle \sigma V_t \rangle$ should be replaced by σV_D. The character of ordinary ohmic resistivity and ambipolar diffusion is quite different. Ordinary resistivity annihilates lines of force; thus magnetic flux is not conserved. Ambipolar diffusion makes a motion of the lines of force relative to the neutral matter possible. But the lines of force are frozen in the ionized component of the gas and thus flux is conserved. However, ambipolar diffusion sometimes makes it possible that steep gradients arise in the magnetic field, and then the time scale for the effects of the ohmic resistivity can be appreciably shortened.

In general, one should be somewhat careful when applying the order-of-magnitude estimates given in Table 1. For ambipolar diffusion the time scale may be much longer than would correspond to the result derived from the last expression in equation (26) if the field is nearly force-free. But in large regions there may be small regions where the gradients of the magnetic field or the temperature gradients are large. In those regions L will be much smaller than has been assumed and the dissipative time scales will be shortened.

Keeping these reservations in mind we inspect Table 1. The mean free path is small compared to the length scales of interest; thus a hydrodynamic description would seem applicable. This need not be true in shock waves where the L given is meaningless. The mean free path is much longer than the Larmor radius. Shocks may have a fine structure on the scale of the Larmor radius if collisions are infrequent (see, for example, Lüst 1960). Such a fine structure may have important effects on cosmic rays as the Larmor radii for the cosmic-ray particles are much larger than those for the thermal particles. The shocks might well keep the distribution function of cosmic rays in the halo isotropic. From the table it appears that effects of ambipolar diffusion can be important in H I regions, while the effects of heat conduction could perhaps be of interest in the halo, but only in directions parallel to the magnetic field. Radiative losses are likely to be important in all cases; thus everywhere in interstellar space energy sources are needed to maintain the temperatures at their observed levels.

§ 3. THE STRENGTH OF THE GALACTIC MAGNETIC FIELD

In Table 1 we have given 10 μG as a representative value of the magnetic field strength in most of the Galaxy. A more precise evaluation of the field intensity is of fundamental importance for our further considerations. Two schools of thought appear to have developed. Some think that in the galactic plane a field of a few μG is appropriate, while others consider a value ten times as large more likely. The difference is important because in the first case the magnetic energy density $B^2/(8\pi)$ is much smaller than the kinetic energy density of random motions in the interstellar gas; in the second case the magnetic energy is the larger of the two and the magnetic field may be expected to have appreciable dynamic effects. Although at the moment it may not be possible to make a conclusive choice, it seems of interest to review the available evidence critically and to see what future improvements are likely. It will appear that most of the evidence points to a rather strong field through a large part of the galactic disk. It is especially important in the following to note exactly what is measured by the various methods. Also it should be kept in mind that the magnetic field strength need not be the same everywhere, and so the claim of some investigators that they have measured *the* galactic magnetic field should be taken *cum grano salis*.

The methods of determining the strength of magnetic fields in the Galaxy can be divided in two groups. First, there are methods which are based on the effects of the magnetic field on the emission and propagation of electromagnetic radiation. The second group consists of methods based on the dynamical effects of magnetic fields. The methods are listed in Table 2, where it is also indicated what physical quantity is measured and what typical values of B are obtained for regions in the galactic disk and halo. It will appear in the further discussion that some of these values may be based on incorrect or uncertain interpretation.

3.1. THE ZEEMAN EFFECT

The Zeeman effect in the 21-cm line provides the most direct evidence on magnetic fields in H I regions. In the longitudinal effect the line is split in two components of opposite circular polarization separated in frequency by $\Delta\nu = 2.8\, B_{||}\, (\mu G)$ c/s. Because the width of the line is typically measured in kc/s the components cannot be observed separately. But $\Delta\nu$ can be obtained by observation of the shift of the mean frequency of the line between the two circular polarizations. Suppose that along the line of sight the field changes sign. Then the Zeeman effects in the regions of opposite field will cancel each other in these measurements. If the components cannot be observed separately only the mean value of $B_{||}$ along the line of sight and over the beamwidth of the observing instrument can be obtained. Thus the Zeeman effect only gives a lower limit to $|B|$. In the transverse Zeeman effect only a small broadening of the line could, in principle, be observed in switching between orthogonal linear polarizations. But because broadening effects add quadratically this effect is too small to be measurable.

Most Zeeman effect measurements have been made in absorption lines which sometimes are very deep and narrow. In Table 3 we have assembled the results

TABLE 2

DETERMINATIONS OF THE MAGNETIC FIELD STRENGTH IN THE GALACTIC DISK AND HALO*

METHOD	QUANTITY MEASURED	B (μG)		MAIN SOURCE OF UNCERTAINTY
		Disk	Halo	
Methods involving electromagnetic radiation:				
Zeeman effect...............	$B_{||}$	< 5	....	⎰Small-scale structure in
Faraday effect..............	$n_H B_{||}$	....	....	⎱ H I clouds
	$n_e B_{||}$	....	....	
Synchrotron radiation........	$k|B_\perp|^{3/2}$	25	6	k; Nature of non-thermal radio radiation
Existence interstellar polarization	B^2	> 1	....	Nature of dust grains
Dynamic determinations:				
Alignment interstellar polarization......................	B^2	30	....	Interpretation
Cosmic ray confinement......	B^2	....	6	Assumed confinement
Virial theorem..............	B^2	....	<20	Matter in halo
Star formation, structure H II regions	B^2	< 5	....	Interpretation
Solar wind.................	B^2	70	....	Theory and observation

* $B_{||}$ and $B_\perp$ are field components parallel and transverse to the line of sight, n_H and n_e are the neutral hydrogen and thermal electron densities, and k is the density of relativistic electrons.

TABLE 3

MEASURED ZEEMAN EFFECTS IN 21-CM ABSORPTION LINES*

Source	(km/sec)	Davies *et al.* (1960)	Weinreb (1962)	Davies *et al.* (1962)	Morris *et al.* (1963)
Cas A............	− 1	+ 1± 4	<3	....	+2±2
	−38	+ 1± 7	....	....	....
	−48	− 3± 7	....	....	....
Tau A............	+10	+10±10	<5	< 5	....
				25	≪25
Sag A............	− 53	+14±40	....	....	....

* The absorption features are identified by their velocities in the second column, while the remaining columns give the values of $B_{||}$ in μG measured by different authors.

obtained by Davies, Slater, Shuter, and Wild (1960), Weinreb (1962), Davies, Verschuur, and Wild (1962), and Morris, Clark, and Wilson (1963). Davies *et al.* (1962) claim to have measured some fields of about 5 μG in some clouds and none in others. Their values for Tau A are based on an analysis in which the line is assumed to be due to two overlapping clouds, one with a rather strong field, the other with no measurable field. However, the results of Weinreb and Morris *et al.* do not confirm the measurements by Davies *et al.*

3.2. The Faraday Effect

The Faraday effect is the rotation of the plane of polarization of an electromagnetic wave in a dispersive medium. Polarized radiation emerges from some radio sources and measurement of the orientation of the plane of polarization as a function of frequency gives useful data on the medium in front of the source, if the source polarization is independent of frequency. This is certainly the case if the Faraday effect within the 21-cm absorption line is considered. The index of refraction and thus the speed of propagation differs slightly for the two circular polarizations if a magnetic field is present in an H I region. The resulting phase difference rotates the plane of polarization of a linearly polarized beam by an angle ψ given by B. G. Clark (1963), where

$$\psi(\nu) = 17.4\, B_{||}(\mu G) T_s \frac{d}{d\nu}\left[\text{Cauchy principal}\atop\text{value} \int_{-\infty}^{+\infty} \frac{\tau(\nu_0)\,d\nu_0}{\nu_0 - \nu}\right]\text{radians}, \quad (27)$$

with T_s the spin temperature of the hydrogen and τ the optical depth. At the moment the measurements appear possible for the cloud in front of the Crab nebula (Tau A), and, according to Clark, the sensitivity would be about the same as that of the Zeeman effect method. Again the mean value of $B_{||}$ is measured. A difficulty would seem to be that the Crab nebula has a width of about 4' and that the polarization is rather non-uniform over the object. Thus, different optical depths in front of different parts of the nebula could also change the orientation of the plane of polarization.

The more common Faraday effect occurs if a plane-polarized electromagnetic wave traverses a magneto-ionic medium. In ionized hydrogen the rotation of the plane of polarization is given by

$$\psi = 0.81\lambda^2 \int_0^L B_{||}(\mu G)\, n_e\, d\,s\,(\text{pc})\,\text{radians} \quad (28)$$

if the wavelength in meters is λ and the path traversed by the radiation L. Polarized radio radiation has been observed in some galactic sources, in many extragalactic sources, and in the general non-thermal radio radiation of the Galaxy. At the wavelengths where Faraday rotation becomes important, the degree of polarization also tends to decrease, indicating differential Faraday rotation, possibly inside the source. Of course, systematic Faraday rotation can also occur in the source, and it is uncertain what part of the rotation actually takes place in the galactic interstellar medium, especially for the extragalactic sources where the intergalactic medium could add further complications.

But the data available now (Gardner and Whiteoak 1962; Seielstad, Morris, Radhakrishnan, and Wilson 1963) indicate that the Faraday rotation for the extragalactic sources depends on galactic latitude. If this is confirmed by other sources, at least part of the effect is galactic.[2] For $b = 20°$ the case of Centaurus A is typical. Cooper and Price (1962) obtain a mean rotation measure (the value of ψ for $\lambda = 1$ m) of 65 radians in three positions separated by a few degrees, with only small individual deviations from the mean. This corresponds to $\langle B_{||} (\mu G) n_e \rangle \, L(pc) = 80$. Suppose the effect arises in the galactic disk. Then $L = 400$ pc and $\langle B_{||} (\mu G) n_e \rangle = 0.2$. On the average probably $n_e < 0.1$ cm^{-3} and then $\langle B_{||} \rangle > 2\mu G$. This would be very difficult to interpret on the basis of a low field picture, because then the field could hardly be in one direction all along the line of sight and, if it is not, then $|\langle B_{||} \rangle| \ll \langle |B_{||}| \rangle$. If the effect arises in the galactic halo, the pronounced dependence on galactic latitude is more difficult to understand. With $L = 20$ kpc we have $\langle B_{||} (\mu G) n_e \rangle = 4 \times 10^{-3}$. With $n_e = 5 \times 10^{-4}$ cm^{-3} as in the Spitzer halo, $\langle B_{||} \rangle = 8\mu G$, which is already too high even for $\langle |B_{||}| \rangle$. If the Faraday rotation is galactic, it thus appears to indicate appreciable regularity in the field, and the results would be definitely incompatible with a weak quasi-turbulent field. Some regularity is also suggested by the small variation of the rotation measure across Centaurus A. In the case of the Crab nebula the value of ψ at 21 cm is about 60° (Morris and Radhakrishnan 1963), and if $L = 1000$ pc we find $\langle B_{||} (\mu G) n_e \rangle = 0.025$ in the disk in this direction, but the effect can also arise within the source.

The observation of rather large polarization (several per cent) in the galactic non-thermal radio radiation (Westerhout, Seeger, Brouw, and Tinbergen 1962; Wielebinski and Shakeshaft 1962) at 400 Mc/s is potentially of great interest.

Observations of Faraday rotation are just beginning, however (Muller, Berkhuijsen, Brouw, and Tinbergen 1963), and all that can be said now is that rotation measures of several radians are present. Future investigations on the Faraday effect should greatly enhance our knowledge of magnetic fields and electron densities in the Galaxy.

3.3. Synchrotron Radiation

Synchrotron radiation from the Galaxy is observed at radio frequencies. From all over the sky non-thermal radio radiation reaches the earth. Some of the emission originates in discrete sources, but most of it is thought to be produced in a more continuous distribution (cf. chapter 11, this volume). An analysis of the 85 Mc/s radiation has been made by Mills (1959), who suggests that most of the

---

[2] Recent data for twenty-nine sources quite clearly show that most of the effect must in fact be galactic (Seielstad et al. 1964). The Faraday rotations vary over the sky in a systematic fashion and reveal a large-scale field pattern (Morris and Berge 1964) that is somewhat difficult to interpret. A further discussion of some implications has been given by Woltjer (1965).

radiation comes from a spheroidal halo (axial ratio 2 : 1) with a semi-major axis somewhat larger than 12 kpc. The radiation shows some concentration toward the galactic plane and also a slight concentration toward the galactic center. Mills claims that in the radiation from the disk the spiral arms are visible. It is important to examine the distribution of the emission in some detail.

The existence of the halo has generally been accepted, although it may be difficult to demonstrate it convincingly from the data on the radio emission in our Galaxy alone. But the fact that some other Sb and Sc galaxies have halos (though it is not a general class property) and arguments based on the isotropy of cosmic rays give some additional support. On the other hand it has become increasingly clear that the distribution of radio emission at high galactic latitudes shows considerable large- and small-scale structure, such as for example the strong spur of emission which emerges from the galactic plane around $l^{II} = 30°$. Because these features extend to high latitudes they cannot be very distant, but on the other hand it would seem that the volume emissivity would become quite high if they were too near, nearer than a kpc say. It would be fallacious, however, to think that all radiation at high latitudes might thus be quite local. If, for example, we inspect the 400 Mc/s survey reproduced by Westerhout et al. (1962), we find for the brightness temperatures near the galactic center about 300°, near the anticenter 39°, and near the north galactic pole 23°. Thus, the mean emission between the sun and the center is 13°/kpc, and if we were to assume a homogeneous emitting layer the total width near the sun would have to be 3.5 kpc, unless an unexpectedly large extragalactic component were present. Clearly the assumptions are such that this is a lower limit. Thus it is quite clear that, whatever the details, the non-thermal radio radiation is characterized by little central concentration, but also by little concentration toward the galactic plane. Oort (1963c) has stressed that no stellar population with such a behavior is known. Therefore it appears probable that the halo emission originates in a rather continuous (not necessarily uniform) field distribution and not in a large number of unresolved discrete sources, like supernova remnants and similar objects. Irregularities in the emission then are due to variations in the magnetic field strength or in the density of relativistic electrons. From Mills' detailed analysis of the smoothed halo distribution, the volume emissivity of the central part of the halo at 85 Mc/s is 1.5×10^{-39} erg sec^{-1} cm^{-3} (c/s)$^{-1}$. Near the sun it would be $\frac{2}{3}$ of this and beyond the solar orbit it would decrease more rapidly.

The non-thermal radio radiation is somewhat stronger near the galactic plane. This additional radiation—in the model of Mills about ten per cent of the total at 85 Mc/s—is usually referred to as the disk component. According to Mills, the emissivity in the central parts of the disk and in the spiral arms amounts to ten times that for the inner parts of the halo, or about 1.5×10^{-38} erg sec^{-1} cm^{-3} (c/s)$^{-1}$ at 85 Mc/s, while between the spiral arms the emissivity would be lower. The distribution of synchrotron radiation which would be expected from a system of spiral arms has been investigated in more detail by Hanbury Brown and Hazard (1960) and by Field (1960). They show that if the radiation is isotropic the spiral arms would appear much more conspicuous in the distribution of the radiation over the sky than is observed and conclude that the radiation is anisotropic. It could then be produced in magnetic fields which would be well aligned along the arms. Mills (1961), however, has pointed out that it is not possible to obtain a unique solution which gives both the emission as a function of the distance to the center and the anisotropy of the radiation. Moreover, it is very doubtful that the actual spiral arms are sufficiently regular to produce these effects. The 22-cm surveys, in which mainly the ionized hydrogen is seen—certainly an isotropic radiator well concentrated in the spiral arms—do not exhibit much more marked effects of spiral structure than the 85 Mc/s survey. Apparently the arms in the Galaxy are not regular. This is plausible from a comparison with photographs of external galaxies.

Shain (1959) has measured the non-thermal radio radiation produced in front of some nearby H II regions. Taking his data at face value and converting his results at 19.7 Mc/s to Mills' frequency with a spectral index of -0.5, the emissivity in the arm near the sun is about the same as the value quoted by Mills as an average for a typical spiral arm. This good agreement may well be fortuitous, but since no other data are available we shall adopt for the non-thermal emission at 85 Mc/s near the sun the value 1.5×10^{-38} erg cm^{-3} sec^{-1} (c/s)$^{-1}$. It would be very valuable if Shain's results could be extended, since his procedure leads to a direct determination of the emissivity in different directions and at different distances from the sun.

The origin of the disk emission is still a point of discussion. It would seem natural to suppose that the same mechanism is at work as in the halo, namely, the radiation of relativistic electrons in interstellar magnetic fields. But it has also been suggested that the radiation could be produced in a collection of discrete sources, probably supernova remnants. This idea is not so implausible, since a source like Cas A radiates already at a power level equal to three per cent of that for the whole disk. Of course, only a few sources of such high brightness occur—and they are readily isolated from the background—but objects of the same kind in a later stage of evolution, like the Cygnus loop and IC 443, might be more numerous and less easily separable from the background. But the volume emissivity in the Cygnus loop is only two orders of magnitude larger than that in the disk component, and within 500 pc from the sun about a hundred such objects would be needed. The Cygnus loop is at 800 pc, and it seems most unlikely that there would be so many nearer objects of the same kind. Also the width of the non-thermal emission in the disk is larger than the width of the layer of gas. If remnants of supernovae of Type II produced the radiation, the opposite situation would be expected, because supernovae of Type II appear to be massive stars, and it is known that the layer of O and B stars is slightly thinner than the layer of gas. Thus it seems unlikely that a large part of the disk component consists of unresolved discrete sources.

Of course, the separation into disk and halo components is somewhat artificial, as the same physical mechanism accounts for both. Both show considerable fluctuations, probably indicating structure in the magnetic field. These fluctuations are especially noticeable in the direction of the galactic anticenter where the smoothing effects of superposition along the line of sight are smallest. From the results of Davies and Hazard (1962), who surveyed the region at 237 Mc/s with a one-degree beam, it appears that the mean temperature on the galactic equator is about 160° K with typical fluctuations of about 20 per cent over regions of several degrees across. It must be stressed again that there is no reason to suppose that these fluctuations are incompatible with emission in a *continuous* medium. In fact, it would have been surprising if the field had been so regular that the halo and disk emission were much smoother.

The spectrum of the galactic radio emission is still somewhat uncertain. Values of about 0.6 for the spectral index were obtained in the later fifties [the spectral index is the exponent a in the spectral distribution $J(\nu) \propto \nu^{-a}$]. Costain (1960) obtained $a = 0.37 \pm 0.04$. Turtle, Pugh, Kenderdine, and Paul-iny-Toth (1962) conclude $a = 0.5$ or 0.6 around 100 Mc/s, less at lower frequencies and more at higher frequencies. No clear differences between different regions have been found. For the moment we shall take $a = 0.5$.

The synchrotron emission from a distribution of relativistic electrons with a differential energy spectrum given by

$$n(E)dE = kE^{-\beta} dE,\qquad(29)$$

where E is measured in Bev, is

$$J(\nu) = k \left(10^5 B \sin \theta \right)^{(\beta+1)/2} \left(10^{-8}\nu \right)^{-(\beta-1)/2} Q(\beta).\qquad(30)$$

The angle θ is the angle between the momentum vector of the electrons and $\boldsymbol{B}$. In the neighborhood of $\beta = 2$, $Q(\beta)$ does not depend very critically on β. Numerically we have $Q(2) = 3.09 \times 10^{-27}$. The value $\beta = 2$ corresponds to a spectral index 0.5 of the radio emission. The radiation is emitted in a narrow cone around the momentum vector of an electron in the neighborhood of a frequency ν_c, given by

$$\nu_c = 1.61 \times 10^{13} BE^2 \sin \theta.\qquad(31)$$

Since only radiation from electrons with their momentum vector along the line of sight is observed, the angle θ is also the angle between the line of sight and $\boldsymbol{B}$ in a region from which radiation is observed. The radiation is characterized by a strong (typically about 75 per cent) linear polarization (Westfold 1959), with the electric vector perpendicular to the projection of $\boldsymbol{B}$. If the distribution function of the particle momenta is not strongly anisotropic within the width of the

emission cone from a single electron (typically a minute of arc) the remainder
of the radiation is not polarized.

If we suppose that the directions of B have a sufficiently random distribution
and average over the angle θ, we find from the observed volume emissivity near
the sun (eq. [30]) that $kB^{3/2} = 1.9 \times 10^{-10}$. The value of k can be obtained from
measurements of the flux of cosmic-ray electrons near the earth. The measurements are difficult because cosmic-ray protons are so much more abundant. At
the moment the only relevant data are those obtained by Earl (1961), who detected 9 supposedly extraterrestrial electrons with energies around 1 bev. Only
a very rough estimate of k can be obtained from such a small number. Making
some correction for solar effects this leads to a value around 1×10^{-12} (Woltjer
1963a). Because of the poor statistics and other uncertainties it cannot be excluded that the actual value of k may ultimately turn out to be much lower,
but it seems unlikely that it could be more than, say, three times larger since
a much larger flux would almost certainly have been detected. With the adopted
value for k we obtain for spiral arms near the sun $B = 35 \mu$G.[3] Taking a factor
of three as the maximum uncertainty of k in the upward direction, we find that
B certainly should exceed 17 μG. These results are consistent with earlier estimates made independently by Biermann and Davis (1960) and Woltjer (1961)
on the basis of an upper limit on k obtained earlier by Critchfield, Ney, and
Oleska (1952). If the field were the same inside and outside the spiral arms, then
near the sun we would have $B = 20 \mu$G.

If we wish to determine the field strength in other parts of the Galaxy we
must make an assumption about the variation of the density of relativistic electrons with position. If a particle that gyrates in a magnetic field moves through
a spatially varying magnetic field, its magnetic moment $mv^2 \sin^2 \theta/B$ is conserved if the length scale characteristic for the field variations is much larger
than the Larmor radius. The kinetic energy of the particle in a static field is
also a constant. Thus, if the particle moves in the direction of decreasing field
intensity, its momentum vector will become more parallel to B. If it moves in
the opposite direction, the motion will become more transverse, until the momentum parallel to the field has become zero. Then the particle is reflected. Let
us suppose that we have a region of varying magnetic fields and that all parts of
the region are interconnected by field lines along which the particles can reach
the different parts of the region. If a steady state has been reached, Liouville's

---

[3] Recently, Agrinier *et al.* (1964) have measured an integral flux of electrons with energies
above 4.5 Bev of 6.6×10^{-4} cm^{-2} sec^{-1} sterad^{-1}. Since the measurements were made during
solar minimum, solar modulation effects should be quite small at these energies. Some knowledge of the spectrum is required to derive the flux of the electrons that are mainly responsible
for the 85 Mc/s radio emission. Up to 1000 Mc/s the spectral index is near 0.50. If the spectrum is unchanged at higher frequencies, we find $B = 3.0 \times 10^{-5}$G in the spiral arms; if beyond 1000 Mc/s we take $\alpha = 0.75$, this becomes 1.8×10^{-5}G, while with $\alpha = 1.00$ we find
1.4×10^{-5}G. In a field of 2×10^{-5}G we have for electrons of 4.5 Bev approximately $\nu_c = 5000$
Mc/s.

theorem states that the distribution function of the particles will be constant along any trajectory in phase space.

We can envisage two different situations. Let us first suppose that the distribution function of particle momenta is isotropic in the region of lowest magnetic field strength. Then in the region of stronger field all angles θ between 0 and $\pi/2$ can occur. According to Liouville's theorem, the distribution function will be the same everywhere, and thus the density of particles will be constant in the region.

If, on the other hand, we suppose that all particles are produced in a region of high field strength, with an isotropic momentum distribution there, and if the regions of lower field strength have been populated wholly by particles which originated in the high field region, the situation is quite different. If the field

TABLE 4

SYNCHROTRON EMISSION AS A FUNCTION OF
MAGNETIC FIELD STRENGTH*

B/B_0	k/k_0	J_{anisotr}	$B^{3/2}$
1.	1	1	1
0.9.	0.68	0.34	0.86
0.8.	0.55	0.16^5	0.72
0.7.	0.45	0.08	0.59
0.6.	0.37	0.037	0.47
0.5.	0.29	0.015	0.36
0.4.	0.22	0.005	0.25

* The particle density k for the case where particles are only produced in the region where the field is B_0, the synchrotron volume emissivity in that case and the synchrotron emissivity for the isotropic case, which varies as $B^{3/2}$.

intensity in the region of production is B_0, only particles with a pitch angle θ smaller than $\sin^{-1}(B/B_0)$ will be found in the region where the field is B. From Liouville's theorem, the distribution function in the allowed parts of phase space is again constant. The density then decreases proportional to the solid angle subtended by the cone which envelops the possible momentum vectors. The density of the particles thus varies as $1 - (1 - B/B_0)^{1/2}$ or, if B/B_0 is small, approximately as $\frac{1}{2} B/B_0$. The synchrotron emission from these electrons is even smaller than would follow from the decrease of k alone, because the average value of $\sin \theta$ is also decreased. If B/B_0 is small, we have approximately $\langle (\sin \theta)^{3/2} \rangle = (2/7) (B/B_0)^{7/4}$, a result which has been derived by Sciama (1962). In the case of a small B/B_0 the synchrotron volume emissivity thus varies as $B^{17/4}$. The radiation is strongly anisotropic, most of it being emitted in directions which make an angle slightly smaller than $\theta_{\max}$ with B. In Table 4 we have given the particle density and the emission for the two different cases as a function of B/B_0. For values of B/B_0 smaller than those given in the table, the expressions given for small B/B_0 can be used.

If there are regions in the Galaxy which are not connected by magnetic field lines nothing can be said about the relative densities in such regions.

Cosmic-ray results indicate that relativistic particles in our region of the Galaxy have a rather strictly isotropic momentum distribution. Also, it appears from the chemical composition of the cosmic rays that the particles do not stay very long in the plane of the Galaxy, where they suffer collisions with the interstellar gas atoms. Thus the available evidence, which admittedly is meager, may be taken to indicate that the particles travel rather freely through at least part of the Galaxy. The evidence is consistent with the supposition that the distribution function is isotropic everywhere, but this interpretation of the data does not appear certain, because the sun is situated in a region of comparatively strong field. Nevertheless, some anisotropy might be expected in the latter case, because there would also be particles which have been accelerated in regions of still higher field strength. And it may be reasonable to suppose that hydromagnetic shocks propagate through the halo, which because of their small-scale structure (smaller than the Larmor radius of the relativistic particles) could effectively randomize the momentum vectors of the cosmic rays. We thus shall assume that the particle density is constant (some aspects of the other point of view have been investigated by Sciama 1962), but near the boundary of the halo the density must go down if the relativistic particle density in the universe is small. Still it is interesting to note that if there are regions where the particles do not have an isotropic distribution function, small variations in the field could lead to very large emission fluctuations, both because of the strong dependence of the emissivity on B and the anisotropy of the radiation. In all previous discussions we have neglected the radiative losses of the electrons. This is justified, since the electrons can traverse the Galaxy at least a thousand times before this becomes important; and it is probable that most of them escape from the halo before that.

If we put k equal to a constant, the distribution of synchrotron emission gives us immediately the distribution of $B^{3/2}$. From the data discussed before, we find in the central parts of the halo a B which is four times smaller than near the sun, while in the central parts of the disk it would be only slightly larger than near the sun if the radiation there is not concentrated in spiral arms. If it is, it might be two or three times larger. If the momenta of the electrons would not have been assumed to be randomized, we would have found that the magnetic field need nowhere deviate more than 30 per cent from its mean value in a sphere with a radius of 8 kpc around the galactic center.

G. Clark (1963) has shown that synchrotron radiation in the X-ray region could conceivably also be observed. In collisions between cosmic-ray nuclei of very high energy (10^{15} ev), gamma rays and energetic electrons are formed in equal numbers. The gamma rays produce a characteristic type of air showers on earth. The electrons radiate their energy very near to the point of their creation in the interstellar magnetic field. The spectral distribution of the radiation depends on the magnetic field strength. Wavelengths of a few angstroms are typical. However, the observed intensities appear rather high, and it may well be that other galactic sources of emission or even intergalactic emission are dominant.

3.4. OPTICAL POLARIZATION

The polarization of the light of distant stars is probably produced by the absorption of light in interstellar clouds by elongated dust grains. According to Davis and Greenstein (1951), the field strength should be at least of the order of a few times 10^{-5} gauss if the grains are paramagnetic. Henry (1958) has shown that for ferromagnetic particles a field of 10^{-6} gauss would suffice, and Wickramasinghe (1962) has shown the same for graphite flakes. Since the nature of the dust grains is still uncertain, it is not yet clear whether the absolute value of the field indicated by the polarization is larger than the mean field which follows from the Zeeman effect.

In many regions the polarization vectors are relatively well aligned. Davis (1951) and Chandrasekhar and Fermi (1953) have estimated the field strength from the dispersion of the polarization vectors around the mean. The idea behind this method is that if the field is weak the cloud motions will distort it so much that the scatter of the polarizations would become large. In a transverse hydromagnetic wave there is equipartition between the kinetic energy and the magnetic energy of the perturbation. If the perturbation of the field is b, the field itself B, the mean-square angular spread of the polarization vectors around the mean a^2, and the velocity dispersion of the clouds in one dimension q, we have, for not too large values of a,

$$a^2 = \left\langle \frac{b^2}{B^2} \right\rangle = \frac{4\pi\rho q^2}{B^2}. \tag{32}$$

For four regions where the dispersion is rather low, Stranahan (1954) found on the average $a \approx 0.12$ radians. With $q = 7$ km/sec and a density of one hydrogen atom per cm^3, we obtain $B = 33$ μG. However, the result may be uncertain as long as we have no better knowledge about the field structure inside and outside of the interstellar clouds. Also, Spitzer (1954) has pointed out that if a magnetic field were produced by interstellar turbulence and subsequently drawn out by the galactic differential rotation the mean-square magnetic field perpendicular to the galactic plane could well be weaker than the field parallel to the plane, and polarization results like those which are observed could be expected. It is not quite clear, however, whether on such a model the small dispersion found in certain regions can be quantitatively accounted for.

3.5. COSMIC-RAY CONFINEMENT

According to Biermann and Davis (1960), it is unlikely that cosmic rays can be confined in the galactic halo if their energy density exceeds the magnetic energy density, at least if not much matter is present in the halo. The argument

may be made precise on the basis of the virial theorem. Let us consider the
zz-component of equation (9) for an isolated stationary system. Then the left-
hand side of the equation and the surface integrals vanish. If not much mass
is present in the halo, T_{zz} and W_{zz} can be neglected. Then equation (9) becomes

$$-2\,\mathfrak{M}_{zz} + \mathfrak{M} + U = 0\,, \tag{33}$$

or

$$U = \mathfrak{M}_{zz} - \mathfrak{M}_{xx} - \mathfrak{M}_{yy}\,. \tag{34}$$

Therefore,

$$\mathfrak{M} > \mathfrak{M}_{zz} > U\,. \tag{35}$$

Thus, the magnetic energy density must on the average certainly be larger than
one-third of the cosmic-ray energy density (for a relativistic gas the pressure
entering U is one-third of the energy density). Near the earth the energy density
of cosmic rays is about 1.4×10^{-12} erg cm^{-3}. If the density of cosmic rays is constant throughout the halo and the disk, the root-mean-square field strength in
the halo should thus be larger than 3.5 μG. If, as is more likely, the energy
density of the cosmic rays is about equal to the magnetic energy density, this
value is increased by a factor 1.7.

If much matter is present in the halo, this reasoning is no longer valid. Then
the weight of the gas high up in the halo could be in equilibrium with the
pressure of cosmic rays. This is a situation in which a heavy gas is supported
in a gravitational field by a light gas of the same pressure. A weak magnetic field would be sufficient to couple the cosmic-ray gas to the thermal gas.
However, in such a case Taylor instabilities seem likely. In such instabilities
the light gas and the heavy gas exchange places and potential energy is re-
leased. If the magnetic field is weak, it cannot affect the energy balance in the
instability in a significant way. Only if the field is strong could it perhaps
stabilize the situation, because then so much energy is needed to twist the field
that the release of gravitational energy might be compensated. Thus, even if
much matter were present in the halo the field is still likely to be rather strong.
Of course, the argument depends on the supposition that no significant cosmic-
ray pressure is present outside the Galaxy.

3.6. The Virial Theorem

The virial theorem puts an upper limit on the field strength. If not much mass
is present in the halo, we can proceed, following Biermann and Davis (1960)
from equation (22), which connects the lag velocity of the gas in the galactic
plane with the total magnetic and cosmic-ray energies. If the total mass of gas
in the disk is 2×10^9 solar masses, the rotational velocity 250 km/sec, and the
volume of the halo equal to that of a sphere with radius 10 kpc, then the average
lag velocity due to the cosmic-ray energy alone is 7 km/sec. If the magnetic
energy is equal to the cosmic-ray energy this figure is doubled. A mean halo
field of 10 μG would produce a lag velocity of 30 km/sec. Since a much larger

lag velocity for the gas in the disk seems impossible, the mean field can hardly exceed this value. Also, the radius of the halo cannot be much larger than 10 kpc if no matter is present outside the disk.

If matter is present in the halo, we have from equation (11) that the absolute value of the total gravitational energy of the matter should be larger than the sum of the magnetic and cosmic-ray energies. With 10^9 solar masses in the halo supported by the magnetic field, it appears that the mean field in the Galaxy still should be less than 20 μG. Thus, unless there is much more gaseous matter in the Galaxy than is suspected at the moment, it seems that the mean field definitely should be smaller than a few times 10^{-5} gauss. If we adopt a value of the field near the sun of 30 μG, a model like that of Sciama (1962) where the synchrotron emission depends very steeply on the magnetic field and where the mean field is only slightly less than the field near the sun, already strains the possibilities.

3.7. STAR FORMATION

Star formation is seriously impeded by magnetic fields, and the structural features of H II regions and their surroundings would be expected to be strongly influenced by magnetic fields. Spitzer (1963) concludes that a uniform field of more than a few μG is extremely unlikely. It is not certain that this conclusion still holds if the field has small-scale structure in the interstellar clouds (Woltjer 1963a). It would seem that a detailed study of these phenomena in the presence of different kinds of magnetic fields would be very much worthwhile.

3.8. THE SOLAR WIND

The solar wind is the systematic outflow of gas from the solar corona. Near the earth the velocity of the gas is several hundred km/sec and the density a few atoms per cm³. Recent discussion indicates that somewhere a shock will occur in the solar wind, beyond which the velocity will be smaller and the density larger. The location of the shock depends on the pressure in the interstellar medium. Brandt (1962) has presented evidence, based on observations of comet tails, that the shock is at 2 A.U. from the sun. Kinetic pressure in interstellar space is inadequate for this. If the interstellar pressure is predominantly magnetic, the shock at 2 A.U. would indicate a field of 70 μG, or maybe somewhat less. Clearly the result is uncertain, as the observational and theoretical knowledge of the solar wind still is inadequate.

3.9. CONCLUSION

If we inspect the data in Table 2 in the light of the foregoing discussion, we note that outside the interstellar gas clouds the available indications point to a field of the order of a few times 10^{-5} G in the galactic disk. On the other hand, both the Zeeman effect and the arguments based on star formation indicate that in interstellar clouds the mean field is an order of magnitude smaller. It would seem that these data can be brought into harmony if the field in an interstellar cloud is really much weaker than in a typical interstellar region, or if the field has a small-scale structure inside the clouds. In the first case, mechanical equilibrium requires the gas pressure to be of the order of $B^2/8\pi$, where B is the field outside the cloud. This leads to cloud densities of the order of a few times 10^3 atoms per cm^3. It is not probable that many clouds of such high density do exist. It is also difficult to see how such clouds could remain in existence for a long time if the field did not have a small-scale structure. The clouds would be confined by the outside field in two dimensions, but they would expand freely along the field lines.

The alternative would seem to be that the field inside most of the cloud has almost the same strength as the outside field, but that the field has small-scale structure. The field would be largely force free, since the thermal energy in the cloud is small compared to the magnetic energy. Such a cloud field could be confined by the general galactic field. The cloud field itself could then confine the gas of the cloud in three dimensions. It seems that most data can be reconciled on the basis of such a model. Some aspects have been further discussed by Woltjer (1963a). Inside the cloud ambipolar diffusion processes are important, and after some time the small-scale structure could be partly dissipated, thus making star formation possible. On the outside of the cloud the gas becomes ionized and the conductivity high. Small clouds, which, for example, have been expelled from stars with the magnetic fields they contain, may merge into the existing clouds and thus add to the small-scale field. Some further aspects of the magnetic fields in interstellar gas clouds have been given by Grzedzielski (1962). Detailed observational and theoretical investigations of the structure of interstellar gas clouds are much needed.

§ 4. THE GALACTIC HALO

In Section 3.3 we have described how the galactic disk is enveloped by an extended distribution of magnetic fields ($B \sim 6$ μG) and cosmic rays. But we have not yet specified the state of matter in the halo or its dynamical properties. In most discussions the interstellar gas clouds at high galactic latitudes are of importance, and we shall first discuss these.

4.1. INTERSTELLAR GAS CLOUDS IN THE HALO

Münch and Zirin (1961) have analyzed data on 46 interstellar components in 24 stars more than 200 pc from the galactic plane. On the average, the stars which are farthest from the plane have the largest number of absorption components with Doppler shifts in excess of 10 km/sec. The inference is that a population of high-velocity clouds extends at least up to 1 kpc from the plane. Negative velocities predominate, but it should be emphasized that the statistics are quite limited. From the equivalent width of the Ca II lines Münch and Zirin obtained the number of Ca^+ ions along the line of sight. If the abundance ratios Ca^+/(all Ca) and (all Ca)/H are known, a relation between the diameter of the cloud and its density or mass can be obtained. Because in all cases—and especially in H I regions—the abundance of Ca^+ is only a few per cent or less of the total Ca abundance the results depend strongly on the somewhat uncertain estimates of the ionization equilibrium. In Table 5 we give results for a typical cloud, obtained on the basis of the calculations of Münch and Zirin. As soon as hydrogen is slightly ionized the H I calculations become invalid. Also the results for a composite cloud model of H I surrounded by a thin shell of H II would turn out somewhat differently.

An analysis by Takakubo of individual H I clouds at latitudes around 20° (reported by Blaauw 1963), has led to a picture in which typical clouds in the neighborhood of the sun have masses of 50 solar masses, hydrogen densities of 20 cm^{-3} and diameters of 6 pc. About ten such clouds are intersected by a straight line of 1-kpc length in the galactic plane. If the Münch-Zirin clouds

TABLE 5

Physical Parameters in a Typical Münch-Zirin
Cloud as a Function of Mass*

$M(\odot)$	HI, $T=100°$			HI, $T=10000°$			HII, $T=10000°$		
	n_H	h	nT	n_H	h	nT	n_H	h	nT
1......	0.9	4	90	6	2	60000	0.11	8	2200
10.....	.6	10	60	4	5	40000	.07	20	1400
100.....	.4	25	40	2	14	20000	.05	50	900
1000.....	0.2	62	20	1	34	10000	0.03	125	600

* The hydrogen density is n_H (cm^{-3}), the total particle density is n (cm^{-3}), and the diameter is h (pc).

are similar clouds at larger distances from the galactic plane, it would appear that clouds expand by a factor of 2 or 3 in moving into the halo if they remain H I or a factor of 7 if they become ionized.

Recently some high-velocity clouds have been discovered (Muller, Oort, and Raimond 1963) which must be located well outside the galactic disk. A survey of less than a hundred points at ±40° latitude has yielded three clouds with radial velocities in excess of 100 km/sec. The most extreme is a cloud with a velocity of −175 km/sec and a projected density of 2×10^{20} hydrogen atoms per cm^2. All three clouds have negative radial velocities. The internal velocity spread is large, about ±12.5 km/sec. At the moment the nature of these clouds is uncertain. Conceivably they could be condensations in the intergalactic medium of the Local Group, but if they are within the galactic halo, they need not be so very different from the Münch-Zirin clouds. It is a complete mystery how clouds can attain such high velocities. In addition to these very high-velocity objects, the 21-cm profiles also show wings and peaks with velocities of up to ±70 km/sec. Taking all evidence together, it appears rather clear that some neutral hydrogen is definitely present in the halo and that its mean density averaged over a halo with 10 kpc radius cannot be much less than 10^{-3} atoms per cm^3.

The existence of interstellar gas clouds in the halo poses the problem of their equilibrium. If they moved in empty space they would expand with a velocity of the order of three times the sound velocity, and Münch and Zirin show that if the clouds had been formed in the galactic plane they would now be too diffuse to be observed. Also, in that case, one would expect an excess of positive velocities. Thus the clouds are apparently confined by the halo medium. Three possible confinement mechanisms have been envisaged, by a hot medium, by a cool quasi-turbulent medium, or by a magnetic field.

4 2. The Hot Halo

Spitzer (1956) has proposed that the clouds are in equilibrium with a hot tenuous gas. The gas is assumed to be in hydrostatic equilibrium in the galactic gravitational field. If the temperature were low, the gas would not extend far from the galactic plane; if the temperature were too high the gas would escape. Assuming that the product nT in the clouds is about 10^3, a halo temperature of $10^6 °$ K and a particle density of 10^{-3} cm^{-3} appeared reasonable. The hot gas is cooled by direct radiative processes in a time that is somewhat shorter than the age of the Galaxy. In a stationary state about 10^{39} ergs/sec should be supplied to compensate for these radiative losses. This is of the same order of magnitude as that required for the maintenance of cloud motions in the galactic disk and a factor of ten less than what is needed for the acceleration of cosmic rays. One supernova of type I per 200 years would be sufficient if the energy of all the moving material were thermalized. It is difficult to obtain experimental verification of the Spitzer halo since its surface brightness, both in the continuum and in emission lines, would be very low. Faraday rotation measurements might be useful, but a large body of information is needed before the halo effects can be established with certainty.

The cool clouds may have important effects on the halo medium. Not only could the total mass of the clouds well exceed that of the halo gas, but if clouds form from the halo medium or if existing clouds absorb heat from it, the energy losses from the halo may be much larger than the direct radiative losses. If we consider that about one Münch-Zirin cloud is seen in front of a typical halo star, the radiation from all these clouds would be about 10^{37} ergs/sec for H I at 100°, about 500 times larger for H I at 10000°, and 10^{40} ergs for H II at 10000°. The latter figure is ten times larger than the direct radiation from the halo medium. If no magnetic fields were present, the clouds would be heated by conduction from the halo medium. From the discussion of Münch and Zirin it appears that for H I clouds the energy supplied is a factor of 10^2 to 10^4 larger than the amount that can be radiated, while for H II regions a balance can be achieved. If a large-scale magnetic field is present, a reduction of the heat transport by a factor of three seems likely, but if the field is on a small scale, the reduction factor is probably larger. Thus, at the moment the situation in the clouds remains unclear—although Münch and Zirin show that some clouds certainly will be ionized by the high-latitude O and B stars—and the energy losses by the halo medium also remain uncertain. Cloud formation in the halo would also be important in this connection. Field (1963) has shown that in the absence of magnetic fields the halo medium would be unstable against the formation of condensations, and he estimates the growth time of these as 0.6×10^9 years. If such a condensation begins to form, it could be expected to fall toward the galactic plane before cloud densities are reached, but with suitable magnetic fields the situation might be different and deserves further study.

The equilibrium of the halo in the galactic gravitational field has not been discussed. Much would depend on the rotation of the halo, on magnetic fields, and on the detailed manner in which mass and energy are supplied. In the absence of direct interaction with the matter in the disk (through a magnetic field), the xx and yy components of the virial theorem yield, in the case of axial symmetry,

$$\int \rho (u_{\varpi}^2 + u_{\varphi}^2)\, d\tau + 2\int P d\tau + \int \rho \varpi \frac{\partial \Phi}{\partial \varpi}\, d\tau = 0. \tag{36}$$

Since $|\partial \Phi / \partial \varpi|$ decreases with increasing $|z|$, since the pressure term is rather large, and since motions other than pure rotation may well be present, the rotational velocities in the halo should on the average be well below the circular velocities in the disk. For example, if only the pressure effects are considered for a temperature of $10^{6\,\circ}$ K and if $\partial \Phi / \partial \varpi$ is taken independent of z, typical lag velocities of 30 km/sec are obtained.

If the rotation of the halo is not too important dynamically (as would certainly be the case in the inner parts if it rotates as a solid body), the pressure would become quite large in the inner regions of the Galaxy. If cooling of the halo by interstellar clouds is important, the cooling effects per unit mass would be strongest in the interior of the Galaxy. Thus, if no corresponding increase in the heating rate occurred, the inner region of the halo would cool, the surrounding matter would lose its support, and the halo material would begin to fall inward. In this way an influx of matter toward the inner parts of the Galaxy could occur. This could be of interest in connection with the outflow of matter observed in the galactic disk.

On the basis of considerations on the dynamics of the Local Group of galaxies, Kahn and Woltjer (1959) have suggested that surrounding the halo a rather hot (5×10^5 degrees) tenuous ($n_e = 10^{-4}$ cm^{-3}) gas is present. Their conclusion that this gas would confine the halo magnetic field by its pressure now seems difficult to accept, since they underestimated the magnetic field strength in the halo and neglected the cosmic-ray pressure. Still the presence of such gas might have non-negligible effects on the structure of the halo. But it does not seem impossible that the Spitzer halo and the Kahn-Woltjer medium are really one and that instabilities may permit inward leakage of the intergalactic gas. Let us neglect for a moment streaming effects and suppose that the outer parts of the halo are in hydrostatic equilibrium and that an adiabatic equation of state may be used. Then from the parameters of the intergalactic medium we obtain for the solar neighborhood $T = 2 \times 10^6$ and $n_e = 8 \times 10^{-4}$. But this is an overestimate because of the magnetic field in the halo and cooling effects. It would then appear possible to combine this model with a model of a non-rotating halo with an inward flow of matter. The mass and energy balance would be simple. Mass would flow into the halo from the outside and be deposited in the inner parts of the Galaxy. The potential energy of the matter in the gravitational field would serve to heat the gas and to provide the kinetic energy associated with the inward flow. The mass of the inner regions of the Galaxy would slowly increase. All these considerations are speculative, but they indicate the need for a much deeper analysis of the dynamics of halo models of the Spitzer type.

4.3. The Cool Halo

Quite a different picture has been developed by Pikelner and Shklovsky (1957, 1959), who conclude that the halo has a high density (0.01 cm^{-3}) and a relatively low temperature (10^4 degrees) and is supported mechanically not by a hydrostatic pressure like the Spitzer halo, but by hydromagnetic pressure waves, which could originate in the central regions of the Galaxy. In an ordinary gas such pressure waves would rapidly dissipate and heat the gas until a Spitzer-type halo would result. But Pikelner and Shklovsky argue that the magnetic field will greatly reduce the dissipation. In fact, Pikelner (1957) has shown that for a hydromagnetic shock which propagates transverse to a magnetic field this reduction may be quite large, a factor of 40 in a typical example. However, one would think that for shocks which propagate parallel to the field the dissipation would be unchanged and that one cannot gain a large factor this way, though more extensive study on this point would be desirable. It might also be that the presence of cosmic rays reduces the dissipation considerably if the cosmic-ray particles are bound to the ordinary gas through the magnetic field (see also, Parker 1958). But to reduce the dissipation significantly in all three dimensions it would seem that the field should have a random structure on a scale of the order of the mean free path of the thermal particles in the gas ($\sim 10^{14}$ cm). Pikelner and Shklovsky obtain the magnetic field strength from the condition that the magnetic energy density should exceed the cosmic-ray energy density. They argue that since the radio data show that magnetic fields and cosmic rays are present up to 10 kpc from the center, the layers above 10 kpc should have enough weight to compensate the pressure of these, and this leads to their density estimate. This reasoning is based on the assumption that cosmic rays cannot be confined by a large-scale field. But Wentzel (1957) has shown that relativistic particles can be confined in a large-scale force-free field, and there is no reason why the same result should not hold for other kinds of large-scale fields. If the field is large-scale, a simple pressure balance cannot be postulated, since the tension along the lines of force should also be taken into account. In the situation envisaged by Pikelner and Shklovsky it is difficult to see how Rayleigh-Taylor instabilities are to be avoided, since the light gas (cosmic rays and small-scale magnetic fields) is supporting the heavy gas in a gravitational field. The energy which is needed to maintain their model is estimated by Pikelner and Shklovsky as 3×10^{41} erg/sec. If such a high figure is correct the halo would be the dominant energy sink in the galactic energy balance. It is now somewhat doubtful whether this energy can be obtained from turbulence in the central region of the Galaxy, as it has been shown (Rougoor and Oort 1960) that the motions there represent a systematic outward flow rather than turbulence.

The high density and low temperature of the Pikelner-Shklovsky halo make an observational check more feasible. If the halo gas is predominantly neutral, as suggested by Pikelner and Shklovsky, then with a hydrogen density of 0.01 cm^{-3}, a velocity dispersion of ± 100 km/sec and a path length of 10 kpc, a mean brightness temperature of about one degree in the 21-cm line could be expected. But a distribution of more condensed clouds in the Spitzer halo could produce a similar result. In fact, it might be somewhat doubtful whether a uniform halo medium of such a low density could be neutral, since a rather large number of stars could contribute to the radiation fields below the Lyman limit. Minkowski and Osterbrock (1959) have made an estimate of the ultraviolet radiation in the globular cluster M3. Because the number of RR Lyrae stars in the Galaxy is about a factor of 1000 larger than that in M3, it might be reasonable to multiply their result with the same factor, in which case the total ionized volume in the halo would be equal to $2 \times 10^9 \, n_H^{-2}$ pc^3. The stars observed by Münch and Zirin (1961) would already contribute ten per cent of this amount. If the radius of the halo is taken as 10 kpc, it follows that the halo material would be ionized if the halo had a uniform density of less than 0.02 atoms cm^{-3}. Any radiation that leaks from the galactic disk would still further increase this figure. If the Pikelner-Shklovsky halo were ionized, it could only be observed with great difficulty. Münch and Zirin show that a cool halo with electron density of 0.1 cm^{-3} can be excluded, but since the Pikelner-Shklovsky estimate is a factor of ten less, more refined measurements are needed.

Pikelner and Shklovsky themselves adduce the measurements of Reber and Ellis (1956) from which absorption of low-frequency radio radiation in the halo would follow. These results are still quite uncertain. Haddock, Schulte, and Walsh (1963) claim that the spectrum of the galactic non-thermal radio radiation continues unchanged down to 2 Mc/s, while Hoyle and Ellis (1963) discuss results by Ellis which would indicate considerable absorption already above 5 Mc/s. These authors consider this as evidence for the existence of a 300 pc thick layer of ionized hydrogen with a mean density of 0.1 particle per cm^3. Such a medium would appear to be incompatible with the measurements of Münch and Zirin. In conclusion it would appear that the Pikelner-Shklovsky halo model is not entirely convincing; but, on the other hand, the difference between this model and a hot halo with cool clouds may be partly academic.

4.4. The Magnetic Halo

If the halo clouds have internal magnetic fields of the kind needed in the disk clouds to explain the Zeeman effect measurements, no gaseous medium is required to confine the clouds (Woltjer 1963a). In the disk the cloud equilibrium would be almost entirely determined by the balance of magnetic stresses inside and outside the cloud. With a magnetic field of 6 μG in the halo we have $B^2/8\pi = 1.4 \times 10^{-12}$, while according to Table 5 the value of nkT in H II clouds (or in H I at 1000°) is near 10^{-13}. Thus the magnetic stresses would still be dominant. Suppose now that a disk cloud moves into the halo. The external field decreases by a factor of 4, and to maintain equilibrium the internal field should change by about the same factor. This corresponds to an increase in linear dimension by a factor of two, which is not inconsistent with the Münch-Zirin data. It thus appears that the parameters of the halo gas cannot be determined convincingly from the cloud-equilibrium considerations and that for the moment the gas density in the halo remains somewhat uncertain. But there is a good prospect that future 21-cm, long-wavelength continuum, optical absorption line, and Faraday effect studies will greatly clarify the situation.

§ 5. THE GALACTIC DISK, SPIRAL STRUCTURE

Observationally much more is known about the disk than about the halo, but the dynamical situation is still obscure. The main features of the disk—largely revealed by 21-cm observations—are the following: around the center of the Galaxy, marked by the radio source Sagittarius A (a strong source of both thermal and non-thermal radiation) a rapidly rotating disk of gas is found with a radius of 700 pc, a total half thickness of 100 pc, and a mean hydrogen density of 2 atm/cm³. The disk may have some internal structure. At less than a hundred pc from the center the rotational velocity is already 200 km/sec. Beyond 100 pc from the center the rotational velocity remains roughly constant at about 250 km/sec. No radial motions have been observed in this inner disk.

At about 4000 pc from the center an expanding arc or ring (the 3-kpc arm) is situated. The full half-width in the z-direction is 130 pc, and if the width in the radial direction is assumed to be three times as large the density is about 2 atoms cm⁻³. The rotational velocity is about 200 km/sec and the radial velocity equals 53 km/sec. Between the inner disk and this structure at 4000 pc is a very confused region where most of the matter ($n_H = 0.3$ cm⁻³) appears to be moving outward with radial velocities of up to 200 km/sec and sometimes low rotational motions.

The main part of the gas is found between 5 and 15 kpc, while some gas appears to extend to nearly 20 kpc from the center. The half thickness is about 270 pc within the solar orbit (10 kpc) and increases farther out. Averaged over the whole region the density is about 0.5 hydrogen atoms cm⁻³. No large (10 km/sec) systematic radial motions are observed. The rotational velocity is about 250 km/sec and decreases very slowly beyond the solar orbit. Up to about 12 kpc from the center the layer of gas is very flat, but farther out rather large systematic deviations occur. But the most noticeable is the distribution of the gas in the plane of the Galaxy, which is suggestive of the spiral structure observed in other galaxies. It should be remembered that the distribution of matter can be obtained from the 21-cm observations only on the basis of some kinematic model. Most models which have been used in the analysis were strictly axisymmetric and no radial motions were assumed. Since spiral structure clearly indicates deviations from axial symmetry and since radial motions may well be associated with it, only the most general features of the distribution of gas can be trusted. A line from the galactic center through the sun probably crosses four major arms between 5 and 15 kpc. If our Galaxy could be approximated by a two-armed logarithmic spiral with each branch represented by an equation $\varpi = \varpi_0 \exp{(m\varphi)}$, where φ is the galactocentric longitude, we would have $m \approx 0.11$ corresponding to a 6° inclination of the spiral arms, but it is not at all clear that such a representation is really possible. Usually it is assumed that the spiral pattern is trailing, i.e., that the spirals open up in a direction opposite to the direction of rotation. In our Galaxy this would be hard to prove conclusively, but in external galaxies most investigators are now convinced that this is the prevailing situation. It must be emphasized, however, that the assumption that our Galaxy has a regular spiral structure is not at all a firm conclusion from the available data which indicate much irregularity. A more extensive summary of the 21-cm data on our Galaxy has recently been given by Oort (1963a). A small part only of the hydrogen in the disk is ionized. Over most of the disk the ionized fraction amounts to a few per cent, but around 5 kpc from the center it may exceed ten per cent.

5.1. The Galactic Nucleus

The galactic nucleus is of special interest because of recent suggestions that the nuclei of galaxies have an important role in the formation and evolution of stellar systems (Ambartzumian 1958), that the explosions of multiple (Burbidge 1962) or very massive (Hoyle and Fowler 1963) supernovae in the nuclei provide the energy for strong radio sources, and that in the galaxy M82 matter is observed that may in fact recently have been expelled from the nuclear regions (Lynds and Sandage 1963). None of these suggestions is very certain but they indicate that a close study of galactic nuclei is important.

According to Westerhout (1958) the radio source Sagittarius A is partly thermal and partly non-thermal. The thermal component is due to about $3 \times 10^7 \, n_e^{-1}$ solar masses of ionized hydrogen (electron density n_e). Later observations have shown that the source has considerable structure (Drake 1959) and that part of the gas is concentrated in a cloud of a few pc radius with a density of a few times 10^3 electrons cm^{-3}. The total amount of gas (10^5 solar masses) is of the same order as that found in the nuclei of some elliptical galaxies and the same ionization mechanism (ultraviolet radiation from evolved stars, Minkowski and Osterbrock 1959) may be operative. If the gravitational field in the galactic nucleus is that of a homogeneous sphere, which at 100 pc from the center yields a circular velocity of 200 km/sec, the radius of an isothermal gas sphere at 10000° K would be 7 pc, and thus the inner condensation could well be in hydrostatic equilibrium.

The non-thermal radiation originates in an ellipsoidal volume with semi-axes of about 200 pc and 100 pc according to Westerhout. From Woltjer's (1959a) discussion it appears that if the energy densities of relativistic electrons and magnetic field are equal, the field strength is 2×10^{-5} G and the total magnetic and electron energies about 5×10^{51} ergs each. But if the relativistic electron density were the same as near the earth, the field would have to be near 10^{-3} G. Such a strong field cannot be contained in the nucleus. From the virial theorem (11) we have, for an isolated source in a steady state,

$$\int \left(\frac{B^2}{8\pi} + 3P \right) d\tau \leq \int \rho x_i \frac{\partial \Phi}{\partial x_i} d\tau = \frac{3}{5} \frac{GMM_g}{R}, \qquad (37)$$

where it is supposed that the mass of gas M_g homogeneously fills a sphere with radius R; M is the total mass within R, also distributed uniformly. With $M_g = 10^5$ solar masses, $R \approx 20$ pc and $M = 3 \times 10^8$ solar masses, we obtain $B < 8 \times 10^{-5}$ G. Of course, more gas of lower density may be present beyond 20 pc, and this could make a somewhat larger B possible. If B equals the upper limit, the density of relativistic electrons is a hundred times larger than near the sun. Secondary production of the electrons by cosmic rays of the same flux as near the earth seems inadequate, and we conclude that the cosmic-ray production per unit volume is somewhat larger in the galactic center than in most of the Galaxy. If an appreciable part of cosmic rays is produced in processes directly or indirectly associated with stars, this need not surprise us. It also would appear necessary that the field in the nucleus is such that it can store the relativistic particles effectively.

The rotating disk around the galactic nucleus does not show signs of important radial motions. It thus appears that the nuclear region of the Galaxy within 700 pc from the center is rather "quiet" with no evidence of violent events.

5.2. RADIAL FLOW IN THE CENTRAL REGION

The region between 1 kpc and 4 kpc from the center presents more difficulties. Two outstanding features of the Rougoor-Oort (1960) analysis of the observations are (1) that the matter in this region moves outward with a velocity that decreases with increasing distance from the center, and (2) that the rotational velocities appear low in the region with large radial velocities, but not very different from the expected circular velocity in the "3-kpc" arm, that is the outermost feature with an appreciable radial velocity.

The general thinking appears to have been that the flow pattern is steady, but it would appear equally possible that the outward motions are an inter-

mittent or even very rare occurrence. If the flow is steady, three questions need
be considered, namely, the origin of the gas, the source of the outward momentum, and the source of the angular momentum for the outward moving gas.
Mass loss from evolving stars appears definitely insufficient to supply the one
or two solar masses per year that are needed, and the only possibility would
seem to be that matter flows in from the halo and is subsequently directed outward in the plane by magnetic fields, which in principle also can take care of
the angular momentum. We shall return to this question in the general discussion of the spiral-structure problem. It will appear that the required field
strengths are uncomfortably high and that the geometry of the field also gives
difficulties. Moreover, stationary magnetic fields can do no work, and a source
of energy for the circulation is needed.

At the other extreme of the range of possibilities is the recent suggestion of
Burbidge and Hoyle (1963) that the galactic halo owes its existence to an explosive event in the nucleus and that this same event is responsible for the outward
motion of the gas in the disk. An obvious difficulty in such a picture is that the
slowest gas is in front of the faster moving gas, while in an explosive event the
opposite might be expected. This difficulty can be circumvented if the gas of
highest velocity has been rather suddenly retarded by the gas already present
in the disk.

The gas at 3.7 kpc has a radial velocity of 53 km/sec. If no gas had been
swept up and if the matter had moved from 100 pc from the center to its present
location without additional acceleration, an initial velocity of 600 km/sec would
have been needed to overcome the gravitational force, and the explosive event
would have occurred 17×10^6 years ago. But the fact that gas with 150 km/sec
velocity is found farther inward would indicate that the explosion actually took
place less than 10×10^6 years ago. The gas that accelerated the 3-kpc arm
should have a higher velocity, 250 km/sec, say, and if the impact had been
sufficiently recent so that not much deceleration had taken place, the present
velocity of the arm would indicate that 80 per cent of the arm mass was already
present before the event. This is in line with the observations that the mass per
unit arm length in the "3-kpc" arm is not very different from that in the other
spiral arms in our Galaxy. The angular-momentum problem is automatically resolved, because the larger part of the mass was rotating before the impact. An
appreciable amount of energy must be dissipated, for an impact velocity of 250
km/sec about 10^{14} erg/gram or with a time scale of 3×10^6 years about 1 erg
gram^{-1} sec^{-1}. Radiative losses for an H I region at 100° K are 2×10^{-4} n_H
erg gram^{-1} sec^{-1}, at 10000° K 20 times larger and for an H II region (at 10000°
K) 5 n_H erg gram^{-1} sec^{-1}. If a magnetic field is present in the arm, some hydrogen might be ionized and some could remain rather cool and be dragged along
by the field. Considerable temperature variations would seem likely and are
indicated by the observation that the line width of the 21-cm line is appreciably smaller in absorption than in emission. As the absorption coefficient

of neutral hydrogen varies as T^{-1}, the cooler matter is preferentially observed in absorption.

A difficulty in this model is the present structure within 700 pc from the center. It is almost inconceivable that the rotating disk would not have been swept away, unless the gas is concentrated in very dense clouds, which is not completely excluded if the halo pressure is high near the galactic center. If the disk has been formed during the last 10^7 years about 0.3 solar masses per year must have been deposited. If gas is ejected in the galactic plane, a much larger amount would be expected to be injected into the halo if the explosion were more or less isotropic. Since this matter has had less retardation it would be somewhat farther from the center.

The most serious difficulties of this model are the fact that the observations suggest, but do not prove, that the matter with velocities of 150 km/sec to 200 km/sec is located *much* nearer to the center than the 3-kpc arm and that the total amount of matter ejected in the disk must be of the order of 10^7 solar masses. Including that gone into the halo, an explosion energy of the order of 10^{57} erg would appear indicated. Of course a multiple explosion also could explain the kinematic situation, but then everything becomes rather arbitrary.

A number of other suggestions do not appear very likely. Hoyle and Ireland (1961) considered the possibility that a rapidly rotating, very massive halo drags the gas along in the azimuthal direction, and thus provides angular momentum to the outward streaming gas. Woltjer (1963b) indicated that sudden star formation in a partly magnetically supported ring of gas can initiate radial motions. B. Lindblad (1962) suggests that a dispersion ring suitably oriented could give some apparently radial motions. Quantitatively these different ideas are not very promising.

5.3. THE DISTRIBUTION OF GAS IN THE z-DIRECTION

The flatness of the gas layer within the solar orbit indicates that the locus of the points where $\partial \Phi / \partial z = 0$ is to a very good approximation a plane. Since the stellar component in the Galaxy, which produces most of the gravitational field, probably has had a long enough lifetime for appreciable dynamical relaxation (phase mixing) to have taken place, this need not surprise us. However, outside the solar orbit the gas layer bends in a systematic way. Kahn and Woltjer (1959) have shown that it is improbable that this is due to a curvature of the $\partial \Phi / \partial z = 0$ surface. Tidal effects associated with the Magellanic Clouds seem insufficient to produce these effects (Burke 1957; Kerr, Hindman, and Carpenter, 1957) even if rather large masses for the Magellanic Clouds are assumed (Lozinskaya and Kardashev 1962). Kahn and Woltjer have shown that the motion of the Galaxy through a possible gaseous medium in the Local Group of galaxies could create a pressure distribution around the halo of the correct magnitude and geometry to push the outer parts of the layer of gas out of the galactic plane, if the Galaxy moves in a more or less radial orbit with respect to the center of the Local Group.

5.4. SPIRAL STRUCTURE

The spiral-like arrangement of the luminous matter is one of the most conspicuous features in many galaxies, but no satisfactory explanation has yet been proposed. Arguments of varying weight have been presented in favor of gravitational, hydromagnetic, or fundamental theories. At the moment it is not clear that a single theory will suffice to explain the spiral structure in all galaxies. It would appear most fruitful then to investigate various mechanisms that could be of importance in detail, and in a more quantitative fashion than has been done heretofore, not so much to find "the" explanation, but to obtain a better idea of what possibilities exist. In the following sections we shall first discuss the kinematic problems associated with the existence of spiral structure. Subsequently, we shall consider what effects magnetic fields can produce in a galaxy in which the gravitational field is axisymmetric. We conclude with a brief outline of theories in which gravitational effects are dominant. It is convenient to subdivide the spiral galaxies into three groups.

Barred Spirals have a basically non-axisymmetric mass distribution and gravitational field. Prendergast (1963) has shown that the barred spirals can be qualitatively understood on the basis of an analysis of the motion of a pressure-free fluid in a rotating non-axisymmetric gravitational field.

Spiral-like Galaxies are galaxies that appear axisymmetric at least in a general way. They show spiral structure, but no systematic spiral pattern can be recognized. The structure rather consists of separate spiral segments or spiral arcs. Examples in the Hubble-Sandage Atlas (Sandage 1961) are NGC 2841 and NGC 5055.

Spiral Galaxies have a large-scale spiral pattern that pervades an appreciable part of the main body of the galaxy. Examples in the Hubble-Sandage Atlas are NGC 5364 and M81, both with two arms, while probably galaxies like M101 and NGC 1232 with more than two arms also belong in this group. Of course, as the number of arms increases the contrast with the preceding class becomes less clear.

Unfortunately no detailed kinematical data on these galaxies are available; only rotation curves have been obtained in a number of cases. Also, at best we know something about the light distribution in some galaxies, but the mass distribution and more specifically the mass concentration in the spiral arms remain uncertain. Gas and young stars are abundant in the spiral arms, but they may represent only part of the matter.

In our own Galaxy more information is available on the neutral hydrogen gas. But because the distance of elements of gas can only be obtained from the measured radial velocities in conjunction with a kinematic model, difficulties of interpretation are serious. It is even difficult to be sure that seen from the out-

side our Galaxy would present a systematic pattern, though this may not be unlikely. The atomic hydrogen density in between the arms in our Galaxy is probably at least three times smaller than in the arms, but again the contrast in the
total mass density is uncertain. Clearly a knowledge of the mass contained in
the spiral arms is a prerequisite for the evaluation of gravitational effects in the
theory of spiral structure.

5.4.1. *Kinematical problems.*—The first difficulty in the theory of spiral structure is of a kinematical character and well known (cf., for example, Burbidge
and Prender ;ast 1960; Oort 1963c). Suppose that the material elements which
constitute the spiral structure, in a galaxy with a large-scale spiral pattern,
move in circular orbits with a velocity that is independent of azimuth. Consider a piece of spiral arm that makes locally an angle ψ with the azimuthal
direction (positive for trailing arms). Consider two neighboring points on the
spiral arm (supposed to be infinitely thin for the moment) separated by $\Delta\varphi$ in
galactocentric longitude and thus by $\varpi\Delta\varphi \tan \psi$ in radial distance. Here ϖ, φ,
and z define a galactocentric system of cylindrical coordinates. If we count
galactocentric longitudes positive in the same direction as galactic longitudes,
our Galaxy rotates in the direction of decreasing φ. To first order the difference
in the angular velocity at the two points considered is $\varpi\Delta\varphi \tan \psi \, (\partial\Omega/\partial\varpi)$. Thus
the time in which the spiral pattern is locally uncoiled, that is the time in which
$|\psi|$ becomes $\pi/2$, is given by

$$
T_{sp} = \frac{-\Delta\varphi}{\varpi\Delta\varphi \tan\psi \, (\partial\Omega/\partial\varpi)} = \frac{-1}{\varpi \tan\psi \, (\partial\Omega/\partial\varpi)}
$$

$$
= \frac{T_{rot}}{2\pi \tan\psi \, (\partial \ln\Omega/\partial \ln\varpi)} ,
$$

(38)

where T_{rot} is the local time of revolution. For small $|\psi|$, $-T_{sp}$ is also the time in
which ψ would be halved. In typical cases the linear rotation velocity changes
only slightly in the region of spiral structure. Thus, with $\Omega \propto \varpi^{-1}$ and with ψ
equal to 0.11 r ıd (as a rough estimate for our Galaxy), we would have about
$T_{sp} = 1.6 \, T_{rot}$. For the galaxies without a general pattern this may not be too
serious, but for the true spiral galaxies this seems an embarrassingly short time
scale in which to form, to develop fully, and to dissolve again a large-scale pattern. It thus appears that the assumption that the material elements of the
spiral structure rotate in circular orbits with constant velocities is incorrect. In
principle, two ways seem open to resolve the difficulties.

It could be supposed that the spiral pattern represents a compression wave
th ıt propagates through the galactic disk. For example, if the matter in the arms
moves in circular orbits, but with variable angular velocity, a pattern could already be obtained, and the velocity of the pattern would have no direct relation
to the velocity of the matter in the pattern. More generally, if the matter moves
in on the averaged closed trajectories, the density contrast between the arms

and the space in between could be brought about by the crowding of the trajectories in the pattern and by the variable velocity along the trajectory for each element of matter. Then the spiral arms must have finite thickness and the interarm region cannot be empty. Such a picture resolves the kinematical difficulties, but of course a dynamic justification is needed.

The alternative possibility, at first sight quite simple, would be that matter streams along the arms. Such a model could even yield very thin arms with no matter in between. Again the winding problem would be resolved, but an equally serious kinematic problem arises with the equation of continuity. If the spiral pattern is to remain stationary it should rotate as a solid body with arbitrary angular velocity Ω_{sp}. If the matter moves along the arms and if the azimuthal velocity is u_φ the radial velocity component is given by

$$u_\varpi = - (\Omega_{sp}\varpi - u_\varphi)\tan\psi . \tag{39}$$

Upon integration over φ and over the width of the galactic disk, the equation of continuity $\partial\rho/\partial t = -\nabla\cdot(\rho u)$ yields

$$\int_0^{2\pi} d\varphi \int_{-z}^{+z} \frac{\partial\rho}{\partial t}\, dz = - \int_0^{2\pi} d\varphi \Big[\int_{-z}^{+z} \frac{1}{\varpi}\frac{\partial}{\partial\varpi}(\varpi\rho u_\varpi)\, dz + \rho u_z\Big|_{-z}^{+z} \Big]. \tag{40}$$

If no matter flows into or out of the disk and if $\bar\rho$, the density averaged over φ and z, and u_φ are taken independent of ϖ (which applies reasonably well to the gas in our Galaxy), we have

$$\frac{\partial\bar\rho}{\partial t} = - \frac{1}{\varpi}\frac{\partial}{\partial\varpi}(\overline{\varpi\rho u_\varpi}) = - \bar\rho \tan\psi \left(2\Omega_{sp} - \frac{u_\varphi}{\varpi}\right). \tag{41}$$

Thus the flow has considerable divergence, and the density chan ;es by a factor of e in a time

$$T_\rho = \frac{1}{|\tan\psi\,(2\Omega_s - u_\varphi/\varpi)|} = \frac{T_{rot}}{2\pi\tan\psi}\frac{1}{|2(T_{rot}/T_{sp}) - 1|}. \tag{42}$$

Since in a good part of a galaxy the last factor will be of order unity, the difficulties with the continuity equation occur on typically the same time scale as those with the winding of the spiral pattern on the simple picture of pure rotation. If more precise values for $\bar\rho$ and u_φ are taken (see Table 6) the results remain qualitatively the same.

Of course the application of the equation of continuity to the gas raises some questions, because the effects of star formation and stellar mass loss should also be taken into account. However, according to Schwarzschild (1963), the turn-over time for the gas is of the order of 10^9 years and thus rather long to affect the above estimates, especially so because the highly uncertain birth rate of very early-type stars is irrelevant, since they shed mass not very far from the place where they were born. Nevertheless these effects certainly will have to be included in any final theory.

Two ways out again appear possible. We could suppose that gas flows from the halo into the disk and vice versa in just such a way that the surface term in equation (40) compensates for the volume term. The inflow of gas should take place only over the spiral arms, while the outflow probably should also occur over the interarm regions, because the effects of star formation and stellar mass loss tend to transport matter from the arms to the regions in between. The model becomes highly complex in this case, and the whole problem of the condensation of the halo medium and the mass balance of the halo would have to be discussed. Alternatively we could envisage with Oort (1963b) that the gas flows back rather directly in between the arms both in the disk and perhaps through the lower parts of the halo. Such a model of course approaches the compression-wave type of picture rather closely.

We now make some numerical estimates with parameters suitable for our Galaxy, for which of course the existence of a large-scale pattern is still in doubt. Near the sun we take $\varpi_0 = 10$ kpc, $\Omega = -2.5 \times 10^{-8}$ rad/yr, $\partial\Omega/\partial\varpi = 3 \times 10^{-9}$ rad/yr/kpc, and thus $T_{\rm rot} = 2.5 \times 10^8$ years, and $\psi = 0.11$ rad. Then from equation (38) we have $T_{\rm sp} = 1.21\, T_{\rm rot} = 3 \times 10^8$ years. Suppose now that matter streams along the arms and that equation (39) is applicable. If u_ϖ is known near the sun $\Omega_{\rm sp}$ can be determined.

From the solar motion with respect to different objects, differential radial motions between various galactic subsystems could be obtained. No such motions have been detected, and the consensus appears to be that differential radial motions between the gas and most of the stars in the solar neighborhood are less than 1 or 2 km/sec. Kerr (1962) has suggested that the small differences between the rotation curves determined at Leiden and Sydney provide evidence for an outward motion of the local standard of rest and thus for an outward motion of both the gas and most of the stars near the sun. Kerr estimated the velocity in the radial direction as 7 km/sec. The suggestion has even been made that this motion and the observed outward flow nearer to the galactic center (3-kpc arm and related phenomena) indicate a general outflow of matter in the galactic plane. Many reasons can be advanced, however, which indicate that this picture is very unconvincing.

1) Different reduction methods used for the discussion of the Leiden and Sydney observations could account for part of the difference between the rotation curves.

2) The argumentation indicates a belief in the strict axial symmetry of the Galaxy. However, no steady state with systematic outward motions and strict axisymmetry is possible for the stellar system.

3) There is no valid reason for supposing that the velocity field in the gas should be strictly axisymmetric. High-resolution data (Burke et al. 1963) on the Andromeda Nebula show that asymmetries can be expected. The longitude distribution of the deviations from flatness of the galactic gas layer also indicates that axial symmetry is only limited.

4) A picture in which the gas moves out systematically from the 3-kpc arm

region to beyond the solar orbit does not resolve the kinematical difficulties associated with spiral structure, and the picture would encounter very serious dynamical difficulties.

We thus would consider it likely that the local standard of rest as usually defined moves around the galactic center in a circular orbit. The fact that near the sun no differential motion in the radial direction between stars and gas is observed then indicates that in equation (39) Ω_{sp} has to be chosen such that u_ϖ vanishes near the sun. This special position of the sun is, of course, rather disturbing. Thus we have

$$u_\varpi = -\left[u_\varphi(\varpi_0)\frac{\varpi}{\varpi_0} - u_\varphi(\varpi) \right] \tan\psi . \qquad (43)$$

TABLE 6

MODEL OF THE GALACTIC DISK, WITH GAS STREAMING
ALONG THE SPIRAL ARMS*

ϖ (kpc)	u_φ (km/s)	N_H (10^{20} cm^{-2})	u_ϖ (km/s)	T_ρ (10^8 y)	$[\rho u_z]_{-z}^{+z}$ (10^{-8} ⊙ pc^{-2}y^{-1})	B_φ (μG)	$u_\varphi-\theta$ (km/s)
6...	−234	4.8	− 9	9	−0.5	92	+60
8...	−248	6.5	− 5	7	+0.8	79	+28
10...	... −250	4.7	0	3	+1.3	66	0
12...	−238	6.4	+ 7	2	+2.9	52	− 20
14...	−226	7.0	+14	120	+0.1	33	−35
16...	−214	2.0	+20	1	−1.9	14	−44
18...	−203	0.3	+27	0.3	−0.7	4	−57

* The velocities of the gas u_φ are taken as an average of the Leiden and Sydney results ($\varpi < 10$ kpc) and from Schmidt's model in chapter 22 ($\varpi \geq 10$ kpc). The hydrogen surface density N_H as determined by van Woerden is taken from Oort (1963a). The radial velocity u_ϖ is computed from equation (43) with tan $\psi = 0.11$. The time T_ρ in which the density would change by a factor e if $u_z = 0$ and the flow out of the galactic plane ρu_z for the case $\partial\rho/\partial t = 0$ are determined from equation (40). Finally the magnetic field B_φ and the difference of the rotational velocity of the gas and the circular velocity are derived from equations (46) and (49). As explained in the text it is unlikely that the model can represent the galactic disk.

Within the solar orbit matter moves inward, while farther out the flow is outward. In Table 6 we give the values of u_ϖ calculated from this equation for different values of ϖ. The times T_ρ are also given, as well as the matter exchange term with the halo for a steady state. It is seen that near the sun about 1 or 2 times 10^{-8} ⊙ pc^{-2} y^{-1} should condense from the halo. Let us now compare this picture with observation. Small radial motions within the solar orbit would be hard to detect, because of confusion with the regions near the center. But outward motions in the direction of the anticenter in excess of a few km/sec should be observable without difficulty. Inspection of the 21-cm results shows that such motions are absent. Thus, either equation (43) is not applicable or the angle of inclination decreases farther out. In fact, it is not uncommon in galaxies that the spiral structure is surrounded by a circular ring. McGee and Murray (1961) have shown that matter streams in from both galactic poles. This may be a purely local phenomenon, but if it is not, the order of magnitude agreement between their (quite uncertain) figure of about $6 \times 10^{-8} \odot \text{pc}^{-2} y^{-1}$ and the results of Table 6 is suggestive. Thus, at the moment a final conclusion about the compatibility of this model with observation still would be somewhat premature, although on the whole the difficulties appear rather serious.

5.4.2. *Radial flow with magnetic fields.*—Consider a galaxy with an axisymmetric gravitational field. If the gas behaves as a perfect fluid, only magnetic forces can account for the radial motions discussed in the preceding section. Typically, in the region of spiral structure $u_\varphi \approx$ constant and thus the angular momentum per unit mass must be changed if an element of gas moves systematically in or out. To construct a complete hydromagnetic model for the spiral structure would be quite difficult, but some results can be obtained in a simpler manner.

Let us consider the following situation (a somewhat similar case has been discussed by Wentzel 1961, 1963). In the central plane of a galaxy matter flows along an axisymmetric field in a frame of reference rotating with angular velocity Ω. The lines of force are spirals with constant inclination ψ. In the central plane $u_z = 0$ and $B_z = 0$. The system is in a steady state. Referring all physical parameters to an inertial frame, we have

$$B_\varpi = - B_\varphi \tan \psi ,$$
$$u_\varpi = - (\Omega \varpi - u_\varphi) \tan \psi . \tag{44}$$

The φ-component of the equation of motion (1) becomes

$$B_\varpi \frac{\partial}{\partial \varpi} (\varpi B_\varphi) = 4\pi \rho u_\varpi \frac{\partial}{\partial \varpi} (\varpi u_\varphi). \tag{45}$$

With equation (44) this becomes

$$\frac{\partial}{\partial \varpi} (\varpi^2 B_\varphi^2) = - 8\pi \varpi \rho (\Omega \varpi - u_\varphi) \frac{\partial}{\partial \varpi} (\varpi u_\varphi), \tag{46}$$

and if we consider a case in which ρ and u_φ are constant, we obtain upon integration

$$B_\varphi^2 = \frac{Q\varpi_0^2}{\varpi^2} - 8\pi \rho u_\varphi (\tfrac{1}{3}\Omega\varpi - \tfrac{1}{2}u_\varphi), \tag{47}$$

with $Q\varpi_0^2$ a constant of integration. The radial component of the equation of motion is

$$\frac{\partial}{\partial \varpi} (\varpi^2 B_\varphi^2) = 8\pi \varpi \rho (u_\varphi^2 - \Theta^2) - 4\pi \varpi^2 \rho \frac{\partial}{\partial \varpi} u_\varpi^2, \tag{48}$$

with Θ the circular velocity ($\Theta^2/\varpi = \partial \Phi / \partial \varpi$). With equations (44) and (46) we obtain

$$\Theta^2 - u_\varphi^2 = - (u_\varphi - \Omega\varpi) \frac{\partial}{\partial \varpi} (\varpi u_\varphi) - \tfrac{1}{2}\varpi \frac{\partial}{\partial \varpi} [(\Omega\varpi - u_\varphi)^2 \tan^2 \psi]. \tag{49}$$

If the angle ψ is small, the last term is almost negligible, and if we take again u_φ a constant, we have

$$\Theta^2 - u_\varphi^2 = - u_\varphi (u_\varphi - \Omega \varpi). \tag{50}$$

Beyond ϖ_0 $(= u_\varphi/\Omega)$ the gas rotates below the circular velocity, while for $\varpi < \varpi_0$ it rotates faster. It is interesting to note that the angle of inclination ψ is not very important in the dynamics of this problem if it is not too large. Also from equation (50) it appears that the differences between the gas velocity and the circular velocity do not depend directly on the magnetic field strength and that these differences tend to be of the same order of magnitude as the circular velocity itself.

In Table 6 we have given the value of B_φ (calculated from eq. [46] with the constant of integration chosen in such a way that the field vanishes near 18 kpc, which gives the smallest possible values for B_φ^2) and the values of $u_\varphi - \Theta$ (calculated from eq. [49]). It appears that the magnetic field is unlikely to be so large; also the deviations from circular velocities appear too great. Of course, the calculations are illustrative only, the more so because u_φ outside the solar orbit has not been observed, but only extrapolated from the values farther in on the basis of a model that was based on the assumption that $u_\varphi - \Theta$ is essentially zero.

If we try to apply the preceding discussion to a model of a stationary outflow of matter from the galactic nuclear region, we directly encounter the difficulty that an outflow corresponds to the opposite sense of winding of the field lines. Thus, we would have to suppose that the spiral arms have a different sense in different parts of the Galaxy, and this appears rather difficult. The strength of the field required ($\sim$50 μG) also would be rather on the high side. The kinematical pattern would be really quite complex if we were to consider all these flows. Near the center matter would flow in from the halo, but around 4 or 5 kpc the matter must evaporate again because there the outward flow from the inner parts and the inward flow from the outer parts meet. Near the sun the matter would again flow into the galactic plane, and far out it should move again into the halo. Thus, if a model of this kind is envisaged, the simplest possibility is extremely complicated.

The model described thus can hardly represent the central plane of the Galaxy even in a qualitative fashion, but this need not surprise us. Since the mean free path of the interstellar gas clouds is of the same order as the width of the galactic disk, a discussion of the central plane only is too limited in scope. More seriously, we have assumed $B_z = 0$, but it can be shown that if the field near the sun exceeds 10 μG, the equilibrium of the spiral arms in the z-direction requires helical field lines winding around the arms (Woltjer 1963b), and thus a rather strong B_z field should be present in the disk. This has the consequence that the system cannot be strictly axisymmetric.

Let us consider again the equation of motion (1). We take the φ-component and integrate it over φ (0 to 2π) and over the width of the disk ($-z$ to $+z$).

After a few partial integrations in which use is made of $\nabla \cdot \boldsymbol{B} = 0$ and $\nabla \cdot (\rho \boldsymbol{u}) = -\partial \rho / \partial t$, we obtain

$$\frac{\partial}{\partial t} \int_0^{2\pi} d\varphi \int_{-z}^{+z} \rho u_\varphi d z$$

$$= \int_0^{2\pi} d\varphi \left\{ \int_{-z}^{+z} d z \left[\frac{1}{\varpi^2} \frac{\partial}{\partial \varpi} \left(\frac{\varpi^2 B_\varpi B_\varphi}{4\pi} - \varpi^2 \rho u_\varpi u_\varphi \right) - \frac{\rho}{\varpi} \frac{\partial \Phi}{\partial \varphi} \right] \quad (51) \right.$$

$$\left. + \left(\frac{B_\varphi B_z}{4\pi} - \rho u_\varphi u_z \right) \Big|_{-z}^{+z} \right\}.$$

Thus, the angular-momentum balance in the disk does not only depend on magnetic and gravitational forces in the disk, but also on the magnetic coupling to the halo and on the angular momentum of the matter that streams in from the halo. Let us suppose we have a steady state, and let us further write $B_\varphi = \bar{B}_\varphi + \delta B_\varphi$, with the bar denoting an average over φ and z and similar expressions for the other variables. Then this equation can be rewritten as

$$0 = \int_0^{2\pi} d\varphi \left[\!\!\left[\int_{-z}^{+z} d z \left\{ \frac{\bar{B}_\varpi}{4\pi\varpi} \frac{\partial}{\partial \varpi} (\varpi \bar{B}_\varphi) - \frac{\langle \rho u_\varpi \rangle}{\varpi} \frac{\partial}{\partial \varpi} (\varpi \bar{u}_\varphi) \right. \right. \right.$$

$$+ \frac{1}{\varpi^2} \frac{\partial}{\partial \varpi} \left[\frac{\varpi^2 \delta B_\varpi \delta B_\varphi}{4\pi} - \varpi^2 \delta (\rho u_\varpi) \delta u_\varphi \right] - \frac{\delta \rho}{\varpi} \frac{\partial \Phi}{\partial \varphi} \right\} \quad (52)$$

$$\left. \left. + \left(\frac{B_z \delta B_\varphi}{4\pi} - \rho u_z \delta u_\varphi \right) \Big|_{-z}^{+z} \right]\!\!\right].$$

Thus, if the magnetic surface term vanishes, if the matter exchange with the halo takes place with the local angular momentum, and if the gravitational term and the terms that are quadratic in the deviations from the mean can be neglected, the result of equation (45) is again obtained. But if matter streams in from the halo with a different angular momentum the situation can be different. Thus it would not be inconceivable that a system of streaming motions through the halo could be devised that would reduce the field strength needed in the disk (an example of such a model is that described by Oort in chap. 21, this volume). Then the model becomes really highly complex, and a discussion of the way in which matter is ejected into the halo and in which it condenses again into the plane becomes of prime importance.

The ϖ-component of equation (1) yields upon integration a somewhat lengthy expression. The main novel term is $\partial B_z^2 / \partial \varpi$. Suitably chosen this term could smooth the excessive differences between the gas velocity and the circular velocity obtained before.

Until now we have omitted the induction equation from our discussion. It is not clear how well the lines of force of the general galactic field are tied to the matter in the interstellar gas clouds, and the correct equation for our case is somewhat in doubt (Woltjer 1963b), but it appears that this equation will in general cause additional difficulties.

Thus, at the moment no final conclusion on the streaming model can be reached; but the difficulties that are encountered appear serious.

5.4.3. *Other hydromagnetic and hydrodynamic theories.*—Hoyle and Ireland (1960) considered spiral arms as magnetic tubes that are winding up. As the winding becomes too tight, whole loops of the spiral structure are supposed to be lifted out of the galactic plane and into the halo. And it is even suggested that this could contribute appreciably to the halo field. It is argued that the spiral loops can rise from the galactic plane because the matter streams downward along the lines of force, but no quantitative discussion of the instability is given and the mechanism must remain in doubt. Also the situation in many galaxies does not look very much as if the structure has already been wound to the breaking point. And at best the rather irregular spiral system could be explained in this way, but not the systems with a large-scale pattern. Nevertheless, the possibility of removing some loops out of the plane remains interesting and should be considered more thoroughly. In a later investigation, Hoyle and Ireland (1961) give arguments why most field lines in the halo cannot have their origin in the spiral arms in the disk and suggest that the rapid rotation in the inner part of the Galaxy can be used to twist the field lines in the spiral arms in such a way that the field in the arms becomes helical (Ireland 1961*a*, *b*). It is not clear that this suggestion is compatible with their first model.

Oki, Fujimoto, and Hitotuyanagi (1961) discussed on the basis of the exact equations the evolution of a magnetic field with lines of force that spiral outward, and confirm that if the situation remains two-dimensional the age of a spiral arm cannot much exceed the period of revolution. They evaluate rather precisely the radial motions that arise during the winding of the field lines. Wentzel (1960) discusses the evolution of a large cloud complex with a magnetic field and shows that it is drawn into a spiral that cannot become too thin because of the magnetic pressure.

Elvius and Herlofson (1960; see also Elvius and Lindblad 1959) proposed that the gas is situated in rings rather than in spiral arms. They suppose that a magnetic field is embedded in the gas and that therefore the rings rotate faster than would correspond to the circular velocity. Actually, as we have discussed before, a lag velocity would be more likely. They then argue that if star formation occurs, the stars will move out of the arm, because they do not experience the magnetic forces, and form a spiral pattern. It is not clear that in this way a systematic spiral pattern that extends over a not very small part of the Galaxy can be produced. But also the fact that H II regions, which are associated with stars of a very brief lifetime, delineate the spiral structure so well cannot be fitted in the model except by additional hypotheses. Still the idea that stars and gas can under certain circumstances behave rather differently is certainly a valid one.

Other extremely speculative ideas have been advanced in which ad hoc hypotheses abound. As a somewhat quantitative discussion is usually lacking, it does not seem worthwhile to consider these further.

Theories of a more purely gas-dynamical nature have also been considered.

Somewhat before the time that adequate data about galaxies became available, von Weizsäcker (1947) showed that much that was known about the interstellar medium could be understood on the basis of turbulence theory. Heisenberg and von Weizsäcker (1948) argued that differential rotation makes spirals from irregular bodies, but that too much winding of the spirals is prevented by the turbulence which dissolves the spiral arms when they become too thin. From the observed small number of windings von Weizsäcker concluded that turbulent velocities are of the same order of magnitude as rotational velocities. It would seem doubtful to us that under those circumstances a large-scale spiral pattern could be present. Gradually the turbulence theories have gone out of fashion, because random velocities are not so very large and because it is not at all clear that the motions in the interstellar gas are turbulent in the hydrodynamic sense. The turbulence was supposed to be maintained by the differential rotation, but as remarked by various authors circular motions are stable for large Reynolds numbers if $d(\varpi^2\, u_\varphi^2)/d\varpi > 0$ in a two-dimensional galaxy. This condition is amply satisfied in most galaxies. But, as will be seen in our further discussion, in the presence of gravitation it is not at all clear that this is a relevant criterion.

A quite different hydrodynamical model has been mentioned by Oort (1963b), who considered the transport of angular momentum due to the exchange of gas between spiral arms. By its nature this mechanism, if it really operates effectively, can only assist the formation and maintenance of spiral structure but certainly cannot be the sole factor as it requires tight winding of the structure and as it does not help in understanding the outermost spiral arms.

5.4.4. *Gravito-gas dynamic considerations.*—Gravitation is the dominant force in any galaxy, and thus it might seem plausible that gravitation would play a fundamental role in the development of spiral structure. As several attempts based on gravitation were on the whole not very successful or convincing, the interest shifted partly to other theories; but the neglect of gravitation in some of these may well have been unjustified. Quite recently the hydrodynamic stability of gaseous (or stellar) disks and its relevance to spiral structure have been studied by Lin and Shu (1964) and Toomre (1964), and we shall first discuss some aspects of this work.

Suppose an axisymmetric gaseous disk of zero thickness, in which $P = 0$ and $u_{\varpi_0} = 0$ suffers arbitrary small displacements with components only in the plane of the disk. After linearizing the continuity equation, the equation of motion, and Poisson's equation, we have—with σ the surface density and primed quantities the first-order perturbations—

$$\frac{\partial \sigma'}{\partial t} + \frac{1}{\varpi}\frac{\partial}{\partial \varpi}(\varpi \sigma_0 u_\varpi') + \frac{\sigma_0}{\varpi}\frac{\partial u_\varphi'}{\partial \varphi} + \frac{u_{\varphi_0}}{\varpi}\frac{\partial \sigma'}{\partial \varphi} = 0, \tag{53}$$

$$\frac{\partial u_\varpi'}{\partial t} + \frac{u_{\varphi_0}}{\varpi}\frac{\partial u_\varpi'}{\partial \varphi} - \frac{2u_{\varphi_0}u_\varphi'}{\varpi} = -\frac{\partial \Phi'}{\partial \varpi}, \tag{54}$$

$$\frac{\partial u'_\varphi}{\partial t} + \frac{1}{\varpi}\frac{\partial (\varpi u_{\varphi 0})}{\partial \varpi}\, u'_\varpi + \frac{u_{\varphi 0}}{\varpi}\frac{\partial u'_\varphi}{\partial \varphi} = -\frac{1}{\varpi}\frac{\partial \Phi'}{\partial \varphi}, \tag{55}$$

$$\frac{1}{\varpi}\frac{\partial}{\partial \varpi}\left(\varpi\frac{\partial \Phi'}{\partial \varpi}\right) + \frac{1}{\varpi^2}\frac{\partial^2 \Phi'}{\partial \varphi^2} + \frac{\partial^2 \Phi'}{\partial z^2} = 4\pi G\sigma'\delta(z). \tag{56}$$

The last equation is the *three*-dimensional Poisson equation and δ is the delta function. For the axisymmetric isothermal gas an investigation of the stability had already been made by Bel and Schatzman (1958) who consider only the two-dimensional Poisson equation, which is not appropriate for a disk. Pacholczyk (1961, and further references there) has included the effects of magnetic fields in the analysis and also considers the stability problem in relation to the spiral structure.

Since the equilibrium state is axisymmetric and time independent, a Fourier analysis in φ and t is useful, and we write for a typical Fourier component

$$\sigma' = \mathrm{Re}\{\tilde{\sigma}(\varpi)\exp[i(\omega t + m\varphi)]\} \tag{57}$$

and similar expressions for the other primed variables. Here ω and $\tilde{\sigma}$ are generally complex and Re denotes the real part. Writing $\tilde{\sigma}(\varpi) = a(\varpi)\exp[ib(\varpi)]$ with a and b real, and also $\omega = \omega_r + i\omega_i$, we have

$$\sigma' = a(\varpi)\exp(-\omega_i t)\cos[\omega_r t + m\varphi + b(\varpi)]. \tag{58}$$

As remarked by Lin and Shu, the density maxima thus are spirals (trailing if $db/d\varpi > 0$) which rotate with angular velocity ω_r and which grow exponentially in time if $\omega_i < 0$. In the linear theory the different modes (different m and ω) are independent. Of course, the pattern obtained by superposing two modes generally does not rotate as a solid body.

To see what really happens, the growth of the different modes must be followed in the region where the linear theory is no longer valid, but this is exceedingly difficult. One might, however, expect (though this is certainly not always true) that the modes, which in the linear theory have the fastest growth rate ($-\omega_i$ large), most likely will show up also in the finite amplitude case. Thus it would be interesting to know whether a disk-like galaxy would be unstable especially for perturbations that correspond to two-armed spirals ($m = 2$).

A full stability analysis has not yet been made, but Toomre (1964) has discussed the axisymmetric case ($m = 0$), which although not directly relevant to the spiral problem leads to interesting results. To see the essence of Toomre's analysis we note that if

$$\sigma' = J_0(a\varpi)\exp(i\omega t), \tag{59}$$

with J_0 a Bessel function of the first kind, the solution of Poisson's equation is

$$\Phi' = \frac{2\pi G}{a} J_0(a\varpi)\exp(-a|z|)\exp(i\omega t). \tag{60}$$

If now a is large enough, $J_0(a\varpi)$ varies much more rapidly than ϖ, $u_{\varphi 0}$, or σ_0, and a local analysis in which these quantities are treated as constants may yield useful results. It can be verified that in this approximation equations (59) and (60) indeed lead to a consistent solution of the other hydrodynamic equations, provided we satisfy the condition

$$\omega^2 = \frac{1}{\varpi^3}\frac{d}{d\varpi}(\varpi u_{\varphi 0})^2 - 2\pi G a \sigma_0 = \kappa_0^2 - 2\pi G a \sigma_0, \tag{61}$$

where the epicyclic frequency, κ, thus is treated as a constant. For solid-body rotation κ is strictly constant, and the solution is exact if $d\sigma_0/d\varpi = 0$. From equation (61) it appears that a pressure-free disk is always unstable against perturbations of small enough wavelength (large a). But in the interstellar gas pressure effects are not completely negligible. Toomre treats the effects of random motions in the equilibrium state from the point of view of the Boltzmann equation, which is appropriate for the case of stars. For the gas we can simply include the ∇P term in the equation of motion. For a uniform disk it is found that to the right-hand side of equation (61) a term $+(\gamma P_0/\rho_0)a^2 = c_0^2 a^2$, with c_0 the sound velocity, should be added. Thus pressure effects stabilize the small wavelengths and the rotation stabilizes the long wavelengths. Let us consider the gas in the galactic disk. With $\sigma = 10^{-3}\,\mathrm{g\,cm^{-2}}$ and $\kappa = 10^{-15}\,\mathrm{sec^{-1}}$ instability for the zero-pressure case is obtained if $\lambda = 2\pi/a < 600$ pc. But pressure effects stabilize the situation at all wavelengths if $c_0 > 2\pi G\sigma_0/\kappa_0 \approx 4$ km/sec.

However, these figures are not meaningful as the disk of gas is gravitationally coupled to the disk of stars. As the total mass of the disk is ten times larger than that of the gas, the stability condition for the disk as a whole would appear not to be satisfied by a large margin, and this is confirmed by Toomre's analysis. Toomre in fact suggests that the instabilities have increased the velocity dispersion of the stars until a marginally stable situation was reached. The wavelength at which stabilization is most difficult is equal to $8\pi^2 G\sigma_0/\kappa^2$, which for the gas alone comes to somewhat more than a kiloparsec and for the disk of gas and stars at several kiloparsecs.

The treatment of the non-axisymmetric modes is much more difficult. In the case of solid-body rotation solutions can still be found, and Toomre gives an expression for ω. But in the more interesting case of differential rotation the situation is obscure. Toomre obtains spiral modes that are wrapped up as time progresses, while Lin considers spiral modes in solid-body rotation. Both follow from a local analysis. The results are not necessarily contradictory. Clearly there is considerable freedom in the set of basic functions in which one expands the perturbations. But this also makes it somewhat doubtful whether firm conclusions concerning the spiral structure can be made from the work up until now. Clearly some exact (numerical) solutions would be very helpful.

Thus the self-gravitation of the matter in the disk may be of great importance in the development of spiral structure. In a way a certain connection with the point of view of B. Lindblad is established; although the purely stellar dynamical theories of spiral structure are somewhat outside the scope of this chapter, we shall briefly discuss the picture developed by B. Lindblad and P. O. Lindblad. For details on a number of concepts involved the reader is referred to chapter 21. A comparison between the work of the Lindblads and that of Lin and Toomre is difficult because particle orbits are extensively used in the former. In principle, however, a theory based on particle orbits and a theory based on the Boltzmann equation for the stars should yield identical results; in the present state of development of the different theories this is not necessarily true.

At the basis of the Lindblad theories (B. Lindblad and Langebartel 1953; B. Lindblad 1959, 1962, 1963) are the possible density waves that can occur in a very flat stellar system. In the inner regions of a galaxy with nearly constant angular velocity—this is not so in our Galaxy—bar-type density waves are particularly important. These waves have a tendency to concentrate the disk matter in a bar-like structure. The density maxima rotate with an angular velocity which is near to the local circular angular velocity. The second type of density concentrations are the dispersion rings (chap. 21). They rotate with an angular velocity ω' equal to $\omega - \kappa/(d\kappa/d\varpi)$. In a large part of the Galaxy $d\kappa/d\varpi$ is not so very different from 2, and the dispersion orbits are closed in a coordinate system rotating with angular velocity ω'. Lindblad considers that dispersion rings may grow by capture from adjacent orbits. A massive bar-type density wave or dispersion ring creates a rotating non-axisymmetric gravitational field, which produces effects elsewhere in the system. The bar-type waves which rotate almost with the local circular velocity have strong effects rather nearby; the dispersion rings which rotate much slower have resonance effects much farther out. Extensive numerical calculations of such waves and rings and their effects on the surrounding matter have been made by P. O. Lindblad (1960, 1963) and a number of interesting results were obtained. In these calculations the potential is a superposition of the old Schmidt model of the Galaxy, which is treated as a fixed unperturbable system, and a set of mass points which move in a gravitational field which is the sum of the Schmidt field and the field they produce themselves. First the permanence of some dispersion orbits over several periods is checked. Then the effects of the dispersion ring on the motion of massless particles at various distances from the galactic center are discussed, and it is demonstrated that large effects occur only around the resonance distance. In a typical case the ring was supposed to have a mass of 1.5 per cent of the mass of the Galaxy. Dispersion rings well within the solar orbit produce little effect, but a ring with axial ratio 0.8 at about the solar orbit produced strong effects at a distance of about 1.6 times the solar distance. When the dispersion ring interacts with an equally massive circular ring the effects are more striking and the rings are destroyed, while spiral-like structures appear. Also when the matter in the outer ring is distributed over two or three rings a similar development occurs. The spiral-like features first open up in the direction of rotation. Later they are transformed into trailing arms by the differential rotation.

In P. O. Lindblad's computations on the bar-type waves an inner ring is perturbed in such a way that it oscillates between circular and elongated shape under the effects of two of these waves. The initial perturbation of the ring with a mass equal to 4.5 per cent of that of the Galaxy is such that in part of the ring the density is more than twice as large as in the least dense part. Repeating the computation with a ring of half the mass, the wave died out rapidly. A very interesting calculation was made with three rings at $\frac{1}{4}$, $\frac{1}{2}$, and $\frac{3}{4}$ of the radius of the solar orbit. The total mass of the initially circular rings is quite large, ten per cent of the mass of the Galaxy. The middle ring again carries bar-type waves. After 400×10^6 years leading arms are developed, which have disappeared 100×10^6 years later; trailing arms appear in the next 100×10^6 years after which the structure dissolves. The very interesting thing is that at the change from leading to trailing arms the matter of the second and third rings is effectively interchanged, and in the end the points of the outer ring lie well within those of the middle ring. With five rings that contain a total of eight per cent of the galactic mass the situation is qualitatively similar. Again the rings that surround the wave-carrying ring are destroyed and mixed, but the inner and outer rings survive. For further results and especially for the figures that exhibit the computations the reader is referred to Lindblad's papers (1960, 1963). At the end of the calculations the velocity dispersion of the particles is usually quite large, and no further formation of interesting structures is expected.

In considering the relation between these computations and the phenomena observed in galaxies the following points should be considered:

1) The ring-like structures make it probably easier to produce observable spiral structure than a continuum would.

2) Rather large initial perturbations of a special kind are imposed. It is somewhat uncertain that there would not be other modes which would grow faster from random small perturbations.

3) The masses of the rings are large—much larger than the total mass of gas in our Galaxy.

4) The matter moves originally in circular orbits; this is the least stable situation, because random motions tend to damp the resonant effects.

5) Nevertheless, the fact that a rather small perturbation can even interchange the matter of different rings is quite interesting. Generally the effects that are produced are surprisingly large. But it is not obvious that the interchange is possible in the case of gas. On the other hand, in a gas the random motions are damped and this may prove helpful.

In a general way, then, these calculations amply confirm the importance of self-gravitation. But we find it somewhat difficult to see what would happen to a smooth gaseous disk from the calculations that are available. Thus, in summary, no satisfactory theory of spiral structure is yet available. Magnetic fields by themselves or hydrodynamic effects by themselves appear inadequate. Gravitational effects almost certainly are not negligible. Probably all three types of effects are important and will have to be included in a full theory. But it would not seem too implausible to suppose that gravitational effects are first and (magneto-)hydrodynamic effects second, rather than vice versa.

5.4.5. *The equilibrium in a spiral arm.*—The equilibrium of the matter in a spiral arm also raises some problems other than those of spiral structure. The interstellar polarization results have usually been considered as evidence for a magnetic field parallel to the axis of a spiral arm. Chandrasekhar and Fermi (1953) already noted that if the field is of uniform direction, the magnetic pressure and the material pressure tend to expand the arm while the gravitational forces have the opposite effect. From this balance of forces they derived a magnetic field strength of a few micro gauss. It is clear that if the field is much stronger difficulties arise, and the only way to resolve these is by having helical windings around the spiral arms (Woltjer 1963b), in which case the field in the arms may become nearly force-free. Such helical field lines could have observable effects. In fact, the first suggestion of such fields came from the analysis of the data on interstellar polarization (Shajn 1956). A later discussion by Ireland (1961b) confirms this. Ireland (1961a) also investigated the effect that such helical fields would have on the synchrotron radiation from the arms. In the future the polarization observations in the radio continuum probably will give the most definite results on the spiral-arm field near the sun. The stability of such a spiral-arm model has recently been investigated by Setti (1965). The origin of helical windings is still in doubt; perhaps they are not systematic windings but have been produced by the z-motion of the gas ejected by supernovae and H II regions.

§ 6. CONCLUSION

In the preceding sections we have discussed the evidence on the strength of the magnetic field and concluded that a field of around 30 μG in the spiral arms and 6 μG in the halo appears probable, at least if the field in the interstellar gas clouds is indeed a small-scale field. The topology of the field is more uncertain, although the interstellar polarization data appear to indicate a field parallel to the spiral arms near the arm axis, while considerations on the equilibrium of the spiral arms and on the confinement of cosmic rays in the halo indicate that strong meridional field components must also be present. The existence of matter in the halo appears very likely, but its properties are still in doubt. Some cool neutral gas has been detected and it appears not improbable that also some hot gas may occur. The precise situation in the halo may have a profound influence on the dynamics of the gas in the disk. The dynamical situation in the disk is still quite obscure. It appears likely that both gravitational effects and magnetic fields have an important role in producing the phenomenon of spiral structure, but the precise mechanisms remain in doubt, partly because the analysis of somewhat realistic theoretical models is so extremely difficult.

The origin of the Galaxy falls outside the scope of this chapter. The early evolution of the gaseous system and the gradual conversion of the gas into stars have to a large extent determined the present properties of the stellar system, but because the gas is a much more dissipative medium the direct effects of the initial state on the present behavior of the gas appear limited. This is not the case for the magnetic field because the decay time of any large-scale magnetic field in the Galaxy must be exceedingly long. The origin of the galactic field presents in fact considerable difficulties. The simplest possibility might be that the field is primeval, but cosmology provides as yet no basis for any particular hypothesis. The alternative—perhaps more in accordance with present scientific philosophy—would be that the field was produced during the life of the Galaxy, perhaps in the initial phases when the gas density still was high. But the high conductivity of the matter is a serious hindrance in that case and no plausible suggestions have been made. Conceivably one can make a small-scale field with the help of the quasi-turbulent motions in the interstellar gas, but a large-scale field with a non-negligible flux through regions a kiloparsec or so across, is quite a different problem.

REFERENCES

AGRINIER, B., BOELLA, G.,
  DEGLI, ANTONI G., DIL-
  WORTH, C., KOECHLIN,
  Y., PARLIER, B., SCARSI,
  L., and SIRONI, G.   1964   *Phys. Rev. Letters*, **13**, 377.

AMBARTZUMIAN, V. A.   1958   *11th Solvay Conference*, p. 241.

BEL, N., and
  SCHATZMAN, E.   1958   *Rev. Mod. Phys.*, **30**, 1015.

BERNSTEIN, I. B.,
  FRIEMAN, E. A.,
  KRUSKAL, M. D., and
  KULSRUD, R. M.   1958   *Proc. Roy. Soc. London, Ser. A*, **244**, 17.

BIERMANN, L., and
  DAVIS, L.   1960   *Zs. f. Ap.*, **51**, 19.

BIERMANN, L., and
  SCHLÜTER, A.   1950   *Zs. f. Naturforsch.*, **5a**, 237.

BLAAUW, A.   1963   *Interstellar Matter in Galaxies*, ed. L. WOLTJER
                  (New York: W. A. Benjamin, Inc.), p. 48.

BRANDT, J. C.   1962   *Icarus*, **1**, 1.

BROUW, W. N.,
  MULLER, C. A., and
  TINBERGEN, J.   1962   *B.A.N.*, **16**, 213.

BURBIDGE, G. R.   1962   *Nature*, **190**, 1053.

BURBIDGE, G. R., and
  HOYLE, F.   1963   *Ap. J.*, **138**, 57.

BURBIDGE, G. R., and
  PRENDERGAST, K. H.   1960   *Ap. J.*, **131**, 243.

BURKE, B. F.   1957   *A.J.*, **62**, 90.

BURKE, B. F., TURNER,
  K. C., and TUVE, M. A.   1963   *A.J.*, **68**, 274.
CHANDRASEKHAR, S.   1957   *Ann. of Phys.*, **2**, 615.
   1960   *J. Math. Anal. and Applied*, **1**, 240.

CHANDRASEKHAR, S.,
  and FERMI, E.   1953   *Ap. J.*, **118**, 113.
CLARK, B. G.   1963   *Nature*, **197**, 474.
CLARK, G.   1963   *Nuova Cimento*, **30**, 727.
COOPER, B. F. C., and
  PRICE, R. M.   1962   *Nature*, **195**, 1084.
COSTAIN, C. H.   1960   *M.N.*, **120**, 248.
CRITCHFIELD, C. L.,
  NEY, E. P., and
  OLESKA, S. O.   1952   *Phys. Rev.*, **85**, 461.
DAVIES, R. D., and
  HAZARD, C.   1962   *M.N.*, **124**, 147.
DAVIES, R. D.,
  SLATER, C. H.,
  SHUTER, W. L. H., and
  WILD, P. A. T.   1960   *Nature*, **187**, 1088.
DAVIES, R. D.,
  VERSCHUUR, G. L., and
  WILD, P. A. T.   1962   *Nature*, **196**, 563.
DAVIS, L.   1951   *Phys. Rev.*, **81**, 890.
DAVIS, L., and
  GREENSTEIN, J. L.   1951   *Ap. J.*, **114**, 206.
DRAKE, F. D.   1959   *A.J.*, **64**, 329 (also *Sky and Telescope*, **18**, 428).
EARL, J. A.   1961   *Phys. Rev. Letters*, **6**, 125.
ELVIUS, A., and
  HERLOFSON, N.   1960   *Ap. J.*, **131**, 304.
ELVIUS, A., and
  LINDBLAD, P. O.   1959   *Arkiv f. Astr.*, **2**, 393.
FERRARO, V. C. A.   1937   *M.N.*, **97**, 458.
FIELD, G. B.   1960   *Pub. A.S.P.*, **72**, 303.
   1963   *Interstellar Matter in Galaxies*, ed. L. WOLTJER
       (New York: W. A. Benjamin, Inc.), p. 183.

GARDNER, F. F., and
  WHITEOAK, J. B.   1962   *Phys. Rev. Letters*, **9**, 197.
GRZEDZIELSKI, S.   1962   *Acta Astr.*, **12**, 154.
HADDOCK, F. T.,
  SCHULTE, H. F., and
  WALSH, D.   1963   *A.J.*, **68**, 75.
HAIN, K., LÜST, R., and
  SCHLÜTER, A.   1957   *Zs. f. Naturforsch.*, **12a**, 833.
HANBURY BROWN R., and
  HAZARD, C.   1960   *Observatory*, **80**, 137.

HEISENBERG, W., and
  WEIZSÄCKER, C. F. VON   1948   *Zs. f. Phys.*, **125**, 290.
HENRY, J.   1958   *Ap. J.*, **128**, 497.
HOYLE, F., and
  ELLIS, G. R. A.   1963   *Australian J. Phys.*, **16**, 1.
HOYLE, F., and
  FOWLER, W. A.   1963   *M.N.*, **125**, 169.
HOYLE, F., and
  IRELAND, J. G.   1960   *M.N.*, **120**, 173.
                          1961   *Ibid.*, **122**, 35.
IRELAND, J. G.   1961*a* *Observatory*, **81**, 131.
                          1961*b* *M.N.*, **122**, 461.

KAHN, F. D., and
  WOLTJER, L.   1959   *Ap. J.*, **130**, 705.
KERR, F. J.   1962   *M.N.*, **123**, 327.
KERR, F. J.,
  HINDMAN, J. V., and
  CARPENTER, M. S.   1957   *Nature*, **180**, 677.
KRUSKAL, M. D., and
  SCHWARZSCHILD, M.   1954   *Proc. Roy. Soc. London, Ser. A*, **223**, 348.
LIN, C. C., and SHU, F. H.   1964   *Ap. J.*, **140**, 646.
LINDBLAD, B.   1959   *Hdb. d. Phys.*, ed. S. FLÜGGE (Berlin: Springer-
                                  Verlag), **53**, 21.
                          1962   *Problems of Extragalactic Research*, ed. G. L. Mc-
                                  VITTIE (New York: Macmillan and Co.), p. 146.
                          1963   *Stockholm Ann.*, **22**, No. 5.

LINDBLAD, B., and
  LANGEBARTEL, R. G.   1953   *Stockholm Ann.*, **17**, No. 6.
LINDBLAD, P. O.   1960   *Stockholm Ann.*, **21**, No. 4.
                          1963   *Interstellar Matter in Galaxies*, ed. L. WOLTJER
                                  (New York: W. A. Benjamin, Inc.), p. 222.

LOZINSKAYA, T. A., and
  KARDASHEV, N. S.   1962   *A.J.U.S S.R.* **39**, 840.
LÜST, R. M.   1960   *Rev. Mod. Phys.*, **32**, 706.
LYNDS, C. R., and
  SANDAGE, A. R.   1963   *Ap. J.*, **137**, 1005.
McGEE, R. X., and
  MURRAY, J. D.   1961   *Australian J. Phys.*, **14**, 260.
MATHIS, J. S.   1962   *Ap. J.*, **136**, 374.
MILLS, B. Y.   1959   "Paris Symposium on Radio Astronomy," *I.A.U.
                                  Symp.*, No. 9, p. 431.
                          1961   *Observatory*, **81**, 75.

MINKOWSKI, R., and
  OSTERBROCK, D. E.   1959   *Ap. J.*, **129**, 583.
MORRIS, D., and BERGE,
  G. L.   1964   *Ap. J.*, **139**, 1388.

MORRIS, D., CLARK, B. G.,
and WILSON, R. W. 1963 *Ap. J.*, **138**, 889.
MORRIS, D., and
RADHAKRISHNAN, V. 1963 *Ap. J.*, **137**, 147.
MULLER, C. A.,
BERKHUIJSEN, E. M.,
BROUW, W. N., and
TINBERGEN, J. 1963 *Nature*, **200**, 155.
MULLER, C. A.,
OORT, J. H., and
RAIMOND, E. 1963 *C.R. Acad. Sci. Paris*, **257**, 1661.
MÜNCH, G., and
ZIRIN, H. 1961 *Ap. J.*, **133**, 11.
OKI, T., FUJIMOTO, M.,
and HITOTUYANAGI, Z. 1961 *Sendai Astr. Rap.*, No. 78.
OORT, J. H. 1963a *Interstellar Matter in Galaxies*, ed. L. WOLTJER
(New York: W. A. Benjamin, Inc.), p. 3.
1963b *Ibid.*, p. 234.
1963c *Ibid.*, p. 316.
OSTERBROCK, D. E. 1961 *Ap. J.*, **134**, 270.
PACHOLCZYK, A. G. 1961 *Ann. d'ap.*, **24**, 326.
PARKER, E. N. 1958 *Phys. Rev.*, **109**, 1328.
PIKELNER, S. B. 1957 *A.J. U.S.S.R.*, **34**, 314.
PIKELNER, S. B., and
SHKLOVSKY, I. S. 1957 *A.J. U.S.S.R.*, **34**, 145.
1959 *Ann. d'ap.*, **22**, 913.
PRENDERGAST, K. H. 1963 *Interstellar Matter in Galaxies*, ed. L. WOLTJER
(New York: W. A. Benjamin, Inc.), p. 217.
REBER, G., and
ELLIS, G. R. 1956 *J. Geophys. Res.*, **61**, 1.
ROUGOOR, G. W., and
OORT, J. H. 1960 *Proc. Nat. Acad. Sci.*, **46**, 1.
SANDAGE, A. R. 1961 Carnegie Inst. Washington, Pub. No. 618.
SCHLÜTER, A. 1957 *Zs. f. Naturforsch.*, **12a**, 855.
SCHWARZSCHILD, M. 1963 *Interstellar Matter in Galaxies*, ed. L. WOLTJER
(New York: W. A. Benjamin, Inc.), p. 266.
SCIAMA, D. W. 1962 *M.N.*, **123**, 317.
SEIELSTAD, G. A.,
MORRIS, D., and
RADHAKRISHNAN, V. 1964 *Ap. J.*, **140**, 53.
SEIELSTAD, G. A.,
MORRIS, D.,
RADHAKRISHNAN, V.,
and WILSON, R. W. 1963 *Observations Owens Valley Obs.*, No. 7.
SETTI, G. 1965 *B.A.N.*, in press.
SHAIN, C. A. 1959 "Paris Symposium on Radio Astronomy," *I.A.U.
Symp.*, No. 9, 451.

SHAJN, G. A.	1956	*A.J. U.S.S.R.*, **33**, 469.
SPITZER, L.	1954	*Ap. J.*, **120**, 1.
	1956	*Ibid.*, **124**, 20.
	1962	*Physics of Fully Ionized Gases* (2d ed.; New York: Interscience Publishers).
	1963	*Interstellar Matter in Galaxies*, ed. L. WOLTJER (New York: W. A. Benjamin, Inc.), p. 98.
	1965	This Compendium, Vol. **7**.
STRANAHAN, G.	1954	*Ap. J.*, **119**, 465.
TOOMRE, A.	1964	*Ap. J.*, **139**, 1217.
TURTLE, A. J., PUGH, J. F., KENDERDINE, S., and PAULINY-TOTH, I. I. K.	1962	*M.N.*, **124**, 297.
WEINREB, S.	1962	*Ap. J.*, **136**, 1149.
WEIZSÄCKER, C. F. VON	1947	*Zs. f. Ap.*, **24**, 181.
WENTZEL, D. G.	1957	*Ap. J.*, **126**, 559.
	1960	*B.A.N.*, **15**, 103.
	1961	*Nature*, **189**, 907.
	1963	*Ann. Rev. Astr. and Astrophys.*, **1**, 195.
WESTERHOUT, G.	1958	*B.A.N.*, **14**, 215.
WESTERHOUT, G., SEEGER, CH. L., BROUW, W. N., and TINBERGEN, J.	1962	*B.A.N.*, **16**, 187.
WESTFOLD, K. C.	1959	*Ap. J.*, **130**, 241.
WICKRAMASINGHE, N. C.	1962	*M.N.*, **125**, 87.
WIELEBINSKI, R., and SHAKESHAFT, J. R.	1962	*Nature*, **195**, 982.
WOLTJER, L.	1959a	*Ap. J.*, **130**, 38.
	1959b	*Ibid.*, p. 405.
	1961	*Ibid.*, **133**, 352.
	1963a	*Interstellar Matter in Galaxies*, ed. L. WOLTJER (New York: W. A. Benjamin, Inc.), p. 88.
	1963b	*Ibid.*, p. 247.
	1965	*Proceedings 13th Solvay Congress*, in press.

The Plan of Selected Areas

A. BLAAUW

Kapteyn Laboratory, Groningen

AND

T. ELVIUS

Uppsala Observatory

IN 1906, J. C. Kapteyn issued the booklet *Plan of Selected Areas*, containing a proposal "to bring together, as far as is possible with such an effort, all the elements which at the present time must seem most necessary for a successful attack on the sidereal problem, that is: the problem of the structure of the sidereal world." It was meant to serve as a basis for the coordination of observational programs dealing with the problem of the space distribution and the motions of the stars. (At that time, extragalactic objects had not yet been recognized as such.) The Plan has contributed greatly to the researches which, first, revealed the proper nature of the Galaxy as a stellar system of finite dimensions, and, next, led to our present knowledge of detailed properties of the space distribution and motions of different components of the galactic population. It continues to be of great significance for galactic research in the present time. For this reason, a brief account and some particulars of the Plan are given below.

The basic data, i.e., coordinates of the areas and first desiderata for observations were given in Kapteyn's original proposal. Progress reports on these and subsequent observational programs, carried out on the basis of the Plan have been issued from time to time; the "First and Second Report" by Kapteyn in 1911 (published by the Astronomical Laboratory at Groningen), the "Third Report" by P. J. van Rhijn in 1923 (also published by the Laboratory), the fourth one by the same author in 1930 (in the *Bulletin of the Astronomical Institutes of the Netherlands*, **6,** 75). Subsequent accounts have been published in the *Transactions of the International Astronomical Union;* those in volumes V to X by P. J. van Rhijn as reports of Commission 32 (Selected Areas), and those in volumes XI A and XII A by T. Elvius as reports of the subcommittee on the Selected Areas of Commission 33 (Structure and Dynamics of the Galactic Sys-

tem). The report in volume IX (published in 1957) contains a complete list of
all publications that ever appeared in relation to the Plan of Selected Areas up
to about 1955. The subsequent reports give supplementary lists.

The Plan of Selected Areas consisted of two parts: (a) the Systematic Plan,
consisting of 206 areas, regularly distributed over the sky, and (b) the Special
Plan, consisting of 46 areas located at points of special interest in the Milky
Way. By far the most attention has been given to the Systematic Plan which,
due to the unbiased way in which the areas were chosen, has met the aim of the
project in the most satisfactory way. These areas are in zones at intervals of 15°
in declination. The coordinates of their centers, i.e., both the galactic coordinates (l^{II}, b^{II}) and the equatorial ones for 1950 with the precession per 100 years
are given in Table 1.

The individual stars in the areas of the Systematic Plan may be identified

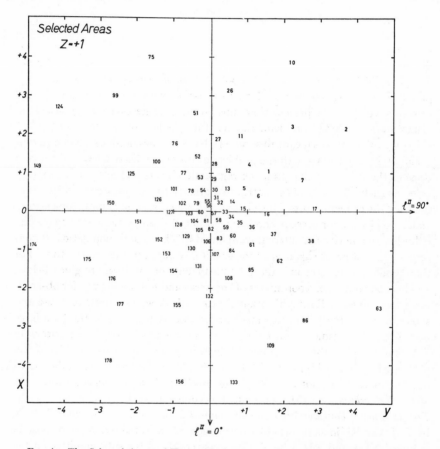

Fig. 1.—The Selected Areas of Kapteyn's Systematic Plan with galactic latitudes $b^{II} >$
$+10°$. The numbers of the areas are placed at the positions x, y where the lines of sight cross the
plane $z = +1$.

by means of references to the *Durchmusterung* catalogues published in the *Harvard Annals*, Vols. 101–3 by E. C. Pickering, J. C. Kapteyn, and P. J. van Rhijn (1918–24), and in the Mt. Wilson Catalogue for the areas 1 to 139 (*Papers of the Mount Wilson Observatory*, Vol. 4; Carnegie Inst. Publ. No. 402) by F. H. Seares, J. C. Kapteyn, and P. J. van Rhijn (1930). These contain coordinates and photographic magnitudes. Objective prism spectral types down to about photographic magnitudes 13 and 12, respectively, are given for the northern sky in the *Bergedorfer Spektral Durchmusterung*, Vols. 1 to 5 published by A. Schwassmann and P. J. van Rhijn (1935–53), and for the southern sky in the *Potsdam Spektral Durchmusterung* (Publ. Astroph. Obs. Potsdam, Vols. 27 and 28, by F. Becker and H. Brück, 1929–38). These two *Durchmusterung* catalogues cover large regions around the area centers (12 and 16–24 square degrees, respectively). For spectral and other data for fainter stars, in usually smaller regions, we refer to the reports referred to above. Charts for areas 1–139, based on the *Mount Wilson Catalogue*, were published by A. Brun of Le Breuil-Allier, France.

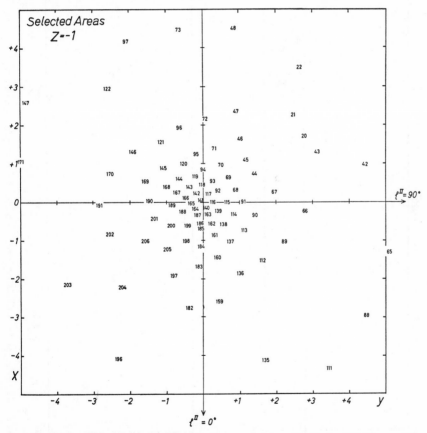

FIG. 2.—The Selected Areas of Kapteyn's Systematic Plan with $b^{II} < -10°$. The numbers are placed at the positions x,y where the lines of sight cross the plane $z = -1$.

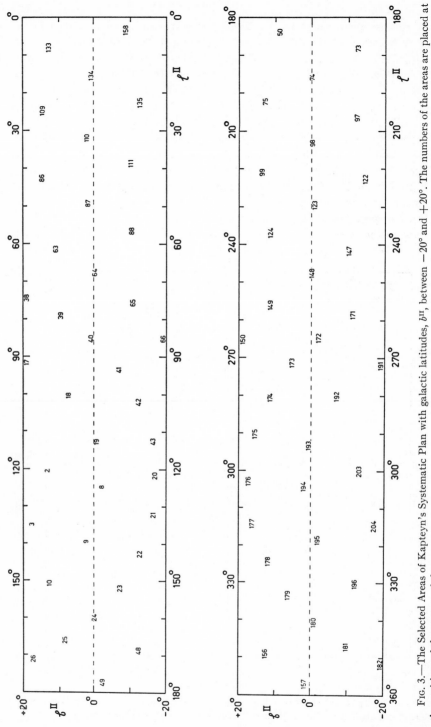

Fig. 3.—The Selected Areas of Kapteyn's Systematic Plan with galactic latitudes, b^{II}, between $-20°$ and $+20°$. The numbers of the areas are placed at the positions of the centers of the areas.

TABLE 1

LIST OF THE SELECTED AREAS OF THE SYSTEMATIC PLAN

Area No.	l^{II}	b^{II}	R.A. Dec. (1950)		Precession (100 yrs)	
1.....	124°.1	+28°.0	8ʰ50ᵐ1	+88°50′	....	
2.....	120.4	+13.2	0 7.7	+75 37	+ 5ᵐ4	+33′
3.....	135.1	+17.6	4 14.3	+75 8	+12.6	+15
4.....	139.9	+31.7	8 10.0	+74 41	+12.0	−18
5.....	124.7	+42.6	12 30.0	+74 43	+ 4.0	−33
6.....	108.3	+36.3	16 12.9	+74 43	− 2.2	−15
7.....	108.6	+20.8	20 23.1	+75 20	− 1.8	+20
8.....	124.7	− 2.1	1 3.1	+60 26	+ 6.2	+32
9.....	139.3	+ 2.4	3 8.0	+60 31	+ 8.0	+23
10.....	150.7	+12.7	5 12.5	+60 14	+ 8.9	+ 7
11.....	156.8	+26.2	7 11.4	+59 55	+ 8.8	−10
12.....	156.5	+40.7	9 6.9	+59 28	+ 7.7	−24
13.....	144.6	+53.3	11 6.0	+59 34	+ 6.0	−32
14.....	114.7	+57.6	13 23.9	+59 14	+ 3.8	−31
15.....	95.2	+48.9	15 18.1	+59 39	+ 2.2	−22
16.....	88.5	+33.3	17 29.7	+59 48	+ 1.3	− 4
17.....	91.7	+19.5	19 23.7	+60 16	+ 1.5	+12
18.....	100.3	+ 7.1	21 25.3	+60 23	+ 2.7	+26
19.....	112.8	− 0.7	23 25.3	+60 16	+ 4.5	+33
20.....	121.9	−17.0	0 42.8	+45 36	+ 5.6	+33
21.....	132.1	−16.5	1 39.0	+45 15	+ 6.1	+30
22.....	142.8	−12.9	2 41.3	+45 23	+ 6.6	+25
23.....	152.2	− 7.4	3 42.5	+45 10	+ 7.0	+19
24.....	160.1	− 0.2	4 42.6	+44 56	+ 7.2	+11
25.....	166.2	+ 8.0	5 40.7	+44 52	+ 7.3	+ 3
26.....	171.0	+17.4	6 39.7	+44 47	+ 7.3	− 6
27.....	174.5	+27.9	7 41.6	+44 43	+ 7.1	−14
28.....	176.0	+38.7	8 43.4	+44 49	+ 6.8	−22
29.....	175.4	+49.2	9 42.2	+44 36	+ 6.4	−28
30.....	170.1	+58.9	10 39.9	+44 54	+ 5.9	−31
31.....	157.7	+68.1	11 39.7	+44 23	+ 5.3	−33
32.....	120.4	+72.8	12 53.3	+44 34	+ 4.6	−32
33.....	91.5	+68.4	13 52.0	+44 55	+ 4.1	−29
34.....	76.9	+60.3	14 49.8	+44 48	+ 3.6	−25
35.....	70.9	+50.1	15 50.6	+44 41	+ 3.3	−18
36.....	70.5	+40.0	16 47.5	+45 15	+ 3.0	−10
37.....	71.6	+28.9	17 50.4	+44 59	+ 2.9	− 1
38.....	74.7	+19.3	18 47.5	+45 13	+ 2.9	+ 7
39.....	79.1	+ 9.4	19 48.6	+44 58	+ 3.2	+15
40.....	85.3	+ 0.8	20 48.7	+45 11	+ 3.5	+22
41.....	93.3	− 7.0	21 52.0	+45 14	+ 3.9	+28
42.....	102.3	−12.4	22 51.2	+45 26	+ 4.4	+32
43.....	112.7	−16.4	23 52.5	+45 7	+ 5.0	+33
44.....	117.3	−31.9	0 26.6	+30 27	+ 5.3	+33
45.....	133.1	−31.4	1 28.8	+30 26	+ 5.6	+31
46.....	147.9	−27.2	2 32.0	+30 23	+ 5.9	+26
47.....	159.0	−21.3	3 26.1	+30 10	+ 6.1	+21
48.....	168.9	−12.4	4 26.2	+30 17	+ 6.3	+13
49.....	177.5	− 2.4	5 27.2	+29 42	+ 6.4	+ 5

TABLE 1—*Continued*

Area No.	l^{II}	b^{II}	R.A. Dec. (1950)		Precession (100 yrs)	
50.....	184°0	+ 8°9	6ʰ27ᵐ2	+29°48′	+ 6ᵐ4	− 4′
51.....	189.2	+20.9	7 27.2	+29 54	+ 6.3	−12
52.....	193.9	+33.7	8 29.1	+29 50	+ 6.1	−20
53.....	197.5	+46.2	9 28.0	+29 47	+ 5.9	−26
54.....	200.1	+58.8	10 26.8	+29 45	+ 5.6	−31
55.....	200.6	+73.1	11 32.6	+29 43	+ 5.3	−33
56.....	199.6	+79.2	12 0.6	+29 23	+ 5.1	−33
57.....	65.5	+85.5	13 6.4	+29 44	+ 4.8	−32
58.....	44.5	+73.8	14 2.2	+29 26	+ 4.5	−29
59.....	45.4	+60.3	15 4.1	+29 38	+ 4.2	−23
60.....	47.8	+48.7	15 58.0	+29 41	+ 4.0	−17
61.....	51.7	+35.4	17 0.9	+29 56	+ 3.9	− 9
62.....	55.8	+23.8	17 56.9	+30 0	+ 3.8	− 0
63.....	61.4	+10.8	19 1.9	+30 4	+ 3.9	+ 9
64.....	67.5	− 0.2	20 0.0	+30 8	+ 4.0	+17
65.....	75.6	−10.7	21 1.1	+30 22	+ 4.2	+24
66.....	85.1	−19.5	22 0.2	+30 24	+ 4.5	+29
67.....	97.5	−26.9	23 3.4	+30 26	+ 4.8	+32
68.....	110.6	−46.1	0 13.6	+15 37	+ 5.2	+33
69.....	133.1	−46.6	1 17.7	+15 26	+ 5.3	+32
70.....	152.8	−42.1	2 18.7	+15 14	+ 5.5	+27
71.....	167.0	−34.8	3 13.8	+15 11	+ 5.6	+22
72.....	178.6	−24.7	4 12.8	+15 18	+ 5.7	+15
73.....	188.5	−12.5	5 16.9	+15 3	+ 5.7	+ 6
74.....	196.0	+ 0.2	6 17.9	+15 9	+ 5.7	− 3
75.....	202.5	+12.9	7 16.8	+15 5	+ 5.7	−11
76.....	209.2	+26.2	8 17.8	+14 51	+ 5.6	−19
77.....	216.1	+38.2	9 12.8	+14 18	+ 5.5	−25
78.....	224.4	+52.3	10 15.7	+14 55	+ 5.4	−30
79.....	240.2	+65.6	11 19.6	+14 34	+ 5.2	−33
80.....	269.0	+75.0	12 14.5	+14 43	+ 5.1	−33
81.....	328.8	+75.7	13 14.5	+14 24	+ 4.9	−32
82.....	6.3	+66.3	14 16.4	+15 6	+ 4.8	−28
83.....	19.3	+54.6	15 11.3	+14 39	+ 4.7	−22
84.....	29°2	+40.9	16 14.3	+14 52	+ 4.6	−15
85.....	36.0	+28.0	17 12.3	+14 56	+ 4.5	− 7
86.....	42.6	+14.6	18 13.3	+15 1	+ 4.5	+ 2
87.....	49.2	+ 1.7	19 13.3	+15 5	+ 4.6	+10
88.....	56.5	− 10.5	20 12.3	+15 19	+ 4.6	+18
89.....	65.0	−21.9	21 10.4	+15 22	+ 4.7	+25
90.....	77.1	−33.1	22 14.4	+15 25	+ 4.8	+30
91.....	92.2	−41.7	23 15.5	+15 16	+ 5.0	+33
92.....	124.9	−62.1	0 52.6	+ 0 26	+ 5.1	+33
93.....	154.2	−58.1	1 52.6	+ 0 35	+ 5.1	+29
94.....	175.3	−49.2	2 53.6	+ 0 22	+ 5.1	+24
95.....	188.8	−38.1	3 52.6	+ 0 9	+ 5.1	+18
96.....	198.3	−26.0	4 50.6	+ 0 5	+ 5.1	+10
97.....	206.6	−12.1	5 54.6	+ 0 0	+ 5.1	+ 1
98.....	213.3	+ 0.0	6 49.6	− 0 13	+ 5.1	− 7
99.....	220.9	+13.8	7 52.6	− 0 28	+ 5.1	−16
100.....	228.6	+26.7	8 51.6	− 0 21	+ 5.1	−23
101.....	239.0	+39.9	9 54.6	− 0 14	+ 5.1	−29
102.....	253.2	+50.4	10 52.6	− 0 36	+ 5.1	−32
103.....	274.6	+59.2	11 52.6	− 0 17	+ 5.1	−33

TABLE 1—*Continued*

Area No.	l^{II}	b^{II}	R.A. Dec. (1950)		Precession (100 yrs)	
104.....	298°5	+62°3	12ʰ40ᵐ6	− 0° 16′	+ 5ᵐ1	−33′
105.....	326.8	+60.0	13 35.6	− 0 25	+ 5.1	−31
106.....	351.5	+51.7	14 39.6	− 0 13	+ 5.1	−26
107.....	5.7	+41.3	15 36.6	− 0 10	+ 5.1	−20
108.....	15.7	+29.3	16 34.6	− 0 16	+ 5.1	−12
109.....	25.0	+14.6	17 42.6	− 0 11	+ 5.1	− 3
110.....	32.0	+ 2.1	18 39.6	+ 0 3	+ 5.1	+ 6
111.....	38.7	−10.2	19 35.6	+ 0 17	+ 5.1	+14
112.....	46.9	−24.1	20 39.6	+ 0 21	+ 5.1	+21
113.....	56.2	−36.8	21 39.6	+ 0 14	+ 5.1	+27
114.....	69.5	−48.3	22 39.6	+ 0 26	+ 5.1	+31
115.....	89.8	−57.5	23 40.6	+ 0 37	+ 5.1	+33
116.....	90.1	−75.0	0 15.5	−14 33	+ 5.1	+33
117.....	148.8	−75.7	1 14.5	−14 24	+ 4.9	+32
118.....	185.6	−65.8	2 17.4	−14 36	+ 4.8	+28
119.....	199.5	−54.4	3 12.3	−14 39	+ 4.7	+22
120.....	209.4	−40.9	4 14.3	−15 2	+ 4.6	+15
121.....	216.4	−26.9	5 17.3	−14 47	+ 4.6	+ 6
122.....	222.8	−14.5	6 14.3	−15 11	+ 4.5	− 2
123.....	229.6	− 0.8	7 17.3	−15 5	+ 4.6	−11
124.....	237.1	+11.3	8 16.3	−15 19	+ 4.6	−19
125.....	245.7	+22.7	9 14.4	−15 22	+ 4.7	−25
126.....	257.8	+33.9	10 18.4	−15 15	+ 4.9	−30
127.....	272.4	+41.4	11 15.5	−15 36	+ 5.0	−33
128.....	291.6	+46.4	12 16.6	−15 27	+ 5.2	−33
129.....	312.8	+46.8	13 16.7	−15 16	+ 5.3	−32
130.....	330.3	+42.8	14 10.7	−15 24	+ 5.4	−28
131.....	346.8	+34.7	15 13.8	−15 21	+ 5.6	−22
132.....	359.0	+24.5	16 14.8	−15 7	+ 5.7	−15
133.....	8.2	+12.6	17 15.9	−15 13	+ 5.7	− 6
134.....	15.6	+ 0.9	18 12.9	−14 59	+ 5.7	+ 2
135.....	22.6	−12.6	19 15.8	−14 55	+ 5.7	+11
136.....	28.5	−25.2	20 12.8	−15 1	+ 5.6	+18
137.....	35.7	−38.3	21 12.8	−14 38	+ 5.5	+25
138.....	44.3	−51.8	22 13.7	−14 45	+ 5.4	+30
139.....	59.2	−65.0	23 16.6	−14 34	+ 5.2	+33
140.....	19.1	−79.8	0 3.6	−29 23	+ 5.1	+33
141.....	245.0	−85.8	1 5.4	−29 34	+ 4.8	+32
142.....	225.0	−73.1	2 5.2	−29 36	+ 4.5	+29
143.....	225.0	−60.8	3 2.1	−29 28	+ 4.2	+23
144.....	228.3	−47.5	4 4.0	−29 52	+ 4.0	+16
145.....	231.8	−35.2	5 1.9	−29 56	+ 3.9	+ 8
146.....	236.1	−23.0	6 0.9	−30 0	+ 3.8	− 0
147.....	241.9	−10.3	7 4.9	−30 15	+ 3.9	− 9
148.....	247.7	+ 0.1	8 0.0	−30 18	+ 4.0	−17
149.....	256.3	+11.5	9 6.1	−30 22	+ 4.2	−24
150.....	265.3	+19.9	10 2.2	−30 15	+ 4.5	−29
151.....	277.4	+26.7	11 2.4	−30 36	+ 4.8	−32
152.....	297.6	+32.1	12 27.6	−30 17	+ 5.3	−33
153.....	312.0	+31.4	13 24.8	−30 36	+ 5.6	−31
154.....	326.4	+28.0	14 24.9	−30 14	+ 5.9	−27
155.....	339.6	+21.0	15 29.1	−30 0	+ 6.1	−20
156.....	349.3	+12.5	16 27.1	−29 57	+ 6.3	−13
157.....	357.2	+ 1 9	17 28.2	−30 12	+ 6.4	− 5

TABLE 1—*Continued*

Area No.	l^{II}	b^{II}	R.A.	Dec. (1950)	Precession (100 yrs)	
158.....	3°7	− 8°8	18^h26^m2	−29°58′	+ 6^{m}4	+ 4′
159.....	9.3	−20.7	19 26.2	−29 44	+ 6.3	+12
160.....	13.8	−33.5	20 28.1	−29 50	+ 6.2	+20
161.....	17.9	−46.8	21 30.9	−29 37	+ 5.9	+27
162.....	20.8	−58.8	22 26.8	−29 25	+ 5.6	+31
163.....	20.8	−71.4	23 24.7	−29 44	+ 5.3	+33
164.....	307.7	−72.9	0 41.4	−44 24	+ 4.7	+33
165.....	277.8	−70.1	1 36.1	−44 55	+ 4.2	+31
166.....	258.6	−62.3	2 37.9	−44 37	+ 3.7	+26
167.....	251.5	−52.0	3 39.7	−44 40	+ 3.3	+19
168.....	250.3	−41.2	4 40.5	−45 4	+ 3.0	+11
169.....	251.2	−30.7	5 40.5	−44 59	+ 2.9	+ 3
170.....	254.1	−20.6	6 39.5	−45 3	+ 2.9	− 6
171.....	258.4	−11.1	7 38.5	−45 7	+ 3.1	−14
172.....	264.7	− 1.9	8 41.7	−45 21	+ 3.4	−22
173.....	271.3	+ 5.3	9 36.9	−45 14	+ 3.8	−27
174.....	280.4	+11.4	10 39.2	−45 26	+ 4.3	−31
175.....	290.4	+15.5	11 39.5	−45 27	+ 4.9	−33
176.....	303.1	+17.3	12 49.8	−45 16	+ 5.6	−33
177.....	314.3	+16.2	13 51.1	−45 5	+ 6.2	−30
178.....	324.3	+11.8	14 51.3	−45 42	+ 6.7	−24
179.....	333.4	+ 6.3	15 51.5	−45 19	+ 7.0	−18
180.....	340.8	− 0.8	16 49.6	−45 5	+ 7.2	−10
181.....	347.2	− 9.7	17 51.7	−44 51	+ 7.3	− 1
182.....	351.8	−19.7	18 53.6	−44 56	+ 7.3	+ 8
183.....	354.9	−30.5	19 56.5	−44 52	+ 7.0	+16
184.....	356.3	−40.3	20 52.4	−44 39	+ 6.7	+23
185.....	354.9	−51.3	21 54.1	−44 36	+ 6.3	+28
186.....	349.4	−60.1	22 46.9	−44 44	+ 5.8	+32
187.....	333.5	−69.0	23 49.6	−44 43	+ 5.2	+33
188.....	294.8	−57.3	1 23.9	−59 34	+ 3.8	+31
189.....	274.3	−48.3	3 25.1	−59 30	+ 2.2	+21
190.....	268.7	−34.1	5 23.7	−59 57	+ 1.3	+ 5
191.....	271.8	−19.5	7 23.7	−60 26	+ 1.4	−12
192.....	280.3	− 6.8	9 27.4	−60 13	+ 2.7	−26
193.....	293.3	+ 0.7	11 29.3	−60 27	+ 4.6	−33
194.....	304.4	+ 2.1	13 0.1	−60 26	+ 6.1	−32
195.....	318.7	− 1.7	15 0.9	−60 12	+ 7.9	−24
196.....	330.4	−12.0	17 6.4	−60 4	+ 8.9	− 8
197.....	337.0	−25.4	19 5.4	−59 35	+ 8.8	+ 9
198.....	336.3	−40.1	21 2.9	−59 48	+ 7.8	+24
199.....	325.2	−52.8	23 1.1	−59 44	+ 6.1	+32
200.....	305.3	−42.6	0 23.2	−74 43	+ 4.3	+33
201.....	287.9	−35.4	4 26.8	−74 53	− 2.4	+13
202.....	288.6	−20.5	8 28.2	−75 10	− 1.6	−20
203.....	300.0	−13.1	12 2.6	−75 27	+ 5.2	−33
204.....	314.7	−17.2	16 6.2	−75 8	+12.5	−16
205.....	319.5	−31.7	20 11.1	−75 1	+12.1	+18
206.....	302.8	−27.9	2 26.8	−89 29	....	......

Because of their uniform distribution on the sky, the Selected Areas of the Systematic Plan are particularly suitable for investigations at the intermediate and high galactic latitudes. At low latitudes they need to be supplemented because these areas are not all located at strategic positions with regard to the principal structural features of the Galaxy as they are known now. Even here, however, they are a good basis for exploratory work and useful as magnitude sequences.

Figures 1 and 2 illustrate the directions of the areas at intermediate and high galactic latitudes (those with $|b^{\mathrm{II}}| > 10°$). They show the coordinates x (toward $l^{\mathrm{II}} = 180°$) and y (toward $l^{\mathrm{II}} = 90°$), parallel to the galactic plane, of the intersections of the directions of the areas with the planes $z = \pm 1$. Figure 3 shows the distribution, in new galactic coordinates, for the areas between $-20°$ and $+20°$ latitude. These figures may serve to facilitate the choice of the areas for particular problems.

The rich material already collected for the stars in the Selected Areas will become of still greater significance when more accurate photometric and spectroscopic data have been obtained and the proper motions have increased in accuracy due to the increased time basis.

Index